D0019471

"HAMILTON SHOULD HAVE A BRILLIANT FUTURE AS ONE OF THE BEST NEW AUTHORS TO APPEAR IN RECENT YEARS."
—*Science Fiction Age*

"ABSOLUTELY VINTAGE SCIENCE FICTION.... HAMILTON PUTS [SF] BACK INTO INTERSTELLAR OVER-DRIVE. An intergalactic adventure story laced with ironies, insights, and held together by a transcending central plot."
—*The Times* (London)

"A SWEEPING, PANORAMIC NOVEL THAT IS LIKELY TO ATTRACT A LEGION OF FANS. This should be one of the major publishing events in the genre this year."
—*Science Fiction Chronicle*

"PAINTED ON THE VAST CANVAS OF CLASSIC SPACE OPERA. . . . The story builds to an explosive climax."
—*SFX*

"ELOQUENT AND INGENIOUS. . . . A host of believable characters deploy against rich descriptions of worlds and living starships."
—*Daily Telegraph* (London)

PETER F. HAMILTON

THE
REALITY
DYSFUNCTION

PART 1: EMERGENCE

ASPECT®

NEW YORK   BOSTON

WARNER BOOKS EDITION

Cover design by Don Puckey and Carol Russo
Cover illustration by Jim Burns

Aspect is a registered trademartk of Warner Books, Inc.

This Warner Books Edition is published by arrangement with Macmillan U.K.

Warner Books, Inc.
1271 Avenue of the Americas
New York, NY 10020

Visit our Web site at
www.warnerbooks.com

W A Time Warner Company

Printed in the United States of America

First Warner Books Printing: July, 1997

15   14

1

Space outside the attack cruiser *Beezling* tore open in five places. For a moment anyone looking into the expanding rents would have received a true glimpse into empty infinity. The pseudofabric structure of the wormholes was a photonic dead zone, a darkness so profound it seemed to be spilling out to contaminate the real universe. Then ships were suddenly streaking up out of the gaping termini, accelerating away at six gees, twisting round on interception trajectories. They were different from the spherical Garissan naval craft which they had tracked between the stars, graceful, streamlined teardrop shapes. Larger and dangerously powerful. Alive.

Nestled snugly in the armoured and sealed command capsule at the heart of the *Beezling*, Captain Kyle Prager was shocked out of a simple astrogration review by a datavised proximity alert from the flight computer. His neural nanonics relayed information from the ship's external sensor clusters directly into his brain. Out here in the great emptiness of interstellar space starlight wasn't powerful enough to provide an optical-band return. He was relying on the infrared signature alone, arching smears of pinkness which the discrimination programs struggled to resolve. Radar pulses were fuzzed and hashed by the ships' electronic-warfare pods.

The combat programs stored in the memory clusters of his neural nanonics went into primary mode. He datavised a quick sequence of instructions into the flight computer, desperate for more information. Trajectories from the five newcomers were computed, appearing as scarlet vector lines curving through space to line up ominously on the *Beezling* and her two escort frigates. They were still accelerating, yet there was no reaction-drive exhaust plume. Kyle Prager's heart sank. "Voidhawks," he said. On the couch next to him, Tane Ogilie, the *Beezling*'s patterning-node officer, groaned in dismay. "How did they know?"

"Confederation Navy Intelligence is good," Kyle Prager retorted. "They knew we'd try a direct retaliation. They must have monitored our naval traffic and followed us." In his mind a black pressure was building. He could almost sense the antimatter-confinement chambers inside the *Beezling*, twinkling like devilish red stars all around him.

Antimatter was the one anathema which was universal throughout the Confederation. No matter what planet or asteroid settlement you were brought up on, they all condemned it.

The penalty if a Confederation Navy ship caught them was an immediate death sentence for the captain, and a one-way ticket on a drop capsule to a penal planet for everyone else on board.

There was no choice, of course, the *Beezling* needed the fantastic delta-V reserve which only antimatter provided, far superior to the usual fusion drives of Adamist starships. The Omutan Defence Force ships would be equipped with antimatter drives. They have it because we have it; we have it because they have it. One of the oldest, and feeblest, arguments history had produced.

Kyle Prager's shoulder muscles relaxed, an involuntary submission. He'd known and accepted the risk, or at least told himself and the admirals he did.

It would be quick and painless, and under ordinary circumstances the crew would survive. But he had orders from the Garissan Admiralty. Nobody was to be allowed access to the Alchemist which the *Beezling* was carrying; and certainly not the Edenists crewing the voidhawks: their bitek science was powerful enough already.

"A distortion field has locked onto us," Tane Ogilie reported. His voice was strained, high. "We can't jump clear."

For a brief moment Kyle Prager wondered what it would be like to command a voidhawk, the effortless power and total superiority. It was almost a feeling of envy.

Three of the intercepting ships were curving round to chase the *Beezling*, while the frigates, *Chengho* and *Gombari*, only rated one pursuer each.

Mother Mary, with that formation they must know what we're carrying.

He formed the scuttle code in his mind, reviewing the procedure before datavising it into the flight computer. It was simple enough, shutting down the safeguards in the main drive's antimatter-confinement chambers, engulfing nearby space with a nova-blast of light and hard radiation.

I could wait until the voidhawks rendezvoused, take them with us. But the crews are only doing their job.

The flimsy infrared image of the three pursuit craft suddenly increased dramatically, brightening, expanding. Eight wavering petals of energy opened outwards from each of them, the sharp, glaring tips moving swiftly away from the centre. Analysis programs cut in; flight vector projections materialized, linking all twenty-four projectiles to the *Beezling* with looped laserlike threads of light. The exhaust plumes were hugely radioactive. Acceleration was hitting forty gees. Antimatter propulsion.

"Combat wasp launch," Tane Ogilie shouted hoarsely.

"They're not voidhawks," Kyle Prager said with grim fury. "They're fucking blackhawks. Omuta's hired blackhawks!" He datavised an evasion manoeuvre order into the flight computer, frantically activating the *Beezling*'s defence procedures. He'd been almost criminally negligent in not identifying the hostiles as soon as they emerged. He checked his neural nanonics; elapsed time since their emergence was seven seconds. Was that really all? Even so, his response had been woefully sloppy in an arena where milliseconds was the most precious currency. They would pay for that, maybe with their lives.

An acceleration warning blared through the *Beezling*—audio, optical, and datavise. His crew would be strapped in, but Mother Mary alone knew what the civilians they carried were doing.

The ship's acceleration built smoothly, and he felt the nanonic membrane supplements in his body hardening, supporting his internal organs against the gee force, preventing them from being pushed through his spine, ensuring an undiminished blood supply to his brain, forestalling blackout. *Beezling* shuddered violently as its own volley of combat wasps launched. Acceleration reached eight gees, and carried on building.

In the *Beezling*'s forward crew module, Dr Alkad Mzu had been reviewing the ship's status as it flew towards their next jump coordinate at one and a half gees. Neural nanonics processed the raw data to provide a composite of the starship's external sensor images, along with flight vector projections. The picture unfurled behind her retinas, scintillating ghost shadows until she closed her eyelids. *Chengho* and *Gombari* showed as intense streaks of blue-white light, the glare from their drive exhausts overwhelming the background starfield.

It was a tight formation. *Chengho* was two thousand kilometres away, *Gombari* just over three thousand. Alkad knew it took superb astrogation for ships to emerge within five thousand kilometres of each other after a jump of ten light-years. Garissa had spent a lot of money on equipping its navy with the best hardware available.

Money which could have been better spent at the university, or on supporting the national medical service. Garissa wasn't a particularly rich world. And as to where the Department of Defence had acquired such large amounts of antimatter, Alkad had studiously avoided asking.

"It will be about thirty minutes before the next jump," Peter Adul said.

Alkad cancelled the datavise. The sensor visualization of the ships faded from her perception, replaced by the spartan grey-green composite of the cabin walls. Peter was standing in the open oval hatch, wearing a dark turquoise ship-suit, padded on all the joints to protect him from bruising knocks in free fall. He smiled invitingly at her. She could see the worry behind the bright, lively eyes.

Peter was thirty-five, a metre eighty tall, with skin actually darker than her own deep ebony. He worked in the university mathematics department, and they had been engaged for eighteen months. Never the outgoing boisterous type, but quietly supportive. One person who genuinely didn't seem to mind the fact that she was brighter than him—and they were rare enough. Even the prospect of her being for ever damned as the Alchemist's creator left him unperturbed. He had actually accompanied her to the ultra-secure navy asteroid base to help with the device's mathematics.

"I thought we could spend them together," he said.

She grinned back up at him and slipped out of the restraint net as he sat on the edge of her acceleration cushioning beside her. "Thanks. Navy types don't mind being cooped up by themselves during realignment. But it certainly gets to me." Various hums and buzzes from the ship's environmental systems invaded the cabin, crewmembers talking softly at their stations, vague words echoing along the cramped companionways. *Beezling* had been assembled specifically to deploy the Alchemist device, its design concentrating on durability and performance; crew comforts had come a long way down the navy's priority list.

Alkad swung her legs over the side of the cushioning ledge, feet *pulled* down to the decking by the strong gravity, and leaned against him, thankful for the warmth of the contact, his just being there.

His arm went round her shoulders. "What is it about the prospect of incipient mortality which gets the hormones flowing?"

She smiled and pressed harder into his side. "What is it in the male make-up that simply being awake gets your hormones going?"

"That's a no?"

"That's a no," she said firmly. "There's no door, and we'd do ourselves an injury in this gravity. Besides, there will be plenty of time once we get back."

"Yes." If we do. But he didn't say that out loud.

That was when the acceleration warning sounded. Even then it took them a second to react, breaking through the initial moment of shock.

"Get back on the cushioning," Peter yelled as the gee force leapt upwards. Alkad attempted to swing her legs back up on the ledge. They were made of uranium, impossibly heavy. Muscles and tendons grated horribly as she strained against the weight.

Come on. It's easy. It's only your legs. Dear Mother, how many times have you lifted your legs? Come on!

Neural-nanonic nerve-impulse overrides bullied her thigh muscles. She got one leg back on the cushioning. By that time the acceleration had reached seven gees. She was stuck with her left leg on the floor, foot slipping along the decking as the enormous weight of her thigh pushed down, forcing her knee joint open.

The two opposing swarms of combat wasps engaged; attacking and defending drones splitting open, each releasing a barrage of submunitions. Space seethed with directed energy beams. Electronic warfare pulses popped and burned up and down the electromagnetic spectrum, trying to deflect, goad, confuse, harass. A second later it was the turn of the missiles. Solid kinetic bullets bloomed like antique shotgun blasts. All it took was the slightest graze, at those closing velocities both projectile and target alike detonated into billowing plumes of plasma. Fusion explosions followed, intense flares of blue-white starfire flinging off violet coronae. Antimatter added its vehemence to the fray, producing even larger explosions amid the ionic maelstrom.

The nebula which blazed between the *Beezling* and her attackers was roughly lenticular, and over three hundred kilometres broad, choked with dense cyclonic concentrations, spewing tremendous cataracts of fire from its edges. No sensor in existence could penetrate such chaos.

Beezling lurched round violently, drive deflector coils working at maximum pitch, taking advantage of the momentary blind spot to change course. A second volley of combat wasps shot out of their bays around the attack cruiser's lower hull, just in time to meet a new salvo fired from the blackhawks.

Peter had barely managed to roll off the acceleration couch where he was sitting, landing hard on the floor of Alkad's cabin, when the terrible acceleration began. He watched helplessly as Alkad's left leg slowly gave way under the crushing gee force; her whimpering filling him with futile guilt. The composite deck was trying to ram its way up through his back. His neck was agony. Half of the stars he could see were pain spots, the rest were a datavised nonsense. The flight computer had reduced the external combat arena to neat ordered graphics which buffeted against priority metabolic warnings. He couldn't even focus his thoughts on them. There were more important things to worry about, like how the hell was he going to force his chest up so he could breathe again?

Suddenly the gravity field shifted. He left the decking behind, and slammed into the cabin wall. His teeth were punched clean through his lip; he heard his nose break with an ugly *crunch*. Hot blood squirted into his mouth, frightening him. No wound could possibly heal in this environment. He would very probably bleed to death if this went on much longer.

Then gravity righted again, squeezing him back against the decking. He screamed in shock and pain. The datavised visualization from the flight computer had collapsed into an eerily calm moire pattern of red, green, and blue lines. Darkness was encroaching around the edges.

The second clash of combat wasps took place over a wider front. Sensors and processors on both sides were overloaded and confused by the vivid nebula and its wild energy efflux. New explosions were splattered against the background of destruction. Some of the attacking combat wasps pierced the defensive cordon. A third volley of defenders left the *Beezling*.

Six thousand kilometres away, another nuclear-fuelled nebula burst into existence as the *Chengho* fought off its solitary hunter's swarm of combat wasps. The *Gombari* wasn't so fortunate. Its antimatter-confinement chambers were shattered by the incoming weapons. *Beezling*'s sensor filters engaged instantly as an ephemeral star ignited. Kyle Prager lost his datavised visualization across half of the universe. He never saw the blackhawk which attacked the frigate wrenching open a wormhole interstice and vanish within, fleeing the lethal sleet of radiation its attack had liberated.

The combat wasp closing on *Beezling* at forty-six gees analysed the formation of the robot defenders approaching it. Missiles and ECM pods raced away, fighting a fluid battle of evasion and deception for over a tenth of a second. Then the attacker was through, a single defender left between it and the starship, moving to intercept, but slowly, the defender had only just left its launch cradle, accelerating at barely twenty gees.

Situation displays flipped into Kyle Prager's mind. The blackhawks' positions, their trajectories. Combat wasp performance. Likely reserves. He reviewed them, mind augmented by the tactics program, and made his decision, committing half of his remaining combat wasps to offensive duties.

Beezling rang like a bell as they launched.

At a hundred and fifty kilometres from its prey, the incoming combat wasp's guidance processors computed it wouldn't quite reach the starship before it was intercepted. It ran through the available options, making its choice.

At a hundred and twenty kilometres away it loaded a deactivation sequence into the hardware of the seven antimatter-confine chambers it was carrying.

At ninety-five kilometres away the magnetic field of the first confinement chamber snapped off. Forty-six gravities took over. The frozen pellet of antimatter was smashed into the rear wall. Long before contact was actually made the magnetic field of the second confinement chamber was switched off. All seven shut down over a period of a hundred picoseconds, producing a specifically shaped blast wave.

At eighty-eight kilometres away, the antimatter pellets had annihilated an equal mass of matter, resulting in a titanic energy release. The spear of plasma which formed was a thousand times hotter than the core of a star, hurtling towards the *Beezling* at relativistic velocities.

Sensor clusters and thermo-dump panels vaporized immediately as the stream of disassociated ions slammed into the *Beezling*. Molecular-binding force generators laboured to maintain the silicon hull's integrity, a struggle they were always destined to lose against such ferocity. Breakthrough occurred in a dozen different places at once. Plasma surged in, playing over the complex, delicate systems like a blowtorch over snow crystals.

The luckless *Beezling* suffered a further blow from fate. One of the plasma streams hit a deuterium tank, searing its way through the foam insulation and titanium shell. The cryogenic liquid reverted to its natural gaseous state under immense pressure, ripping the tank open, and blasting fragments in every direction. An eight-metre section of the hull buckled upwards, and a volcanic geyser of deuterium haemorrhaged out towards the stars past shredded fingers of silicon.

Combat wasp explosions were still flooding surrounding space with torrents of light and elementary particles. But the *Beezling* was an inert hulk at the centre of a dissipating halo, her hull fissured, reaction drive off, spinning like a broken bird.

The three attacking blackhawk captains observed the last volley of *Beezling*'s combat wasps lock on to their own ships and race vengefully across the gulf. Thousands of kilometres away, their colleague scored a debilitating strike on the *Chengho*. And the *Beezling*'s combat wasps had halved the separation distance.

Energy patterning cells applied a terrible stress against the fabric of space, and the blackhawks slipped into the gaping wormholes which opened, contracting the interstices behind them. The *Beezling*'s combat wasps lost track of their targets; on-board processors began to scan round and round in an increasingly futile attempt to re-acquire the missing signatures as the drones rushed further and further away from the disabled warship.

The return of consciousness wasn't quite as welcome as it should have been, even though it meant that Dr Alkad Mzu was still alive. Her left leg was a source of nauseous pain. She could remember hearing the bones snapping as her knee hinged fully open. Then came the twists of a shifting gravity field, far more effective than any torturer. Her neural nanonics had damped down the worst of the pain, but the *Beezling*'s final convulsion had brought a blessed oblivion.

How in Mother Mary's name did we survive that?

She thought she had been prepared for the inherent risk of the mission failing, for death to claim her. Her work at the university back on Garissa made her all too aware of the energy levels required to push a starship through a ZTT jump, and what would happen should an instability occur in the patterning nodes. It never seemed to bother the navy crew, or rather they were better at hiding it. She knew also that there was a small chance they would be intercepted by Omutan naval craft once the *Beezling* emerged above their target star. But even that wouldn't be so bad, the end should a combat wasp break through *Beezling*'s defensive shield would probably be instantaneous. She even acknowledged that the Alchemist might malfunction. But this . . . Hunted down out here, unprepared physically or mentally, and then to survive, however tenuously. How could the good Mother Mary be so callous? Unless perhaps even She feared the Alchemist?

Residual graphics seemed to swirl obstinately among the ailing thoughts of her consciousness. Vector lines intersected their original jump coordinate thirty-seven thousand kilometres ahead. Omuta was a small, unremarkable star directly in front of the coordinate. Two more jumps, and they would have been in the system's Oort cloud, the sparse halo of ice-dust clouds and slumbering comets which marked the boundary of interstellar space. They were approaching from galactic north, well outside the plane of the ecliptic, trying to avoid detection.

She had helped plan the mission profile, offering her comments to a room full of senior navy staff who were visibly nervous in her presence. It was a syndrome which had affected more and more people in the secret military station as her work progressed.

Alkad had given the Confederation something new to fear, something which surpassed even the destructive power of antimatter. A star slayer. And that prospect was as humbling as it was terrifying. She had resigned herself that after the war billions of planet dwellers would look up at the naked stars, waiting for the twinkling light which had been Omuta to vanish from the night sky. Then they would remember her name, and curse her to hell.

All because I was too stupid to learn from past mistakes. Just like all the other dreaming fools throughout history, wrapped up with seductive, clean equations, their simplistic, isolated elegance, giving no thought to the messy, bloody, *physical* application that was their ultimate reality. As if we didn't have enough weapons already. But that's human nature, we've always got to go one better, to increase the terror another notch. And for what?

Three hundred and eighty-seven Dorados: large asteroids with a nearly pure metal content. They were orbiting a red-dwarf sun twenty light-years away from Garissa, twenty-nine light-years from Omuta. Scoutships from both inhabited systems had stumbled across them virtually simultaneously. Who had actually been first would never now be known. Both governments had claimed them: the wealth contained in the lonely metal chunks would be a heady boost for the planet whose companies could mine and refine such plentiful ore.

At first it had been a squabble, a collection of *incidents*. Prospecting and survey ships dispatched to the Dorados had been attacked by "pirates." And, as always, the conflict had escalated. It ceased to be the ships, and started to become their home asteroid ports. Then nearby industrial stations had proved tempting targets. The Confederation Assembly's attempt to mediate had come to nothing.

Both sides had called in their registered naval reserves, and started to hire the independent traders, with their fast, well-equipped ships capable of deploying combat wasps. Finally, last month, Omuta had used an antimatter bomb against an industrial asteroid settlement in the Garissa system. Fifty-six thousand people had been killed when the biosphere chamber ruptured, spewing them out into space. Those who survived, another eighteen thousand with their mashed fluid-clogged lungs, decompressed capillaries, and dissevered skin, had strained the planet's medical facilities close to breaking point. Over seven hundred had been sent to the university's medical school, which had beds for three hundred. Alkad had witnessed the chaos and pain first hand, heard the gurgling screams that never ended.

So now it was retaliation time. Because, as everybody knew, the next stage would be planetary bombardment. And Alkad Mzu had been surprised to find her nationalistic jingoism supplanting the academic aloofness which had ruled her life to date. Her *world* was being threatened.

The only credible defence was to hit Omuta first, and hit it hard. Her precious hypothetical equations had been grasped at by the navy, which rushed to turn them into functional hardware.

"I wish I could stop you from feeling so much guilt," Peter had said. That was the day they had left the planet, the two of them waiting in the officers' mess of a navy spaceport while their shuttle was prepared.

"Wouldn't you feel guilty?" she asked irritably. She didn't want to talk, but she didn't want to be silent either.

"Yes. But not as much as you. You're taking the blame for the entire conflict. You shouldn't do that. Both of us, all of us, everyone on the planet, we're all being propelled by fate."

"How many despots and warlords have said that down the centuries? I wonder," she retorted.

His face managed to be sad and sympathetic at the same time.

Alkad relented, and took his hand. "But thank you for coming with me, anyway. I don't think I could stand the navy people by myself."

"It will be all right, you know," he said softly. "The government isn't going to release any details, least of all the name of the inventor."

"I'll be able to walk straight back into the job, you mean?" she asked. There was too much bitterness in her voice. "As if nothing had happened?" She knew it wouldn't happen that way. Intelligence agencies from half the governments in the Confederation would find out who she was, if they hadn't already. Her fate wouldn't be decided by any cabinet minister on politically insignificant Garissa.

"Maybe not nothing," he said. "But the university will

still be there. The students. That's what you and I live for, isn't it? The real reason we're here, protecting all that."

"Yes," she said, as if uttering the word made it fact. She looked out of the window. They were close to the equator here, Garissa's sun bleaching the sky to a featureless white glare. "It's October back there now. The campus will be knee deep in featherseeds. I always used to think that stuff was a bloody great nuisance. Whoever had the idea of founding an African-ethnic colony on a world that's three-quarters temperate zones?"

"Now that's a tired old myth, that we have to be limited to tropical hellholes. It's our society which counts. In any case, I like the winters. And you'd bitch if it was as hot as this place the whole year round."

"You're right." She gave a brittle laugh.

He sighed, studying her face. "It's their star we're aiming for, Alkad, not Omuta itself. They'll have a chance. A good chance."

"There are seventy-five million people on that planet. There will be no light, no warmth."

"The Confederation will help. Hell, when the Great Dispersal was at its peak, Earth was deporting over ten million people a week."

"Those old colony-transport ships have gone now."

"Earth's Govcentral is still kicking out a good million a week even now; and there are thousands of military transports. It can be done."

She nodded mutely, knowing it was all hopeless. The Confederation couldn't even get two minor governments to agree to a peace formula when we both wanted it. What chance has the Assembly got trying to coordinate grudgingly donated resources from eight hundred and sixty disparate inhabited star systems?

The sunlight pouring through the mess window deepened to a sickly red and started to fade. Alkad wondered woozily if the Alchemist was already at work on it. But then the stimulant programs steadied her thoughts, and she realized she was in free fall, her cabin illuminated by a weak pink-tinged emergency light. People were floating around her. *Beezling*'s crew, murmuring in quiet worried tones. Something warm and damp brushed against her cheek, sticking. She brought her hand up instinctively. A swarm of dark motes swam across her field of view, glistening in the light. Blood!

"Peter?" She thought she was shouting his name, but her voice seemed very faint. "Peter!"

"Easy, easy." That was a crew-member. Menzul? He was holding her arms, preventing her from bouncing around the confined space.

She caught sight of Peter. Two more crew were hovering over him. His entire face was encased by a medical nanonic package which looked like a sheet of thick green polythene.

"Oh, merciful Mary!"

"He's OK," Menzul said quickly. "He'll be all right. The nanonic package can cope."

"What happened?"

"A squadron of blackhawks caught us. An antimatter blast breached the hull. Screwed us pretty good."

"What about the Alchemist?"

Menzul shrugged loosely. "In one piece. Not that it matters much now."

"Why?" Even as she asked she didn't want to know.

"The hull breach wrecked thirty per cent of our jump nodes. We're a navy ship, we can jump with ten per cent knocked out. But thirty . . . Looks like we're stuck out here; seven light-years from the nearest inhabited star system."

At that moment they were precisely thirty-six and a half light-years from their G3 home star, Garissa. If they had trained the *Beezling*'s remaining optical sensors on the faint diamond of light far behind, and if those sensors possessed sufficient resolution, then in thirty-six years, six months, and two days they would have seen a brief surge in the apparent magnitude as Omuta's mercenary ships dropped fifteen antimatter planet-buster bombs on their home world. Each one had a megatonnage blast equivalent to the asteroid impact which wiped out the dinosaurs on Earth. Garissa's atmosphere was ruined beyond redemption. Superstorms arose which would rage for millennia to come. By themselves, they weren't fatal. On Earth, the shielded arcologies had sheltered people from their heat-wrecked climate for five and a half centuries. But unlike an asteroid impact, where the energy release was purely thermal, the planet-busters each emitted the same amount of radiation as a small solar flare. Within eight hours, the rampaging storms had spread the nuclear fallout right across the planet, rendering it completely uninhabitable. Total sterilization took a further two months.

2

The Ly-cilph home planet was located in a galaxy far removed from the one which would ultimately host the human Confederation. Strictly speaking it wasn't a planet at all, but a moon, one of twenty-nine orbiting a gas supergiant, a formidable orb two hundred thousand kilometres in diameter, itself a failed brown-dwarf star. After its accretion had finished it lacked enough mass for fusion ignition; but none the less its inexorable gravitational contraction generated a massive thermal output. What was ostensibly its nightside fluoresced near the bottom end of the visible spectrum, producing a weary emberlike glow which fluctuated in continental-sized patterns as the dense turbulent clouds raged in never ending cyclones. Across the dayside, where lemon-shaded rays from the K4 primary sun fell, the storm bands shone a lambent salmon-pink.

There were five major moons, with the Ly-cilph planet the fourth out from the cloud tops, and the only one with an atmosphere. The remaining twenty-four satellites were all barren rocks: captured asteroids, junk left over from the solar system's formation, all of them less than seven hundred kilometres in diameter. They ranged from a baked rock ball skimming one thousand kilometres above the clouds, from which the metal ores had boiled away like a comet's volatiles, up to a glaciated planetoid in a retrograde orbit five and a half million kilometres out.

Local space was hazardous in the extreme. A vast magnetosphere confined and channelled the supergiant's prodigious outpouring of charged particles, producing a lethal radiation belt. Radio emission was a ceaseless white-noise howl. The three large moons orbiting below the Ly-cilph homeworld were all inside the radiation belt, and completely sterile. The innermost of the three was chained to the ionosphere with a colossal flux tube, along which titanic energies sizzled. It also trailed a plasma torus around its orbital path, the densest ring of particles inside the magnetosphere's comprehensive embrace. Instant death to living tissue.

The tidal-locked Ly-cilph world coasted along seventy thousand kilometres above the tenuous outer fringes of the magnetosphere, beyond the reach of the worst radiation. Occasional palpitations within the flux lines would bombard the upper atmosphere with protons and electrons, sending squalls of solar-bright borealis lights slithering and twisting silently across the rusty sky.

Atmospheric composition was an oxygen-nitrogen mix, with various sulphurous compounds, and an inordinately high water-vapour level. Mist, fog, and stacked cloud layers were the norm. Proximity to the infrared glow of the supergiant gave it a perpetual tropical climate, with the warm, wet air of the nearside constantly on the move, rushing around to the farside where it cooled, radiating its thermal load away into space, and then returning via storms which traversed the poles. Weather was a drab constant, always blowing, always raining, the strength of the gusts and downpours dictated by the orbital location. Night fell in one place, at one time. On the farside, when supergiant and planet were in an inferior conjunction, and the hellish red cloudscape eclipsed the nearside's brief glimpse of the sun.

It was a cycle which was broken only once every nine years, when a new force was applied to the timeless equation. A four-moon conjunction, which brought chaos and devastation to the surface with storms of biblical ferocity.

The warmth and the light had incubated life on this world, as they had on countless billions throughout the universe. There had been no seas, no oceans when the first migratory interstellar germ fell onto the pristine planet, rooting its way into the mucky stain of chemicals infecting the bubbling muddy waters. Tidal forces had left a smooth surface, breaking down mountains, grinding away at the steppes left over from the time of formation. Lakes, rivers, and flood plains covered the land, steaming and being rained on. There was no free oxygen back then, it was all combined with carbon.

A solid stratum of white cloud ensured the infrared radiation found it hard to escape, even in the centre of the farside. Temperatures were intolerably high.

The first life, as always, was algae, a tough slime which spread through the water, seeping down rivers and streams to contaminate the lakes, hurried through the air by the tireless convection currents. It altered and adapted over geological eras, slowly learning to utilize the two contrasting light sources as an additional energy supply. Success, when it came, was swift, mere millennia. Oxygen poured forth. Carbon was digested. The temperature fell. The rain quickened, thinning the clouds, clearing the sky. Evolution began once more.

For millions of years, the planet's governing nine-year cycle was of no importance. Storms and hurricanes were an irrelevance to single-cell amoebas floating sluggishly through the lakes and rivers, nor did they matter to the primitive lichens which were creeping over the rocks. But the cells adrift in the water gradually began to form cooperative colonies, and specialization occurred. Jelly-like worms appeared in the lakes, brainless, instinct-driven and metabolically inefficient, little more than mobile lichen. But it was a start. Birth and death began to replace fission as the premier method of reproduction. Mutations crept in, sometimes producing improvements, more often resulting in inviability. Failed strains were rapidly culled by merciless nature. Divergence appeared, the dawn of a million species; DNA strands lengthened, a chemical record of progress and blind alleys. Crawling creatures emerged onto the lakesides, only to be scalded by the harsh chemicals making up the atmosphere. Yet they persisted.

Life was a steady progression, following a pattern which was as standard as circumstances would allow. There were no such things as ice ages to alter the direction which this world's creatures were taking, no instabilities causing profound climate changes. Only the nine-yearly storms, appearing without fail, which became the dominant influence. The new animals' breeding cycles were structured around it, plant growth was restricted by it.

The planet matured into a jungle world, a landscape of

swamps and lush verdancy, where giant ferns covered the surface from pole to pole, and were themselves webbed and choked with tenacious creepers reaching for the clear sky. Floating weeds turned the smaller lakes into vast marshlands. Elaborate ruff flowers vied for the attention of insects and birds, seed pods with skirts of hardened petals flew like kites through the air. Wood was non-existent, of course, wood required decades of uninterrupted growth to form.

Two wildly different flora genealogies sprang up, with the terminator as an unbreachable dividing line, and battleground. Farside plants adapted to the sun's yellow light: they were capable of tolerating the long nights accompanying conjunction, the cooler temperatures. Nearside was the province of red light, falling without end: its black-leafed plants were taller, stronger, more vigorous, yet they were unable to conquer farside. Night killed them, yellow light alone was insufficient to drive their demanding photosynthesis, and the scattered refraction of red light by the thick atmosphere never carried far enough, haunting the land for a couple of hundred kilometres beyond the terminator.

The animals were more adaptive, ranging freely across farside and nearside. Dinosaur-analogues never appeared, they were too big, requiring too much time to grow. Apart from bird-analogues, lizard creatures with membranous wings, most animals were smallish, reflecting their aquatic heritage. All were cold-blooded, at home in the muddy streams and weed-clogged pools. They retained that ancestral trait out of pure necessity. For that was where their eggs were laid, buried deep and safe in the mud of the lakebeds, hidden away from the worst ravages of the storm. That was how all life survived while the winds scoured the world, as seeds and eggs and spores, ready to surge forth when stability returned in a few short weeks.

On such an inimical world life can evolve in one of two ways. There are the defeated, littered on countless planets across the cosmos, weak, anaemic creatures huddled in their dead-end sanctuaries, a little protective niche in the local ecology, never rising above a rudimentary level, their very lack of sophistication providing them with the means of continuation. Or there are the triumphant, the creatures which refuse to be beaten, which fight tooth and nail and claw and tentacle against their adversity; those for which circumstances act as an evolutionary spur. The dividing line is thin; it might even be that a devastating storm every eight years could bring genetic ruination. But nine years . . . nine proved enough time to ensure survival, allowing the denizens to rise to the challenge rather than sink back into their ubiquitous mires.

The Ly-cilph claimed such a victory. A mere eight hundred million years after life had begun on their world they had reached their pinnacle of evolution. They became transcendent entities.

Their nine-year cycle starts in a fish form, hatching from the black egg-clusters concealed below the mud. Billions of free-floating slugs emerge, two centimetres long, and are eaten by faster, meaner predators as they gorge themselves on the abundant sludge of decayed vegetation putrefying in the water. They grow and change over three years, losing their tails, developing a snail-like skirt. They cling to the bottom of their lakes, an ovoid body ninety centimetres high, with ten tentacles rising up from the crown. The tentacles are smooth, sixty centimetres long, devoid of suckers, but with a sharp curved horn on the tip; and they're fast, exploding like a nest of enraged pythons to snatch their ignorant prey swimming overhead.

When their full size has been reached they slide up out of the water to range through the planetwide jungle. Gills adapt to breathe the harsh musky air, tentacle muscles strengthen to support the drooping limbs away from the water's cosy buoyancy. And they eat, rummaging through the matted undergrowth with insistent horns to find the black, wizened nutlike nodes that have been lying there neglected since the storm. The nodes are made up of cells saturated with chemical memory tracers, memories containing information, the knowledge accumulated by the Ly-cilph race throughout time. They bring understanding, an instant leap to sentience, and trigger the telepathic centre of their brains. Now they have risen above a simple animal level of existence they have much to converse about.

The knowledge is mainly of a philosophical nature, although mathematics is highly developed; what they know is what they have observed and speculated upon, and added to with each generation. Farside night acts as a magnet as they gather to observe the stars. Eyes and minds linked by telepathy, acting as a gigantic multi-segment telescope. There is no technology, no economy. Their culture is not orientated towards the mechanical or materialistic; their knowledge is their wealth. The data-processing capacity of their linked minds far exceeds that of any electronic computer system, and their perception is not limited to the meagre electromagnetic wavelengths of the optical bands.

Once awoken, they learn. It is their purpose. They have so little time in their corporeal form, and the universe they find themselves in, the splendour of the gas supergiant and its multifarious satellites, is large. Nature has ordained them as gatherers of knowledge. If life has a purpose, they speculate, then it must be a journey to complete understanding. In that respect intellect and nature have come to a smooth concordance.

In the ninth year after their hatching, the four large innermost moons line up once more. The distortion they cause in the supergiant's magnetosphere acts like an extension to the flux tube. The agitated particles of the ionosphere which use it as a conduit up to the first moon's plasma torus now find themselves rising higher, up to the second moon, then the third, higher still, fountaining out of the magnetosphere altogether. The Ly-cilph world swings round into their path.

It is not a tight directed beam; up at the mushrooming crown the protons and electrons and neutrons have none of the energy they possessed when the roiling flux lines flung them past the first moon. But as always it is the sheer scale of events within the gas supergiant's domain which proves so overwhelming.

The Ly-cilph world takes ten hours to traverse through the invisible cloud of ions loitering outside the flux lines. In that time, the energy which floods into the atmosphere is more than sufficient to destroy the equilibrium of the slowly circulating convection currents.

The deluge arrives at the end of the planet's one and only mating season. The Ly-cilph and their non-sentient cousins have produced their eggs and secreted them into the lakebeds. Plants have flowered and scattered their seeds across the landscape. Now there is only the prospect of death.

When the first titanic bursts of azure lightning break overhead, the Ly-cilph stop their analysing and deliberations, and begin to impart all they know into the empty cells of the nodes which have grown out of their skin like warts around the base of their tentacles.

The winds howl, voicing the planet's torment. Gusts are strong enough to break the metre-thick stems of the fern trees. Once one goes it starts a domino effect in the jungle. Destruction spreads out in vast ripples, looking like bomb blasts from above. Clouds are torn apart by the violence, reduced to cotton tufts spinning frantically in the grip of small, ferocious whirlwinds. Micro-typhoons plunge back and forth, accelerating the obliteration of the jungle.

All the while the Ly-cilph remain steadfast, their adhesive skirts anchoring them to the ground as the air around them fills with broken fronds and shredded leaves. The nodes, now saturated with their precious heritage, drop off like ripe fruit. They will lie hidden amongst the grass and roots for another three years.

Nearside is ablaze with potent lightstorms. High above the tattered clouds, the aurora borealis forms a veil across the sky, a garish mother-of-pearl haze riddled with thousands of long, lurid scintillations, like giant shooting stars. Beyond that, the conjunction is joined, three moons sliding into alignment, bathed in an eerie trillion-amp phosphorescence. An epicentre to one of the gas supergiant's planet-swallowing cyclones.

The particle jet has reached its zenith. The flux tube's rain of energy penetrates the tormented lower atmosphere. It is embraced by the Ly-cilph. Their minds consume the power, using it to metamorphose once again. The nodes brought them sentience, the supergiant's surplus energy brings them transcendence. They leave the chrysalis of the flesh behind, shooting up the stream of particles at lightspeed, spacefree and eternal.

The liberated minds swarm above their abandoned world

for several days, watching the storms abate, the clouds re-form, the old convection currents return to their familiar courses. The Ly-cilph have achieved incorporeality, but their perspective, shaped by the formative material exis-tence, remains unchanged. As before, they deem the purpose of their life is experience, perhaps eventually to be followed by understanding. The difference is that they are no longer restricted to a single world and brief glimpses of the stars; now the entire universe is laid out before them, they wish to know it all.

They begin to drift away from the odd planet which birthed them, tentatively at first, then with greater boldness, dispersing like an expanding wave of eager ghosts. One day they will return to this point, all the generations of Ly-cilph that ever lived. It will not happen while the primary star still burns; they will travel until they meet the boundary of the universe as it contracts once more, following the galactic su-perclusters as they fall into the reborn dark mass at the cen-tre, the cosmic egg regathering all it has lost. Then they will be back, congregating around the black star husk, sharing the knowledge they have brought, searching through it for that elusive ultimate understanding. And after understanding they will know what lies beyond, and with that a hope of a further switch to yet another level of existence. Possibly the Ly-cilph will be the only entities to survive the present uni-verse's final reconfiguration.

But until then they are content to observe and learn. Their very nature precludes them from taking part in the myriad dramas of life and matter unfolding before their ethereal senses.

Or so they believe.

3

Iasius had come back to Saturn to die.

Three hundred and fifty thousand kilometres above the gas giant's wan beige cloudscape the wormhole terminus expanded, and the voidhawk slipped out into real space. Sensors mounted on the strategic-defence satellites patrolling the gas giant's designated starship emergence zone found the infrared glow straight away, as radar waves tickled the hull. *Iasius* hailed the nearest habitat with its affinity, and identified itself. The satellite sensors slid their focus away, resuming their vigil.

Captain and crew borrowed the bitek starship's paramount senses to observe the glorious ringed planet outside, whilst all the time their minds wept with the knowledge of what was to come. They were flying above the gas giant's sunlit hemisphere, a nearly full crescent showing. The rings were spread out ahead and two degrees below them, seemingly solid, yet stirring, as if a gritty gas had been trapped between two panes of glass. Starlight twinkled through. Such majestic beauty seemed to deny their terrible reason for returning.

Iasius's affinity touched their minds. **Feel no sorrow,** the bitek starship said silently. **I do not. What is, is. You have helped to fill my life. For that I thank you.**

Alone in her cabin, Captain Athene felt her mental tears become real. She was as tall as any woman of the hundred families, whose geneticists had concentrated on enhancing sturdiness so their descendants could comfortably spend a lifetime coping with the arduous conditions of spaceflight. Her carefully formatted evolution had given her a long, handsome face, now heavily wrinkled, and rich auburn hair which had lost its youthful sheen to a lustrous silver. In her immaculate ocean-blue ship-tunic she projected a regal quality of assurance, which always elicited total confidence from her crews. But now her composure had vanished, expressive violet eyes reflecting the utter anguish welling up inside.

No, Athene, please don't.

I can't help it, her mind cried back. **It's so unfair. We should go together, we should be allowed.**

There was an eldritch caress down her spine, more tender than any human lover could ever bestow. She had felt that same touch on every day of all her hundred and eight years. Her only true love. None of her three husbands received as much emotional devotion as *Iasius*, nor, she admitted with something approaching sacrilege, had her eight children, and three of them she had carried in her own womb. But other Edenists understood and sympathized; with their communal affinity there was no hiding emotions or truth. The birthbond between the voidhawks and their captains was strong enough to survive anything the universe could possibly throw at them. Except death, the most private section of her mind whispered.

It is my time, *Iasius* said simply. There was an overtone of contentment within the silent voice. If the voidhawk had had lungs, Athene thought it would have sighed at that moment.

I know, she said wistfully. It had been increasingly obvious during the last few weeks. The once omnipotent energy patterning cells were now struggling to open a wormhole interstice. Where over half a century ago there had been a feeling that a single swallow manoeuvre could span the galaxy, the pair of them now experienced a muted sense of relief if a planned fifteen light-year swallow was accomplished only a light-month short of the required coordinate. **Damn the geneticists. Is parity so much to ask for?** she demanded.

One day perhaps they will make ship and captain live as long as each other. But this which we have now, I feel a rightness to it. Someone has to mother our children. You will be as good a mother as you have been a captain. I know this.

The sudden burst of self-satisfied conviction in the mental voice made her grin. Sticky lashes batted some of the moisture away. **Raising ten children at my age. Goodness!**

You will do well. They will prosper. I am happy.

I love you, *Iasius*. If I was allowed to have my life again, I would never change a second of it.

I would.

You would? she asked, startled.

Yes. I would spend one day as a human. To see what it was like.

Believe me, both the pleasures and the pain are greatly exaggerated.

Iasius chuckled. Optically sensitive cells protruding like blisters from its hull located the Romulus habitat, and the starship felt for its mass with a tiny ripple in the spacial distortion field its energy patterning cells were generating. The habitat's solidity registered in its consciousness, a substantial mote orbiting the outside edge of the F-ring. Substantial but hollow, a bitek polyp cylinder forty-five kilometres long, ten wide; it was one of the two original voidhawk bases germinated by the hundred families back in 2225. There were two hundred and sixty-eight similar habitats orbiting Saturn now, along with their subsidiary industrial stations, their numbers tangible evidence of just how important the bitek starships had become to the whole Edenist economy.

The starship sent power flashing through its patterning cells, focusing energy towards infinity, the loci distorting space outside the hull, but never enough to open a wormhole interstice. They rode the distortion wave towards the habitat like a surfer racing for the beach, quickly accelerating to three gees. A secondary manipulation of the distortion field generated a counter-acceleration force for the benefit of the crew, providing them an apparent acceleration of one gee. A smooth and comfortable ride, unmatched by Adamist starships with their fusion drives.

Athene knew she would never be quite so comfortable if she ever took a trip in a voidhawk again. With *Iasius* she could always feel the nothingness of the vacuum flowing by; a sensation she equated with being in a rowing-boat on some country river, and letting her hand trail through the calm water. Passengers never received that feeling. Passengers were meat.

Go on, she told the starship. **Call for them.**

All right.

She smiled for both of them at the eagerness in the tone.

Iasius called. Opening its affinity full, projecting a wordless shout of joy and sorrow over a spherical zone thirty astronomical units in radius. Calling for mates.

Like all voidhawks, *Iasius* was a creature of deep space, unable to operate close to the confines of a strong gravity field. It had a lenticular shape, measuring one hundred and ten metres in diameter, thirty metres deep at the centre. The hull was a tough polyp, midnight blue in colour, its outer layer gradually boiling away in the vacuum, replaced by new cells growing up from the mitosis layer. Internally, twenty per cent of its mass was given over to specialist organs—nutrient reserve bladders, heart pumps supplying the vast capillary network, and neuron cells—all packaged together neatly within a cylindrical chamber at the centre of the body. The remaining eighty per cent of its bulk was made up from a solid honeycomb of energy patterning cells which generated the spatial distortion field it used for both propulsion modes. It was those cells which were decaying in ever larger quantities. Like human neurons they were unable to regenerate effectively, which dictated the starship's life expectancy. Voidhawks rarely saw out more than a hundred and ten years.

Both the upper and lower hull surfaces had a wide circular groove halfway out from the middle, which the mechanical systems were slotted into. The lower hull groove was fitted mainly with cradles for cargo-pods, the circle of folded titanium struts interrupted only by a few sealed ancillary systems modules. Crew quarters nestled in the upper hull groove, a chrome-silver toroid equipped with lounges, cabins, a small hangar for the atmospheric flyer, fusion generators, fuel, life-support units. Human essentials.

Athene walked around the toroid's central corridor one last time. Her current husband, Sinon, accompanied her as she performed her final sacrosanct duty: initiating the children who would grow up to be the captains of the next generation. There were ten of them, zygotes, Athene's ova fertilized with sperm from her three husbands and two dear lovers. They had been waiting in zero-tau from the moment of conception, protected from entropy, ready for this day.

Sinon had provided the sperm for only one child. But walking beside her, he found he held no resentment. He was from the original hundred families; several of his ancestors had been captains, as well as two of his half-siblings; for just one of his own children to be given the privilege was honour enough.

The corridor had a hexagonal cross-section, its surface made out of a smooth pale-green composite that glowed from within. Athene and Sinon walked at the head of the silent procession of the seven-strong crew, air whirring softly from overhead grilles the only sound. They came to a section of the corridor where the composite strip of the lower wall angle merged seamlessly with the hull, revealing an oval patch of the dark blue polyp. Athene stopped before it.

This egg I name *Oenone*, Iasius said.

The polyp bulged up at the centre, its apex thinning as it rose, becoming translucent. Red rawness showed beneath it, the crest of a stem as thick as a human leg which stretched right down into the core of the starship's body. The tumescent apex split open, dribbling a thick gelatinous goo onto the corridor floor. Inside, the sphincter muscle at the top of the red stem dilated, looking remarkably similar to a waiting toothless mouth. The dark tube inside palpitated slowly.

Athene held up the bitek sustentator, a sphere five centimetres in diameter, flesh-purple, maintained at body temperature. According to the data core on the zero-tau pod it had been kept in, the zygote inside was female; it was also the one Sinon had fathered. She bent down and pushed it gently into the waiting orifice.

This child I name Syrinx.

The little sustentator globe was ingested with a quiet wet slurp. The sphincter lips closed, and the stem sank back down out of sight. Sinon patted her shoulder, and they gave each other a proud smile.

They will flourish together, *Iasius* said proudly.
Yes.

Athene walked on. There were another four zygotes left to initiate, and Romulus was growing larger outside.

The Saturn habitats were keening their regret at *Iasius*'s call. Voidhawks throughout the solar system answered with pride and camaraderie; those that weren't outbound with cargo abandoned their flights to flock around Romulus in anticipation.

Iasius curved gently round the non-rotational dock at the northern endcap. With her eyes closed, Athene let the affinity bond image from the voidhawk's sensor blisters expand into her mind with superhuman clarity. Her visual reference of the habitat altered as the endcap loomed large beyond the rim of the starship's hull. She saw the vast expanse of finely textured red-brown polyp as an approaching cliff face; one with four concentrically arrayed ledges, as if ripples had raced out from the axis in some distant time, only to be frozen as they peaked.

The voidhawk chased after the second ledge, two kilometres out from the axis, swooping round to match the habitat's rotation. Adamist reaction-drive spaceships didn't have anything like the manoeuvrability necessary to land on the ledges, and they were reserved for voidhawks alone.

Iasius shot in over the edge, seeming to hover above the long rank of mushroomlike docking pedestals which protruded from the floor, before choosing a vacant one. For all its bulk, it alighted with the delicate grace of a hummingbird.

Athene and Sinon felt the gravity fade down to half a gee as the distortion field dissipated. She watched the big flat-tyred crew bus rolling slowly towards the bitek starship, elephant-snout airlock tube held upwards.

Come along, Sinon urged, his mind dark with emotion. He touched her elbow, seeing all too plainly the wish to remain during the last flight.

She nodded her head reluctantly. "You're right," she said out loud.

I'm sorry that doesn't make it any easier.

She gave him a tired smile and allowed him to lead her

out of the lounge. The bus had arrived at the rim of the void-hawk. Its airlock tube lengthened, sliding over the upper hull surface to reach the crew toroid.

Sinon diverted his attention away from his wife to the flock of voidhawks matching pace with the ledge. There were over seventy waiting, latecomers rising into view as they left their crews behind on the other ledges. The emotional backwash from the waiting bitek starships was impossible to filter out, and he could feel his own blood singing in response.

It wasn't until he and Athene reached the passage to the airlock that he noticed an irregularity in the flock. *Iasius* obligingly focused on the starship in question.

That's a blackhawk! Sinon exclaimed.

Amidst the classic lens shapes it seemed oddly asymmetric, drawing the eye. A flattened teardrop, slightly asymmetric, with the upper hull's dorsal bulge fatter than that on the lower hull; from what he supposed was prow to stern it measured an easy hundred and thirty metres; the blue polyp hull was mottled with a tattered purple web pattern.

The larger size and various unorthodox configurations which set the blackhawks apart, their divergence from the voidhawk norm (some called it evolution), came about because of their captains' requirement for greater power. Actually, improved combat performance was what they were after, Sinon thought acrimoniously. The price for that agility usually came in the form of a shorter lifespan.

That is the *Udat*, *Iasius* said equably. **It is fast and powerful. A worthy aspirant.**

There's your answer, then, Athene said, using affinity's singular-engagement mode so the rest of the crew were excluded from the exchange. She had a gleam in her eye as they paused by the airlock's inner hatch.

Sinon pulled a sour face, then shrugged and walked off down the tube to the bus, giving her the final moment alone with her ship.

There was a hum in the corridor she had never heard before, a resonance coming from *Iasius*'s excitement. When she put her fingers to the sleek composite wall there was nothing, no tremor or vibration. Perhaps it was only in her mind. She turned and looked back into the toroid, the familiar confined corridors and lounges. Their whole world.

"Goodbye," she whispered.

I will love you always.

The crew bus trundled back over the ledge towards the cliff of polyp, nuzzling up to a metal airlock set into the base. *Iasius* laughed uproariously across the communal affinity band; it could feel the ten eggs inside its body, glowing with vitality, their urgency to be born. Without warning it streaked away from the pedestal, straight towards the waiting flock of its cousins. They scattered in delighted alarm.

This time there was no counter-acceleration force required for the crew toroid, no protection for fragile humans. No artificial safety limits. *Iasius* curved sharply, pulling an easy nine gees, then flattened its trajectory to fly between the endcap and the giant metal arm of the counter-rotating dock. Weak pearl-white sunlight fell on the hull as it moved out of the ledge's shadow. Saturn lay ahead, the razor-sharp line of the rings bisecting it cleanly. The bitek starship headed in for the planet-swathing streamers of ice crystals and primitive molecules at twelve gees, stray dust-motes and particles brushed smoothly aside by the distortion field's bow wave. Enthusiastic voidhawks raced after it, looking more and more like a stippled comet's tail as they emerged into the light.

In the crew quarters, metal was buckling under its new and enormous weight. Empty lounges and corridors were filled with drawn-out creaking sounds, composite furniture was splintering, collapsing onto the floor, each fresh fragment hitting with the force of a hammer blow, leaving a deep indentation. The cabins and galley were awash with water that squirted from broken pipes, strange ripples quivered across the surface as *Iasius* performed minute course adjustments.

Iasius entered the rings, optical-band perception degrading rapidly as the blizzard raging outside the hull thickened. It curved round again, bending its path in the direction which the ring particles orbited, but always at an angle, al-

ways heading inwards towards the massive presence of the
gas giant. It was a glorious game, dodging the larger chunks,
the dagger fragments of ice which glittered so coldly, the
frosted boulders, sable-black chunks of near-pure carbon.
The bitek starship soared around them all, spiralling, diving,
swooping in huge loops, heedless of the stress, of the toll its
frenzy extracted from the precious patterning cells. Energy
was free, coursing through the ring. Cosmic radiation, the
planet's undulating magnetic flux, the doughty gusts of solar
wind; *Iasius* swept it all in with the distortion field, concentrating it into an abundant coherent stream which the patterning cells absorbed and redirected.

By the time it reached the Encke division the power surplus was enough to energize the first egg. *Iasius* let out a
shrill cry of triumph. The other voidhawks responded. They
had followed tenaciously, striving to match the giddy helter-
skelter route *Iasius* had flown, boring down the passage it
had broken through the ring mass, desperately deflecting the
whirling particles tossed about by its wake. The leader of the
flock kept changing, none could equal the speed, nor match
the carefree audacity; often they were caught out by the savage turns, overshooting, blundering about in a squall of
undisturbed particles. It was a test of skill as well as power.
Even luck played a part. Luck was a trait worth inheriting.

When *Iasius* called the first time, *Hyale* was the closest, a
mere two hundred kilometres behind. It surged forward, and
Iasius relented, slowing fractionally, holding a straight
course. They rendezvoused, *Hyale* sliding in to hold position ten metres away, their hulls overlapping perfectly. Ring
particles skidded round them like snow from a ski blade.

Hyale began to impart its compositional pattern through
their affinity bond, a software DNA flowing into *Iasius* with
a sense of near orgasmic glory. *Iasius* incorporated the
Hyale's structural format into the vast energy squirt it discharged into the first egg.

The egg, *Acetes*, awoke in a blaze of wonder and exhilaration. Alive with racing currents of power, every cell
charged with rapture and purpose and the urge to burst into
immediate growth.

Iasius filled space with its glee.

Acetes found itself propelled out into the naked vacuum. Shattered fragments of *Iasius*'s hull were spinning away, a dark red hole set in midnight blue receding at a bewildering speed.

Free! the egg sang. **I'm free!**

A huge dark bulk hung above it. Forces it could sense but couldn't understand were slowing its wild tumbling. The universe seemed to be composed entirely of tiny splinters of matter pervaded by glowing energy bands. Voidhawks flashed past at frightening velocities.

Yes, you are free, *Hyale* said. **I bid you welcome to life.**

What is this place? What am I? Why can't I move like you? *Acetes* struggled to make sense of the scraps of knowledge fluttering around its racing mind, *Iasius*'s final gift.

Patience, *Hyale* counselled. **You will grow, you will learn. The data you possess will be integrated in time.**

Acetes cautiously opened its affinity sensitivity to cover the whole of Saturn's environment, and received a chorus of greetings from the habitats, an even greater wave of acknowledgement from individual adult Edenists, excited trills from children; and then its own kind offered encouragement, infant voidhawks nesting within the rings.

Its tumbling halted, it hung below *Hyale*'s lower hull, looking round with raw senses. *Hyale* began to alter their trajectory, moving the egg into a stable circular orbit around the gas giant where it would spend the next eighteen years growing to full size.

Iasius plunged on towards the cloudscape, ploughing a dark telltale furrow through the rings for any entity watching with the right kind of senses. Its flight produced enough power to energize two more eggs, *Briseis* and *Epopeus*, while it was still in the A-ring. *Hesperus* emerged while it was passing through the Cassini division. *Graeae, Ixion, Laocoön* and *Merope* all awoke in the B-ring, to be borne away by the voidhawks whose compositional patterns they had been given.

Udat caught up with *Iasius* near the inner edge of the B-ring. It had been a long, arduous flight, straining even the blackhawk's power reserves, testing manoeuvrability as seldom before. But now *Iasius* was calling for a mate again, and *Udat* glided across the gap until their distortion fields merged and the hulls almost touched. It sent *Iasius* its own compositional pattern through the affinity bond, swept away by a fervent gratification.

I thank you, *Iasius* said at the end. **I feel this one will be something special. There is a greatness to it.**

The egg cannoned up from its ovary, sending out a cascade of polyp flakes, and *Udat* was left to exert its distortion field to brake the intrigued, eager infant as *Iasius* departed. The puzzled blackhawk had no chance to ask what it had meant by that last enigmatic statement.

I welcome you to life, *Udat* said formally, when it had finally stopped the seven-metre globe from spinning.

Thank you, *Oenone* replied. **Where are we going now?**

To a higher orbit. This one is too close to the planet.

Oh! A pause as it probed round with immature senses, its giddy thoughts quietening down. **What is a planet?**

The last egg was *Priam*, ejected well below the meagre lip of the B-ring. Those voidhawks remaining in the flight, now down to some thirty strong, peeled away from *Iasius*. They were already dangerously close to the cloudscape which dominated a third of the sky; gravity was exerting its malign influence on local space, gnawing at the fringes of their distortion fields, impairing the propulsive efficiency.

Iasius continued to descend, its lower, faster orbit carrying it ahead of the others. Its distortion field began to falter, finally overwhelmed by the intensity of the gravitational effect five hundred kilometres above the gas giant.

The terminator rose ahead, a black occlusion devouring the silently meandering clouds. Faint phosphene speckles swam through the eddies and peaks, weaving in and out of the thicker ammonia-laden braids, their light ebbing and kindling in hesitant patterns. *Iasius* shot into the penumbra, darkness expanding around it like an elemental force. Saturn had ceased to be a planet, an astronomical object, it was becoming hugely solid. The bitek starship curved down at an ever increasing angle. Ahead of it was a single fiery streak, growing brighter in its optical sensors. The darkside equator, that frozen remote wasteland, was redolent with sublime grandeur.

Ring particles were falling alongside *Iasius*, a thick, dark rain, captured by the gossamer fingers of the ionosphere, a treacherously insistent caress which robbed them of speed, of altitude. And, ultimately, existence.

When they had been lured down to the fringes of the ionosphere, icy gusts of hydrogen molecules burnt around them, emitting banners of spectral flame. They dipped rapidly as atmospheric resistance built, first glowing like embers, then crowned by incandescent light; sunsparks, stretching a hundred-kilometre contrail behind them. Their billion-year flight ended swiftly in a violent spectacle: a dazzling concussion which flung out a shower of twinkling debris, quickly extinguished. All that remained was a tenuous trail of black soot which was swept up by the howling cyclones.

Iasius reached the extremity of the ionosphere. The light of the dying ring particles was hot on its lower hull. A tremulous glow appeared around its rim. Polyp began to char and flake away, orange flecks bulleting off into the distance. The bitek starship began to lose peripheral senses as its specialist receptor cells grew warm. Denser layers of hydrogen pummelled the hull. The desent curve began to get bumpy, vexatious supersonic winds were beginning to bite. *Iasius* flipped over. The abrupt turn had disastrous consequences on its avian glide; with the hull's blunt underside smashing head on into the hydrogen, the starship was suddenly subjected to a huge deceleration force. Dangerous quantities of flame blossomed right across the hull as broad swaths of polyp ablated. *Iasius* started to tumble helplessly down towards the scorching river of light.

The retinue of voidhawks watched solemnly from their safe orbit a thousand kilometres above, singing their silent hymn of mourning. After they had honoured *Iasius*'s passing with a single orbit they extended their distortion fields, and launched themselves back towards Romulus.

The human captains of the voidhawks involved with the mating flight and the *Iasius*'s crew had passed the time of the flight in a circular hall reserved for that one purpose. It reminded Athene of some of the medieval churches she had visited during her rare trips to Earth, the same vaulted ceiling and elaborate pillars, the intimidating air of reverence, though here the polyp walls were a clean snow-white, and instead of an altar there was a fountain bubbling out of an antique marble Venus.

She stood at the head of her crew, the image of Saturn's searing equator lingering in her mind. A last gentle emanation of peacefulness as the plasma sheath wrapped *Iasius* in its terminal embrace.

It was over.

The captains stopped by one at a time to extend their congratulations, their minds touching hers, bestowing a fragile compassion and understanding. Never, ever a commiseration; these gatherings were supposed to be a reaffirmation of life, celebrating the birth of the eggs. And *Iasius* had energized all ten; some voidhawks went to meet the equator with several eggs remaining.

Yes, they were right to toast *Iasius*.

He's coming over, look, Sinon said. There was a mild tone of resentment in the thought.

Athene raised her eyes from the captain of the *Pelion*, and observed Meyer making his way through the crowd towards her. The *Udat*'s captain was a broad-shouldered man in his late thirties, black hair cut back close to his skull. In contrast to the silky blue ceremonial ship-tunics of the voidhawk captains he wore a functional grey-green ship's one-piece and matching boots. He nodded curtly in response to the formal greetings he received.

If you can't say anything nice, Athene told Sinon, using singular-engagement mode, **don't say anything at all.** She didn't want anything to spoil the wake; besides she felt a certain sympathy for someone so obviously out of place as Meyer was. Nor would it do the hundred families any harm to introduce some diversity into their stock. She kept that thought tightly locked at the core of her mind, knowing full well how this bunch of traditionalists would react to such heresy.

Meyer stood before her, and inclined his head in a swift bow. He was a good five centimetres shorter than her, and she was one of the smaller Edenists in the hall.

Captain— she began. She cleared her throat. No fool like an old one; his affinity bond was with *Udat* alone. A unique neuron symbiont meshed with his medulla, providing him with a secure link to its clone-analogue in the *Udat*, nothing like the hereditary Edenist communal affinity. "Captain Meyer, my compliments to your ship. It was an excellent flight."

"Thank you for saying so, Captain. It was an honour to take part. You must be proud all the eggs were energized."

"Yes." She lifted her glass of white wine in salute. "So what brings you to Saturn?"

"Trade." He glanced round stiffly at the other Edenists. "I was delivering a cargo of electronics from Kulu."

Athene felt like laughing out loud, his freshness was just the tonic she needed. She put her arm through his, ignoring the startled looks it caused, and drew him away from the rest of the crew. "Come on, you're not comfortable with them. And I'm too old to be bothered by how many navy flight code violation warrants are hanging over your head. *Iasius* and I left all that behind us a long time ago."

"You used to be in the Confederation Navy?"

"Yes. Most of us put in a shift. We Edenists have a strong sense of duty sequenced into us."

He grinned into his glass. "You must have been a formidable team, that was some mating flight."

"History now. What about you? I want to hear all about life on the knife edge. The gung-ho adventures of an independent trader, the shady deals, the wild flights. Are you fabulously wealthy? I have several granddaughters I wouldn't mind getting rid of."

Meyer laughed. "You have no grandchildren. You're too young."

"Nonsense. Stop being so gallant. Some of the girls are older than you." She enjoyed drawing him out, listening to his stories, his difficulties in making the repayments to the bank for the loan he'd taken to buy *Udat*, his anger at the shipping cartels. He provided a welcome anodyne to the black fissure of emptiness which had opened in her heart, the one that would never close.

And when he left, when the wake was over, the thanks

given, she lay on her new bed in her new house and found ten young stars burning brightly at the back of her mind. *Iasius* had been right after all, hope was eternal.

For the next eighteen years *Oenone* floated passively within the B-ring where *Udat* had left it. The particles flowing around it were occasionally deluged with bursts of static, interacting with the gas giant's magnetosphere to stir the dust grains into aberrant patterns, looking like the spokes of a massive wheel. But for most of the time they obeyed the simpler laws of orbital mechanics, and whirled obediently around their gravitonic master without deviation. *Oenone* didn't care, both states were equally nourishing.

As soon as the blackhawk departed, the egg began to ingest the tides of mass and energy which washed over its shell. Elongating at first, then slowly bloating into two bulbs over the course of the first five months. One of these flattened out into the familiar voidhawk lens shape, the other remained globular, squatting at the centre of what would ultimately evolve into the bitek starship's lower hull. It extruded fine strands of organic conductor, which acted as an induction mechanism, picking up a strong electrical current from the magnetosphere to power the digestive organs inside. Ice grains and carbon dust, along with a host of other minerals, were sucked into pores dotting the shell and converted into thick protein-rich fluids to supply the multiplying cells within the main hull.

At the core of the nutrient-production globe, the zygote called Syrinx began to gestate inside a womb-analogue organ, supported by a cluster of haematopoiesis organs.

Human and voidhawk grew in union for a year, developing the bond that was unique even among Edenists. The memory fragments which had come from *Iasius*, the navigation and flight instincts it had imparted at the birth, became a common heritage. Throughout their lives they would always know exactly where the other was; flight trajectories and swallow manoeuvres were a joint intuitive choice.

Volscen arrived a year to the day after *Iasius*'s last flight, rendezvousing with the fledgeling voidhawk egg as it orbited contentedly amid the ring. *Oenone*'s nutrient-production globe disgorged the womb-analogue and its related organs in a neat package, which the *Volscen*'s crew retrieved.

Athene was waiting just inside the airlock as they brought the organ package on board. It was about the size of a human torso, a dark crinkled shell sprayed with rays of frost where liquids had frozen during its brief exposure to space. They started to melt as soon as it came into contact with the *Volscen*'s atmosphere, leaving little viscous puddles on the green composite decking.

Athene could sense the infant's mind inside, quietly cheerful, with a hint of expectancy. She searched through the background whispers of the affinity band for the insect-sentience of the package's controlling bitek processor, and ordered it to open.

It split apart into five segments like a fruit; fluids and mucus spilled out. At the centre was a milk-coloured sac connected to the organs with thick ropy cords, pulsing rhythmically. The infant was a dark shadow, stirring in agitation as the unaccustomed light shone on her. There was a gurgling sound as the package voided its amniotic fluid across the floor, and the sac began to deflate. The membrane peeled back.

Is she all right? *Oenone* asked anxiously. The mental tone reminded Athene of a wide-eyed ten-year-old.

She's just perfect, Sinon said gently.

Syrinx smiled up at the expectant adults peering down at her, and kicked her feet in the air.

Athene couldn't help but smile back down at the placid infant. It's all so much easier this way, she thought, at a year old they are much better able to cope with the transition; and there's no blood, no pain, almost as though we weren't meant to have them ourselves.

Breathe, Athene told the baby girl.

Syrinx spluttered on the gummy mass in her mouth and spat it out. With her affinity sensitivity opened to the full, Athene could feel the passage of the coolish air down into the baby's lungs. It was strange and uncomfortable, and the lights and colours were frightening after the pastel dream images of the rings which she was used to. Syrinx began to cry.

Crooning sympathy both mentally and verbally Athene unplugged the bitek umbilical from her navel, and lifted the baby out of the sac's slippery folds. Sinon hovered around her with a towel to wipe the girl down, radiating pride and concern. *Volscen*'s crew began to clear up the pulpy mess of the package, ready to dump it out of the airlock. Bouncing Syrinx on her arm, Athene moved down the corridor towards the lounge that was serving as a temporary nursery.

She's hungry, *Oenone* said. A thought which was vigorously echoed by Syrinx.

Stop fussing, Athene said. **She'll be fed once we've dressed her. And we've got another six to pick up yet. She's going to have to learn to take her turn.**

Syrinx let out a plaintive mental wail of protest.

"Oh, you are going to be a bonny handful, aren't you?"

She was, but then so were all of her nine siblings as well. The house Athene had taken was a circular one, consisting of a single-storey ring of rooms surrounding a central courtyard. Its walls were polyp, and its curved roof was a single sheet of transparent composite which could be opaqued as required. It had been grown to order by a retired captain two hundred years previously when arches and curves were the fashion, and there wasn't a flat surface anywhere.

The valley it sat in was typical of Romulus's interior, with low, rolling sides, lush tropical vegetation, a stream feeding a series of lakes. Small, colourful birds glided through the branches of the old vine-webbed trees, and the air was rich with the scent of the flower cascades. It resembled a wilderness paradise, conjuring up images of the pre-industrial Amazon forests, but like all the Edenist habitats every square centimetre was meticulously planned and maintained.

Syrinx and her brothers and sisters had the run of it as soon as they learnt to toddle. Nothing harmful could happen to children (or anybody else) with the habitat personality watching the entire interior the whole of the time. Athene and Sinon had help, of course, both human nursery workers and the housechimps, monkey-derived bitek servitors. But even so, it was exhausting work.

As she grew up it was obvious that Syrinx had inherited her mother's auburn hair and slightly oriental jade eyes; from her father she got her height and reach. Neither parent claimed responsibility for her impetuosity. Sinon was terribly careful not to display any public favouritism, though the whole brood soon learnt to their creative advantage that he could never say no or stay cross with his daughter for long.

When she was five years old the whispers in her sleep began. It was Romulus who was responsible for her education, not *Oenone*. The habitat personality acted as her teacher, directing a steady stream of information into her sleeping brain; the process was interactive, allowing the habitat to quiz her silently and repeat anything which hadn't been fully assimilated the first time. She learnt about the difference between Edenists and Adamists, those humans who had the affinity gene and those who didn't, the "originals", whose DNA was geneered but not expanded. The flood of knowledge sparked an equally impressive curiosity. Romulus didn't mind, it had infinite patience with all its half-million strong population.

This difference seems silly to me, she confided to *Oenone* one night as she lay in her bed. **The Adamists could all have affinity if they wanted to. It must be horrible to be so alone in your head. I couldn't live without you.**

If people don't want to do something, you shouldn't force them, *Oenone* replied.

For a moment they shared the vista of the rings. That night *Oenone* was orbiting high above the dayside of the saffron gas giant planet; it loomed through the misty particle drifts, a two-thirds crescent which always held her entranced. Sometimes she seemed to spend the whole night watching the colossal cloud armies at war.

It's still silly of them, she insisted.

One day we will visit Adamist worlds, then we'll understand.

I wish we could go now. I wish you were big enough.

Soon, Syrinx.

For ever.

I'm thirty-five metres broad now. The particles have been thick this month. Just another thirteen years.

Double for ever, the six-year-old replied brokenly.

Edenism was supposed to be a completely egalitarian society. Everybody had a share in its financial, technical, and industrial resources, everybody (thanks to affinity) had a voice in the consensus which was their government. But in all the Saturn habitats the voidhawk captains formed a distinct stratum of their own, fortune's favourites. There was no animosity from the other children, neither the habitat personality nor the adults would tolerate that, and animosity couldn't be hidden with communal affinity. But there was a certain amount of manoeuvring; after all, the captains would one day choose their own crews from the people they could get on with. The inevitable childhood groups which formed did so around the cub captains.

By the time she was eight, Syrinx was the best swimmer out of all her siblings, her long spidery limbs giving her an unbeatable advantage over the others in the water. The group of children she led spent most of their time playing around the streams and lakes of the valley, either swimming or building rafts and canoes. This was around the time they discovered how to fox Romulus's constant surveillance, misusing affinity to generate loitering phantasms in the sensor cells which covered every exposed polyp surface.

When they were nine years old she challenged her brother Thetis to an evasion race as a way of testing their new-found powers. Both teams of children set off on their precarious rafts, gliding down the stream out of the valley. Syrinx and her juvenile cohorts made it all the way down to the big salt-water reservoir which ringed the base of the southern endcap. That was where their punts became useless in the hundred-metre depth; and so there they drifted in happy conspiracy until the axial light-tube dimmed before responding to the increasingly frantic affinity calls from their parents.

You shouldn't have done it, *Oenone* chided solemnly that evening. **You didn't have any life jackets.**

But it was fun. And we had a real zing of a ride back in

the Hydro Department officer's boat. It was so fast, there was spray and wind and everything.

I'm going to speak to Romulus about your moral responsibility traits. I don't think they integrated properly. Athene and Sinon were very worried, you know.

You knew I was all right; so Mother must have known as well.

There is such a thing as propriety.

I know. I'm sorry, really. I'll be nice to Mother and Father tomorrow, promise. She rolled over onto her back, pulling the duvet a little tighter. The ceiling was transparent, and she could just make out the dim silverish moon-glow of the habitat's light-tube through the clouds. I imagined it was you I was riding on, not just a stupid raft.

Did you?

Yes. There was that unique flash of oneness as their thoughts kissed at every level of consciousness.

You're just trying to gain my sympathy, *Oenone* accused.

Course I am. That's what makes me me. Am I really horrible, do you think?

I think I will be glad when you're older, and more responsible.

I'm sorry. No more raft rides. Honest. She giggled. It was still heaps of fun, though.

Sinon died when the children were eleven; he was a hundred and sixty-eight. Syrinx cried for days, even though he had done his best to prepare the children. "I'll always remain with you," he told the dejected group when they gathered round his bed. Syrinx and Pomona had picked fresh angel-trumpets from the garden to be put into vases beside the bed. "We have continuity, us Edenists. I'll be a part of the habitat personality, I'll see what you're all up to, and we can talk whenever you want. So don't be sad, and don't be frightened. Death isn't something to be afraid of, not for us." And I want to watch you grow up and start your captaincy, he told Syrinx privately. You're going to be the best captain ever, Sly-minx, you see. She gave him a tentative smile, and then hugged his frail form, feeling the hot, sweaty skin, and hearing in her mind his inner wince as he shifted his position.

That night she and *Oenone* listened to his memories as they fled his decaying brain, a bewildering discharge of images and smells and emotional triggers. That was when she first found out about the nagging worry he held about *Oenone*, the tiny shred of doubt which persisted about the voidhawk's unusual co-parent. His concern hanging in the darkened bedroom like one of the phantasms she bamboozled the habitat receptor cells with.

See, Sly-minx, I told you I'd never desert you. Not you.

She smiled into the empty air as his distinctive mental tone sounded in her head. Nobody else ever called her that, only Daddy. There was a curious background burble, as if a thousand people were all holding whispered conversations somewhere far behind him.

But the next morning, the sight of his body wrapped in a white shroud being carried out of the house to be buried in the habitat's arbour was too much for her, and the tears began.

"How long will he live for in the habitat multiplicity?" she asked Athene after the short burial ceremony.

"As long as he wants," Athene said slowly. She never lied to any of the children, but there were times when she wished she wasn't so damn noble. "Most people retain their integrity for about a couple of centuries within the multiplicity, then they just gradually blend in to the overall habitat personality. So even then they don't vanish completely. But at that, it's a lot better than any heavenly salvation which Adamist religions offer their followers."

Tell me about religion, Syrinx asked the habitat personality later that day. She was sitting at the bottom of the garden, watching fast bronze-coloured fish sliding through the big stone-lined lily pond.

It is an organized form of deity worship, usually originating in primitive cultures. Most religions perceive God as male, because they all have their roots in a time prior to female emancipation—which serves to illustrate how contrived they are.

But people still follow them today?

A majority of Adamists retain their faith, yes. There are several religions current in their culture, notably the Christian and Muslim sects. Both convey the belief that holy prophets walked the Earth at some time in the past, and both promise a form of eternal salvation for those who adhere to the teachings of said prophets.

Oh. Why don't Edenists believe, then?

Our culture proscribes nothing providing it doesn't harm the majority. You may, if you wish, practise the worship of any god. The major reason no Edenist chooses this action is that we have extremely stable personalities. We can look at the whole concept of God and spirituality from a vantage point built on logic and physics. Under such an intensive scientific scrutiny, religion always fails. Our knowledge of quantum cosmology is now sufficiently advanced to eliminate the notion of God altogether. The universe is an entirely natural phenomenon, if extraordinarily complex. It was not created by an external act of will.

So we don't have souls?

The concept of soul is as flawed as that of religion. Pagan priests preyed on people's fear of death by promising them there was an afterlife in which they would be rewarded if they lived a good life. Therefore belief in your soul is also an individual choice. However, as Edenists have continuation through becoming part of a habitat personality, no Edenists have required this particular aspect of faith. Edenists know their existence does not end with physical death. We have, to some extent, superseded religion thanks to the mechanics of our culture.

But what about you? Do you have a soul?

No. My mentality is, after all, the summation of individual Edenists. Nor was I ever one of God's creatures. I am entirely artificial.

But you're alive.

Yes.

So if there were souls, you'd have one.

I concede your argument. Do you think there are souls?

Not really. It seems a bit silly. But I can see how Adamists believe in it so easily. If I didn't have the option of transferring my memories into a habitat, I'd want to believe I had a soul, too.

An excellent observation. It was the memory transfer ability which resulted in the mass excommunication of Christian Edenists by Pope Eleanor in 2090. When our founder Wing-Tsit Chong became the first human to transfer his memories into a habitat neural stratum, the Pope denounced his action as sacrilegious, an attempt to avoid divine judgement. Subsequently the affinity gene was declared to be a violation of divine heritage; the Vatican was afraid it placed too great a temptation before the devout. An Islamic proclamation was issued along similar lines a year later, proscribing the faithful from having the gene sequenced into their children. It was the start of the divergence between Edenist and Adamist culture, and also effectively ended Adamist use of bitek. Without affinity control, bitek organisms have little practical use.

But you said there are lots of different religions; how can there be many gods? There can't be more than one Creator, surely? That's a contradiction.

A good point. Several of the largest wars Earth has known have been fought over this issue. All religions claim theirs is the true faith. In actuality, any religion is dependent solely on the strength of conviction in its followers.

Syrinx gave up, and rested her head in her hands as she watched the fish scuttle under the big pink water lilies. It all sounded highly unlikely to her.

What about you? she asked *Oenone.* Are you religious?

I don't see the need to pray to an unseen deity for anything. I know what I am. I know why I am. You humans seem to delight in building your own complications.

Syrinx stood up, smoothing down her black mourning dress. The fish dived for deep cover at the sudden movement. Thanks a bunch.

I love you, *Oenone* said. I'm sorry you're upset over Sinon. He made you happy. That's good.

I won't cry any more, she told herself, Daddy's there whenever I want to talk to him. There, that must mean I've got a properly integrated personality. So that's all right.

If only it didn't hurt so much deep inside her chest, about where her heart was.

By the time she reached fifteen, her education was concentrating on subjects necessary for captaining a ship. Engineering and power systems, Confederation space law, astrogration, bitek life-support organs, mechanics, fluid behaviours, superconductivity, thermodynamics, fusion physics. She and *Oenone* listened to long lectures on the abilities and limits of voidhawks. There were practical lessons too, how to use spacesuits, practising fidgety repairs in low gravity, and acclimatization trips to the voidhawk ledges outside. Running through shipboard routines.

She was perfectly at home in free fall. Floating balance was geneered into all Edenists, and the hundred families went further with their manipulation, toughening and thickening internal membranes to withstand high-gee acceleration. Edenists were loath to use nanonic-supplement boosting unless there was no alternative.

By her mid-teens she was losing her puppy fat (not that she'd ever had much to start with) and beginning to acquire her definitive adult features. The carefully modified genes of her ancestors had bestowed her with a long face that had slightly sunken cheeks, emphasizing strong bones, and a wide mouth which could deliver a dazzling smile whenever she chose. She was as tall as most of her brothers, and her figure was filling out to her complete satisfaction. At this time she had grown her hair halfway down her back, knowing she would never have the opportunity again: when she started operational flying it would have to be cut short. Long hair was at best a nuisance and at worst a hazard in a starship.

When she was seventeen she had a month-long *affaire* with Aulie, who was forty-four, which made it doomed from the start, which made it *so* romantic. She enjoyed her time with Aulie unashamedly, as much for the mild censure and gossip it generated among her friends and family as the new styles of euphoria she experienced under his knowledgeable tuition. Now he was someone who *really* knew how to exploit free fall.

Teenage Edenist sexuality was one of the most talked about and envied legends among their Adamist counterparts. Edenists didn't need to worry about disease, not with their immunology systems; and affinity ensured that there were no problems of jealousy, or even possessive domination. Honest lust was nothing to be ashamed of, it was a natural aspect of teenage hormones on the boil, and there was also ample room for genuine one-to-one attraction. So given that even trainee captains only had five hours of practical engineering and technology lessons each day, and by their midteens Edenists needed at most six hours' sleep per night, the rest of the time was spent pursuing orgasmic release in a manner which would have impressed even the Romans.

Then her eighteenth birthday came around. Syrinx almost couldn't bring herself to leave the house that morning. Athene had worn her usual cheerful face, emotions hidden beyond even the most sensitive prying. But Syrinx knew exactly how much the sight of all ten children preparing to go hurt her. She had hung back after the formal breakfast, but Athene had shooed her out of the kitchen with a brief kiss. "It's the price we all pay," she said. "And believe me, it's worth it."

Syrinx and her siblings suited up and walked out onto the innermost ledge of the northern endcap, progressing with long lopes in the quarter gravity. There were a lot of people milling around outside the airlocks, service personnel, the crews of voidhawks currently perched on pedestals. All of them were eagerly awaiting the arrival of the newest voidhawks. The swirl of expectancy from them and other Edenists in the habitat caught her by surprise, but at least it helped quell her own nerves.

I'm the one that should be nervous, *Oenone* protested.
Why? All this comes naturally to you.
Ha!
Are you ready?
We could wait a little longer, see if I grow some more.

You haven't grown for two months. And you're quite big enough already.

Yes, Syrinx, the starship said, so meekly that she had to smile.

Come on, remember I was apprehensive with Hazat. That turned out to be fantastic.

I hardly think you can compare sex with spaceflight. And I wouldn't call that apprehension, more like impatience. There was a tone of pique in the mental voice.

Syrinx put her hands on her hips. **Get on with it.**

Oenone had been steadily absorbing electricity from the nutrient-production globe for the last month; with its growth phase finally complete the demand on the induction pick-off cables by the globe's organs had fallen off sharply, allowing the starship to begin the long powering-up process of its patterning cells. Now the energy levels were high enough to initiate a distortion field, which would enable it to suck power directly out of space. If it didn't get the distortion field right the cells would power down, and a rescue mission would have to be launched. In the past such missions hadn't always been a hundred per cent successful.

With Syrinx's pride and encouragement bolstering its mind, *Oenone* started to separate from the nutrient-producing globe. Fibrous tubes tore along their stress lines. Warm fluids squirted into space, acting like crude rocket engines, adding to the pressure on the remaining tubes. Organic conductors snapped and sealed, their ends whipping back and forth in the expanding cloud of vaporized fluid. The final tube broke, and the globe lurched away like a punctured balloon.

See? Easy, Syrinx said. The two of them were remembering together, reviewing the miragelike memories of a voidhawk called *Iasius*. To generate a distortion field you just had to trigger the initial energy flash through the patterning cells like *so*. Energy began to flow inside the labyrinthine honeycomb of patterning cells, compressing, the density building towards infinity in mere nanoseconds.

The distortion field flared outwards, billowing wildly.

Steady, Syrinx instructed gently. The field's fluctuations began to damp down. It changed shape, becoming more stable, twisting the radiation of local space into a viable stream. The patterning cells began to absorb it. There was a heavenly sensation of satisfaction gusting out to the stars.

Yes! We did it. They embraced mentally. Congratulations were flung at them from Edenists and voidhawks alike. Syrinx searched round to see that all her siblings and their craft had generated stable distortion fields. As if Athene's children would fail!

Together *Oenone* and Syrinx began to experiment, changing the shape of the field, altering its strength. The voidhawk began to move, rising up out of the rings, into clear space, seeing the stars unencumbered for the first time. Syrinx thought she could feel the wind blowing in her face, ruffling her hair. She was some ancient mariner standing on the wooden deck of her sailing ship, speeding across an endless ocean.

Three hours later *Oenone* slipped into the gap between Romulus's northern endcap and the counter-rotating dock. It began to curve round, racing after the ledge.

Syrinx saw it expand from nowhere out of the spinning starfield. **I can see you!** It had been so long.

And I you, *Oenone* replied lovingly.

She jumped for joy, legs sending her flying three metres above the ledge.

Careful, *Oenone* said.

Syrinx just laughed.

It slid in over the edge, and hovered above the pedestal closest to her. When it settled she began to glide-run towards it, whooping exuberantly, arms windmilling for balance. *Oenone*'s smooth midnight-blue hull was marbled by a fine purple web.

4

The Ruin Ring formed a slim dense halo three kilometres thick, seventy kilometres broad, orbiting five hundred and eighty thousand kilometres above the gas giant Mirchusko. Its albedo was dismayingly low; most of the constituent particles were a dowdy grey. A haze of small particles could be found up to a hundred kilometres outside the main band in the ecliptic plane; dust mainly, flung out from collisions between larger particles. Such meagre dimensions made the Ruin Ring totally insignificant on a purely astronomical scale. However, the effect it had on the course of human events was profound. Its existence alone managed to bring the richest kingdom in history to the verge of political chaos, as well as posing the Confederation's scientific community the greatest mystery it had ever known, one which remained unsolved a hundred and ninety years after its discovery.

It could so easily have gone unnoticed by the Royal Kulu Navy scoutship *Ethlyn*, which investigated the system in 2420. But system survey missions are too expensive to mount for the crew to skimp on detail even though it is obvious there is no terracompatible planet orbiting the star, and naval captains are chosen for their conscientious nature.

The robot probe which *Ethlyn* fired into orbit around Mirchusko performed standard reconnaissance fly-bys of the seven moons above a hundred and fifty kilometres in diameter (anything smaller was classed as an asteroid), then moved on to analyse the two rings encircling the gas giant. There was nothing extraordinary or even interesting about the innermost: twenty thousand kilometres broad, orbiting three hundred and seventy thousand kilometres out, the usual conglomeration of ice and carbon and rocky dust. But the outer ring had some strange spectrographic lines, and it occupied an unusually high orbit. *Ethlyn*'s planetary science officer raised the probe's orbit for a closer look.

When the achromatic pictures relayed from the probe's optical sensors began to resolve, all activity on board the *Ethlyn* came to an abrupt halt as the crew abandoned their routine to assess the scene. The ring which had the mass of a modestly sized moon was composed entirely of shattered xenoc habitats. *Ethlyn* immediately deployed every robot probe in its inventory to search the rest of the system, with depressingly negative results. There were no other habitats, no survivors. Subsequent searches by the small fleet of Kulu research ships which followed also produced a resounding blank. Neither could any trace of the xenoc race's home-world be found. They hadn't originated on any planet in the Ruin Ring's system, nor had they come from any of the surrounding stars. Their origin and death were a complete enigma.

The builders of the wrecked habitats were called the Laymil, though even the name wasn't discovered for another sixty-seven years. It might seem that the sheer quantity of remnants would provide archaeologists and xenoc investigators with a superabundance of research material. But the destruction of the estimated seventy thousand plus habitats had been ferocious, and it had happened two thousand four hundred years previously. After the initial near-simultaneous detonation a cascade of secondary collisions had begun, a chain reaction lasting for decades, with gravel and boulders pulverizing large shell sections, setting off another round of collisions. Explosive decompression tore apart the living cells of plants and animals, leaving already badly eviscerated corpses to be decimated still further by the punishing sleet of jagged fragments. And even after a relative calm fell a century later, there was the relentless chafing of the vacuum, boiling surface molecules away one by one until only phantom-thin outlines of the original shape were left.

In another thousand years the decay would have precluded almost any investigation into the Laymil. As it was, the retrieval of useful artefacts was a dangerous, frustrating, and generally poorly rewarded task. The Laymil research project, based in Tranquillity, a custom-grown bitek habitat orbiting seven thousand kilometres above the Ruin Ring, depended on scavengers to do the dirty work.

The scavengers who ventured into the Ruin Ring were driven by a variety of reasons; some (mostly the younger ones) thought it was adventurous, some did it because they had no choice, for some it was a last resort gamble. But all of them kept going in the hope of that one elusive Big Find. Intact Laymil artefacts raised huge prices on the collector's market: there was a limited and diminishing source of unique alien *objets*, and museums and private collectors were desperate to obtain them.

There existed no prospecting technology which could sift through the Ruin Ring particles and identify the gems amid the dross; scavengers had to don their spacesuits and get out there amid the hurtling shell splinters and go through it all one piece at a time, using hands and eyeballs. Most of them earned enough from what they found to keep going. Some were better at it than others. Luck, they called it. They were the ones who found a couple of the more intriguing pieces each year, items which would tide them over in high style for months at a time. Some were exceptionally lucky, returning time and again with pieces the collectors and research project simply had to have. And some were suspiciously lucky.

If pressed, Joshua Calvert would have to admit membership of the second category, though it would be a self-deprecating acknowledgement. He had pulled six decent pieces out of the Ring in the last eight months; a pair of reasonably intact plants, a couple of circuit boards (fragile but OK), half of a rodentlike animal, and the big one, an intact egg, seven centimetres high. Altogether they had brought in three-quarters of a million fuseodollars (the Edenist currency, used as a base currency by the Confederation as a whole). For most scavengers that would have been enough to retire on. Back in Tranquillity people were shaking their heads and wondering why he kept returning to the Ring. Joshua was twenty-one, and that much money could keep him in a satisfactorily high-rolling style for life.

They wondered because they couldn't feel the intense need burning in him, surging down every vein like a living current, animating each cell. If they had known about that tidal-force drive they might have had an inkling of the unquiet nature lurking predator-fashion behind his endearing grin and boyish looks. He wanted one hell of a lot more than three-quarters of a million. In fact it was going to take nearer five million before he was anywhere near satisfied.

Living in a high-rolling style wasn't even an option as far as he was concerned. A life spent doing nothing but keeping a careful eye on your monthly budget, everything you did limited by the dividends of prudent investments? That sounded like living death to him, suspended inanimation, strictly loser's territory.

Joshua knew just how much more to life there could be. His body was perfectly adapted to handle free fall, a combination of useful physiological traits geneered into his family by wanderlust ancestors long distant. But it was just a consort to his mind, which was hardwired into the most riotous human trait, the hunger for new frontiers. He had spent his early childhood listening to his father telling and retelling stories of his own captaincy: the smuggling flights, outsmarting Confederation Navy squadrons, the fights, hiring out as mercenary warriors to governments and corporations with a grudge, of travelling the universe at will, strange planets, fanciful xenocs, willing women in ports scattered across the colonized galaxy. There wasn't a planet or moon or asteroid settlement in the Confederation they hadn't explored and populated with fanciful societies before the old man finally found the combination of drugs and alcohol which could penetrate the beleaguered defences of his enhanced organs. Every night since he was four years old Joshua had dreamed that life for himself. The life Marcus Calvert had blown, condemning his son to sit out his own existence in a habitat on the edge of nowhere. Unless . . .

Five million Edenist fuseodollars, the price of repairing his father's starship—although admittedly it might even cost more, the shape old *Lady Mac* was in after so many years of neglect. Of leaving bloody boring backward Tranquillity. Of having a real life, free and independent.

Scavenging offered him a realistic way, an alternative to indenturing his soul to the banks. That money was out here in the Ruin Ring, waiting for him to pick it up. He could feel the Laymil artefacts calling to him, a gentle insistent prickling at the back of his conscious mind.

Some called it luck.

Joshua didn't call it anything. But he knew nine times out of ten when he was going to strike. And this time was it. He had been in the Ring for nine days now, nudging cautiously through the unending grey blizzard gusting outside the spaceplane's windscreen, looking at shell fragments and discarding them. Moving on. The Laymil habitats were remarkably similar to Tranquillity and the Edenist habitats, biologically engineered polyp cylinders, although at fifty kilometres long and twenty in diameter they were fatter than the human designs. Proof that technological solutions were the same the universe over. Proof that the Laymil were, at that level at least, a perfectly ordinary spacefaring race. And giving absolutely no hint of the reason behind their abrupt end. All their wondrous habitats had been destroyed within the period of a few hours. There were only two possible explanations for that: mass suicide, or a weapon. Neither option sat comfortably in the mind; they opened up too many dark speculations, especially among the scavengers who immersed themselves in the Ruin Ring, constantly surrounding themselves with the physical reality of that terrifying unknowable day over two and a half thousand years ago. A third option was the favourite speculation of scavengers. Joshua had never thought of one.

Eighty metres ahead of him was a habitat shell section, one of the larger ones; roughly oval, two hundred and fifty metres at its widest. It was spinning slowly about its long axis, taking seventeen hours to complete each revolution. One side was the biscuit-coloured outer crust, a tough envelope of silicon similar to Adamist starship hulls. The xenoc researchers back in Tranquillity couldn't work out whether or not it was secreted by the habitat's internal polyp layers; if so then Laymil biological engineering was even more advanced than Edenism's bitek. Stacked above the silicon were various strata of polyp, forty-five metres thick, dulled and darkened by vacuum exposure. Sitting on top of the polyp was a seam of soil six metres deep, frozen and fused into a concrete-hard clay. Whatever vegetation had once grown here had been ripped away when the habitat split open, grass and trees torn out by the roots as typhoons spun and roared for a few brief seconds on their way to oblivion. Every square centimetre of surface was pockmarked by tiny impact craters from the millennia-long bombardment of Ring gravel and dust.

Joshua studied it thoughtfully through the gritty mist of particles blurring its outlines. In the three years he had been scavenging he'd seen hundreds of shell fragments just like it, barren and inert. But this one had something, he knew it.

He switched his retinal implants to their highest resolution, narrowed the focus, and scanned the soil surface back and forth. His neural nanonics built up a cartographic image pixel by pixel.

There were foundations sticking up out of the soil. The Laymil used a rigidly geometric architecture for their buildings, all flat planes and right angles. No one had ever found a curving wall. This outline was no different, but if the floorplan was anything to go by it was larger than any of the domestic residences he had explored.

Joshua cancelled the cartographic image, and datavised an instruction into the spaceplane's flight computer. Reaction-control-thruster clusters in the tail squeezed out hot streams of ions, and the sleek craft began to nose in towards the foundations. He slipped out of the pilot's seat where he'd been strapped for the last five hours, and stretched elaborately before making his way out of the cockpit into the main cabin.

When the spaceplane was being employed in its designed role of a starship's ground to orbit shuttle the cabin was fitted with fifteen seats. Now he was using it purely to ferry himself between Tranquillity and the Ruin Ring, he had stripped them out, utilizing the space for a jury-rigged freefall shower, a galley, and an anti-atrophy gym unit. Even with a geneered physique he needed some form of exercise; muscles wouldn't waste away in free fall, but they would weaken.

He started to take off his ship's one-piece. His body was slim and well muscled, the chest slightly broader than average, pointers to the thickened internal membranes, and a metabolism which refused to let him bloat no matter how much he ate or drank. His family's geneering had concentrated purely on the practicalities of free-fall adaptation, so he was left with a face that was rather too angular, the jaw too prominent, to be classically handsome, and mouse-brown hair which he kept longer than he ought to for flying. His retinal implants were the same colour as the original irises: blue-grey.

Once he was naked he used the tube to pee in before putting on his spacesuit, managing to avoid any painful knocks while he pulled the suit equipment from various lockers. The cabin was only six metres long, and there were too many awkward corners in too little space. Every movement seemed to set something moving, food wrappers he'd misplaced flapping about like giant silver butterflies and crumbs imitating bee swarms. When he got back to port he would have to have a serious cleaning session, the space-plane's life-support filters really weren't designed to cope with so much crap.

In its inactive state the Lunar State Industrial Institute (SII) programmable amorphous silicon spacesuit consisted of a thick collar seven centimetres high with an integral respirator tube, and a black football-sized globe attached to the bottom. Joshua slipped the collar round his neck, and bit the end of the tube, chewing his lips round until it was comfortable. When he was ready he let go of the handhold, making sure he wasn't touching anything, and datavised an activation code into the suit's control processor.

The SII spacesuit had been the astronautics industry standard since before Joshua was born. Developed by the Confederation's only pure Communist nation, it was produced in the Lunar city factories and under licence by nearly every industrialized star system. It insulated human skin perfectly against the hostile vacuum, permitted sweat transpiration, and protected the wearer from reasonably high radiation levels. It also gave complete freedom of motion.

The globe began to change shape, turning to oil and flowing over him, clinging to his skin like a tacky rubber glove. He closed his eyes as it slithered over his head. Optical sensors studding the collar section datavised an image directly into his neural nanonics.

The armour which went on top of his new shiny-black skin was a dull monobonded-carbon exoskeleton with a built-in cold-gas manoeuvring pack, capable of withstanding virtually any kinetic impact the Ruin Ring would shoot at him. The SII suit wouldn't puncture, no matter what struck him, but it would transmit any physical knock. He ran both suit and armour checklists again while he clipped tools to his belt. Both fully functional.

When he emerged into the Ruin Ring the first thing he did was datavise a codelock order to the outer hatch. The airlock chamber was unprotected against particle bombardment, and there were some relatively delicate systems inside. It was a thousand to one chance, but five or six scavengers disappeared in the Ring each year. He knew some scavengers and even starship crews who had grown blasé about procedures, always moaning at Confederation Astronautics Board operational safety requirements. More losers, probably with a deep death-wish.

He didn't have to worry about the rest of the spaceplane. With its wings retracted, it was a streamlined fifteen-metre needle, designed to take up as little room in a starship's hangar as possible. Its carbotanium fuselage was tough, but for working the Ruin Ring he had coated it with a thick layer of cream-coloured foam. There were several dozen long score lines etched into it, as well as some small blackened craters.

Joshua orientated himself to face the shell section, and fired the manoeuvring pack's gas jets. The spaceplane began to shrink behind him. Out here in deep space the sleek shape seemed completely incongruous, but it had been the only craft he could use. Seven additional reaction-mass tanks and five high-capacity electron-matrix cells were strapped around the tail, also covered in foam, looking like some kind of bizarre cancerous growths.

The detritus of the Ruin Ring drifted unhurriedly around him, a slow-tempo snowstorm, averaging two or three particles per cubic metre. Most of it was soil and polyp, brittle, petrified chips. They brushed against the armour, some bouncing off, some fragmenting.

There were other objects too, twisted scraps of metal, ice crystals, smooth rounded pebbles, lengths of cabling gradually flexing. None of them had any colour; the F3 star was one-point-seven-billion kilometres away, too distant to produce anything other than a pallid monochrome even with the sensors' amplification. Mirchusko was just visible, a bleached, weary, green bulk, misted over like a dawn sun behind a band of cloud.

Whenever Joshua went EVA it was always the absolute quiet which got to him. In the spaceplane there was never any silence; the hums and whines of the life support, sudden *snaps* from the thruster-nozzle linings as they expanded and contracted, gurgles from the makeshift water lines. They were constant reassuring companions. But out here there was nothing. The suit skin clogged his ears, muffling even the sound of his own breathing. If he concentrated he could just make out his heartbeat, waves breaking on a very distant shore. He had to battle against the sense of smothering, the universe contracting.

There was something drifting in amongst the particles, a long feather-shape. He shifted the suit sensors' focus, glad of the diversion. It was a complete bough from a tree, about five metres away on his left. The forked branches were the palest grey, tapering down to small twigs laden with long triangular leaves; the end which had broken away from the trunk was barbed with narrow blades of wood.

Joshua datavised an order into the manoeuvring pack, and curved round to catch the bough. When he reached it he closed his gauntleted hand around the middle. It was like trying to grasp a sculpture of sun-baked sand. The wood crumbled below his fingers, dissociating into minute flakes. Tremors ran along the branches, shaking the origami leaves as if they were in a breeze. He caught himself listening for the dry rustle, then he was suddenly in the heart of an expanding cloud of ash. He watched it for a long regretful moment before unclipping the slim sampler box from his belt in a reflex action, and swatting a few of the flakes.

The gas jets fired, agitating the cloud, and he emerged into a clearer section of space. The shell section was twenty metres away. For a disconcerting moment it looked like solid ground, and he was falling towards it. He shut down the collar sensor input for half a second, redefining his visual orientation in his mind. When the image came back, the shell section was a vertical cliff face, and he was flying towards it horizontally. Much better.

The soil was in shadow, although no part of the shell section was truly black, there was too much scattered light from Mirchusko for that. He could clearly see the foundations now, walls of black glass, snapped off a metre above the frozen quagmire of lustreless soil. The largest room had some kind of mosaic flooring, and a quarter of the small tiles were still in place. He halted seven metres from the darkened shell surface, and slid sideways. When he switched on the armour suit's lights, white spot beams picked out an elaborate pattern of green, scarlet, and mauve tiles. From where he was it looked almost like a giant eight-taloned claw. Rivulets of water had solidified over it. They sparkled in the twin beams.

Joshua assigned the image a file code, storing it in an empty neural nanonic memory cell. The mosaic would bring in about thirty thousand fuseodollars, he guessed, if he could chip the hundreds of tiles out without breaking them. Unlikely. And the water, or whatever, would have to be scraped or evaporated away first. Risky. Even if he did work out a suitable method, it would probably take at least a week. That couldn't have been the siren call he'd heard with his mind.

The gas jets burped again.

He began to build up a picture of the edifice as he glided over the stumpy walls: it was definitely a public building of some description. The room with the tile floor was probably a reception hall; there were five equally spaced gaps in one wall which suggested entrance doors. Corridors led off from the other three walls, each with ten small rooms on either side. There was a T-junction at the end of each of them, more corridors, more side rooms. Offices? There was no way of telling, nothing had been left when the building took flight, whirling off into space. But if it were a human building, he would call them offices.

Like most scavengers, Joshua thought he knew the Laymil well enough to build up a working image. In his mind they weren't so much different from humans. Weird shape, trisymmetric: three arms, three legs, three stumpy serpentlike sensor heads, standing slightly shorter than a man. Strange biochemistry: there were three sexes, one female egg-carrier, two male sperm-carriers. But essentially human in basic motivation; they ate and shitted, and had kids, and built machines, and put together a technological civilization, probably even cursed their boss and went for a drink after work. All perfectly normal until that one day when they encountered something they couldn't handle. Something which either had the power to destroy them in a couple of hours, or make them destroy themselves.

Joshua shivered inside the perfectly regulated environment of the SII suit. Too much time in the Ruin Ring could do that, set a man to brooding. So call the cramped square rooms offices, and think what happens in human offices. Over-paid intransigent bureaucrats endlessly shuffling data.

Central data-storage system!

Joshua halted his aimless meander around the serrated foundations and flew in close to the nearest office. Low, craggy black walls marked out a square five metres to a side. He got to within two metres of the floor and stopped, hanging parallel to it. Gas from the manoeuvring jets coaxed little twisters of dust from the network of fine fissures lacing the rumpled polyp surface.

He started at a corner, switching the sensors to cover an area of half a square metre, then fired the jets to carry him sideways. His neural nanonics monitored the inertial guidance module in a peripheral mode, allowing him to give his full attention to the ancient polyp as the search navigation program carried him backwards and forwards across the floor, each sweep overlapping the last by five centimetres.

He had to keep reminding himself of scale, otherwise he might have been flying an atmosphere craft over a desert of leaden sand. Deep dry valleys were actually impact scratches, sludgy oases marked where mud particles had hit, kinetic energy melting them, only to re-freeze immediately.

A circular hole one centimetre in diameter. Expanded to fill half his vision. Metal glinted within, a spiral ramp leading down. Bolt hole. He found another one; this time the bolt was still inside, sheared off. Two more, both with snapped bolts. Then he found it. A hole four centimetres across. Frayed cable ends inside waved at him like seaweed fronds. The optical fibres were unmistakable, different tolerances to the Kulu Corporation standard he was used to but apart from that they could have been human made. A buried communication net, which must logically be linked with the central data-storage system. But where?

Joshua smiled around the respirator tube. The entrance hall gave access to every other part of the building, why not the maintenance ducts? It fell into place without even having to think. So obvious. Destiny, or something close. Laughter and excitement were vibrating his nerves. This was it, the Big Strike. His ticket out into the real universe. Back in Tranquillity, in the clubs and scavenger pubs, they would talk in envious respectful tones about Joshua and his strike for decades. He'd made it!

The datavised order he shot into the manoeuvring pack sent him backing away from the office's floor. His suit sensors clicked down the magnification scale, jumping his vision field back to normal in a lurching sequence of snapshots. The pack rotated him ninety degrees, pointing him at the mosaic, and he raced towards it, pale white ribbons of gas gushing from the jet nozzles.

That was when he saw it. An infrared blob swelling out of the Ruin Ring. Impossible, but there it was. Another scavenger. And there was no way it could be a coincidence.

His initial surprise was replaced by a burst of dangerous anger. They must have tracked him here. It wouldn't have been particularly difficult, now he thought about it. All you needed was an orbit twenty kilometres above the Ring plane, where you could watch for the infrared signature of reaction drives as scavenger craft matched orbits with their chosen shell sections. You would need military-grade sensors, though, to see through all the gunk in the Ring. Which implied some pretty cold-blooded planning on someone's part. Someone determined in a way Joshua had never been. Someone who wouldn't shrink from eliminating the scavenger whose craft they intercepted.

The anger was beginning to give way to something colder.

Just how many scavengers had failed to return in the last few years?

He focused the collar sensors on the still-growing craft, and upped the magnification. Pink smear enveloped by brighter pink mist of the reaction-drive exhaust. But there was a rough outline. The standard twenty-metre-long hexagonal grid of an inter-orbit cargo tug, with a spherical life-support module on one end, tanks and power cells filling the rear cargo cradles, nesting round the reaction drive.

No two scavenger craft were the same. They were put together from whatever was available at the time, whatever components were cheapest. It helped with identification. Everyone knew their friends' ships, and Joshua recognized this one. The *Madeeir*, owned by Sam Neeves and Octal Sipika. Both of them were a lot older than him; they'd been scavengers for decades, one of the few two-man teams working the Ruin Ring.

Sam Neeves: a ruddy-faced jovial man, sixty-five years old now, with fluid retention adding considerable bulk to his torso due to the time he spent in free fall. His body wasn't geneered for long-term zero-gee exposure like Joshua's, he had to go in for a lot of internal nanonic supplements to compensate for the creeping atrophy. Joshua could remember pleasant evenings spent with Sam, back around the time he started out scavenging, eagerly listening to the older man's tips and tall stories. And more recently the admiration, being treated almost like a protégé made good. The not quite polite questions of how come he came up trumps so often. So many finds in such a short time. Exactly how much were they worth? If anyone else had tried prying like that he would have told them to piss off. But not Sam. You couldn't treat good old Sam like that.

Good old fucking Sam.

The *Madeeir* had matched velocities with the shell section. Its main reaction drive shut down, shimmering vapour veil dissipating. The image began to clarify, details filling in. There were small bursts of topaz flame from its thruster clusters, edging it in closer. It was already three hundred metres behind the spaceplane.

Joshua's manoeuvring pack fired, halting him above the mosaic, still in the shell's umbra.

His neural nanonics reported a localized communication-frequency carrier wave switching on, and he just managed to datavise a response prohibition order into his suit transponder beacon as the interrogation code was transmitted. They obviously couldn't see him just yet, but it wouldn't take long for their sensors to pinpoint his suit's infrared signature, not now they had shut down their reaction drive. He rotated so that his manoeuvring pack's thermo-dump fins were pointing at the shell, away from the *Madeeir*, then considered his options. A dash for the spaceplane? That would be heading towards them, making it even easier for their sensors. Hide round the back of the shell section? It would be putting off the inevitable, the suit's regenerator gills could scrub carbon dioxide from his breath for another ten days before its power cells needed recharging, but Sam and Octal would hunt him down eventually, they knew he couldn't afford to stray far from the spaceplane. Thank Christ the airlock was shut and codelocked; it would take time for them to break in however powerful their cutting equipment was.

"Joshua, old son, is that you?" Sam's datavise was muzzy with interference, ghostly whines and crackling caused by the static which crawled through the particles. "Your transponder doesn't respond. Are you in trouble? Joshua? It's Sam. Are you OK?"

They wanted a location fix, they still hadn't seen him. But it wouldn't be long. He had to hide, get out of their sensor range, then he could decide what to do. He switched the suit sensors back to the mosaic floor behind him. The dendrite tendrils of ice cast occasional pinpoint sparkles as they reflected the *Madeeir*'s reaction-control-thruster flames. A coherent-microwave emission washed over him; radar wasn't much use in the Ruin Ring, the particles acted like old-fashioned chaff. To use a scanner which only had the remotest chance of spotting him showed just how serious they were. And for the first time in his life he felt real fear. It concentrated the mind to a fantastic degree.

"Joshua? Come on, Joshua, this is Sam. Where are you?"

The ribbons of frozen water spread across the tiles resembled a river tributary network. Joshua hurriedly accessed the visual file of his approach from his neural nanonics, studying the exact pattern. The grubby ice was thickest in one of the corners, a zone of peaks and clefts interspaced by valleys of impenetrable shadow. He cautiously ordered the manoeuvring pack to push him towards that corner, using the smallest gas release possible, always keeping the thermo-dump fins away from the *Madeeir*.

"Joshua, you're worrying us. Are you OK? Can we assist?"

The *Madeeir* was only a hundred metres away from the spaceplane now. Flames speared out from its thruster clusters, stabilizing its position. Joshua reached the rugged crystalline stalagmites rearing up a couple of metres from the floor. He was convinced he was right; the water had surged up here, escaping its pipes or tubing or whatever had carried it through subterranean depths. He grabbed one of the stalagmites, the armour's gauntlet slipping round alarmingly on the iron-hard ice until he killed his momentum.

Crawling around the tapering cones hunting for some kind of break in the shell was hard work, and slow. He had to brace himself firmly each time he moved a hand or leg. Even with the sensors' photonic reception increased to full sensitivity the floor obstinately refused to resolve. He was having to feel his way round, metre by metre, using the inertial guidance display to navigate to the centre, logically where the break should be. If there was one. If it led somewhere. If, if, if . . .

It took three agonizing minutes, expecting Sam's exuberant mocking laughter and the unbearable searing heat of a laser to lash out at any second, before he found a crevice deeper than his arm could reach. He explored the rim with his hands, letting his neural nanonics assemble a comprehensible picture from the tactile impressions. The visualization that materialized in his mind showed him a gash which

was barely three metres long, forty centimetres wide, but
definitely extending below the floor level. A way in, but too
small for him to use.

His imagination was gibbering with images of the pursuit
Sam and Octal were putting together behind him. Bubbling
up from that strange core of conviction was the knowledge
that he didn't have time to wriggle about looking for a wider
gap. This was it, his one chance.

He levered himself back down to the widest part of the
gash, and wedged himself securely between the puckered
furrows of ice, then took the thermal inducer from his belt.
It was a dark orange cylinder, twenty centimetres long,
sculpted to fit neatly into his gauntleted hand. All scavengers used one: with its adjustable induction field it was a
perfect tool for liberating items frozen into ice, or vacuum-
welded to shell sections.

Joshua could feel his heart racing as he datavised the field
profile he wanted into the inducer's processor, and ordered
his neural nanonics to override his pacemaker, nulling the
adrenalin's effect. He lined the thermal inducer up on the
centre of the gap, took a deep breath, tensed his muscles,
and initiated the program he'd loaded in his neural nanonics.

His armour suit's lights flooded the little glaciated valley
with an intense white glare. He could see dark formless
phantoms lurking within the murky ice. Pressure ridges that
formed sheer planes refracted rainbow fans of light back at
the collar sensors. A gash that sank deep into the shell section's interior, a depth hidden beyond even that intrusive
light's ability to expose.

The thermal inducer switched on simultaneously with the
lights, fluorescing a metre-wide shaft of ice into a hazy red
tube. At the power level he used it turned from solid to liquid to gas in less than two seconds. A thick pillar of steam
howled past him, blasting lumps of solid matter out into the
Ruin Ring. He fought to keep his hold on the ice as the edge
of the stream grazed the armour suit.

"See you, Joshua," Sam's datavise echoed round his
brain, laughing derisively.

The thermal inducer snapped off. A second later the rush
of steam had abated enough to show him the tunnel it had

cut, slick walls reflecting the suit's light like rippled chrome. It ended ten metres down in a polyp cave. Joshua spun round his centre of gravity, fists hammering into the still bubbling ice, clawing desperately for traction on the slippery surface as he dived head-first down the tunnel.

Madeeir's laser struck the ice as his boots disappeared below the floor. Stalagmites blew apart instantly under the violent energy input, ice vaporized across an area three metres wide. A mushroom cloud of livid steam boiled up into space, carrying with it a wavefront of semi-solid debris. The laser shone like a shaft of red sunlight at its centre.

"Got the little shit!" Sam Neeves' triumphant exclamation rang in the ether.

The laser blinked out. Slush splattered against the spaceplane's foam-encased fuselage. A second later it reached the *Madeeir*, pattering weakly against the alithium struts. Reaction-control thrusters flamed momentarily, holding its position steady.

Once the storm of vapour had dwindled away, *Madeeir* refocused its sensor suite on the vibrating shell section. There was no ice left among the building's foundations, the scouring had plucked the tiles free as well, even some of the low-lying walls had been razed by the blast-wave of steam. A roughly circular patch of the polyp floor glowed a dull vermilion. The sheer power of the laser saved Joshua. The soles of his armour suit had been caught in the initial blaze of photons, melting the mono-bonded-carbon boots, boring into the tough black membrane of the SII suit underneath. Even the miraculous Lunar technology couldn't withstand that assault. His skin had charred, broiling the meat, singeing bone.

But the steam which had erupted so violently absorbed a great deal of the laser's power. The seething gas also distorted the beam, and it didn't just surge outwards, it also slammed down through the tunnel, punching at any blockage.

Joshua hurtled out of the gash in the polyp cave's roof, cannoning into the floor, bouncing, arms flailing helplessly. He was almost unconscious from the pain in his feet, the analgesic block his neural nanonics had erected in his cortex was faltering under the nerve impulse overload. Blood was spraying out of his soles from the arteries which hadn't been cauterized by the heat. The SII suit redistributed its molecules, flowing around the roasted feet, sealing the broken blood vessels. He hit the cave roof, recoiling. His neural nanonic circuits were visualizing a physiological schematic of his body, an écorché figure with feet flashing urgent red. Neatly tabulated information that was neither sound nor vision was pulsing into his consciousness, telling him the extent of the wounds. He really didn't want to know, the gruesome details were acting like an emetic.

Steam was still gushing into the cave, building in pressure. He could actually hear the gale screeching its affliction. Caustic probes of red light stabbed down through the gash in the ceiling, fluctuating erratically. He hit the polyp again, jarring his arm. The knocks and spinning and pain were too much; he vomited. The SII suit immediately vented the acidic fluid as his stomach spasmed. He cried out in anguish as the sour juices sloshed round in his mouth, rationality fading away. His neural nanonics recognized what was happening and damped down all external nerve inputs, ordered the suit processor to feed him a draught of cool, clear oxygen, then fired the manoeuvring pack jets at full power to stop his madcap oscillations.

The suspension couldn't have lasted more than ten seconds. When he took notice of the sensor visualization again the red light illuminating the cave had been extinguished, and the steam was rushing back out of the gap, currents tugging him gently back up towards it again. He reached out an arm to steady himself against the ceiling. His fingers closed automatically around a metal conduit pinned to the polyp.

Joshua did a fast double take, then began to scan the suit collar sensors round the cave. There were no ends in sight. It wasn't a cave, it was a passage, slightly curved. The conduit was one of twenty running along the ceiling. They had all broken open below the gash, a familiar feathery fan of ragged photonic cables protruded.

His neural nanonics were clamouring for attention, medical data insistent against his synapses. He reviewed it quickly, quashing the return of the nausea. His soles had burnt down to the bone. There were several options stored in the neural nanonics' medical program. He chose the simplest: shut-off for nerves below the knees, infusing a dose of antibiotics from the armour's emergency pack, and shunting a mild tranquillizer program into primary mode to calm his inflamed thoughts.

While he waited for the drugs to start working he took a more measured assessment of the passage. The polyp had ruptured in several places, water and a syrupy fluid had spouted in, freezing over the walls in long streaks, turning the passage into a winterland grotto. They were boiling now, crusty surface temporarily turned back to a liquid by the retreating steam, frothing like bad beer. When he shone the suit's lights into the rents he could see tubes running parallel to the passage; water ducts, nutrient arteries, sewage ducts—whatever, they were the habitat's utilities. Edenist habitats were riddled with similar channels.

He summoned up the inertial guidance display, and integrated the passage into the data construct of the shell section. If the curve was reasonably constant, one end would emerge from the section's edge after thirty metres. He started to move up the other way, watching the conduits. He didn't have anywhere else to go.

The passage branched, then branched again. One junction had five passages. Ice clogged a lot of the walls, bulging outward in smooth mounds. In several places it was virtually impassable. Once he had to use the thermal inducer again. The conduits were often buried under frosted waves. The destruction had been as great down here as it had everywhere else in the habitat. That should have warned him.

The hemispherical chamber might have held the central storage system for the offices above; there was no way of telling now. The conduits which had led him loyally this far all snaked in through an open archway, then split at the apex three metres over his head, running down the curving walls like silver ribs. There had been a great deal of electronic equipment in here at one time: slate-grey columns, a metre or so high, with radiator fins running down the outside, the equivalent of human processor-module stacks. Some of them were visible, badly vacuum eroded now, their fragile

complex innards mashed beyond salvation, battered ends
sticking out of the rubble. Nearly half of the ceiling had collapsed, and the resulting pile of polyp slivers had agglutin-
ated in an alarmingly concave wall, as though the
avalanche had halted half-way through. If gravity was ever
reapplied here, the whole lot would come crashing down.
Whatever force had rampaged through the chamber when
the habitat broke apart had left total devastation in its wake.

Maybe it was deliberate, he mused, because it's certainly
very thorough. Maybe they didn't want any records to survive?

The manoeuvring pack rotated him, allowing him to perform a complete survey. Over by the archway, a tongue of
that viscous brownish fluid had crept in, stealing along the
wall until the temperature drop congealed it into a translucent solid. A regular outline was just visible below the gritty
surface.

He sailed over, trying to ignore the debilitating effect his
maimed feet were having on the rest of his body. He had developed a splitting headache despite the tranquillizer program, and he'd caught his limbs trembling several times as
he drifted along the passage. The neural nanonics had reported his core temperature dropping one degree. He suspected a form of mild shock was tightening its malicious
grip. When he got back to the spaceplane he was going to
have to use the medical nanonic packages to stabilize himself straight away. That brought a grin. When! He'd almost
forgotten about Sam and Octal.

He was right about the frozen liquid, though. Up close,
with the suit lights on full, he could make out the definite
shape of one of the grey electronics pillars. It was in there
waiting for him; waiting patiently for over two and a half
thousand years, since the time Jesus was nailed to the cross
on a primitive, ignorant Earth, immaculately preserved in
grubby ice against the insidious decay so prevalent in the
Ruin Ring. Every circuit chip, every memory crystal, just
waiting for that first current of electrons to reawaken them.
His Strike!

Now all he had to do was get it back to Tranquillity.

*   *   *

The communication band was devoid of human data traffic as he perched on the lip of the passage, and all his suit communication block could pick up was the usual background pop and fizz of Mirchusko's emissions. He'd experienced a strange kind of joy just seeing the Ruin Ring again after retracing his course down the passage. Hope had dwindled to that extent. But now he felt a stubborn determination rising up against the tranquillizer program muffling his mind.

It was impossible to see his spaceplane or the *Madeeir* from where he was, the passage lip was fourteen metres below the soil seam, a maggot hole in a sheer cliff face. Looking down he could see the ochre silicon envelope thirty-five metres below. And he still didn't like to think of the force it would take to snap something that thick the way he snapped biscuits.

This part of the shell surface was exposed to the sunlight, a pale lemon radiance, alive with flickering ever-changing shadows cast by the unceasing swarm of Ring particles. His inertial-guidance unit was projecting a course vector into his mind, a warm orange tube stretching out to vanishing point somewhere in the Ring ahead of him. He datavised the trajectory into the manoeuvring pack, and its jets pulsed, pushing him gently away from the passage, slipping silently down the imaginary tube.

He waited until he was a kilometre and a half from the cover of the shell section before changing direction, then headed out at a steep angle to his previous course, facing into the sun, nozzles firing continually, building velocity. What he was actually doing was raising his orbital altitude in respect to Mirchusko. A higher altitude would give him a longer orbital period. When he halted he was still in the same inclination as the *Madeeir* and the shell section, but five kilometres higher. In their lower, faster orbit, the ship and shell section began to overhaul him.

He couldn't even see them any more. Five kilometres of particles was as effective a shield as the output from a military electronic-warfare pod. The neural nanonics kept flashing up a graphic overlay for him, a small red circle around the shell section, his one tenuous link with salvation. He had never been so far from the spaceplane before, never been so achingly alone.

His armour suit's communication block began to pick up first scraps of datavised exchanges between Sam and Octal, unintelligible bursts of digital code with a curious echo effect. He was glad of the diversion, using his neural nanonics to try and decrypt the signals. His universe seemed to fill with numbers, galactic constellations of colourless digits, all twisting elusively as he loaded tracer program after tracer program, searching for a pattern.

". . . no chance. It's built for landing security, no telling what'll . . . on a planet. A thermal inducer would just anneal the . . ." That was Octal's datavise, emitted from a suit block. It made sense, he was the younger, fifty-two; Sam would be sitting comfortably back in the *Madeeir* directing his junior to recover what they could from the spaceplane.

Joshua felt a shiver run down his ribcage. The cold of the gas giant's environment was reaching in through the SII suit to close around him.

Sam's datavise: ". . . the tail where the tanks . . . anything large would have to be . . ."

Octal's datavise: ". . . there now. I can see some kind of cradle he's . . . can't be for . . ."

They faded in and out, chattering, snarling at each other. Sam seemed certain that Joshua had picked something up. He listened to it in a waking daze as the *Madeeir* drifted past. Slowly, it was all happening in time stretched thin.

A lump of clear ice coasted past, as broad as his hand. There was a turquoise and orange fish inside, three eyes around a triangular beaklike mouth, staring ahead, as if it was somehow aware of its surroundings, swimming along its eternal migration path. He watched it dwindle away, too numb to try and collect it—gone for ever now.

He had virtually fallen asleep when the inertial-guidance program warned him he was now falling behind the *Madeeir*. The manoeuvring-pack jets began to fire in a long, elaborate pattern, reducing his velocity and altitude again, sending him curving down behind the *Madeeir*.

Sam's datavise: ". . . response from the flight computer . . . photonic interface point . . ."

Octal's datavise: ". . . fission blade won't work, the fucking hatch is monobonded carbon, I'm telling you . . . Why don't you listen, arsehole . . ."

Sam's datavise: ". . . little shit . . . find his body . . . chew on his bones . . ."

The manoeuvring pack took Joshua behind the *Madeeir*, the ship a fuzzed pink outline a kilometre ahead of him. He could catch an intermittent view of it through the swirl of particles. Then he lowered his orbit again, a few hundred metres this time, and orbital mechanics reeled him in towards it with painful slowness.

His approach was conducted solely within its blind spot, a cone extending backwards from its reaction drive. All he had to do was keep the bulk of the engine bay between himself and the sensors protruding from the life-support module, and he would remain undetected, especially in the clutter of the Ruin Ring. He also had the advantage that they thought he was dead. They wouldn't be looking, not for anything as small as a suit.

The last hundred metres were the worst. A quick burst of speed, rushing headlong into the twin pits of the reaction-drive nozzles. If they started up now . . .

Joshua slid between the two fat bell-shapes, and anchored himself on the maze of thrust-distribution struts. The rockets were similar in principle to the engines in his spaceplane, though he didn't know the marque. A working fluid (usually a hydrocarbon) was pumped into an energizer chamber where it was heated to about seventy-five thousand degrees Kelvin by a colossal discharge from the power cells. It was a simple system, with few moving parts, little to go wrong, and cheap to maintain. Scavengers didn't need anything more, the delta-V you needed to travel between Tranquillity and the Ruin Ring was small. Joshua couldn't think of anyone who used a fusion drive.

He began to move around the gimbals, going hand over hand, careful not to jar his feet against anything. The power leads were easy to find, superconductor cables as thick as his arm. He fished round his belt for the fission knife. The ten-centimetre blade glowed a spectral yellow, unusually bright in the shade-soaked engine bay. It made short work of the cables.

Another quick climb brought him up against the hulking tanks. They were covered by a quilt of nultherm insulation blanket. He settled himself at the bottom of one tank, and stripped a patch of the insulation away. The tank itself was a smooth dull silver, merging seamlessly into the turbopump casing at its base. He jammed the thermal inducer into a support-strut joint, squirted on some epoxy to make sure it wouldn't slip, and datavised a series of orders into its processor.

Ten minutes later, the processor switched on the thermal-induction field. Joshua had programmed it to produce a narrow beam, ten centimetres wide, three metres long. Three-quarters of it was actually projected inside the tank, where it started to vaporize the hydrocarbon liquid. Frenzied currents churned, carrying more fluid into the field. Pressure built swiftly, rising to dangerous levels.

The metal shell of the tank wasn't quite so susceptible to the field. Its molecular structure retained cohesion for almost twenty seconds before the sheer quantity of heat concentrated into such a small area disrupted the valency bonds. The metal turned malleable and began to bulge outwards, impelled by the irresistible pressure mounting inside the tank.

In the *Madeeir*'s cramped cabin, Sam Neeves widened his eyes in horror as datavised alarms shrilled in his brain. Complex ship schematics unfurled across his consciousness, fuel sections a frantic red. Emergency safety programs sent a torrent of binary pulses into the engine bay. None of it made any difference to the rising pressure.

They were contingencies for malfunctions, he realized. This was something else, the tank was being subjected to a tremendous energy input. The trouble was external. Deliberate.

"Joshua!" he roared in helpless fury.

After operating for twenty-five seconds at maximum expenditure the thermal inducer's electron matrix was exhausted. The field shut down. But the damage had been done.

The protuberance swelling from the tank was glowing a brilliant coral-pink. Its apex burst open. A fountain of boiling gas streaked out, playing across the engine bay. Thermal blankets took flight, whirling away; composite structures and delicate electronics modules melted, sending out spumes of incendiary droplets. *Madeeir* lurched forward, slewing slowly around its long axis as the rocketlike thrust of the erupting tank shoved against the hull.

"Holy shit," Sam Neeves spat. "Octal! Octal, for Christ's sake get back here!"

"What's happening?"

"It's Joshua, he's fucked us. Get back here. The reaction control can't keep her stable."

Even as he said it the guidance data pouring into his mind showed the thruster clusters losing the battle to hold the ship level. He tried to activate the main drive, the only engines with the strength to compensate for the rogue impulse of the ruptured fuel tank. Dead.

A neural nanonic medical monitor program overrode his pacemaker, calming his frightened heart. Adrenalin buzzed in his head.

Sensors and control linkages from the engine bay were failing at an unbelievable rate. Large areas of the schematic in his mind were an ominous black. The shell section loomed large in the forward sensors.

Joshua watched from behind the relative safety of a boulder three hundred metres away. The *Madeeir* was starting to tumble like the universe's largest drumstick. Sparkly gas spewed out of one end, tracing a wavering arc through space.

"We're going to hit!" Sam Neeves datavised.

The *Madeeir* had already wobbled past the spaceplane, giving Joshua a nasty moment. Now it was careering towards the shell section. He held his breath.

It should have hit, he thought, it really should. But the rotation it had picked up saved it. *Madeeir* flipped over the edge of the polyp cliff as if it was on pivots, its life-support module no more than five metres from the surface. At that speed it would have been split open as though it was made of glass.

Joshua sighed as the gritty tension contracting every tendon drained away. They deserved death, but it would just have to wait now. He had other priorities. Like making sure he lived. At the back of his mind there was a phantom throbbing from his feet. His neural nanonics were reporting his blood was laced with toxins, probably some contamination from the burned flesh, too.

Madeeir raced onwards, deeper into the Ruin Ring. Already two hundred metres beyond the shell section. The plume of gas was visibly weaker.

A small pearl-white mote curved over the edge of the shell section, chasing after the ship. Octal, desperate not to be stranded alone with a spaceplane he couldn't open. If he'd stopped to think, he might have sabotaged Joshua's craft.

Be thankful for small mercies, Joshua told himself.

The manoeuvring pack lifted him from his hiding place behind the boulder. Its gas reserve was down to five per cent. Just enough to get back to the spaceplane. Although he would have found a way even if it was empty. Somehow. Today he was fortune's child.

5

Like a fool Quinn Dexter had been waiting for the jolt, a
blink of cold emptiness which would tell him the voyage
had actually taken place. It hadn't happened, of course. The
crewman had tugged him into the coffin-sized zero-tau pod,
one of thousands arranged in a three-dimensional lattice
within the colonist-carrier starship's vast life-support capsule. Unfamiliar with free fall, and hating the disorientating
giddiness every motion brought, Quinn had meekly allowed
himself to be shoved about like he was so much cargo. The
cortical-suppressor collar pinching his neck made any
thoughts of escape a pitiful fantasy.

Right up until the moment the pod cover had hinged
smoothly over him he refused to believe it was happening,
clinging to the notion that Banneth would pull strings and
get him off. Banneth was plugged into Govcentral's State of
Canada administration as deep as a high magus in a virgin.
One word, one nod of her head, and he would be free once
more. But no. It hadn't happened. Quinn, it seemed, wasn't
important enough. There were hundreds of eager waster
boys and girls in the Edmonton arcology who even now
would be vying to replace him, hungry for Banneth's attention, her bed and her smile, a place in the Light Bringer
sect's hierarchy. Youths with verve, with more style than
Quinn. Youths who would strut rather than sweat when they
were carrying Banneth's cargo of weird persona-sequestrator nanonics into Edmonton. Who wouldn't be dumb
enough to try and run when the police stopped them at the
vac train station.

Even the police had thought Quinn was crazy for doing
that, laughing as they hauled his twitching stunned body
back to Edmonton's Justice Hall. The carton had self-de-

structed, of course, an internecine energy flare reducing the nanonics to indecipherable clusters of crumbling molecules. The police couldn't prove he was carrying anything illegal. But the charge of resisting arrest was good enough for the magistrate to slap an Involuntary Transport order on him.

Quinn had even tried giving the sect's sign to the crewman, the inverted cross, fingers squeezing so tight his knuckles had whitened. *Help me!* But the man hadn't noticed, or understood. Did they even have Light Brother sects out amongst the stars?

The pod cover closed.

Banneth didn't care about him, Quinn realized bitterly. God's Brother, after the loyalty he'd shown her! The atrocious sex she had demanded from him. "My little Sunchild," she had crooned as he penetrated and was penetrated. The pain he had pridefully endured at his initiation to become a sergeant acolyte. The weary hours spent on the most trivial sect business. Helping to recruit his own friends, betraying them to Banneth. Even his silence after he was arrested; the beating the police had given him. None of it meant shit to Banneth. He didn't mean shit to Banneth. That was wrong.

After years bumming round as an ordinary waster kid, it had taken the sect to show him what he really was, an animal, pure and simple. What they'd done to him, what they'd made him do to others, it was liberation, freeing the serpent beast which lurked in the soul of every man. Knowing his true self was glorious. Knowing that he had the power to do what he wanted to others, simply because he chose to. It was a magnificent way to live.

It made the lower ranks obey, out of fear, out of respect, out of adoration. He was more than their chapter leader, he was their saviour. As Banneth was his.

But now Banneth had abandoned him, because Banneth thought him weak. Or perhaps because Banneth knew his true strength, the conviction he had in himself. There were few in the sect who were as committed to worshipping the Night as Quinn. Had she come to see him as a threat?

Yes. That was more likely. The true reason. Everyone feared him, his purity. And by God's Brother they were right to do so.

The pod cover opened.

"I'll get you," Quinn Dexter whispered through clenched teeth. "Whatever it takes, I'm coming after you." He could see it then: Banneth violated with her own persona-sequestrator nanonics, the glittery black filaments worming their way through her cortex, infiltrating naked synapses with obscene eagerness. And Quinn would have the command codes, reducing mighty Banneth to a puppet made of flesh. But aware. Always aware of what she was being made to do. Yes!

"Oh, yeah?" a coarse voice sneered. "Well, cop this, pal."

Quinn felt a red-hot needle jab up his spine pressing in hard. He yelped more with shock than pain, his back convulsing frantically, pushing him out of the pod.

The laughing crewman grabbed him before he hit the mesh bulkhead three metres in front of the pod. It wasn't the same man that had put Quinn into the pod seconds before. Days before. Weeks . . .

God's Brother, Quinn thought, how long has it been? He gripped the mesh with sweaty fingers, pressing his forehead against the cool metal. They were still in free fall. His stomach oscillating like jelly.

"You going to put up a fight, Ivet?" the crewman asked.

Quinn shook his head weakly. "No." His arms were trembling at the memory of the pain. God's Brother, but it had hurt. He was frightened the neural blitz had damaged his implants. That would have been the final irony, to have got this far only for them to be broken. The two nanonic clusters the sect had given him were the best, high quality and very expensive. Both of them had passed undetected in the standard body scan the police had given him back on Earth. They had to, possessing the biolectric pattern-mimic cluster would have qualified him for immediate passage to a penal planet.

Being entrusted with it was another token of the sect's faith in him, in his abilities. Copying someone's biolectric pattern so he could use their credit disk inevitably meant having to dispose of them afterwards. Weaker members might shirk from the task. Not Quinn. He'd used it on over seventeen victims in the last five months.

A quick status check revealed both the nanonic clusters

were still functional. God's Brother hadn't deserted him, not entirely.

"Smart boy. Come on, then." The crewman grabbed Quinn's shoulder, and began to swim along the mesh with nonchalant flips of his free hand.

Most of the pods they passed were empty. Quinn could see the outlines of more pods on the other side of the mesh. The light was dim, casting long grey shadows. Looking round him he knew how a fly must feel crawling about inside an air-conditioning duct.

After the life-support module, there were a couple of long tubular corridors. Crewmen and colonists floated past. One family was clustered around a wailing four-year-old girl who clung to a grab hoop with a death-grip. Nothing her parents could say would make her let go.

They went through an airlock into a long cylindrical compartment with several hundred seats, nearly all of them occupied. Spaceplane, Quinn realized. He had left Earth on the Brazilian orbital tower, a ten-hour journey crammed into a lift capsule with twenty-five other Involuntary Transportees. It suddenly struck him he didn't even know where he was now, nothing had been said about his destination during his fifty-second hearing in front of the magistrate.

"Where are we?" he asked the crewman. "What planet?"

The crewman gave him a funny look. "Lalonde. Why, didn't they tell you?"

"No."

"Oh. Well, you could have copped a worse one, believe me. Lalonde is EuroChristian-ethnic, opened up about thirty years ago. I think there's a Tyrathca settlement, but it's mainly humans. You'll do all right. But take my advice, don't get the Ivet supervisor pissed at you."

"Right." He was afraid to ask what a Tyrathca was. Some kind of xenoc, presumably. He shuddered at that, he who had never ventured out of the arcologies or vac-train stations back on Earth. Now they were expecting him to live under open skies with talking animals. God's Brother!

The crewman hauled Quinn down to the rear of the spaceplane, then took his collar off and told him to find a spare seat. There was a group of about twenty people sitting in the last section, most of them lads barely out of their teens, all with the same slate-grey one-piece jump suit he'd been issued with. IVT was printed in bright scarlet letters on their sleeves. Waster kids. Quinn could recognize them, it was like looking into a mirror which reflected the past. Him a year ago, before he joined the Light Brothers, before his life meant something.

Quinn approached them, fingers arranged casually in the inverted cross sign. Nobody responded. Ah well. He strapped himself in next to a man with a pale face and short-cropped ginger hair.

"Jackson Gael," his neighbour said.

Quinn nodded numbly and muttered his own name. Jackson Gael looked about nineteen or twenty, with the kind of lean body and contemptuous air that marked him down as a street soldier, tough and uncomplicated. Quinn wondered idly what he had done to be transported.

The PA came on, and the pilot announced they would be undocking in three minutes. A chorus of whoops and cheers came from the colonists in the front seats. Someone started playing a mini-synth, the jolly tune grating on Quinn's nerves.

"Balls," Jackson Gael said. "Look at 'em, they want to go down there. They actually believe in that New Frontier crap the development company has peddled them. And we've got to spend the rest of our lives with these dickheads."

"Not me," Quinn said automatically.

"Yeah?" Jackson grinned. "If you're rich how come you didn't bribe the captain, have him drop you off at Kulu or New California?"

"I'm not rich. But I'm not staying."

"Yeah, right. After you finish your work-time you're gonna make it as some hotshot merchant. I believe you. Me, I'm gonna keep my head down. See if I can't get assigned to a farm for my work-time." He winked. "Some good-looking daughters in this batch. Lonely for them out there in their little wilderness homesteads. People like you and me, they start looking at us in a better light after a while. And if you ain't noticed yet, there ain't many Ivet fems."

Quinn stared at him blankly. "Work-time?"

"Yeah, work-time. Your sentence, man. Why, you think they were going to turn us loose once we hit the planet?"

"They didn't tell me anything," Quinn said. He could feel the despair opening up inside him, a black gulf. Only now was he beginning to realize how ignorant of the universe outside the arcology he truly was.

"Man, you must've pissed someone off bad," Jackson said. "You get dumped on by a politico?"

"No." Not a politician, somebody far worse, and infinitely subtler. He watched the last colonist family emerge from the airlock, it was the one with the terrified four-year-old girl. Her arms were wrapped tightly round her father's neck and she was still crying. "So what do we do for work-time?"

"Well, once we get down there, you, me, and the other Ivets start doing ten years' hard labour. See, the Lalonde Development Company paid for our passage from Earth, and now they want a return on that investment. So we spend the prime of our life shovelling shit for these colonists. Community maintenance, they call it. But basically we're a convict gang, Quinn, that's what we are; we build roads, clear trees, dig latrines. You name it, every crappy job the colonists need doing, we do it for them. Work where we're told, eat what we're given, wear what we're given, all for fifteen Lalonde francs a month, which is about five fuseodollars' worth. Welcome to pioneer paradise, Quinn."

The McBoeing BDA-9008 spaceplane was a no-frills machine designed for operations on stage one agrarian planets; remote basic colonies where spare parts were limited, and maintenance crews were made up of wash-outs and inexperienced youngsters working their first contract. It was a sturdy delta shape built in a New Californian asteroid settlement, seventy-five metres long, with a wingspan of sixty metres; there were no ports for the passengers, just a single curving transparent strip for the pilot. A fuselage of thermal-resistant boron-beryllium alloy glinted a dull oyster in the sharp light of the F-type star a hundred and thirty-two million kilometres away.

Faint jets of dusty gas spirted out of the airlock chamber

as the seal disengaged. Docking latches withdrew into the bulk of the starship, leaving the spaceplane floating free.

The pilot fired the reaction-control thrusters, moving away from the seamless curve of the huge starship's hull. From a distance the McBoeing resembled a moth retreating from a football. When they were five hundred metres apart, a second, longer, burn from the thrusters sent the spaceplane curving down towards the waiting planet.

Lalonde was a world which barely qualified as terracompatible. With a small axial tilt and uncomfortable proximity to its bright primary, the planet's climate was predominantly hot and humid, a perennial tropical summer. Out of its six continents only Amarisk in the southern hemisphere had been opened for settlement by the development company. Humans couldn't venture into the equatorial zone without temperature-regulated suits. The one, northern, polar continent, Wyman, was subject to severe storms as the hot and cool air fronts clashed around its edges all year long. Shrivelled ice-caps covered less than a fifth of the area normal for terracompatible planets.

The spaceplane sliced cleanly down through the atmosphere, its leading edges glowing a dull cerise. Ocean rolled past below it, a placid azure expanse dotted with volcanic island chains and tiny coral atolls. Pristine clouds boiled across nearly half of the visible surface, generated by the relentless heat. Barely a day went by anywhere on Lalonde without some form of rain. It was one of the reasons the development company had managed to attract funding; the regular heat and moisture was an ideal climate for certain types of plants, rewarding the farmer colonists with vigorous growth and high yields.

By the time the McBoeing dropped to subsonic velocity it had fallen below the vast cloudband sweeping in towards Amarisk's western coast. The continent ahead covered over eight million square kilometres, stretching from the flood plains of the western coast to a long range of fold mountains in the east. Under the midday sun it glared a brilliant emerald, jungle country, broken by huge steppes in the south where the temperature dropped towards subtropical.

Beneath the spaceplane the sea was stained with mud, a

grubby brown blemish extending for seventy to eighty kilometres out from the boggy shore. It marked the mouth of the Juliffe, a river whose main course stretched just under two thousand kilometres inland, way into the foothills guarding the eastern coast. The river's tributary network was extensive enough to rival Earth's Amazon. For that reason alone, the development company had chosen its southern bank as the site of the planet's capital (and sole) city, Durringham.

The McBoeing passed low over the coastal swamps, lowering its undercarriage, bullet-shaped nose lining up on the runway thirty kilometres ahead. Lalonde's only spaceport was situated five kilometres outside Durringham, a clearing hacked out of the jungle containing a single prefabricated metal grid runway, a flight-control centre, and ten hangars made from sun-bleached ezystak panels.

The spaceplane touched down with tyres squealing, greasy smoke shooting up as the flight computer applied the brakes. The nose lowered, and it rolled to a halt, then started to taxi back towards the hangars.

An alien world. A new beginning. Gerald Skibbow emerged from the stuffy atmosphere of the spaceplane's cabin, looking about with reverence. Just seeing the solid picket of raw jungle bubbling around the spaceport's perimeter he knew he'd done the right thing coming here. He hugged his wife, Loren, as they started down the stairs.

"Damn, will you look at that! Trees, real bloody trees. Millions of them. Trillions of them! A whole bloody world of them." He breathed in deep. It wasn't quite what he'd expected. The air here was solid enough to cut with a knife, and sweat was erupting all over his olive-green jump suit. There was a smell, vaguely sulphurous, of something rotting. But by damn it was natural air; air that wasn't laced with seven centuries of industrial pollutants. And that's what really counted. Lalonde was dreamland made real, unspoilt, a world on which the kids could make anything come true just by working at it.

Marie was following him down the stairs, her pretty face registering a slight sulk, nose all crinkled up at the scent of the jungle. Even that didn't bother him; she was seventeen, nothing in life was right when you were seventeen. Give her two years, she'd grow out of it.

His eldest daughter, Paula, who was nineteen, was staring round appreciatively. Her new husband, Frank Kava, stood beside her with his arm protectively round her shoulder, smiling at the vista. The two of them sharing the moment of realization, making it special. Now Frank had what it took, a perfect son-in-law. He wasn't afraid of hard work. Any homestead with Frank as a partner was bound to prosper.

The apron in front of the hangar was made from compacted rock chips, with puddles everywhere. Six harried Lalonde Development Company officers were collecting the passengers' registration cards at the bottom of the steps, running them through processor blocks. Once the data was verified, each immigrant was handed a Lalonde citizenship card and an LDC credit disk with their Govcentral funds converted to Lalonde francs, a closed currency, no good anywhere else in the Confederation. Gerald had known that would happen; he had a Jovian Bank credit disk stashed in an inner pocket, carrying three and a half thousand fuseodollars. He nodded thanks as he received his new card and disk, and the officer directed him towards the cavernous hangar.

"You'd think they'd be a bit better organized," Loren muttered, cheeks puffed against the heat. It had taken fifteen minutes' queueing before they got their new cards.

"Want to go back already?" Gerald teased. He was holding up his citizenship card, grinning at it.

"No, you wouldn't come with me." The eyes smiled, but the tone lacked conviction.

Gerald didn't notice.

In the hangar they joined the waiting passengers from an earlier spaceplane flight, where the LDC officer collectively labelled them Transient Group Seven. A manager from the Land Allocation Office told them there was a boat scheduled to take them upriver to their allocated settlement land in two days. They would be sleeping in a transients' dormitory in Durringham until it departed. And they'd have to walk into town, though she promised a bus for the smaller children.

"Dad!" Marie hissed through her teeth as the groans rose from the crowd.

"What? You haven't got legs? You spent half the time at your day club in the gym."

"That was muscle toning," she said. "Not forced labour in a sauna."

"Get used to it."

Marie almost started to answer back, but caught the look in his eye. She exchanged a slightly worried glance with her mother, then shrugged acceptance. "OK."

"What about our gear?" someone asked the manager.

"The Ivets will unload it from the spaceplane," she said. "We've got a lorry ready to take it into town, it'll go straight onto the boat with you."

After the colonists started their march into town a couple of the spaceport ground crew marshalled Quinn and the other Involuntary Transportees into a work party. So his first experience of Lalonde was spending two hours lugging sealed composite containers out of a spaceplane's cargo hold, and stacking them on lorries. It was heavy work, and the Ivets stripped down to their shorts; it didn't seem to make a lot of difference to Quinn, sweat appeared to have consolidated into a permanent layer on his skin. One of the ground crew told them that Lalonde's gravity was fractionally less than Earth standard; he couldn't feel that, either.

About quarter of an hour into the job he noticed the ground crew had all slunk back into the shade of the hangar. Nobody was bothering with the Ivets.

Two more McBoeing BDA-9008s landed, bringing another batch of colonists down from the orbiting starship. One spaceplane took off, ferrying LDC personnel up to the empty berths; they were going home, their contract time expired. He stopped to watch the big dark delta-shape soar into the sky, dwindling away to the east. The sight laced his thoughts with vicious envy. And still nobody was paying him any attention. He could run, here and now, away into that awesome expanse of untamed land beyond the perimeter. But the spaceport was the place where he wanted to run *to*, and he could well imagine how the homesteaders would treat fugitive Ivets. He might have been stupid enough to be Transported, but he wasn't that naïve. Cursing softly under his breath, he hauled another composite box full of carpentry tools out of the McBoeing's hold and carried it over to the lorry.

By the time the Ivets finished the unloading and began their long trudge into Durringham the clouds from the west had arrived bringing a warm, persistent rain. Quinn wasn't surprised to find his grey jump suit turned out not to be waterproof.

The Lalonde Immigration Registration Department manager's office was in an administration block grafted onto the spaceport's flight-control centre. A long rectangular flat roof structure of ezystak panels clipped onto a metal frame. It had been assembled twenty-five years previously when the first colonists arrived, and its austere fittings were showing their age. Lalonde didn't even rate programmed-silicon constructs for its administration buildings, Darcy thought bleakly; at least the Lunar-built structures had some concessions to comfortable living. If ever a colony project was funded on the cheap, it was Lalonde. But the office did have air-conditioning, powered from solar cells. The temperature was appreciably lower than outside, though the humidity remained constant.

He sat on the settee working his way through the registration cards which the latest batch of arrivals had handed over in exchange for their citizenship and LDC credit disks. The starship had brought five and a half thousand people from Earth; five and a half thousand losers, dreamers, and criminals let loose to wreck another planet in the name of noble destiny. After sixty years in the Edenist Intelligence agency, Darcy couldn't think of Adamists in any other terms. And they claim they're the normal ones, he thought wryly, give me ungodly freakishness every time.

He entered another card's memory into his processor block, glancing briefly at the hologram. A fairly handsome twenty-year-old man, face composed, eyes haunted with fear and hatred. Quinn Dexter, an Involuntary Transportee. The processor block balanced on his lap didn't respond to the name.

The card was tossed onto the growing pile. Darcy picked up another.

"Something you never told me," Nico Frihagen said from behind his desk. "Who are you people looking for?"

Darcy looked up. Nico Frihagen was Lalonde's Immigration Registrar, a grand title for what was essentially a clerk working in the Governor's Civil Administration Division. He was in his late fifties, dourly Slavic in appearance, with rolling jowls and limp receding hair. Darcy suspected his ancestors had had very little to do with geneering. The slobbish civil servant was drinking beer from a tube, an offworld brand, no doubt pilfered from some unsuspecting arrival's farmsteading gear. Spaceport staff had a nice racket going ripping off the new colonists. Nico Frihagen was an essential segment of the scam; a list of belongings was included on the colonists' registration cards.

That readiness to jam his nose in the trough made the registrar an ideal contact for the Edenist operatives. For a straight five hundred fuseodollars a month, Darcy and his partner, Lori, ran through the new immigrants' identification without having to access the colony's civic data store.

Details on the immigrants were sparse, the Lalonde Development Company didn't really care who settled the planet as long as they paid their passage and land registration fee. The company wouldn't declare a dividend for another century yet, when the population had grown above a hundred million and an industrial economy was rising to replace the agrarian beginnings. Planets were always very long term investments. But Darcy and Lori kept ploughing through the data. Routine procedure. Besides, someone might get careless.

"Why do you want to know? Has somebody been showing an interest?" Lori asked, sitting at the other end of the settee from Darcy. A seventy-three-year-old woman with plain auburn hair and a round face, she looked about half of Nico Frihagen's age. Like Darcy she lacked the distinctive height of most Edenists, which made both of them ideal for deep cover work.

"No." Nico Frihagen gestured with the beer tube. "But you've been doing this for three years now, hell probably for three years before that for all I know. It's not just the money, that doesn't mean much to you people. No, it's the time you spend. That's got to mean you're searching for someone important."

"Not really," Lori said. "It's a type of person we're after, not a specific individual."

Good enough, Darcy told her silently.

Let's hope he's satisfied with it, she replied.

Nico Frihagen took a swig of beer. "What type?"

Darcy held up his personal processor block. "The profile is loaded in here, available on a need to know basis. Do you think you need to know, Nico?"

"No. I just wondered. There have been rumours, that's all."

"What sort of rumours, Nico?"

Nico Frihagen gazed out of the office's window, watching an Ivet team unloading a McBoeing BDA-9008. "Upriver. Some settlers vanished, a couple of homesteads up in Schuster County. The sheriffs couldn't find any trace of them, no sign of a struggle, no bodies; just empty houses."

Where the heck is Schuster County? Lori asked.

Darcy queried the bitek processor in his block; a map of the Juliffe's tributary basin bloomed in his mind. Schuster County glowed a soft amber, a sprawling area, roughly rectangular, clinging to the side of the Quallheim River, one of the hundreds of tributaries. **Like Nico said, way upriver. Over a thousand kilometres; it's an area they're just opening up for settlement.**

It could be some kind of big animal. A kroclion, or even something the ecological analysis crew didn't find.

Maybe. Darcy couldn't bring himself to believe that. "So what was the rumour about it, Nico? What are people saying?"

"Not much, not many people know. The Governor wanted it kept quiet, he was worried about stirring up trouble with the Tyrathca farmers, there's a group of them on the other side of the savannah which borders Schuster County. He thought they'd get the blame, so the county sheriff hasn't made an official report. The homesteads have been listed as abandoned."

"When did this happen?" Lori asked.

"Couple of weeks back."

Not much to go on, Lori said.

It's remote enough. The kind of area he'd go to.

I concede that. But what would he want with some hick farmers?

Insufficient data.

Are we going to go and check?

Check what? That the homesteads are empty? We can't go gallivanting off into the jungle over a couple of families who have broken their settlement contract. Goodness, if you stuck me out there in the middle of nowhere, I'd want to run away.

I still say it's odd. If they had been ordinary malcontents, the local sheriff would have known about it.

Yes. But even if we did go, it would take us two or three weeks to reach Schuster County. That means the trail would be well over a month old and cold. How good are you at tracking trails like that through a jungle?

We could take Abraham and Catlin out of zero-tau, use them to scout the area.

Darcy weighed up the options. Abraham and Catlin, their eagles, had enhanced senses, but even so sending them off without even a reasonable idea of where their quarry might be was pointless. They could spend half a year covering Schuster County alone. If they had more operatives he might have sanctioned it, but not with just the two of them. Covering Lalonde's immigrants was a long shot, acting on one piece of dubious information nearly forty years old: that Laton had bought a copy of the original ecological assessment team's report. Chasing off into the hinterlands was completely out of the question.

No, he said reluctantly. **We'll keep them for when we have a definite scent. But there's a voidhawk due from Jospool in a month, I'll ask the captain for a complete survey of Schuster County.**

OK, you're the boss.

He sent the mental image of a grin. They had worked together for too long for rank to be anything other than nominal between them.

"Thanks for mentioning this," Darcy told Nico Frihagen. "It was useful?"

"Could be. We'll certainly show our appreciation."

"Thank you." Nico Frihagen smiled thinly and took another gulp of beer.

He is a disgusting oaf, Lori said.

"We'd be even more grateful if you let us know of any more disappearances," Darcy said.

Nico Frihagen cocked his beer tube in his direction. "Do my best."

Darcy picked up another registration card. The name Marie Skibbow was printed along the top; an attractive teenage girl smiled rebelliously at him from her hologram. Her parents were in for a few years of hell, he decided. Outside the grimy window, thick grey clouds were massing on the western horizon.

The road linking Durringham to the spaceport was a broad strip of pinkish rock chippings slicing straight through the thick jungle. Father Horst Elwes marched towards the capital as best he could with his swelling feet rubbing what felt suspiciously like blisters on both heels. He kept a cautionary eye on the clouds accumulating above the gently waving treetops, hoping the rain would hold off until he made it to the transients' dormitory.

Thin spires of steam drifted out of the chippings around his feet. The narrow gorge between the trees seemed to act as a lens for the sun, and the heat was awesome. A carpet of bushy grass was besieging the edge of the road. Vegetation on Lalonde certainly was vigorous. Birdsong filled the air, a resonant chittering. That would be the chikrows, he thought, reviewing the didactic memory of local conditions which the Church had given him before he left Earth. About the size of a terran pheasant, with bright scarlet plumage. Eatable, but not recommended, the artificial memory informed him.

There wasn't much traffic on the road. Battered lorries rumbling to and from the spaceport, carrying wooden crates and ancient-looking composite cargo-pods, some loaded up with homesteading gear. The spaceport crews riding power bikes with broad, deep-tread tyres, tooting their horns as they sped past, the men shouting at the girls. Several horse-drawn carts trundled by. Horst stared with unashamed delight at the big creatures. He'd never visited his arcology's zoo back on Earth. How strange that the first time he should meet them was on a planet over three hundred light-years from their birthworld. And how could they stand the heat with such thick coats?

There were five hundred members in Group Seven, of which he was included. They had all started off down the road in a tightly packed group following the LDC officer, chattering brightly. Now, after a couple of kilometres, they had become well spread out, and subdued. Horst was close to the rear. His joints were already creaking in protest, and the need for a drink was rising sharply. Yet the air was so moist. Most of the men had shrugged out of their jump suit tops and T-shirts, tying the arms around their waist. So too had several of the women. He noticed that all the locals on power bikes were in shorts and thin shirts; so was the LDC officer leading them, come to that.

He stopped, surprised by the amount of blood pounding away in his cheeks, and gave the seal catch at his neck a full ninety-degree twist. The front of his jump suit split open to reveal his thin powder-blue T-shirt, stained a shade deeper by sweat. The lightweight silk-smooth garment might be ideal for shipboard use, and even in an arcology, but for dealing with raw nature it was ridiculous. Somebody must have got their communication channels fouled up. Surely colonists hadn't been arriving dressed like this for twenty-five years?

A little girl, about ten or eleven years old, was looking up at him. She had that miniature angel's face of all young children, with straight shoulder-length white-blonde hair, gathered into two pony-tails by small red cords. He was surprised to see she was wearing sturdy ankle-length hiker boots, along with baggy yellow shorts and a small white cotton top. A wide-brimmed green felt hat was tilted back sharply. Horst found himself smiling down at her automatically.

"Hello, there. Shouldn't you have got on the bus back at the spaceport?" he asked.

Her face screwed up in indignation. "I'm not a baby!"

"I never said you were. But you could have fooled the development company officer into giving you that lift. I would have done it, if I had the chance."

Her eyes darted to the white crucifix on his T-shirt sleeve. "But you're a priest."

"Father Horst Elwes, *your* priest, if you are in Group Seven."

"Yes, I am. But claiming a lift would have been dishonest," she persisted.

"It would have been sensible. And I'm sure Jesus would understand."

She grinned at that, which made the day seem even brighter to Horst.

"You're nothing like Father Varhoos back home."

"Is that good?"

"Oh, yes." She nodded vigorously.

"Where's your family?"

"There's only me and Mother." The girl pointed to a woman who was walking towards them. She was in her mid-thirties, a strong face with the same fair hair as her daughter. Her robust figure made Horst sigh for what could never be. Not that the Unified Christian Church forbade its priests from marrying, far from it, but even in his prime, twenty years ago, he had been curved in most directions. Now he was what his kinder colleagues described as cuddly, and that was after treating every calorie like an invading virus.

Her name was Ruth Hilton, she told him briskly, and her daughter was Jay. There was no mention of a husband or boyfriend. The three of them started walking down the road together.

"It's nice to see someone was thinking along practical lines," Horst said. "A fine band of pioneers we turned out to be." Ruth was also dressed for the heat, with shorts, cloth hat, and a sleeveless vest; her boots were larger versions of Jay's. She was carrying a well-loaded rucksack; and her broad leather belt had several devices clipped on to it. Horst didn't recognize any of them.

"This is a tropical planet, Father. Didn't the Church give you a generalist didactic memory of Lalonde before you left?" Ruth asked.

"Yes. But I hardly expected to be undertaking a route march the minute we arrived. By my personal timetable, it's only been fifteen hours since I left the arcology abbey."

"This is a stage one colony," Ruth said, without any sympathy. "You think they're going to have the time or the inclination to wet-nurse five thousand arcology dwellers who have never seen the open sky before? Do me a favour!"

"I still think we might have been given some warning. Perhaps a chance to change into more appropriate clothing."

"You should have carried it with you in the zero-tau pod. That's what I did. There's an allowance for up to twenty kilos of personal luggage in the passage contract."

"The Church paid for my passage." Horst answered carefully. He could see Ruth had what it took to survive in this new, demanding world; but she would have to learn to soften her somewhat mercenary attitude or he could imagine himself trying to calm a lynch mob. He forbade a grin. Now that would be a true test of my ability.

"Know what your problem is, Father?" Ruth asked. "Too much faith."

Quite the contrary, Horst thought, I have nowhere near enough. Which is why I'm here in the remotest part of the human dominion, where I can do little or no harm. Though the bishop was far too kind to put it like that.

"What do you intend doing when we reach our destination?" he asked. "Farming? Fishing in the Juliffe, perhaps?"

"Not likely! We'll be self-sufficient, of course, I brought enough seeds for that. But I'm a qualified didactic assessor." She grinned roguishly. "I'm going to be the village schoolmarm. Probably the county schoolmarm, seeing the scraploose way this place is put together. I've got a laser imprinter and every educational course you can think of stored in here." She patted the rucksack. "Jay and I are going to be able to write our own ticket with that. You wouldn't believe the things you're going to need to know once we're dumped in the middle of nowhere."

"I expect you're right," he said without much enthusiasm. Were all the other colonists experiencing the subtle feeling of doubt now they were facing the daunting physical reality of Lalonde? He looked round at the people nearest to him.

They were all plodding along lethargically. A gorgeous teenage girl trudged past, face down, lips set in grim misery. Her jump suit top was tied round her waist; she was wearing a tangerine scoop-neck T-shirt underneath, revealing plenty of smooth skin that was coated in sweat and dust. A silent martyr, Horst decided; he had seen the type often enough when he put in a stint at his arcology's refuge. None of the males nearby paid her the slightest attention.

"You bet I am," Ruth boomed irrepressibly. "Take shoes, now. You probably brought two or three pairs, right?"

"Two pairs of boots, yes."

"Smart. But they're not going to last five years in the jungle, no matter what fancy composite they're made out of. After that you make your own. And for that you come to me for a course in cobbling."

"I see. You have thought this out, haven't you?"

"Wouldn't be here if I hadn't."

Jay smiled up at her mother with complete adoration.

"Isn't an imprinter rather heavy to be lugging about?" Horst asked curiously.

Ruth guffawed loudly, and ran the back of her hand across her brow in a theatrical motion. "Sure is. But it's valuable, especially the newest technical courses, stuff this planet's never heard of. I'm not about to leave that in the hands of the spaceport crew. No way, no how."

A chill of alarm slithered through Horst. "You don't think . . ."

"I'm bloody sure they are. It's what I'd do."

"Why didn't you say something back there?" he demanded in exasperation. "I have reading primer books in my container, medicines, communion wine. Some of us could have remained with it for security."

"Listen, Father, I'm not aiming to be mayor of this group, I'll leave that to some hulking macho male, thank you. And I can't see myself being applauded for standing up in front of that manager woman and saying we should stay behind to stop her friends from stealing our gear. Would you have done that, you with your goodwill to all men?"

"Not publicly, no," Horst said. "But there are ways."

"Well, start thinking of them, because those precious con-

tainers of ours are going to be left piled up in a warehouse
in town for the next couple of days before we set sail. And
we're going to need what's inside them, and I really do
mean *need*; because anyone who thinks that all it takes to
survive out there is determination and honest toil is in for the
shock of their pampered lives."

"Do you always have to be right about absolutely everything?"

"Listen, you're here to look after our souls, Father. You'll
be good at that, I can see, you're the caring type. Deep
down, anyway. But keeping my soul connected to my body,
that's all down to me. And I intend to do the best job I can."

"All right," he said. "It might be a good idea for me to
speak with some of our group this evening. Perhaps we
could organize some kind of watch at the warehouse."

"Wouldn't be a bad idea to see if we can acquire replacements for anything that's gone walkabout, as well. There's
bound to be other groups' gear stored with ours, it shouldn't
be too difficult."

"Alternatively, we could go to the Sheriff's office, and
ask them to find anything that's been stolen from us," Horst
said forcibly.

Ruth laughed out loud.

They walked on in silence for several minutes.

"Ruth?" he asked eventually. "Why have you come
here?"

She exchanged a mournful glance with Jay, the two of
them suddenly vulnerable. "I'm running away," she said.
"Aren't you?"

Durringham had been founded in 2582, a couple of (Earth)
years after the Confederation inspection team had confirmed
the results of the land venture company's ecological analysis crew, agreeing that Lalonde had no biota exceptionally
hazardous to humans—a certificate which was vital for any
planet seeking to attract colonists. The hiatus was due to the
venture company (which had bought the settlement rights
from the scoutship which discovered the planet) attracting
partners, and turning itself into the Lalonde Development
Company. With enough financial backing to establish a

working spaceport and provide a minimal level of civil administration, as well as securing an agreement with the Edenists to germinate a bitek habitat above Murora, the system's largest gas giant, the task of attracting colonists began in earnest.

After reviewing the predominantly South-East Asian catchment profiles and intended culture-base of other stage one colony planets in the same sector as Lalonde, the LDC board decided to concentrate on EuroChristian-ethnic stock to give themselves an adequate immigrant pool. They wrote a broadly democratic constitution which would come into effect over a century, with the LDC turning over local civil administration functions to elected councils, and ultimately the governorship to a congress and president at the end of the first hundred years. Theory had it that when the process was complete Lalonde would have developed a burgeoning industrial/technological society, with the LDC as the largest across-the-board shareholder in the planet's commercial enterprises. That was when the real profits would start to roll in.

At the start of the preliminary stage, cargo starships delivered thirty-five dumpers into low orbit: squat, conical, atmospheric-entry craft, packed full of heavy machinery, supplies, fuel, ground vehicles, and the prefabricated sections of runway. The dumpers were aerobraked below orbital velocity, and one by one began their long fiery descent curve towards the jungle below. They rode the beacon signals down to land beside the Juliffe's southern bank, spread out in a line fifteen kilometres long.

Each dumper was thirty metres high, fifteen metres across its base, weighing three hundred and fifty tonnes fully loaded. Small fins around the base steered them with reasonable accuracy through the atmosphere until they were seven hundred metres above the ground, by which time they had slowed to subsonic speed. A cluster of eight giant parachutes lowered them for the final few hundred metres, bringing them to a landing which resembled a controlled crash to the small flight-control team watching from a safe distance. They were designed for a one-way trip; where they landed, they stayed.

Construction crews followed them down in small VTOL spaceplanes, and began unloading. When the dumpers had been emptied they formed environment-proof accommodation for the crews' families and offices for the governor's civil administration staff.

The jungle surrounding the dumpers was levelled first, a chop and burn policy producing a wide swath of desolated foliage and charred animals; the spaceport clearing followed. After the runway grids were assembled, a second wave of workers arrived in the McBoeings, along with more equipment. This time they had to build their own accommodation, using the profusion of logs the earlier crews had left scattered across the ground. Rings of crude wooden cabins sprang up around all of the dumpers, looking as if they were rafts floating on a sea of mud. Stripped of its scrub cover, subject to continual heavy plant traffic and Lalonde's daily rains, the rich black loam was reduced to a fetid-smelling sludge which was over half a metre thick in places. The rock crushers worked continuously throughout the planet's twenty-six-hour day, but they could never supply enough chippings to stabilize the expanding city's quagmire roads.

The view from the scuffed and algae-splattered window of Ralph Hiltch's office, on the third floor of the dumper which housed the Kulu Embassy, showed him the sun-soaked timber-plank roofs of Durringham spread out across the gently undulating land next to the river. The conglomeration was devoid of any methodical street pattern. Durringham hadn't been laid down with logical forethought, it had erupted like a tumour. He was sure even Earth's eighteenth-century cities had more charm than this. Lalonde was his fourth offworld assignment, and he had never seen anything more primitive. The weather-stained hulls of the dumpers rose above the shanty-town precincts like arcane temples, linked to the ramshackle buildings with a monstrous spider web of sable-black power cables slung between tall poles. The dumpers' integral fusion generators provided ninety per cent of the planet's electrical power, and Durringham was completely dependent on their output.

By virtue of the Royal Kulu Bank taking a two per cent stake in the LDC, Kulu's Foreign Office had acquired the dumper for its staff as soon as the start-up phase of colonization was over, ousting the Governor's Aboriginal Fruit Classification Division in the process. Ralph Hiltch was grateful for the political arm-twisting manoeuvre of twenty years ago; it allowed him to claim an air-conditioned office, and a tiny two-room apartment next door. As the Commercial Attaché he was entitled to a bigger apartment in the embassy's residential block outside, but his actual position as Head of Station for the Kulu External Security Agency operation on Lalonde meant he needed the kind of secure quarters which the old dumper with its carbotanium structure could provide. Besides, like everything else in Durringham, the residential block was made of wood, and leaked something rotten.

He watched the near-solid cliff of silver-grey rain sweeping in from the ocean, obscuring the narrow verdant line peeping above the rooftops to the south which marked the boundary of the jungle. It was the third downpour of the day. One of the five screens on the wall opposite his desk showed a real-time weather-satellite image of Amarisk and the ocean to the west, both covered by spiral arms of cloud. To his wearily experienced eye the rain would last for a good hour and a half.

Ralph eased himself back in his chair and regarded the man sitting nervously on the other side of his desk. Maki Gruter tried not to shift about under the stare. He was a twenty-eight-year-old grade three manager working for the Governor's Transport Office, dressed in fawn shorts and a jade shirt, his lemon-yellow cagoule hanging off the back of his chair. Like almost everyone else in Lalonde's civil administration he was for sale; they universally regarded this backwoods posting as an opportunity to rip off both the LDC and the colonists. Ralph had recruited Maki Gruter two and a half years ago, a month after he himself had arrived. It wasn't so much an entrapment exercise as simply making a selection from a host of eager volunteers. There were times, Ralph reflected sagely, when he would like to see an official who wouldn't sell out for just a sniff of the ubiquitous Edenist fuseodollar. Once his duty tour on Lalonde was finished in another three years he would have to go through innumerable refresher courses. Subversion was so easy here.

In fact there were times when he questioned the whole point of the ESA mounting an operation on what was basically a jungle populated by psychological Neanderthals. But Lalonde was only twenty-two light-years from the Principality of Ombey, the Kulu Kingdom's newest dominion star system, itself only just out of stage-two development. The ruling Saldana dynasty wanted to make sure that Lalonde didn't mature along hostile lines. Ralph and his colleagues were assigned to watch the colony's political evolution, occasionally offering covert assistance to aspirants with coincident policies; money, or black data on opposing candidates, it didn't make any difference in the end. The formative years of a colony's independence set the political agenda for centuries to come, so the ESA did its best to make sure the first elected leaders were ideologically benign as regards the Kingdom. Placemen, basically.

It made sense if you took the long-term consequences into account; a few million pounds spent now as opposed to the billions any form of naval action would cost once Lalonde had a technoeconomy capable of building military starships. And God knows, Ralph thought, the Saldanas approached every problem from that angle—with their life-expectancy long term was the only term they understood.

Ralph smiled pleasantly at Maki Gruter. "Anyone of any interest in this batch?"

"Not that I can see," the civil servant said. "All Earth nationals. Usual Ivet types, waster kids dumb enough to get caught. No political exiles, or at least, none listed." Behind his head, the screen displaying the vectors of Lalonde's miserly orbital traffic showed another spaceplane docking with the vast colonist-carrier starship.

"Fine. I'll have it checked, of course," Ralph said expectantly.

"Oh, right." Maki Gruter's mouth twitched in a half-embarrassed grin. He pulled out a processor block and datavised the files over.

Ralph observed the information flood into his neural nanonics, assigning it to spare storage cells. Tracer programs ran through the fifty-five hundred names, comparing them to his primary list, the most troublesome of Earth's political agitators known to the ESA. There was no match-up. Later he would datavise the files into a processor block, running a comparison with the huge catalogue of recidivist names, facial images, and in some cases DNA prints which the ESA had trawled from right across the Confederation.

He glanced out through the window again to see a group of the new arrivals slogging along the mushy road which led down the side of the square of grass and straggly roses which passed for the embassy gardens. The rain had arrived, drenching them in seconds. Women, children, and men with their hair beaten down, jump suits clinging to their bodies like a dark, crinkled, lizard hide, all looking thoroughly wretched. There might have been tears on their faces, but he couldn't tell with the rain. And they still had another three kilometres to go before they reached the transients' dormitories down by the river.

"Christ, look at them," he murmured. "And they're supposed to be this planet's hope for the future. They can't even organize a walk from the spaceport properly, none of them thought to take waterproofs."

"Have you ever been to Earth?" Maki Gruter asked.

Ralph turned away from the window, surprised by the younger man's question. Maki was normally keen to simply collect the money and run. "No."

"I have. That planet is one giant hive queen for misbegottens. Our noble past. Compared to that, what this planet offers in the way of a future doesn't look so bad."

"Yeah, maybe." Ralph opened a drawer and took out his Jovian Bank credit disk.

"There's someone else going upriver with this batch of colonists," Maki said. "My office had to arrange a berth for him, that's how I know."

Ralph stopped in the act of authorizing the usual three-hundred-fuseodollar payment. "Who's that?"

"A marshal from the Sheriff's Office. Don't know his name, but he's being sent up to Schuster County to scout round."

Ralph listened to Maki Gruter explain about the missing

homestead families, his mind running over the implications. Somebody in the Governor's Office must consider it important, he thought, there were only five marshals on the planet: combat specialists with nanonic-boosted metabolisms, and well armed. Colony Governors deployed them to sort out severe problems, like bandits and potential revolts, problems that had to be eliminated fast.

Another of Ralph's briefs was to watch for pirate activity in the Lalonde system. Prosperous Kulu with its large merchant fleet was engaged in a constant battle with mercenary vessels. Undisciplined, under-policed colony planets with woefully deficient communications were an ideal market for stolen cargoes, and most of the immigrants were at least bright enough to bring a credit disk primed with fuseodollars. The contraband was invariably sold deep in the hinterlands, where dreams soured within weeks when it became clear just how tough it was to survive outside the enclosed comfort of an arcology, and nobody was going to question where sophisticated power hardware and medical packages came from.

Perhaps those families had questioned the source of their windfall?

"Thanks for telling me," he said, and upped the payment to five hundred fuseodollars.

Maki Gruter smiled in gratitude as his credit disk registered the financial bonus. "My pleasure."

Jenny Harris came in a minute after the transport manager left. A thirty-year-old ESA lieutenant, on her second off-world mission. She had a flat face, her nose slightly crooked, with short dark ginger hair, and a slim figure which belied her strength. Ralph had found her a competent officer in the two years she'd been on Lalonde, if a little bit too rigorous in applying agency procedure to every situation.

She listened attentively as Ralph repeated what Maki Gruter had told him.

"I haven't heard any word on unexplained hardware appearing upriver," she said. "Just the usual black-market activity, selling off the gear which the spaceport crews lift from new colonists."

"What assets have we got up in the Schuster area?"

"Few," she said reluctantly. "We mainly rely on our contacts in the Sheriff's Office for reports on contraband, and the boat crews fill in a bit more of the picture. Communication is the problem, naturally. We can give our upriver assets communication blocks, but the Confederation Navy satellites would spot any transmissions even if they were prime encrypted."

"OK," Ralph nodded. It was an old argument, urgency against exposure risk. At this stage of its development nothing on Lalonde was considered urgent. "Do we have anyone going upriver?"

Jenny Harris paused as her neural nanonics reviewed schedules. "Yes. Captain Lambourne is due to take a new colonist group upriver in a couple of days, they're settling land just past Schuster itself. She's a good courier, I use her to collect reports from our in situ assets."

"Right, ask her to find out what she can, about the missing families and whether or not there's been any unexplained equipment appearing up there. In the meantime I'll contact Solanki, see if he's heard anything about it." Kelven Solanki worked at the small Confederation Navy office in Durringham. Confederation Navy policy was that even the humblest of colony worlds was entitled to the same degree of protection as any of the developed planets, and the office was supposed to be visible proof of that. To underline the fact, Lalonde received a twice-yearly visit by a frigate from the 7th Fleet, based at Roherheim, forty-two light-years away. Between visits, a flock of ELINT sensor satellites watched over the star system, reporting their observations directly to the navy office.

Like Ralph and the ESA, their secondary role was to keep an eye out for pirate activity.

Ralph had introduced himself to Lieutenant-Commander Solanki soon after he arrived. The Saldanas were strong supporters of the Confederation, so cooperation as far as locating pirate activity was concerned was a sensible arrangement. He got on reasonably well with the commander, partly due to the navy's mess, which served arguably the best meals in the city, and neither of them made any mention of Ralph's other duties.

"Good idea," Jenny Harris said. "I'll meet with Lambourne tonight, and brief her on what we want. She'll want paying," she added in a cautionary tone.

Ralph requested Lambourne's file from his neural nanonics, shaking his head ruefully when he saw how much the woman cost them. He could guess how much she would ask for this fact-finding mission upriver. "OK, I'll authorize it. Try and keep her under a thousand, please."

"Do my best."

"Once you've dealt with her, I want you to activate an asset in the Governor's office, find out why the Honourable Colin Rexrew thinks it's necessary to send a marshal to investigate some missing farmers no one has ever heard of before."

After Jenny Harris left he datavised the list of new arrivals into his processor block for analysis, then sat back and thought about how much to tell Commander Solanki. With a bit of luck he could drag out the meeting and get himself invited to dinner at the mess.

6

Twenty-two thousand kilometres ahead of *Oenone*, the tiny blue ion-manoeuvring jets of the Adamist starship *Dymasio* were consumed by the interstellar night. Syrinx watched through the voidhawk's optical senses as the intense pinprick of light dwindled away to nothing. Directional vectors swirled away at the back of her mind, an unconscious calculation performed in conjunction with *Oenone*'s spacial instinct. The *Dymasio* had lined up on the Honeck star system eight light-years away, the alignment checked out perfectly.

I think this is it, she told Thetis. *Graeae*, her brother's voidhawk, was drifting a thousand kilometres to one side of *Oenone*; the two voidhawks had their distortion fields reduced to a minimum. They were operating in full stealth mode, with minimal energy expenditure. There wasn't even any gravity in the crew toroid. The crew hadn't eaten any hot meals, there had been no waste dumps, all of them peeing and crapping into sanitary bags, and there was definitely no hot water. Blanket webs of heat-duct cables had been laid over *Oenone*'s hull and crew toroid alike, then smothered by a thick light-absorbent insulation foam. All the starship's waste heat was siphoned off by the blankets and radiated away through a single dump panel, always orientated away from their prey. Holes had been left for *Oenone*'s sensor blisters, but that was all. *Oenone* kept complaining that the covering itched, which was ridiculous, but Syrinx held her peace—for now.

I agree, Thetis replied.

Syrinx felt a shiver of trepidation mingling with a release of pent-up tension. They had been following the *Dymasio* for seventeen days, keeping twenty to thirty thousand kilometres behind as it zigzagged between uninhabited star systems on a totally random course designed to spot and shake off any possible pursuer. A chase of that nature was demanding and difficult, putting a strain on even Edenist psyches, let alone the twenty-strong Adamist naval marine squad they were carrying. Seeing the way their hard-pressed captain, Larry Kouritz, had maintained discipline throughout the mission had sparked a rare respect. And there weren't many Adamists who rated that.

With the final coordinate insertion manoeuvres complete, she could imagine the *Dymasio* retracting its sensors and thermo-dump panels, configuring itself for the jump, charging its patterning nodes with energy. **Ready?** she asked *Oenone*.

I'm always ready, the voidhawk replied tartly.

Yes, she would be very glad when this mission was over. It had been Thetis who persuaded her to sign on with the Confederation Navy for a seven-year tour, Thetis with his strong sense of duty and commitment, goaded by a wilful zest. Syrinx had always intended to put in a naval stint, Athene had often told her rumbustious children of her service days, painting an enticing picture of gallantry and camaraderie. She just hadn't anticipated it to be quite so soon, three years after she and *Oenone* started flying.

With their power and agility, voidhawks were an essential component of the Confederation Navy, employed by Fleet admirals as ideal interception craft. After being fitted out with both offensive and defensive combat systems and an extensive array of electronic sensors, then undergoing a three-month procedural-training course, *Oenone* and *Graeae* had been assigned to the 4th Fleet, operating from the Japanese Imperium capital Oshanko.

Although the Confederation Navy was a dedicated supranational organization, voidhawks always had Edenist crews. Syrinx had kept her original crew: Cacus, the life-support engineer; Edwin, in charge of the toroid's mechanical and electrical systems; Oxley, who piloted both the multifunction service vehicle and the atmospheric ion-field flyer; Tula, the ship's generalist and medical officer. And Ruben, the fusion-generator technician, who had become Syrinx's lover a month after he came aboard, and at a hundred and twenty-five was exactly a century older than her.

It was like Aulie all over again, an aspect which made her feel incredibly girlish and carefree, almost an antithesis of her responsibilities as captain. They slept together when ship's schedules permitted, and spent all their shore leave ranging across whichever planet, habitat, or asteroid settlement they were visiting. Although well into middle age, Ruben, like all Edenists, was still more than capable physically, so their sex life was pretty reasonable; and they both shared a delight in exploring the different cultures flourishing within the Confederation, marvelling in their sheer variety. Through Ruben, and his seemingly inexhaustible patience, she had learned to be far more tolerant of Adamists and their idiosyncrasies. Which was another reason for accepting the Confederation Navy commission.

Then there was also that familiar miscreant thrill to be had from the way everyone regarded their relationship as mildly scandalous. Given their life expectancy, large age gaps were common among Edenist partners, but a hundred years was pushing the limits of propriety. Only Athene didn't make the mistake of objecting, she knew Syrinx far too well for that. In any case, the relationship wasn't that serious; Ruben was convenient, uncomplicated, and fun.

The final crew-member was Chi, who had been posted to *Oenone* by the navy to be their weapons officer. He was a career Confederation Navy man, as far as any Edenist could be in an organization which demanded staff officers renounce their national citizenship (hardly practical for Edenists).

Oenone and *Graeae* had spent four years of patrolling uninhabited star systems, providing occasional random escorts for merchant ships in the hope of engaging pirates, exercised with the Fleet on full-system defence attacks, taken part in a marine assault on an industrial station suspected of building antimatter combat wasps, and making innumerable goodwill calls at ports throughout the 4th Fleet's sector. For the last eight months the Admiralty had assigned them to an independent interception duty, under the command of the Confederation Naval Intelligence Service. This was the third chase flight the CNIS had sent them on: the first ship had been empty when they reached it; the second, a blackhawk, managed to elude them with its longer swallow range, much to Syrinx's extreme chagrin. But the *Dymasio* was undeniably guilty; the CNIS had suspected it of carrying antimatter for some time, and this flight proved it. Now the ship was preparing to enter an inhabited system to make contact with an asteroid separatist group. This time they would make their arrest. This time! *Oenone*'s cabin atmosphere seemed compressed by the prospect.

Even Eileen Carouch, the CNIS lieutenant who was liaising with them, had picked up on the Edenists' expectancy. She was strapped into the couch next to Syrinx, a middle-aged woman with a bland, unmemorable face, the kind Syrinx supposed was ideal for an active agent. But the personality behind it was resolute and resourceful; discovering the *Dymasio*'s hoarded cache was proof of that.

Right now she had her eyes tight closed, accessing the datavised information *Oenone* was providing through bitek processors interfaced with their hardware equivalents, allowing all the Adamists to see what was going on.

"*Dymasio*'s ready to jump," Syrinx said.

"Thank heavens for that. My nerves can't stand much more of this."

Syrinx felt a grin on her lips. She always found a slight edge of tension in her dealings with Adamists on an individual basis; them and their emotions locked inside impenetrable bone, you never knew quite what they felt, which was difficult for the empathic Edenists to handle. But Eileen had turned out to be amazingly blunt with her opinions. Syrinx quite enjoyed her company.

The *Dymasio* vanished. Syrinx felt the sharp kink in space as the ship's patterning nodes warped the fabric of reality around her hull; to *Oenone* the distortion was like a flare. One that was totally quantifiable. The voidhawk instinctively knew the emergence-point coordinate.

Let's go! Syrinx broadcast loudly.

Power flooded through the voidhawk's patterning cells. An interstice was torn open. They plunged into the expanding wormhole. Syrinx could feel *Graeae* generating its own wormhole away to one side, then the interstice closed behind them, sealing them in timeless oblivion. Imagination, twinned with genuine voidhawk sensorium input, provided a giddy rushing sensation for the couple of heartbeats it took to traverse the wormhole. A terminus opened at some indeterminable distance, a different texture of negation, seemingly curving round them. Starlight began to pour in, bending into a filigree of slender blue-white lines around the hull. *Oenone* shot out into space. Stars became hard diamond points again.

The event horizon had evaporated from the *Dymasio*'s hull, depositing the starship five light-days out from Honeck's sun. Its sensor clusters and thermo-dump panels emerged from the hull with the timidity of a hibernating creature venturing out into a spring day. As with all Adamist starships, it took time to check its location, and scan local space for stray comets or rock fragments. That crucial time lapse allowed the tremendous spacial flaws accompanying the opening of the voidhawks' terminuses to remain undetected.

Ignorant of his invisible followers, the *Dymasio*'s captain activated the starship's main fusion drive, heading towards the next jump coordinate.

"It's moving again," Syrinx said. "Preparing to go insystem. Do you want to interdict?" The thought of antimatter being carried into an inhabited system disturbed her.

"What's the new destination?" Eileen Carouch asked.

Syrinx consulted the system's almanac stored in *Oenone*'s memory cells. "It looks like Kirchol, the outer gas giant."

"Any settlements in orbit?" She hadn't quite grasped how to pull information from *Oenone* the way she could from hardware memory cores.

"None listed."

"It has to be heading for a rendezvous, then. Don't interdict it, follow it in."

"Let it into an inhabited system?"

"Sure. Look, if it was just the antimatter we wanted, we could have boarded any time in the last three months. That's how long we've known the stuff was on board. *Dymasio* has visited seven inhabited star systems since we started monitoring it, without threatening any of them. Now my agent confirms the captain has found a buyer with these separatist hotheads, and I want them. This way we can wrap up both supplier and destination. We could even come out of it with the location of the antimatter-production station. Commendations all round, so just be patient."

"OK." **Did you catch all that?** Syrinx asked Thetis.

Certainly did. And she's quite right.

I know, but . . . She broadcast a complex emotional harmonic of eagerness and frustration.

Bear with it, little sister. Mental laughter. Thetis always knew how to tweak her. *Graeae* had been born before *Oenone*, but there was a marked comparison in size; with a hull diameter of a hundred and fifteen metres *Oenone* was the largest of all *Iasius*'s children. And it wasn't until puberty's growth hormones came into effect that Thetis outmatched her in physical tussles. But they had always been the closest, always competing against each other.

I've never met anyone more unsuitable for a captaincy, Ruben chided. **No composure, all teenage recklessness, that's your fault, young lady. I'm jumping ship when this is over, bugger what the contract says.**

She laughed out loud, quickly turning it into a cough for Eileen's benefit. Even though she was used to the degree of honesty which affinity fostered, Ruben always astounded her with his intimate knowledge of her emotional composition. **You don't complain about my other teenage attributes,** she shot back, complete with a very graphic image.

Oh, lady, you just wait till we're off duty.

I'll hold you to that.

The prospect almost made the tense waiting worthwhile.

Because of the need for a more precise trajectory when jumping towards a planet than for an interstellar jump, *Dymasio* spent a good fifty minutes re-aligning its course with considerable accuracy. Once its new orbital vector intersected Kirchol, the starship reconfigured itself for a jump.

Weapons status check, please, Syrinx demanded when the light from *Dymasio*'s dive flame began to fade.

Combat wasps and proximity defence systems online, Chi replied.

OK, everybody, alert status one. We don't know how many hostiles there are going to be around Kirchol, so we'll proceed with extreme caution. The admiral wants this ship interdicted, not destroyed, but if we're outnumbered we let loose the combat wasps and retreat. Let's just hope this is the nest.

She caught an indistinct mental grumble: **It can't possibly be another decoy jump. Please.** From the tiredness of the tone she guessed it was Oxley, who was actually older than Ruben, a hundred and fifty. Sinon had recommended him when she was assembling her first crew. He had stayed on mostly out of loyalty to her when she signed on with the navy. More cause for guilt.

Dymasio jumped.

Kirchol was a muddy brown globe three hundred and seventy thousand kilometres below *Oenone*'s hull, attendant moons glimmering dimly in the exhausted sunlight. The gas giant had nothing like the majesty of Saturn, it was too drab, too listless. Even the stormbands lacked ferocity.

Dymasio and the two voidhawks had emerged above the south pole; insignificant on such a scale, one dull speck, and two coal-black motes, falling with imperceptible slowness as the gravity field tugged at them.

Syrinx opened her mind to Chi, combining *Oenone*'s perceptual awareness with the weapons officer's knowledge of their combat wasps' performance capabilities. Her nerves stretching over a huge volume of space, making a far-off body tremble in reaction.

The *Dymasio* started to transmit a simple radio code, beaming it down towards the gas giant. Given their position, there would be no overspill falling on the populated inner system, Syrinx realized, no chance of being detected even in a few hours when the radio waves finally bridged the gulf.

An answering pulse flashed out from something in orbit around Kirchol, well outside *Oenone*'s mass-detection range. The source point began to move, vaulting out of its orbit at five gees. *Oenone* couldn't detect any infrared trace, and there was no reaction-drive exhaust. The radio signal cut out.

A blackhawk. The thought leapt between the Edenists on both voidhawks, a shared frisson of glee.

It's mine, Syrinx told Thetis on singular-engagement mode. She hadn't forgotten how the last blackhawk had given them the slip. It rankled still.

Oh, come on, he protested.

Mine, she repeated coolly. **You get all the glory nabbing that actual antimatter. What more do you want?**

The next blackhawk we come across is mine.

Of course, she cooed.

Thetis retreated, his subconscious grousing away. But he knew better than try and argue with his sister when she was in that mood.

We're going after it? *Oenone* demanded.

We certainly are, she reassured it.

Good, I didn't like losing that last one. I could have matched its swallow.

No, you couldn't. That was nineteen light-years. You'd damage your patterning cells trying to emulate that. Fifteen light-years is our limit.

Oenone didn't answer, but she could sense the resentment in its mind. She had almost been tempted to try the larger than usual swallow, but fear of injuring the voidhawk held her back. That and the prospect of stranding the rest of the crew in deep space.

I would never harm you or the crew, *Oenone* said gently.

I know. But it was annoying, wasn't it?

Very!

The blackhawk rose up out of the ecliptic plane in a long, graceful curve. Even when it slowed to rendezvous with the *Dymasio* the two waiting voidhawks couldn't discern its shape or size. They were thirty thousand kilometres away, too far for optical resolution, and the slightest use of the distortion effect to probe it would have given them away.

Both target craft used their radios when they were five thousand kilometres apart, a steady stream of encrypted data. It made tracking absurdly easy, *Oenone*'s passive electronic sensor array triangulating them to half a metre. Syrinx waited until they were only two thousand kilometres apart, then issued the order to interdict.

HOLD YOUR LOCATION, *Oenone* bellowed across the affinity band. It detected a mental flinch from the blackhawk. **CANCEL YOUR ACCELERATION, DO NOT ATTEMPT TO INITIATE A SWALLOW. STAND BY FOR RENDEZVOUS AND BOARDING.**

Gravity surged back into the crew toroid, building with uncomfortable speed. *Oenone* and *Graeae* streaked in towards their prey at eight gees. *Oenone* was capable of generating a counter-acceleration force of three gees around the crew toroid, which still left Syrinx subject to a harsh five gees. Her toughened internal membranes could just about take the strain, but she worried that the blackhawk would try to run. Their crews nearly always used nanonic supplements, enabling them to withstand much higher acceleration. If it developed into a straight chase, *Oenone*'s crew were going to suffer, especially Ruben and Oxley.

She needn't have worried. After *Oenone*'s affinity shout, the blackhawk folded in its distortion field. But she was keenly aware of the sullen anger colouring its thoughts, presumably echoing those of its captain. There was a name, too, or rather an insistence of identity: *Vermuden*.

Graeae was broadcasting a radio message at the *Dymasio*, the same demand to maintain position. In the Adamist starship's case, enforcement was a more practical option. The voidhawk reached out with its distortion field, disrupting the quantum state of space around the *Dymasio*'s hull; if it tried to jump away now, the interference would produce instabilities in its patterning nodes, with spectacularly lethal results as the desynchronized energy loci imploded.

Oenone and *Graeae* drew apart as they closed on their respective targets. The *Vermuden* was a sharp profile in Syrinx's mind now, a flattish onion shape one hundred and five metres in diameter, its central spire tapering to a needle-sharp point sixty metres above the hull rim. There was no crew toroid, instead three silvery mechanical capsules were fixed equidistantly around the upper hull; one was a life-support cabin large enough for about five or six people, another was a hangar for a small spaceplane, the third was its cargo hold. Energy currents simmered below its hull, spectral iridescent whirls that suggested extreme agitation.

"Captain Kouritz, you and your squad to the airlock, please," Syrinx said when they began to slow for rendezvous. "Be advised, the blackhawk's cabin space is approximately four hundred cubic metres."

Vermuden hung in space three hundred kilometres away, a dusky crescent, slightly ginger in colour. She could feel Chi locking the proximity defence lasers onto the blackhawk, a mix of electronic and bitek senses providing the focus.

"I'll go with them," Eileen Carouch said. She tapped her restraint-strap release catch.

"Make sure the *Vermuden*'s captain is brought straight back here," Syrinx said. "I'll send one of my people with you to fly *Vermuden* back to Fleet headquarters." Without its captain, the blackhawk would have to obey an Edenist.

Oenone flipped over as it approached *Vermuden*, inverting itself so that it seemed to be descending vertically towards the blackhawk's upper hull. An airlock tube extended out from the crew toroid. The marine squad waited in the chamber behind it, fully armoured, weapons powered up. Gravity throughout the toroid had returned to a welcome Earth standard.

Syrinx ordered the *Vermuden*'s captain to extend the blackhawk's airlock.

The *Dymasio* exploded.

Its captain, faced with the total certainty of a personality debrief followed by a Confederation Navy firing squad, decided his crew and ship were a worthwhile price to pay for taking *Graeae* with him. He waited until the voidhawk was a scant kilometre away, beginning its docking manoeuvres, then turned off the antimatter-confinement chambers.

Five hundred grams of antimatter rushed to embrace an equal mass of ordinary matter.

From *Oenone*'s position, two thousand kilometres away, the elemental energy wavefront split the universe in two. On one side the stars burnt with their usual untroubled tranquillity; opposite that infinity vanished, replaced by a solid flat plane of raging photons.

Syrinx felt the light searing into *Oenone*, scorching optical-receptor cells into crisps. Affinity acted like a conductor for purple-white light, allowing it to shine straight into her own mind, a torrent of photons that threatened to engulf her sanity. In amongst the glare were fissures of darkness, fluttering around like tiny birds caught by a gale. They called out to her as they passed, mental cries, sometimes words, sometimes visions of people and places, sometimes smells—phantasm tastes, a touch, the laughter, music, heat, chill, wetness. Minds transferring into *Oenone*'s neural cells. But broken, incomplete. Flawed.

Thetis! Syrinx cried.

She couldn't find him, not amid such turmoil. And the light had become a pervasive pain. She howled in anguish and hatred.

Vermuden's distortion field distended, strengthened, applying stress against the perpetual structure of reality. An interstice yawned wide.

Chi fired the gamma lasers. But the beams raked emptiness. The interstice was already closing.

Less than two seconds after the *Dymasio* exploded, a blast wave of particles arrived to assault *Oenone*'s hull, supplementing the corrosive electromagnetic radiation already striking against the foam. The voidhawk looked past the immediate chaos, observing *Vermuden*'s wormhole forming, a tunnel through empty dimensions. Size and determinant length defined by the blackhawk's energy input. *Oenone* knew the terminus coordinate exactly, twenty-one light-years away, the blackhawk's utter limit.

This time! *Oenone* thought tempestuously. Energy blazed through its own patterning cells.

No! Syrinx shouted, shocked out of her grief.

There is a way, I know how. Trust me.

She waited helplessly as the interstice engulfed them, some treacherous aspect of her subconscious granting the voidhawk permission, urging them on towards retribution. Worry faded when she saw the wormhole was only thirteen light-years long. As its terminus began to open, she felt the patterning cells activate again. Realization was instantaneous, and she laughed with vengeful fury.

Told you so, *Oenone* said smugly.

The desperate twenty-one light-year swallow had stretched *Vermuden*'s energy loading capacity virtually to breaking point. It could sense its captain prone on his acceleration couch, muscles locked solid, back arched, the exertion twinned. The wormhole's pseudofabric slithered round the hull, not a physical pressure, but tangible none the less. Finally, up ahead, the terminus manifested. Starlight traced strange shapes as it filtered through.

Vermuden popped out into the clean vacuum of normal space, mind radiating vivid relief.

Well done, its captain said. *Vermuden* felt arm and chest muscles slacken, an indrawn breath.

Powerful laserlight illuminated its hull, washing out its optical receptor cells in a pink dazzle. A lens-shaped mass a hundred and fifteen metres in diameter hung eighty metres off its central spire in the direction of Betelgeuse's demonic red gleam.

"What the fuck . . . How?" the captain yelped.

This is just the targeting laser, *Oenone* said. **If I sense any flux change in your patterning cells I'll switch to the gamma lasers and slice you in half. Now extend your airlock. I have some people on board keen to meet you.**

"I didn't know voidhawks could do that," Eileen Carouch said a couple of hours later. *Vermuden*'s captain, Henry Siclari, and the blackhawk's other two crewmen, were in *Oenone*'s brig; and the navy prize crew, headed by Cacus, were familiarizing themselves with the blackhawk's systems. Cacus reckoned they would be able to take the ship back to Oshanko in a day. "Sequential swallows?" Syrinx said. "Nothing to stop them, you just need a voidhawk with an acute spacial sense." **Like you.**

I love you, *Oenone* replied, unabashed by the alternate praise and admonitions the Edenists had been bombarding it with since the manoeuvre.

Got an answer to everything, haven't you? she said. But the humour wasn't there.

Thetis. His broad, smiling face covered in boyish freckles, the uncombed sandy hair, the lanky, slightly awkward body. All the hours together spent roving around Romulus.

He was a part of her identity in the same way as *Oenone*. Soulsibling, so much had been shared. And now he was gone. Torn away from her, torn out of her, the voyages together, frustrations and achievements.

I mourn for him too, *Oenone* whispered into her mind, its thoughts drenched with regret.

Thank you. And *Graeae***'s eggs have been lost as well. What a terrible, filthy thing to do. I hate Adamists.**

No, that is beneath us. See, Eileen and the marines share our loss. It is not Adamists. Only individuals. Always individuals. Even Edenists have our failures, do we not?

Yes. We do, she said, because it was true enough. But there was still that fraction of her mind which remained vacant, the vanished smile.

Athene knew something was shockingly wrong as soon as *Oenone* emerged above Saturn. She was in the garden lounge, feeding two-month-old Clymene from a bitek mammary orb when the cold premonition closed about her. It made her clutch at her second great-great-grandchild for fear of the future and what it held. The infant wailed in protest at the loss of the nipple and the tightness of her grip. She hurriedly handed Clymene back to her great-grandson, who tried to calm the baby girl with mental coos of reassurance. Then Syrinx's alarmingly dulled mind touched Athene, and the awful knowledge was revealed in full.

Is there nothing of him left? she asked softly.

Some, Syrinx said. **But so little, I'm sorry, Mother.**

A single thought would be enough for me.

As *Oenone* neared Romulus it gave up the thought fragments it had stored to the habitat personality. A precious intangible residue of life, the sole legacy of Thetis and his crew.

Athene's past friends, lovers, and husbands emerged from the multiplicity of Romulus's personality to offer support and encouragement, cushioning the blow as best they could. **We will do what we can,** they assured her. She could feel the tremulous remnants of her son being slowly woven into a more cohesive whole, and drew a brief measure of comfort from that.

Although no stranger to death, Athene found this bereavement particularly difficult. Always at the back of her mind was the belief that the voidhawks and their captains were somehow immortal, or at least immune to such wasteful calamity. A foolish, almost childish belief, because they were the children she prized the most. Her last link with *Iasius*, their offspring.

Half an hour later, dressed in a plain jet-black ship-tunic, Athene stood in the spaceport reception lounge, a proud, solitary figure, the lines on her face betraying every one of her hundred and thirty-five years as they never had before. She looked out over the ledge as *Oenone* and its anxious escort of two voidhawks from the Saturn defence squadron crept out of the darkness. *Oenone* sank onto a vacant pedestal with a very human mindsigh of relief. Feed tubes in the pedestal stirred like blind stumpy tentacles, searching for the female orifices on the voidhawk's underside; various sphincter muscles expanded and gripped, producing tight seals. *Oenone* gulped down the nutrient fluid which Romulus synthesized, filling its internal bladders, quenching the thirst which leached vitality from every cell. They hadn't stayed at Oshanko any longer than it took to hand Henry Siclari and his crew over to the Fleet port authorities, and allow Edenist bonding-adjustment specialists to assume command of *Vermuden*. After that Syrinx had insisted on coming direct to Saturn.

Athene looked out at the big voidhawk with real concern rising.

Oenone was in a sorry state: hull foam scorched and flaking, toroid thermo-dump panels melted, electronic sensor systems reduced to rivulets of congealed slag, the sensor blisters that had faced the *Dymasio* roasted, their cells dead.

I'm all right, *Oenone* told her. **It's mostly the mechanical systems that were damaged. And the biotechnicians can graft new sensor blisters into me. I'm never going to complain about being covered in foam again,** it added humbly.

When Syrinx came through the airlock her cheeks had become almost hollow, her hair was hanging limp over her skull, and she walked as though she had been condemned. Athene felt the tears come at last, and put her arms round her woebegone daughter, soothing the drained thoughts with an empathic compassion, the maternal balm.

It's not your fault.

If I hadn't . . .

Don't, Athene ordered sternly. **You owe Thetis and** *Graeae* **this much, not to sink into pointless remorse. You're stronger than that, much stronger.**

Yes, Mother.

He did what he wanted to. He did what was right. Tell me how many millions of lives would have been lost if that antimatter had been used against a naked planetary surface?

A lot, Syrinx said numbly.

And he saved them. My son. Because of him, they will live, and have children, and laugh.

But it hurts!

That's because we're human, more so than Adamists can ever be. Our empathy means we can never hide from what we feel, and that's good. But you must always walk the balance, Syrinx; the balance is the penalty of being human: the danger of allowing yourself to feel. For this we walk a narrow path high above rocky ground. On one side we have the descent into animalism, on the other a godhead delusion. Both pulling at us, both tempting. But without these forces tugging at your psyche, stirring it into conflict, you can never love. They awaken us, you see, these warring sides, they arouse our passion. So learn from this wretched episode, learn to be proud of Thetis and what he accomplished, use it to counter the grief. It is hard, I know; for captains more than anyone. We are the ones who truly open our souls to another entity, we feel the deepest, and suffer the most. And knowing that, knowing what you would endure in life, I still chose to bring you into existence, because there is so much joy to be had from the living.

*   *   *

The circular house snug in arms of its gentle valley hadn't changed, still a frantic noisy vortex of excited children, slightly weary adults, and harassed bitek housechimps. Syrinx might never have been away. With eighteen children, and, so far, forty-two grandchildren, eleven great-grandchildren, and the two newest fourth-generation additions, Athene headed a family that never gave her a moment's rest. Ninety per cent of the adults were involved with spaceflight in one field or another, which meant long absences were the norm. But when they came back, it was the house and Athene they always visited first, staying or passing through as the fancy took them.

"Athene's boarding-house, bordello, and playpen," the old ex-captain had called it on more than one occasion.

The younger children were delighted to see Syrinx, whooping as they gathered round her, demanding kisses and stories of the planets she'd visited, while the adults offered subdued condolences. Being with them, knowing and feeling the heartache being shared, lifted the load. Slightly.

After the evening meal Syrinx went back to her old room, asking to be left alone for a few hours. Ruben and Athene acceded, retreating to the white iron chairs on the patio and conversing on the singular-engagement mode, sober faces betraying their worry.

She lay back on the bed, staring through the transparent roof at the lazy winding valleys beyond the dimming axial light-tube. In the seven years since *Oenone* reached maturity the trees had grown and bushes fattened, expanding the green-on-green patterns of her childhood.

She could feel *Oenone* out on the ledge, hull being cleaned of foam, mobile gantry arms in position, giving technicians full access to the battered crew toroid. Now it had completed its nutrient digestion its mindtone was returning to normal. It was enjoying being the centre of attention, busy conversing with the ledge crews over aspects of the repairs. Two biotechnicians were squatting over a ruined sensor blister with portable probes, taking samples.

Daddy?

I'm here, Sly-minx. I told you I always would be.

Thank you. I never doubted. How is he?

Happy.

A little of the dread lifted from her heart. Is he ready?

Yes. But there was so much missing from recent years. We have integrated what we can. The core of identity is viable but it lacks substance. He remains a child, perhaps the part of him you loved the most.

Can I talk to him yet?

You may.

She was standing barefoot on thick, cool grass beside a broad stream, the axial light-tube shining like a thread of captured sunlight overhead. There were tall trees around her, bowing under the weight of vines hanging between their branches, and long cascades of flowers fell to the floor, some of them trailing in the clear water. Butterflies flapped lazily through the still air, contending with bees for perches on the flowers, birds cheeped all around.

It was the clearing where she had spent so many days as a girl, just past the bottom of the lawn. Looking down she saw she was wearing a simple cotton summer dress with a tiny blue and white check. Long loose hair swirled around skinny hips. Her body was thirteen years old; and she knew why even as she heard the children shouting and laughing. Young enough to be regarded as part of childhood's conspiracy, old enough to be revered, to hold herself aloof and not be resented for it.

They burst into the clearing, six ten-year-old boys, in shorts and T-shirts, bare chested and in swimming trunks, smiling and laughing, strong limbs flashing in the warm light.

"Syrinx!" He was in their middle, sandy hair askew, grinning up at her.

"Hello, Thetis," she said.

"Are you coming with us?" he asked breathlessly.

A raft of rough silicon sheets, foamed aluminium I-beams, and empty plastic drink tanks—familiar enough to bring tears to her eyes—was lying on the bank, half in the water.

"I can't, Thetis. I just came to make sure you're all right."

"Course I'm all right!" He tried to do a cartwheel on the grass, but toppled over and fell into a laughing heap. "We're going all the way down to the salt-water reservoir. It'll be fun, we've not told anyone, and the personality won't see us. We could meet anything down there, pirates or monsters. And we might find some treasure. I'll bring it back, and I'll be the most famous captain in all of the habitat." He scrambled to his feet again, eyes shining. "*Please* come, Syrinx. Please?"

"Another time, I promise."

There were shouts from the other boys as the raft was pushed into the fast-flowing stream. It bobbed about at alarming angles for a few seconds before gradually righting itself. The boys started to pile on.

Thetis's head swivelled between Syrinx and the raft, desperately torn. "Promise? Really promise?"

"I do." She reached out and held his head between her hands, and kissed him lightly on his brow.

"Syrinx!" He squirmed in agitation, colouring as the other boys launched into a flurry of catcalls.

"Here," she said, and took off a slim silver necklace with an intricately carved pale jade stone the size of a grape. "Wear this, it'll be like I'm there with you. And next time I visit, you can tell me all about it."

"Right!" And he ran for the raft, splashing through the shallows as he fumbled to fasten the chain round his neck. "Don't forget, come back. You promised."

How far will he go? she asked Sinon as a soaking Thetis was hauled over the edge of the raft by a couple of his friends.

As far as he wishes.

And how long will it last?

As long as he wants.

Daddy!

I'm sorry, I didn't mean to be flippant. Probably about ten or fifteen years. You see, even childhood will ultimately pale. Games that defy adults and friends that mean the whole world are all very well, but a major part of what a ten-year-old is, is the wish to be old; his actions are a shadow of what he sees as adult behaviour. There is an old saying, that the boy is the father of the man. So when he has had his fill of adventure and realizes he will never be that man, that he is a sterile child,

his identity will fade out of the multiplicity into the overall personality. Like all of us will eventually, Sly-minx, even you.

You mean he will lose hope.

No. Death is the loss of hope, everything else is merely despair.

The children were paddling now, getting the hang of the raft: Thetis was sitting at the front shouting orders, in his element. He looked round, smiled and waved. Syrinx raised a hand.

Adamists lose hope, she said. The *Dymasio*'s captain lost all hope. That's why he did what he did.

Adamists are incomplete. We know we will continue after the body dies; in some way, some fraction of us will linger for hundreds of millennia. For myself, I cannot even contemplate abandoning the multiplicity segment of the personality, not with you and my other children and grandchildren to watch over. Perhaps in ten or fifteen generations, when I can conjure up no sense of attachment, then I may seek full unity with the habitat personality, and transfer my allegiance to all Edenists. But it will be a very long time.

Adamists have their religions. I thought their gods gave them hope.

They do, to the very devout. But consider the disadvantage under which the ordinary Adamist labours. The mythical kingdom, that is all their heaven can ever be, beyond ever knowing. In the end, such belief is very hard for poor sinful mortals to retain. Our afterlife, however, is tangible, real. For us it is not a question of faith, we have fact.

Unless you are Thetis.

Even he survives.

Some of him, a stunted existence. Floating down a river that will never end.

Loved, treasured, welcomed, eternal.

The raft disappeared round a bend, a clump of willows blocking it from sight. High-pitched voices drifted through the air. Syrinx let her hand drop. "I will visit you again, big brother," she told the empty gurgling stream. "Again and again, every time I come back. I will make you look forward to my visits and the stories I bring, I will give you something to hope for. Promise."

In her room she looked up at the darkened indistinct landscape far above. The axial light-tube had been reduced to a lunar presence masked by the evening's first rain-clouds.

Syrinx closed her mind to the other Edenists, closed it to the voidhawks flying outside, closed it to the habitat personality. Only *Oenone* remained. Beloved who would understand, because they were one.

Emerging from the jumble of doubt and misery was the tenuous wish that the Adamists were right after all, and there was such a thing as God, and an afterlife, and souls. That way Thetis wouldn't be lost. Not for ever.

It was such a tiny sliver of hope.

Oenone's thoughts rubbed against hers, soothing and sympathetic.

If there is a God, and if somewhere my brother's soul is intact, please look after him. He will be so alone.

7

Over a thousand tributaries contributed towards the Juliffe's rapacious flow, a wrinkled network of rivers and streams gathering in the rainfall over an area of one and a half million square kilometres. They emptied themselves into the main course at full volume throughout the whole two hundred and ninety-five days of Lalonde's year, bringing with them immense amounts of silt, rotting vegetation, and broken trees. The turbulence and power of the huge flow was such that the water along the last five hundred kilometres turned the same colour and thickness as milky coffee. By the time it reached the coast the river's width had swollen to over seventeen kilometres; and the sheer weight of water backed up for two thousand kilometres behind it was awesome. At the mouth it looked as though one sea was bleeding into another.

For the final hundred-kilometre stretch, the banks on the northern side were non-existent; marshland extended up to a hundred and fifty kilometres into the countryside. Named the Hultain Marsh after the first reckless ecological assessment team member to venture a few brief kilometres inside its fringes, it proved an inhospitable zone of reeds and algae and sharp-toothed lizard-analogue animals of varying sizes. No human explorer ever managed to traverse it; the ecological evaluators contented themselves with Hultain's sketchy report and the satellite survey pictures. When the wind blew from the north, it carried a powerful smell of corruption over the river into Durringham. To the city's residents the Hultain Marsh had virtually assumed the quality of myth, a repository of bad luck and ghoulish creatures.

The land on the Juliffe's southern side, however, rose up to twelve metres above the surging brown waters. Sprawling

aloof along the bank, Durringham was relatively safe from
the most potent of the Juliffe's spring floods. Poised between spaceport and water, the city was the key to colonizing the entire river basin.

The Juliffe provided the Lalonde Development Company
with the greatest conceivable natural roadway into Amarisk's
interior. With its tributaries extending into every valley in the
centre of the landmass, there was no need to hack out and
maintain expensive tracks in the jungle. Abundant wood provided the raw material for boat hulls, the simplest and cheapest form of travel possible. So shipbuilding swiftly became
the capital's principal industry, with nearly a quarter of its
population dependent on the success of the shipyards.

Captains under contract to the LDC would take newly arrived colonist groups upriver, and bring down the surplus
produce from the established farms to be sold in the city.
There were several hundred boats docking and sailing every
day. The port with its jetties and warehouses and fishmar-
kets and shipyards grew until it stretched the entire length of
the city. It was also the logical place to site the transients'
dormitories.

Jay Hilton thought the dormitory was tremendously exciting. It was so different from anything in her life to date. A
simple angled roof of ezystak panels eighty metres long,
supported by a framework of metal girders. There were no
walls, the LDC officer said they would have made it too hot
inside. There was a concrete floor, and row after row of hard
wooden cots. She had slept in a sleeping-bag the first night,
right at the centre of the dormitory with the rest of Group
Seven's kids. It had taken her an age to fall asleep, people
kept talking, and the river made great swooshing noises as it
flowed past the embankment. And she didn't think she
would ever get used to the humidity, her clothes hadn't been
completely dry since she got off the spaceplane.

During the day the dormitory thronged with people, and
the alleyways between the cots were great for chases and
other games. Life underneath its rattling roof was very easy-
going; nothing was organized for the kids, so they were free
to please themselves how they chose. She had spent the sec-

ond day getting to know the other kids in Group Seven. In the morning they ran riot among the adults, then after lunch they had all made their way down to the riverside to watch the boats. Jay had loved it. The whole port area looked like something out of a historical AV programme, a slice of the Earth's Middle Ages preserved on a far planet. Everything was made of wood, and the boats were so beautiful, with their big paddles on each side, and tall iron stacks that sent out long plumes of grey-white smoke.

Twice during the day the sky had clouded over, and rain had fallen like a solid sheet. The kids had all retreated under the dormitory roof, watching spellbound as the grey veil obscured the Juliffe, and huge lightning bolts crashed overhead.

She had never imagined the wild was so wild. But her mother wasn't worried, so she wasn't. Sitting down and just watching had never been such fun before. She couldn't think how wonderful it was going to be actually travelling on a river-boat. From a starship one day to a paddle-steamer the next! Life was glorious.

The food they had been served was strange, the aboriginal fruit was all odd shapes with a mildly spicy flavouring, but at least there wasn't any vat meat like they had at the arcology. After the high tea the staff served for the kids in the big canteen at one end of the dormitory, she went back to the riverside to see if she could spot any aboriginal animals. She remembered the vennal, something like a cross between a lizard and a monkey. It featured prominently in the didactic memory which the LDC immigration advisory team at the orbital-tower base-station had imprinted before she left Earth. In the mirage floating round inside her skull it looked kind of cute. She was secretly hoping she'd be able to have one as a pet once they reached their allotted land upriver.

The embankment was a solid wall of bitek polyp, a dull apricot in colour, preventing any more of the rich black soil from being chewed away by the frighteningly large river. It was thrilling to see so much bitek being used; Jay had never met an Edenist, although back at the arcology Father Varhoos had warned the congregation about them and their soulless technology of perverted life. But using the polyp here was a good idea, the kernels were cheap, and the coral didn't need constant repairs the way concrete would. She couldn't see the harm. The whole universe was being turned upside-down this week.

She slid right down the sloping wall to the water itself, and started walking, hoping to see a xenoc fish. The water here was almost clear. Wavelets lapping on the polyp sent up sprays that showered her bare legs; she was still wearing the shorts and blouse that her mother had made her carry in the zero-tau pod. A lot of the other colonists in Group Seven had spent the morning chasing after their gear in one of the warehouses, trying to find more practical clothes.

Everyone had been envious and admiring of her and mother yesterday. That felt good. So much better than the way people back in the arcology regarded them. She pushed that thought away hurriedly.

Her boots splashed through the shallows, the water droplets slithering off the shiny coating. There were a lot of big pipe outlets venting into the river, along with the drainage gullies which were like medium-sized streams, so she had to be careful as she dodged under the pipes not to get splattered by the discharges. Up ahead was one of the circular harbours, six hundred metres in diameter, also made out of polyp; a refuge where the larger boats could dock in calmer waters. The harbours were spaced every kilometre or so along the embankment, with clusters of warehouses and timber mills springing up on the ground behind them. In between the harbours were rows of wooden jetties sticking out into the river, which the smaller traders and fishing boats used.

The sky was growing darker again. But it wasn't rain, the sun was low in the west. And she was getting very tired, the day here was awfully long.

She ducked under a jetty, hand stroking the black timber pillars. Mayope wood, her eidetic memory said, one of the hardest woods found in the Confederation. The tree had big scarlet flowers. She rapped her knuckles against it experimentally. It really was hard, like a metal, or stone.

Out on the river one of the big paddle-boats was sailing past, churning up a big wake of frothy water as its bows drove against the current. Colonists were lined up along the rails, and they all seemed to be looking at her. She grinned and waved at them.

Group Seven was sailing tomorrow. The *real* adventure. She stared wistfully after the boat as it slipped away upriver.

That was when she saw the thing caught around a support pillar of the next jetty. A dirty yellow-pink lump, about a metre long. There was more of it underwater, she could tell from the way it bobbed about. With a whoop, she raced forwards, feet kicking up fans of water. It was a xenoc fish, or amphibian, or something. Trapped and waiting for her to inspect it. Names and shapes whirled through her mind, the didactic memory on full recall, trying to match up with what she was seeing.

Maybe it's something new, she thought. Maybe they'll name it after me. I'll be famous!

She was five metres away, and still running as hard as she could, when she saw the head. It was someone in the water, someone without any clothes on. Face down! The shock threw her rhythm, and her feet skidded from under her. She yelled as her knee hit the rough, unyielding polyp. She felt a hot pain as she grazed the side of her leg. She finished up flat against the embankment, legs half in the water, feeling numb all over and sick inside. Blood started to well up in the graze. She bit her lip, eyes watering as she watched it, fighting not to cry.

A wave lifted the corpse in the river, knocking it against the support pillar again. Through sticky tears Jay saw that it was a man, all swollen up. His head turned towards her. There was a long purple weal along one cheek. He had no eyes, only empty holes where they should be. His flesh was rippling. Jay blinked. Long white worms with a million legs were feeding on the battered flesh. One oozed out of his half-open mouth like a slender anaemic tongue, its tip waving around slowly as though it was tasting the air.

She threw her head back and screamed.

The rain which came after the sun sank from the sky an hour later that evening was a big help to Quinn Dexter. Between them, Lalonde's three moons conspired to cast a bright spectral phosphorescence on the night-time city: people could see their way quite clearly down the slushy streets, but with the thick clouds scudding overhead the light level was drastically reduced. Durringham didn't have street lighting; individual pubs would floodlight the street outside their entrance, and the bigger cabins had porch lights, but outside their pools of radiance there was only a faint backscatter of photons. In amongst the large industrial buildings of the port where Quinn lurked there wasn't even that, only gloom and impenetrable shadows.

He had slipped away from the transients' dormitory after the evening meal, finding himself a concealing gap between a couple of single-storey outbuildings tacked on to the end of a long warehouse. Jackson Gael was crouched down behind some barrels on the other side of the path. Behind him was the high blank wall of a mill, slatted wooden planks rearing up like a cliff face.

There wouldn't be many people wandering around this part of the port at night, and those that did would probably be colonists waiting for a boat upriver. There was another transients' dormitory two hundred metres to the north. Quinn had decided that colonists would make the best targets.

The sheriffs would pay more attention to a city resident being mugged than some new arrival who nobody cared about. Colonists were human cattle to the LDC; and if the dopey bastards hadn't worked that out for themselves, then more fool them. But Jackson had been right about one thing, the colonists were better off than him. Ivets were the lowest of the low.

They had discovered that yesterday evening. When they finally arrived at the dormitory they were immediately detailed to unload the lorries they had just loaded at the spaceport. After they finished stacking Group Seven's gear in a harbourside warehouse a group of them had wandered off into town. They didn't have any money, but that didn't matter, they deserved a break. That was when they found the grey Ivet jump-suit with its scarlet letters acted like a flashing beacon: *Shit on me.* They hadn't got more than a few hundred metres out of the port before they turned tail and hurried back to the dormitory. They'd been spat on, shouted at, jeered by children, had stones flung at them, and finally someone had let a xenoc animal charge at them. That had frightened Quinn the most, though he didn't show it to the others. The creature was like a cat scaled up to dog size; it had jet-black scales and a wedge-shaped head, with a lot of sharp needle teeth in its gaping mouth. The mud didn't slow it down appreciably as it ran at them, and several Ivets had skidded onto their knees as the group panicked and ran away.

Worst of all were the sounds the thing made, like a drawn-out whine; but there were words in the cry, strangely twisted by the xenoc gullet, human words. "City scum," and "Kid fuckers," and others that were distorted beyond recognition, yet all carrying the same message. The *thing* hated them, echoing its master who had laughed as its huge jaws snapped at their running legs.

Back in the dormitory, Quinn had sat down and started to think for the first time since the police stunned him back on Earth. He had to get off this planet which even God's Brother would reject. To do that he needed information. He needed to know how the local set-up worked, how to get himself an edge. All the other Ivets would dream about leaving, some must have made attempts to escape in the past. The biggest mistake he could make would be rushing it. And dressed in his signpost jump-suit, he wouldn't even be able to scout around.

He had caught Jackson Gael's eye, and flicked his head at the velvet walls of night encircling the dormitory. The two of them slipped out unnoticed, and didn't return till dawn.

Now he waited crouched against the warehouse wall, stripped down to his shorts, nerves burning with excitement at the prospect of repeating last night's spree. Rain was drumming on the rooftops and splashing into the puddles and mud of the path, kicking up a loud din. More water was gurgling down the drainage gully at the side of the warehouse. His skin and hair were soaked. At least the drops were warm.

The man in the canary-yellow cagoule was almost level with the little gap between the outhouses before Quinn heard him. He was squelching through the mud, muttering and humming under his breath. Quinn peered out round the corner. His left eye had been boosted by a nanonic cluster, giving him infrared vision. It was his first implant, and he'd used it for exactly the same purpose back at the arcology: to give him an edge in the dark. One thing Banneth had taught him was never fight until you've already won.

The retinal implant showed him a ghostly red figure weaving unsteadily from side to side. Rain showed as a gritty pale pink mist, the buildings were claret-coloured crags.

Quinn waited until the man had passed the gap before he moved. He slid out onto the path, the length of wood gripped tightly in his hand. And still the man was unaware of him, rain and blackness providing perfect cover. He took three paces, raised the improvised club, then slammed it down at the base of the man's neck. The cagoule's fabric tore under the impact. Quinn felt the blow reverberate all the way back up to his elbows, jarring his joints. God's Brother! He didn't want the man dead, not yet.

His victim gave a single grunt of pain, and collapsed forwards into the mud.

"Jackson!" Quinn called. "God's Brother, where are you? I can't shift him by myself. Get a move on."

"Quinn? Christ, I can't see a bloody thing."

He looked round, seeing Jackson emerge from behind the barrels. His skin shone a strong burgundy in the infrared spectrum, arteries and veins near the surface showing up as brighter scarlet lines.

"Over here. Walk forward three steps, then turn left." He guided Jackson up to the body, enjoying the sense of power. Jackson would follow his leadership, and the others would fall into line.

Together they dragged their victim into the outhouse— Quinn guessed it had been some kind of office, abandoned years ago now. Four bare wooden slat walls and a roof that leaked. Tapers of slime ran down the walls, fungal growths blooming from the cracks. There was a strong citric scent in the air. Overhead the clouds were drifting away inland. Beriana, the second moon, came out, shining a wan lemon light onto the city, and a few meagre beams filtered through the skylight. They were enough for Jackson to see by.

Both of them went over to the pile of clothes they had left heaped on a broken composite cargo-pod. Quinn watched Jackson towelling himself dry. The lad had a strong body, broad shoulders.

"Forget it, Quinn," Jackson said in a neutral voice, but one that carried in the silence following the rain. "I don't turn on to that. Strictly het, OK?" It came out like a challenge.

"Hey, don't lose cool," Quinn said. "I got my eye on someone, and it ain't you." He wasn't entirely sure he could whip the lanky lad from a straight start. Besides he needed Jackson. For now.

He started to pull on the clothes which belonged to one of last night's victims, a green short-sleeved shirt and baggy blue shorts, waterproof boots which were only fractionally too large. Three pairs of socks stopped them from rubbing blisters. He was strongly tempted to take those boots upriver, he didn't like to think what would happen to his feet in the lightweight Ivet-issue shoes.

"Right, let's see what we've got," he said. They stripped the cagoule from the unconscious man. He groaned weakly. His shorts were soiled, and a ribbon of piss ran out of the cagoule.

Definitely a new colonist, Quinn decided, as he wrinkled his nose up at the smell. The clothes were new, the boots were new, he was clean shaven; and he had the slightly overweight appearance of an arcology dweller. Locals were nearly always lean, and most sported longish hair and thick beards.

His belt carried a fission-blade knife, a miniature thermal inducer, and a personal MF flek-player block.

Quinn unclipped the knife and the inducer. "We'll take those with us upriver. They'll come in useful."

"We'll be searched," Jackson said. "Anything you like, we'll be searched."

"So? We stash them in the colonists' gear. We'll be the ones that load it onto the boat, we'll be the ones that unload it at the other end."

"Right."

Quinn thought he heard a grudging respect in the lad's voice. He started frisking the man's pockets, hoping the dampness in the fabric wasn't piss. There was a citizenship card naming their victim as Jerry Baker, a credit disk of Lalonde francs, then he hit the jackpot. "God's Brother!" He held up a Jovian Bank credit disk, holographic silver on one side, royal purple on the other. "Will you look at this. Mr Pioneer here wasn't going to take any chances in the hinterlands. He must have been planning on buying his way out of any trouble he hit upriver. Not so dumb after all. Just his bad luck he ran into us."

"Can you use it?" Jackson asked urgently.

Quinn turned Jerry Baker's head over. A soft liquid moan emerged from his lips at the motion. His eyelids were fluttering, a bead of blood ran out of his mouth; his breathing was erratic. "Shut up," Quinn said absently. "Shit, I hit him too hard. Let's see." He pressed his right thumb against Jerry Baker's, and engaged his second implant. The danger was that with Jerry Baker's nervous system fucked up from the blow, the biolectric pattern of his cells which activated the credit disk might be scrambled.

When the nanonic signalled the pattern had been recorded, he held up the Jovian Bank credit disk and touched his thumb to the centre. Green figures lit up on the silver side.

Jackson Gael let out a fast triumphant hoot, and slapped Quinn on the back. Quinn had been right: Jerry Baker had come to Lalonde prepared to buy himself out of fifteen hundred fuseodollars' worth of trouble.

They both stood up.

"Hell, we don't even have to go upriver now," Jackson said. "We can set up in town. Christ, we can live like kings."

"Don't be bloody stupid. This is only going to be good until he's reported missing, which will be tomorrow morning." His toe nudged the inert form on the wet floor.

"So change it into something; gold, diamonds, bales of cloth."

Quinn gave the grinning lad a sharp look, wondering if he'd misjudged him after all. "This isn't our town, we don't know who's safe, who to grease. Whoever changed that much money would know it was bent, they'd give our descriptions to the sheriffs first chance they got. They probably wouldn't want us upsetting their own operations."

"So what do we do with it, then?"

"We change some of it. These local francs have a cash issue as well as disks. So we spend heavily, and the locals will love giving a pair of dumb-arse colonists their toy francs as change instead of real money. Then we buy a few goodies we can take upriver that will make life a lot easier, like a decent weapon or two. After that . . ." He brought the disk up to his face. "It goes into the mud. We don't leave any evidence, OK?"

Jackson pulled a face, but nodded regretfully. "OK, Quinn. I guess I hadn't thought it through."

Baker moaned again, the wavery sound of a man trapped in a bad dream.

Quinn kicked him absently. "Don't worry about it. Now first help me put Jerry Baker into the drainage gully outside where he'll wash down into the river. Then we'll find somewhere where we can spend his fuseodollars in style." He started looking round for the wooden club to silence Baker and his moaning once and for all.

After visiting a couple of pubs, the place they wound up at was called Donovan's. It was several kilometres away from the port district, safely distant from any Group Seven members who might be having a last night in the big city. In any case, it wasn't the sort of place that the staunchly family types of Group Seven sought out.

Like most of Durringham's buildings, it was single storey, with walls of thick black wood. Stone piles raised it a metre above the ground, and there was a veranda right along the front, with drinkers slouched over the railing, glass tankards of beer in their hands, watching the newcomers with hazed eyes. The road outside had a thick layer of stone chippings spread over it. For once Quinn's boots didn't sink in up to his ankles.

Their clothes marked them down as colonists, machine-made synthetic fabric; locals were dressed in loom-woven

cloth, shirts and shorts hand sewn, solid boots that came up
to the top of their calves, caked in mud. But nobody shouted
a challenge as they walked up the steps. Quinn felt almost
home for the first time since he'd stepped off the spaceplane. These were people he understood, hard workers who
pleased themselves any damn way they chose after dark.
They heard the xenoc animals even before they went
through the open doors. It was that same eerie whine of the
thing which had chased them yesterday evening, only this
time there were five or six of them all doing it at the same
time. He exchanged a fast glance with Jackson, then they
were inside.

The bar was a single plank of wood running along one
side of the main bar, a metre wide, fifteen metres long. People were lined up along it, two deep, the six barmaids hard
pushed to cope.

Quinn waited until he reached the bar, and held up the
Jovian Bank disk. "You take this?"

The girl barely glanced at it. "Yeah."

"Great, two beers."

She started pulling them from the cask.

"It's my last night here before I sail upriver. Do you know
where I can maybe get a bit of sport? Don't want to waste
it."

"In the back." She didn't look up.

"Gee, thanks. Have one yourself."

"A brightlime, thanks." She put his half-litre tankards
down in the puddles on the bar. "Six fuseodollars."

Which Quinn reckoned was three times what the drinks
should cost, unless a brightlime was more expensive than
Norfolk Tears. Yes, the locals knew how to treat transient
colonists. He activated the credit disk, shunting the money
to her bar account block.

The vicious black catlike animals were called sayce, the
local dog-analogue, with a degree more intelligence than
Earth's canines. Quinn and Jackson saw them as soon as
they pushed aside the rug hanging across the doorway and
elbowed their way into Donovan's rear room. It was a bait-
ing arena; three tiers of benches ringing a single pit dug into
the floor and lined with cut stone, five metres in diameter,

three deep. Bright spotlights were strung up on the rafters, casting a white glare on the proceedings. Every centimetre of bench space was taken. Men and women with flushed red faces, cheering and shouting, soaked in sweat. It was hot in the room, hotter than the spaceport clearing at midday. Big cages were lined up along the back wall, sayce prowling about inside, highly agitated, some of them butting the bars of that ubiquitous black wood, emitting their anguished whine.

Quinn felt a grin rising. Now this was more like it!

They found a bench and squirmed on. Quinn asked the man he was next to who was taking the money.

It turned out the bookie was called Baxter, a thin oriental with a nasty scar leading from the corner of his left eye down below his grubby red T-shirt neck.

"Pay out only in Lalonde francs," he said gruffly.

A man mountain with a black beard stood at Baxter's side, and gave Quinn a cannibal look.

"Fine by me," Quinn said amicably. He put a hundred fuseodollars on the favourite.

The fights were impressive, fast, violent, gory, and short. The owners would stand on opposite sides of the pit, holding back their animals, shouting orders into the flat triangular ears. When the sayce had reached a fever pitch of anger they were shoved into the pit. Streamlined black bodies clashed in a snarl of six-clawed paws and snapping jaws, muscle bands like steel pistons bunching and stretching the shiny skin. Losing a leg didn't even slow them down. Quinn saw them tear off legs, jaws, rip out eyes, rake underbellies. The pit floor became slippery with blood, fluid, and sausage-string entrails. A crushed skull usually ended it, the losing sayce being repeatedly smashed against the stone wall until bone splintered and the brain was torn. Their blood was surprisingly red.

Quinn lost money on the first three fights, then picked up a wad of six hundred francs on the fourth, equivalent to a hundred and fifty fuseodollars. He handed a third of the plastic notes to Jackson, and put another two hundred fuseodollars on the next fight.

After seven fights he was eight hundred fuseodollars

down, with two and a half thousand Lalonde francs in his pocket.

"I know her," Jackson said as the next two sayce were being goaded on the side of the pit by their owners. One of them was an old bull, his skin a cross web of scars. That was the one Quinn had put his money on. Always trust in proven survivors.

"Who?"

"Girl over there. She's from Group Seven."

Quinn followed his gaze. The girl was a teenager, very attractive, with longish dark hair falling down over her shoulders. She was wearing a sleeveless singlet with a scoop neck; it looked new, the fabric was shiny, definitely synthetic. Her face was burning with astonishment and excitement, the taste of forbidden fruit, sweetest of all. She was sitting between two brothers, twins, about thirty years old, with sandy blond hair, just beginning to thin. They were dressed in shirts of checked cotton, crudely cut. Both of them had the kind of thick brown skin that came from working outdoors.

"Are you sure?" With the glare of the lights it was difficult for him to tell.

"I'm sure. I couldn't forget those tits. I think she's called Mary, Mandy, something like that."

The sayce were shoved into the pit, and the crowd roared. The two powerful vulpine bodies locked together, spinning madly, teeth and claws slicing through the air.

"I suppose she's entitled to be here," Quinn said. He was annoyed, he didn't need complications like the girl. "I'm going to have a word with Baxter. Make sure she doesn't see you, we don't want her to know we were here."

Jackson gave him a thumbs up and took another gulp from his tankard.

Baxter was standing on the ramp leading from the pit to the cages, head flicking from side to side as he followed the battling beasts. He acknowledged Quinn with a terse nod.

A spume of blood flew out of the pit, splattering the people on the lowest benches. One of the sayce was screeching. Quinn thought it was calling, "Help."

"You done all right tonight," Baxter said. "Break even, beginner's luck. I let you place bigger bets, you want."

"No, I need the money. I'm going upriver soon."

"You build nice home for family, good luck."

"I need more than luck up there. Suppose I bump into one of those?" He flicked a finger at the pit. The old bull had its jaws around the younger sayce's throat, it was slamming its head against the side of the pit, oblivious to the deep gouges the other's claws were raking down its flanks.

"Sayce not like living near river," Baxter said. "Air too wet. You be all right."

"A sayce or one of its cousins. I could do with something with a bit of punch, something that'll stop it dead."

"You bring plenty gear from Earth."

"Can't bring everything we need, the company doesn't let us. And I want some recreational items as well. I thought maybe I could pick it all up in town. I thought maybe you might know who I needed to see."

"You think too much."

"I also pay a lot."

Down in the pit a sayce's head virtually exploded as it was slammed against the wall for the last time. Pulpy gobs of brain sleeted down.

Quinn smiled when he saw the old bull raise its head to its cheering owner and let out a gurgling high-pitched bleat: "Yessss!"

"You owe me another thousand francs," he told Baxter. "You can keep half of it as a finder's fee."

Baxter's voice dropped an octave. "Come back here, ten minutes; I show you man who can help."

"Gotcha."

The old bull sayce was sniffling round the floor of the pit when Quinn got back to Jackson. A blue tongue started to lick up the rich gore sloshing about on the stone.

Jackson watched the spectacle glumly. "She's gone. She left with the twins after the fight. Christ, putting out like that, and she's only been here a day."

"Yeah? Well, just remember she's going to be trapped on a river cruise with you for a fortnight. You can work your angle then."

He brightened. "Right."

"I think I got us what we need. Although God's Brother

knows what kind of weapons they sell in this dump. Crossbows, I should think."

Jackson turned to face him. "I still think we should stay here. What do you hope to do upriver, take over the settlement?"

"If I have to. Jerry Baker isn't going to be the only one who brought a Jovian Bank disk with him. If we get enough of them, we can buy ourselves off this shit heap."

"Christ, you really think so? We can get off? All the way off?"

"Yeah. But it's going to take a big pile of hard cash, that means we've got to separate a lot of colonists from their disks." He fixed the lad with the kind of stare Banneth used when she interviewed new recruits. "Are you up to that, Jackson? I've got to have people who are going to back me the whole way. I ain't got space for anyone who farts out at the first sign of trouble."

"I'm with you. All the way. Christ, Quinn, you know that, I proved that last night and tonight."

There was a note of desperation creeping into the voice. Jackson was insisting on having a part of what Quinn offered. The ground rules were laid out.

So let the game start, Quinn thought. The greatest game of all, the one God's Brother plays for all eternity. The vengeance game. "Come on," he said. "Let's go see what Baxter's got for us."

Horst Elwes checked the metabolic function read-out on his medical block's display screen, then glanced down at the sleeping figure of Jay Hilton. The girl was curled up inside a sleeping-bag, her facial features relaxed into serenity. He had cleaned the nasty graze on her leg, given her an antibiotic, and wrapped the leg in a sheath of epithelium membrane. The tough protective tissue would help accelerate natural dermal regeneration.

It was a pity the membrane could only be used once. Horst was beginning to wonder if he had stocked enough in his medical case. According to his didactic medical course, damaged human skin could rot away if it was constantly exposed to high humidity. And humidity didn't come any higher than around the Juliffe.

He plucked the sensor pad from Jay's neck, and put it back in the medical block's slot.

Ruth Hilton gave him an expectant stare. "Well?"

"I've given her a sedative. She'll sleep for a solid ten hours now. It might be a good idea for you to be at her side when she wakes up."

"Of course I'll be here," she snapped.

Horst nodded. Ruth had shown nothing but concern and sympathy when the sobbing girl had stumbled back into the dormitory, never letting a hint of weakness show. She had held Jay's hand all the time while Horst disinfected the graze, and the sheriff asked his questions. Only now did the worry spill out.

"Sorry," Ruth said.

Horst gave her a reassuring smile, and picked up the medical block. It was larger than a standard processor block, a rectangle thirty-five centimetres long, twenty-five wide and three thick, with several ancillary sensor units, and a memory loaded with the symptoms and treatment of every known human illness. And that was as much a worry as the epithelium membrane; Group Seven was going to be completely dependent on him and the block for their general health for years to come. The responsibility was already starting to gnaw at his thoughts. His brief spell in the arcology refuge had shown him how little use theoretical medicine was in the face of real injuries. He had swiftly picked up enough about first aid to be of some practical use to the hard-pressed medics, but anything more serious than cuts and fractures could well prove fatal upriver.

At least the block had been left in his pod; several other items had gone missing between the spaceport and the warehouse. Damn, but why did Ruth have to be right about that? And the sheriffs hadn't shown any interest when he reported the missing drugs. Again, just like she said.

He sighed and rested his hand on her shoulder as she sat on the edge of the cot, stroking Jay's hair.

"She's a lot tougher than me," he said. "She'll be all right. At that age, horror fades very quickly. And we'll be going upriver straight away. Getting out of the area where it happened is going to help a lot."

"Thank you, Horst."

"Do you have any geneering in your heritage?"

"Yes, some. We're not Saldanas, but one of my ancestors was comfortably off, God bless him, we had a few basic enhancements about six or seven generations ago. Why?"

"I was thinking of infection. There is a kind of fungal spore here which can live in human blood. But if your family had even a modest improvement to your immune system there won't be any problem."

He stood and straightened his back, wincing at the twinges along his spine. It was quiet in the dormitory; the lights were off in the centre where the rest of Group Seven's children had been settled down for the night. Bee-sized insects with large grey wings were swarming round the long light panels that had been left on. He and Ruth had been left alone by the other colonists after the sheriff departed to examine the body in the river. He could see some kind of meeting underway in the canteen, most of the adults were there. The Ivets formed a close-knit huddle in a corner at the other end, all of them looking sullen. And frightened, Horst could tell. Waster kids who had probably never even seen an open sky before, never mind primeval jungle. They had stayed in the dormitory all day. Horst knew he should make an effort to get to know them, help build a bridge between them and the genuine colonists, unite the community. After all, they were going to spend the rest of their lives together. Somehow he couldn't find the energy.

Tomorrow, he promised himself. We'll all be on the ship for a fortnight, that'll give me ample opportunity.

"I ought to be at the meeting," he said. From where he was he could see two people standing up for a shouting match.

"Let 'em talk," Ruth grunted. "It keeps them out of mischief. They won't get anything sorted until after the settlement supervisor shows up."

"He should have been here this morning. We need advice on how to establish our homes. We don't even know the location we've been assigned."

"We'll find out soon enough; and the supervisor will have the whole river trip to lecture us. I expect he's out prowling the town tonight. I can't blame him, stuck with us for the next eighteen months. Poor sod."

"Must you always think the worst of people?"

"It's what I'd do. But that isn't what worries me right now."

Horst sneaked another look at the meeting. They were taking a vote, hands raised in the air. He sat down on the cot facing Ruth. "What does worry you?"

"The murder."

"We don't know it was a murder."

"Get real. The body was stripped. What else could it be?"

"He could have been drunk." Because God knows a drink is what I need just looking at that river.

"Drunk and taking a swim? In the Juliffe? Come on, Horst!"

"The autopsy should tell us if . . ." He trailed off under Ruth's gaze. "No, I don't suppose there will be one, will there?"

"No. He must have been dumped in the river. The sheriff told me that two colonists from Group Three were reported missing by their wives this morning. Pete Cox and Alun Reuther. I'll give you ten to one that body is one of them."

"Probably," Horst admitted. "I suppose it's shocking that urban crime is rife here. Somehow you don't imagine such a thing on a stage one colony world. Then again, Lalonde isn't quite what I imagined. But we'll be leaving it all behind shortly. Our own community will be too small for such things, we will all know each other."

Ruth rubbed at her eyes, her expression haunted. "Horst, you're not thinking. Why was the body stripped?"

"I don't know. For the clothes, I suppose, and the boots."

"Right. Now what sort of mugger is going to kill for a pair of boots? Actually kill two people in cold blood. God, the people here are poor, I'm not denying it, but they're not that desperate."

"Who then?"

She looked pointedly over his shoulder. Horst turned

round. "The Ivets?. That's rather prejudiced, isn't it?" he asked reproachfully.

"You've seen the way they're treated in the town, and we don't treat them any better. They can't move outside the port district without getting beaten up. Not with their jump suits on, and they don't have anything else to wear. So who is more likely to want ordinary clothes? Who isn't going to care what they have to do to get them? And whoever did murder that man did it inside the port, uncomfortably close to this dormitory."

"You don't think it was one of ours?" he exclaimed.

"Let's say, I'm praying it wasn't. But with the way our luck is turning out, I wouldn't count on it."

Diranol, Lalonde's smallest, outermost moon, was the only one of the planet's three natural satellites left in the night sky, a nine-hundred-kilometre globe of rock with a red ochre regolith, half a million kilometres distant. It hovered above the eastern horizon, painting Durringham in a timid rose-pink fluorescence when the power bike skidded to a halt just outside the skirt of light leaking from the big transients' dormitory. Marie Skibbow loosened her grip on Furgus. The ride through the darkened city had been sensational, drawing out every second, filling it with glee and excitement. The walls slashing past, sensed rather than seen, the headlight beam revealing ruts and mud patches on the road almost as soon as they hit them, wind whipping her hair about, eyes stung by the slipstream. Taunting danger with every turn of the wheel, and beating it, *living*.

"Here we go, your stop," Furgus said.

"Right." She swung her leg over the saddle, and stood beside him. Now the weariness swept through her, a frozen wave of depression that hung poised high above, waiting to crash down at the prospect of the future and what it held.

"You're the best, Marie." He kissed her, one hand fondling her right breast through the singlet's fabric. Then he was gone, red tail light sinking into the blackness.

Her shoulders drooped as she made her way into the dormitory. Most of the cots were full, people were snoring, coughing, tossing about. She wanted to turn and run, back to

Furgus and Hamish, back to the dark fulfilment of the last few hours. Her brain was still fizzing from the experiences, the naked savagery of the sayce-baiting, and the jubilant crowd in Donovan's, blood heat inflaming her senses. Then the delicious indecency of the twins' quiet cabin on the other side of town, with their straining bodies pounding against her first singly then both at once. That crazy bike ride in the vermilion moonlight. Marie wanted every night to be the same, without end.

"Where the hell have you been?"

Her father was standing in front of her, mouth all squeezed up that way it did when he was really angry. And for once she didn't care.

"Out," she said.

"Out where?"

"Enjoying myself. Exactly what you think I shouldn't do."

He slapped her on the cheek, the sound echoing from the high roof. "Don't you be so bloody impudent, girl. I asked you a question. What have you been doing?"

Marie glared at him, feeling the heat grow in her stinging cheek, refusing to rub it. "What's next, *Daddy*? Will you take your belt to me? Or are you just going to use your fists?"

Gerald Skibbow's jaw dropped. People on the nearby cots were turning over, peering at them blearily.

"Do you know how late it is? What have you been up to?" he hissed.

"Are you quite sure you want a truthful answer to that, Daddy? *Quite* sure?"

"You despicable little vixen. Your mother's been fretting over you all night. Doesn't that even bother you?"

Marie curled her lip up. "What tragedy could possibly happen to me in this paradise you've brought us to?"

For a moment she thought he was going to strike her again.

"There have been two murders in the port this week," he said.

"Yeah? That doesn't surprise me."

"Get into bed," Gerald said through clenched teeth. "We'll discuss this in the morning."

"Discuss it?" she asked archly. "You mean I get an equal say?"

"For fuck's sake, can it, Skibbow," someone shouted. "We want to get some sleep here."

Under the impotent stare of her father, Marie pulled her shoes off and sauntered over to her cot.

Quinn was still dozing in his sleeping-bag, struggling against the effects of the rough beer he had drunk in Donovan's, when someone gripped the side of his cot and yanked it through ninety degrees. His arms and legs thrashed about in the sleeping-bag as he tumbled onto the floor, but there was no way he could prevent the fall. His hip smacked into the concrete first, jarring his pelvis badly, then his jaw landed. Quinn yelled out in surprise and pain.

"Get up, Ivet," a voice shouted.

A man was standing over him, grinning down evilly. He was in his early forties, tall and well built, with a shock of black hair and a full beard. The brown leather skin of his face and arms was scarred with a lunar relief of pocks and the tiny red lines of broken capillaries. His clothes were all natural fabric, a thick red and black check cotton shirt with the arms torn off, green denim trousers, lace-up boots that came up to his knees, and a belt which carried various powered gadgets and a vicious-looking ninety-centimetre steel machete. A silver crucifix on a slim chain glinted at the base of his neck.

He laughed in a bass roar as Quinn groaned at the hot pain in his throbbing hip. Which was too much. Quinn grappled with the seal catch at the top of the bag. He was going to make the bastard *pay*. The seal opened. His hands came out, and he kicked his legs, trying to shake off the constricting fabric. Somewhere around the edges of his perception the other Ivets were shouting in alarm and jumping over the cots. A huge damp jaw closed around his right hand, *completely* around, sharp teeth pinching the thin skin of his wrist, their tips grating between his tendons. Shock froze him for a horrific second. It was a dog, a hound, a fucking hellhound. Even a sayce would have thought twice before taking it on. The thing must have stood a metre high. It had short grizzled grey fur, a blunt hammerhead muzzle, jowls of black rubber, wet with gooey saliva. Big liquid eyes were fixed on him. It was growling softly. Quinn could feel the vibration all the way along his arm. He waited numbly, expecting the jaws to close, the mauling to begin. But the eyes just kept staring at him.

"My name is Powel Manani," said the bearded man. "And our glorious leader, Governor Colin Rexrew, has appointed me as Group Seven's settlement supervisor. That means, Ivets, I own you: body, and soul. And just to make my position absolutely clear from the start: I don't like Ivets. I think this world would be a better place without putrid pieces of crap like you screwing it up. But the LDC board has decided to lumber us with you, so I am going to make bloody sure every franc's worth of your passage fee is squeezed out of you before your work-time is up. So when I say lick shit, you lick; you eat what I give you to eat; and you wear what I give you to wear. And because you are lazy bastards by nature, there is going to be no such thing as a day off for the next ten years."

He squatted down beside Quinn and beamed broadly. "What's your name, dickhead?"

"Quinn Dexter . . . sir."

Powel's eyebrows lifted in appreciation. "Well done. You're a smart one, Quinn. You learn quick."

"Thank you, sir." The dog's tongue was pressing against his fingers, sliding up and down his knuckles. It felt utterly disgusting. He had never heard of an animal being trained so perfectly before.

"Smartarses are troublemakers, Quinn. Are you going to be a troublemaker for me?"

"No, sir."

"Are you going to get up in the mornings in future, Quinn?"

"Yes, sir."

"Fine. We understand each other, then." Powel stood up. The dog released Quinn's hand, and backed off a pace.

Quinn held his hand up: it glistened from all the saliva;

there were red marks like a tattooed bracelet around his wrist, and two drops of blood welled up.

Powel patted the dog's head fondly. "This is my friend, Vorix. He and I are affinity bonded, which means I can quite literally smell out any scams you dickheads cook up. So don't even try to pull any fast ones, because I know them all. If I find you doing anything I don't like, it will be Vorix who deals with you. And it won't be your hand he bites off next time, he'll be dining on your balls. Do I make myself clear?"

The Ivets mumbled their answer, heads bowed, avoiding Powel's eye.

"I'm glad none of us are suffering any illusions about the other. Now then, your instructions for the day. I will not repeat them. Group Seven is going upriver on three ships: the *Swithland*, the *Nassier*, and the *Hycel*. They are currently docked in harbour three, and they're sailing in four hours. So that is the time you have to get the colonists' gear loaded. Any pods that aren't loaded, I will have you carry on your backs the whole way to the landing site upriver. Do not expect me to act as your permanent nursemaid, get yourselves organized and get on with it. You will be travelling with me and Vorix on the *Swithland*. Now move!"

Vorix barked, jowls peeled back from his teeth. Powel watched Quinn skitter backwards like a crab, then pick himself up and chase off after the other Ivets. He knew Quinn was going to be trouble, after helping to start five settlements he could read the Ivets' thoughts like a personality debrief. The youth was highly resentful, and smart with it. He was more than a waster kid, probably got tied in with some underground organization before he was transported. Powel toyed with the idea of simply leaving him behind when the *Swithland* sailed, let the Durringham sheriffs deal with him. But the Land Allocation Office would know what he'd done, and it would be entered in his file, which had too many incidents already. "Bugger," he muttered under his breath. The Ivets were all outside the dormitory, heading along the path to the warehouse. And it looked like they were gathering round Quinn, waiting for him to start directing them. Oh well, if it came to it, Quinn would just have to have an accident in the jungle.

Horst Elwes had been watching the episode with a number of Group Seven's members, and now he stepped up to Powel. The supervisor's dog turned its neck to look at him. Lord, but it was a brute. Lalonde was becoming a sore test for him indeed. "Was it necessary to be quite so unpleasant to those boys?" he asked Powel Manani.

Powel looked him up and down, eyes catching on the white crucifix. "Yes. If you want the blunt truth, Father. That's the way I always deal with them. They have to know who's in charge from the word go. Believe me, they respect toughness."

"They would also respond to kindness."

"Fine, well you show them plenty of it, Father. And just to prove there's no ill feeling, I'll give them time off to attend mass."

Horst had to quicken his pace to keep up. "Your dog," he said cautiously.

"What about him?"

"You say you are bonded with affinity?"

"That's right."

"Are you an Edenist, then?"

Vorix made a noise that sounded suspiciously like a snicker.

"No, Father," Powel said. "I'm simply practical. And if I had a fuseodollar for every new-landed priest who asked me that I would be a millionaire. I need Vorix upriver; I need him to hunt, to scout, to keep the Ivets in line. Neuron symbionts give me control over him. I use them because they are cheap and they work. The same as all the other settlement supervisors, and half of the county sheriffs as well. It's only the major Earth-based religions which maintain people's prejudice against bitek. But on worlds like Lalonde we can't afford your prissy theological debates. We use what we have to, when we have to. And if you want to survive long enough to fill Group Seven's second generation with your noble bigotry over a single chromosome which makes people a blasphemy, then you'll do the same. Now if you'll excuse me, I have a settlement expedition to sort out." He brushed past, heading for the harbour.

Gerald Skibbow and the other members of Group Seven

followed after him, several of them giving shamefaced glances to the startled priest. Gerald watched Rai Molvi gathering up his nerve to speak. Molvi had made a lot of noise at the meeting last night, he seemed to fancy himself as a leader of men. There had been plenty of suggestions that they form an official committee, elect a spokesperson. It would help the group interface with the authorities, Rai Molvi said. Gerald privately gave him six months before he was running back to Durringham with his tail between his legs. The man was an obvious lawyer type, didn't have what it took to be a farmer.

"You were supposed to be here yesterday to brief us," Rai Molvi said.

"Quite right," Powel said without breaking stride. "I apologize. If you would like to make an official complaint about me, the Land Allocation Office which issues my contract is in a dumper down on the western edge of town. It's only six kilometres."

"No, we weren't going to complain," Rai Molvi said quickly. "But we do need to establish certain facts to prepare ourselves. It would have been helpful had you attended."

"Attended what?"

"Last night's council meeting."

"What council?"

"Group Seven's council."

Powel took a breath. He never did understand why half of the colonists came to Lalonde in the first place. The LDC must employ some pretty amazing advertising techniques back on Earth, he thought. "What was it the council wanted to know?"

"Well . . . where are we going, for a start?"

"Upriver." Powel stretched out the pause long enough to make the other man uncomfortable. "A place called Schuster County, on the Quallheim tributary. Although I'm sure that if you have somewhere else in mind the river-boat captain will be happy to take you there instead."

Rai Molvi reddened.

Gerald pushed his way to the front as they all moved out from under the dormitory's creaking roof. Powel had turned, making for the circular harbour two hundred metres away,

Vorix padding along eagerly behind him. There were several paddle-boats pulled up at the wooden quays inside the artificial lagoon. The bright red specks of scavenging chikrows swirled overhead. The sight with its sense of purpose and adventure was unbeatable, quickening his blood.

"Is there anything we need to know about the paddle-boats?" he asked.

"Not really," Powel said. "They carry about a hundred and fifty people each, and it'll take us about a fortnight to reach the Quallheim. Your meals are provided as part of your transit fee, and I'll be giving talks on the more practical aspects of jungle lore and setting up your home. So just find yourself a bunk, and enjoy the trip, for you won't ever have another like it. After we make landfall the real work begins."

Gerald nodded his thanks and turned back to the dormitory. Let the others pester the man with irrelevant questions, he would get the family packed and onto the *Swithland* straight away. A long river trip would be just what Marie needed to calm her down.

The *Swithland* followed a standard design for the larger paddle-boats operating on the Juliffe. She had a broad, shallow hull made of mayope planks, measuring sixty metres from prow to stern and twenty metres broad. With the water flowing by a mere metre and a half below the deck she could almost have been mistaken for a well-crafted raft had it not been for her superstructure, which resembled a large rectangular barn. Her odd blend of ancient and modern technologies was yet another indicator of Lalonde's development status. Two paddles midway down the hull because they were far simpler to manufacture and maintain than the more efficient screws. Electric motors because the industrial machinery to assemble them was cheaper than the equivalent necessary to produce a steam generator and turbine unit. But then electric motors required a power source, which was a solid-state thermal-exchange furnace imported from Oshanko. Such costly imports would only be tolerated while the number of paddle-boats made the generator and turbine factory uneconomical. When their numbers increased the governing economic equations would change in tandem, quite probably sweeping them away entirely to be replaced with another equally improbable mismatch craft. Such was the way of progress on Lalonde.

The *Swithland* herself was only seventeen years old, and good for another fifty or sixty at least. Her captain, Rosemary Lambourne, had taken out a mortgage with the LDC that her grandchildren would be paying off. As far as she was concerned, that was a bargain. Seventeen years of watching hapless colonists sailing upriver to their dream's ruin convinced her she had done the right thing. Her colonist shipment contract with the Governor's Transport Office was a solid income, guaranteed for the next twenty years, and everything she brought downriver for Durringham's growing merchant community was pure profit, earning hard fuseodollars.

Life on the river was the best, she could hardly remember her existence back on Earth, working in a Govcentral design bureau to improve vac-train carriages. That was somebody else's existence.

A quarter of an hour before they were due to cast off, Rosemary stood on the open bridge, which took up the forward quarter of the superstructure's top deck. Powel Manani had joined her after he had led his horse up the gangplank, tethering it on the aft deck; now the two of them watched the colonists embarking. Children and adults alike shuffled round. The children were mostly gathered round the horse, patting and stroking it gently. Shoulder-bags and larger cases were strewn about over the dark planking. The sound of several heated arguments drifted up to the top deck. Nobody had thought to count how many people were coming on board. Now the boat was overladen, and latecomers were reluctant to find another berth on one of the other ships.

"You got your Ivets organized well," she told the supervisor. "I don't think I've ever seen the gear stowed so professionally before. They finished over an hour ago. The harbour-master ought to nab them from you and put them to work as stevedores."

"Humm," Powel said. Vorix, who was lying on the deck behind them, gave an uneasy growl.

Rosemary grinned at that. Sometimes she wasn't sure who was bonded to who.

"Something wrong?" she asked.

"Someone, actually. They've got themselves a leader. He's going to be trouble, Rosemary. I know he is."

"You'll keep them in line. Hell, you've supered five settlements, and all of them wound up viable. If you can't do it nobody can."

"Thanks. You run a pretty tight ship yourself."

"Keep an eye out for yourself this time, Powel. There's people gone missing up in Schuster County recently. Rumour has it the Governor's none too happy."

"Yeah?"

"The *Hycel* is carrying a marshal upriver. Going to have a scout round."

"I wonder if there's a bounty for finding them? The Governor doesn't like homesteaders ducking out of their settlement contract, it sets a bad example. Everyone would come and live in Durringham otherwise."

"From what I hear, they want to find out what happened to them, not where they are."

"Oh?"

"They just vanished. No sign of a fight. Left all their gear and animals behind."

"Fine, well, I'll keep alert." He took a broad-rimmed hat out of the pack at his feet. It was yellow-green in colour, much stained. "Are we sharing a bunk this trip, Roses?"

"No chance." She leant further over the rail to scan the foredeck for her four children, who along with two stokers were her only other crew. "I've got me a brand-new Ivet as my second stoker. Barry MacArple, he's nineteen, real talented mechanic on both sides of the sheets. I think it shocks my eldest boy. That is, when he actually stops boffing the colonists' daughters himself."

"Fine."

Vorix let out a plaintive whine, and dropped his head onto his forepaws.

"When are you back in Schuster County next?" Powel asked.

"A couple of months, maybe three. I'm taking a group up

to Colane County on the Dibowa tributary next time out. After that I'll be up in your area. Want me to visit?"

He settled the hat on his head, working out agendas and timescales in his mind. "No, it's too soon. This bunch won't have exhausted their gear by then. Make it nine or ten months, let them feel a little deprivation, we'll be able to flog them a bar of soap for fifty fuseodollars by then."

"That's a date."

They shook on it, and turned back to watch the quarrelling colonists below.

Swithland cast off more or less on time. Rosemary's eldest boy, Karl, a strapping fifteen-year-old, ran along the deck shouting orders to the colonists who were helping with the cables. A cheer went up from the passengers as the paddles started turning and they moved away from the quay.

Rosemary was in the bridge herself. The harbour didn't have much spare water anyway, and *Swithland* was sluggish with a hold full of logs for the furnace, the colonists, their gear, and enough food to last them three weeks. She steered past the end of the quay and out into the centre of the artificial lagoon. The furnace was burning furiously, twin stacks sending out a high plume of grey-blue smoke. Standing on the prow, Karl gave her a smiling thumbs-up. He's going to break a lot of female hearts, that one, she thought proudly.

For once there wasn't a rain-cloud to be seen, and the forward-sweep mass-detector showed her a clean channel. Rosemary gave the horn a single toot, and pushed both paddle-control levers forward, moving out of the harbour and onto her beloved untamed river that stretched away into the unknown. How could life possibly be better than this?

For the first hundred kilometres the colonists of Group Seven could only agree with her. This was the oldest inhabited section of Amarisk outside Durringham, settled almost twenty-five years previously. The jungle had been cleared in great swaths, making way for fields, groves, and grazing land. As they stood on the side of the deck they could see herds of animals roaming free over the broad pastures, picking teams working the groves and plantations, their piles of wicker baskets full of fruit or nuts. Villages formed a continual chain along the southern bank, the rural idyll; sturdy, brightly painted wooden cottages set in the centre of large gardens that were alive with flowers, lines of tall, verdant trees providing a leafy shade. The lanes between the trunks were planted with thick grasses, shining a brilliant emerald in the intense sunlight. Out here, where people could spread without constraint, there wasn't the foot and wheel traffic to pound the damp soil into the kind of permanent repellent mud which made up Durringham's roads. Horses plodded along, pulling wains loaded with bounties of hay and barley. Windmills formed a row of regular pinnacles along the skyline, their sails turning lazily in the persistent wind. Long jetties struck out into the choppy ochre water of the Juliffe, two or three to each village. They had constant visitors in the form of small paddle-driven barges eager for the farms' produce. Children sat on the end of the jetties dangling rods and lines into the water, waving at the eternal procession of boats speeding by. In the morning small sailing boats cast off to fish the river, and the *Swithland* would cruise sedately through the flotilla of canvas triangles thrumming in the fresh breeze.

In the evening, when the sky flared into deep orange around the western horizon, and the stars came out overhead, bonfires would be lit in the village greens. Leaning on the deck rail that first night as the fires appeared, Gerald Skibbow was reduced to an inarticulate longing. The black water reflected long tapers of orange light from the bonfires, and he could hear gusty snatches of songs as the villagers gathered round for their communal meal.

"I never thought it could be this perfect," he told Loren.

She smiled as his arm circled her. "It does look pretty, doesn't it. Something out of a fairy story."

"It can be ours, this sort of life. It's waiting up there at the end of the river. In ten years' time we'll be dancing round a bonfire while the boats go by."

"And the new colonists will look at us and dream!"

"We'll have our house built, like a palace made from wood. That's what you'll live in, Loren, a miniature palace that the King of Kulu himself will envy. And you'll have a garden full of vegetables and flowers; and I'll be out in the grove, or tending the herds. Paula and Marie will live nearby, and the grandchildren will run both of us off our feet."

Loren hugged him tightly. He lifted his head and let out a bellow of joy. "God, how could we have wasted so many years on Earth? This is where we all belong, all of us, Loren. We should throw away our arcologies and our starships, and live like the Lord intended. We really should."

Ruth and Jay stood together beside the taffrail and watched the sun sink below the horizon, crowning the vast river with an aura of purple-gold light for one sublime magical minute.

"Listen, Mummy, they're singing," Jay said. Her face was a picture of serenity. The horrid corpse of yesterday was long forgotten; she had found utter contentment with the big beige-coloured horse hitched up to the port railing. Those huge black eyes were so soft and loving, and the feel of its wet nose on her palm when she fed it a sweet was ticklish and wonderful. She couldn't believe something so huge was so gentle. Mr Manani had already said he would let her walk it round the deck each morning for exercise and teach her how to groom it. The *Swithland* was paradise come early. "What are they singing?"

"It sounds like a hymn," Ruth said. For the first time since they had landed she was beginning to feel as though she'd made the right decision. The villages certainly looked attractive, and well organized. Knowing that it was possible to succeed was half the battle. It would be tougher further from the capital, but not impossible. "I can't say I blame them."

The wind had died down, sending flames from the bonfires shooting straight up into the starry night, but the aroma of cooking food stole over the water to the *Swithland* and her two sister craft. The scent of freshly baked bread and thick spicy stews played hell with Quinn's stomach. The Ivets had been given cold meat and a fruit that looked like an orange, except it had a purple-bluish coloured skin and tasted salty. All the colonists had eaten a hot meal. Bastards. But the Ivets were starting to turn to him, that was something. He sat on the deck at the front of the superstructure, looking out to the north, away from all those fucking medieval hovels the colonists were wetting themselves over. The north was dark, he liked that. Darkness had many forms, physical and mental, and it conquered all in the end. The sect had taught him that, darkness was strength, and those that embrace the dark will always triumph.

Quinn's lips moved soundlessly. "After darkness comes the Bringer of Light. And He shall reward those that followed His path into the void of Night. For they are true unto themselves and the nature of man, which is beast. They shall sit upon His hand, and cast down those who dress in the falsehood of Our Lord and His brother."

A hand touched Quinn's shoulder, and the fat priest smiled down at him. "I'm holding a service on the aft deck in a few minutes. We are going to bless our venture. You would be very welcome to attend."

"No, thank you, Father," Quinn said levelly.

Horst gave him a sad smile. "I understand. But the Lord's door is always open for you." He walked on towards the aft deck.

"Your Lord," Quinn whispered to his departing back. "Not mine."

Jackson Gael saw the girl from Donovan's slouched against the port rail just aft of the paddle, head resting on her hands. She was wearing a crumpled Oxford-blue shirt tucked into black rugby shorts, white pumps on her feet, no socks. At first he thought she was gazing out over the river, then he caught sight of the personal MF block clipped to her belt, the silver lenses in her eyes. Her foot was tapping out a rhythm on the decking.

He shrugged out of the top of his grey jump suit, tying the arms round his waist so she wouldn't see the damning scarlet letters. There was no appreciable drop in temperature as the humid air flowed over his skin. Had there ever been a single molecule of cool air on this planet?

He tapped her on the shoulder. "Hi."

A spasm of annoyance crossed her face. Blind mirror irises turned in his direction as her hand fumbled with the little block's controls. The silver vanished to show dark, expressive eyes. "Yeah?"

"Was that a local broadcast?"

"Here? You've got to be kidding. The reason we're on a boat is because this planet hasn't invented the wheel yet."

Jackson laughed. "You're right there. So what were you 'vising?"

"*Life Kinetic*. That's Jezzibella's latest album."

"Hey, I rate Jezzibella."

Her sulk lifted for a moment. "Course you do. She turns males to jelly. Shows us fems what we can all do if we want. She makes herself succeed."

"I saw her live, once."

"God. You did? When?"

"She played my arcology a year ago. Five nights in the stadium, sold out."

"Any good?"

"Supreme." He spread his arms exuberantly. "Nothing like an ordinary Mood Fantasy band, it's almost straight sex, but she went on for hours. She just sets your whole body on fire, what she does with the dancers. They reckoned her AV broadcast pillars were using illegal sense-activant codes. Who gives a shit? You would have loved it."

Marie Skibbow's pout returned. "I'll never know now, will I? Not on this bloody retarded planet."

"Didn't you want to come here?"

"No."

The hot resentment in her voice surprised him. The colonists had seemed such a dopey bunch, every one of them wrapped up in the prospect of all that rustic charm crap spread out along the riverbank. It hadn't occurred to him that they were anything other than unified in their goal. Marie might be a valuable ally.

He saw the captain's son, Karl, making his way down the side of the superstructure. The boy was wearing a pair of white canvas shorts, and rubber-soled plimsolls. *Swithland* was riding some choppy water, but Karl's balance was uncanny, he could anticipate the slightest degree of pitch.

"There you are," he said to Marie. "I've been looking everywhere for you, I thought you'd be at the service the priest's giving."

"I'm not helping to bless this trip," she said smartly.

Karl grinned broadly, his teeth showing a gleam in the deepening twilight. He was a head shorter than Jackson, which put him a few centimetres below Marie's height, and his torso was muscled like a medical text illustration. His family must have had plenty of geneering, he was too perfect. Jackson watched in growing bewilderment as he held his hand out expectantly to the girl.

"Are you ready to go?" Karl asked. "My cabin's up forward, just below the bridge."

Marie accepted the boy's hand. "Sure."

Jackson was given a lurid wink from Karl as he led Marie down the deck. They disappeared into the superstructure, and Jackson was sure he heard Marie giggle. He couldn't believe it. She preferred Karl? The boy was five years younger than him! His fists clenched in anger. It was being an Ivet, he *knew* it was. The little bitch!

Karl's cabin was a compact compartment overlooking the prow, definitely a teenager's room. A couple of processor blocks lay on the desk, along with some micro-tool units and a half-dismantled electronics stack from one of the bridge systems. There were holograms on the wall showing starfields and planets; clothes, shoes, and towels were scattered about on the deck planks. It had about ten times as much space as the cabin the Skibbows and Kavas were forced to share.

The door shut behind Marie, muting the sound of the congregation gathered on the aft deck. Karl immediately kicked off his plimsolls, and unlatched a broad bunk which had been folded flat against the wall.

He's only fifteen years old, Marie thought, but he has got a tremendous body, and that smile . . . God, I shouldn't have allowed him to smooth talk me in here, never mind be thinking of bedding him. Which only made her feel even randier.

The congregation started to sing a hymn, their voices bringing a rich enthusiasm to the slow melody. She thought of her father out there, his eager-to-make-amends expression this morning, telling her how the river trip would show her the wholesome satisfaction to be earned from the quieter side of life and honest labours. So please, darling, try to understand Lalonde is our future now, and a fine future at that.

Marie unbuttoned her shirt under Karl's triumphant gaze, then started on her shorts.

The settlements along the Juliffe changed subtly after the third day. The *Swithland* passed the end of the Hultain Marsh, and villages began to appear on the distant northern bank. They lacked the trimness of the earlier buildings, there were fewer animals and cultivated fields; less jungle had been cleared, and the trees standing so close to the cabins looked far more imposing.

The river branched, but the *Swithland* sailed on purposefully down the main channel. The water traffic began to fall off. These villages were still hard at work to tame the land, they couldn't afford the time it took to make sailing boats. Big barges were chugging down the river, loaded mainly with mayope timber cut by new settlements to sell to the shipyards in the city. But by the end of the first week even the barges were left behind. It simply wasn't economical to carry timber to the capital over such a distance.

There were tributary forks every hour now. The Juliffe was narrower, down to a couple of kilometres, its fast waters almost clear. Sometimes they would sail for five or six hours without seeing a village.

Horst felt the mood on board turning, and prayed that the despondency would end once they made landfall. The devil makes work for idle hands, and it had never been truer than out here. Once they were busy building their village and preparing the land Group Seven would have no time for brooding. But the second week seemed to last for ever, and the daily rains had returned with a vengeance. People were muttering about why they had to travel quite this far from the city for their allocated land.

The jungle had become an oppressive presence on either side, hemming them in, trees and undergrowth packed so tightly that the riverbanks created a solid barricade of leaves extending right down to the water. Foltwine, a tenacious freshwater aquatic plant, was a progressive nuisance. Its long, brown ribbonlike fronds grew just below the surface right across the width of the river. Rosemary avoided the larger clumps with ease, but strands would inevitably wrap themselves around the paddles. The *Swithland* made frequent stops while Karl and his younger sister clambered over them, cutting the tough slippery fronds free with the radiant yellow blades of fission knives.

Thirteen days after they departed from Durringham they had left the Juliffe itself behind and started to sail along the Quallheim tributary. It was three hundred metres wide, fast flowing, with vine-swamped trees thirty metres high forming a stockade on both banks. Away to the south, the colonists could just make out the purple and grey peaks of a distant mountain range. They stared in wonder at the snow-caps shining brightly in the sun; ice seemed to belong to an alien planet, not native to Lalonde.

In the early morning of the fourteenth day after leaving Durringham, a village crept into view as they edged their way up the river, the first they had seen for thirty-six hours. It was set in a semicircular clearing, a bite into the jungle nearly a kilometre deep. Felled trees lay everywhere. Thin towers of smoke rose from a few fire pits. The shacks were crude parodies of the cottages belonging to villages downriver; lashed-up frames with walls and roofs made from panels of woven palm fronds. There was a single jetty that looked terribly unsafe, with three hollowed-out log canoes tied up to it. A small stream trickling through the middle of the clearing into the river was an open sewer. Goats were tied to stakes, foraging in the short grass. Emaciated chickens scratched around in the mud and sawdust. The inhabitants stood about listlessly and watched the *Swithland* go past with numb, hooded eyes. Most of them were wearing shorts and boots, their skin a deep brown, whether from the sun or dirt it was hard to say. Even the apparently eternal chittering of the jungle creatures was hushed.

"Welcome to the town of Schuster," Rosemary said with some irony. She was standing on the bridge, one eye permanently on the forward-sweep mass-detector, watching out for foltwine and submerged snags.

Group Seven's council and Powel Manani were ranged around the bridge behind her, grateful to be in the shade.

"This is it?" Rai Molvi asked, aghast.

"The county capital, yeah," Powel said. "They've been going for about a year now."

"Don't worry," Rosemary said. "The land you've been allocated is another twelve kilometres upriver. You won't have to have much contact with them. No bad thing, too, if you ask me. I've seen communities like this before, they infect their neighbours. Better you have a fresh start."

Rai Molvi nodded briefly, not trusting himself to speak.

The three rivercraft sailed on slowly, leaving behind the shanty town and its torpid inhabitants. The colonists gathered on *Swithland*'s aft deck watched them disappear as the boat rounded a bend in the river, silent and contemplative.

Horst made the sign of the cross, muttering an invocation. Perhaps a requiem would be more appropriate, he thought.

Jay Hilton turned to her mother. "Will we have to live like that, Mummy?"

"No," she said firmly. "Never."

Two hours later, with the river down to a hundred and fifty metre width, Rosemary watched the digits on the inertial-guidance block flick round to match the coordinates the Land Allocation Office had given her. Karl stood on the prow as the *Swithland* crept along at a walking pace, his keen eyes searching the impenetrable green barrier of vegetation along the southern bank. The jungle was steaming softly from the rain of an hour earlier, white tendrils wafting out of the treetops, then spiralling away into the burning azure sky. Small, colourful birds darted about between the branches, shrieking brazenly.

Karl suddenly jumped up and waved to his mother, pointing at the bank. Rosemary saw the tarnished silver pillar with its hexagonal sign on top. It was stuck in the soil five metres above the water. Vines with big purple flowers had already climbed halfway up it.

She gave the horn a triumphant hoot. "End of the line," she sang out. "This is Aberdale. Last stop."

"All right," Powel said, holding up his hands for silence. He was standing on a barrel to address the assembled colonists on the foredeck. "You've seen what can be done with a little bit of determination and hard work, and you've also seen how easy it is to fail. Which road you go down is entirely up to you. I'm here to help you for eighteen months, which is the period your future will be settled in. That's the make or break time. Now, tell me, are you going to make a go of it?"

He received a throaty cheer, and smiled round. "Fine. Our first job is going to be building a jetty so that Captain Lambourne and the other two river-boats can dock. That way we can unload your gear properly, without getting it wet. Now a jetty is an important part of any village on this river. It tells a visitor straight away what sort of community you want to carve out for your selves. You'll notice our good captain wasn't too eager to stop at Schuster. Not surprising, is it? A good jetty is one that the boats are always going to stop at, even out here. It's a statement that you want to take part in what the planet has to offer. It says you want to trade and grow rich. It says that there are opportunities here for clever captains. It makes you a part of civilization. So I think it would be a good idea if we start off as we mean to go on, and build ourselves a solid decent jetty that's going to last out your grandchildren. That's what I think. Am I right?"

The chorus of "Yes!" was deafening.

He clapped his hands together, and hopped down off the barrel. "Quinn?" He beckoned to the lad, who was in the group of quiet Ivets standing in the shade of the superstructure.

Quinn trotted forward. "Yes, sir?"

The respectful tone didn't fool Powel for a second. "The captain is holding station against the current for now. But it's costing her power, so we have to secure the *Swithland* if we want her to stay for any length of time. I want you to ferry a cable out to the shore, and tie it onto a tree large enough to take the strain. Think you can manage that?"

Quinn looked from Powel to the mass of dark green vegetation on the bank then back to Powel. "How do I get over there?"

"Swim, boy! And don't try telling me you can't. It's only thirty-five metres."

Karl came over, uncoiling a rope. "Once you've secured it, we'll haul the *Swithland* into the shallows, and rig a proper mooring," the boy said. "Everyone else can wade ashore from there."

"Great," Quinn said sourly. He took his shoes off, then started to shrug out of his jump suit. Vorix nosed around the two shoes, sniffing eagerly.

Quinn left his shorts on, and sat on the decking to put his shoes back on. "Can Vorix come with me, please?" he asked.

The dog looked round, long tongue hanging out of the side of its big jaw.

"What the hell do you want him with you for?" Powel asked.

Quinn gestured to the jungle with its barrage of animal sounds. "To take care of any wild sayce."

"Get in the water, Quinn, and stop whingeing. There aren't any wild sayce around here." Powel watched as the lad eased himself over the side of the deck and into the river. Jackson Gael lay flat on the deck, and handed the rope down.

Quinn started swimming for the shore with a powerful sidestroke, dragging the rope behind him.

"The kroclions ate all the sayce," Powel yelled after him; then, laughing heartily, went aft to get the jetty-building team organized.

8

Tranquillity: a polyp cylinder with hemispherical endcaps, its shell the colour of fired unglazed clay, sixty-five kilometres long, seventeen kilometres in diameter, the largest of all bitek habitats ever to be germinated within the Confederation. It was drab and uninviting in appearance, and difficult to see from a distance; what little sunlight eventually reached it from the F3 primary one-point-seven billion kilometres away seemed to be repulsed, preferring to flow around the curving shell rather than strike the surface. It was the only human settlement in the star system, orbiting seven thousand kilometres above the Ruin Ring. The shattered remnants of those very remote xenoc cousins were its sole companions. A permanent reminder that for all its size and power, it was terribly mortal. Lonely, isolated, and politically impotent, there should be few people who would choose to live in such a place.

And yet … .

Starships and scavenger vessels on an approach trajectory could discern a stippled haze of light hovering around the endcap orientated to galactic north. A cluster of industrial stations floated in attendance. Owned by some of the largest astroengineering companies in the Confederation, they were permanently busy serving the constant stream of starships arriving and departing. Cargo tugs, fuel tankers, personnel carriers, and multipurpose service vehicles shuttled around them, their reaction drives pulsing out a smog of hot blue ions.

A three-kilometre spindle connected Tranquillity's northern endcap to a non-rotating spaceport: a disc of metal girders, four and a half kilometres in diameter, with a confusing jumble of support facilities, tanks, and docking bays arrayed across its surface, resembling a gigantic metal cobweb that had snagged a swarm of fantastic cybernetic insects. It was as busy as any Edenist habitat, with Adamist starships loading and unloading their cargoes, taking on fuel, embarking passengers.

Behind the tarnished silver-white disc, three circular ledges stood out proud from the endcap: havens for the bitek starships which came and went with quick, graceful agility. Their geometrical diversity fascinated the entire spaceport, and most of the habitat's population; observation lounges overlooking the ledges were popular among the young and not-so-young. Mirchusko was where the blackhawks mated and died and gestated. Tranquillity offered itself as one of their few legitimate home bases. Their eggs could be bought here, changing hands for upwards of twenty million fuseodollars and absolutely no questions.

Around the rim of the endcap hundreds of organic conductor cables stretched out into space; subject to constant dust abrasion and particle impact, they were extruded on a permanent basis by specialist glands to compensate for the near-daily breakages. The habitat's rotation kept the cables perfectly straight, radiating away from the shell like the leaden-grey spokes of some cosmic bicycle wheel. They sliced through the flux lines of Mirchusko's prodigious magnetosphere, generating a gigantic electrical current which powered the biological processes of Tranquillity's mitosis layer as well as the axial light-tube and the domestic demands of its inhabitants. Tranquillity ingested thousands of tonnes of asteroidal minerals each year to regenerate its own polyp structure and invigorate the biosphere, but chemical reactions alone could never produce a fraction of the energy it needed to nurture its human occupants.

Beyond the endcap and the induction cables, exactly halfway down the cylinder, there was a city, home to over three million people: a band of starscrapers wrapped around the median equator, five-hundred-metre-long towers projecting out of the shell, studded with long, curving transparencies that radiated warm yellow light out into space. The view from the luxurious apartments inside was breathtaking; stars alternated with the storm-wracked gas giant and its little empire of rings and moons, eternal yet ever-changing as the cylinder rotated to provide an Earth-standard gravity at the base of the towers. Here, Adamists were granted the sight which was every Edenist's birthright.

Small wonder, then, that Tranquillity, with its liberal banking laws, low income tax, the availability of black-hawks to charter, and an impartial habitat-personality which policed the interior to ensure a crime-free environment (essential for the peace of mind of the millionaires and billionaires who resided within), had prospered, becoming one of the Confederation's premier independent trading and finance centres.

But it hadn't been designed as a tax haven, not at first; that came later, born out of desperate necessity. Tranquillity was germinated in 2428, on the order of the then Crown Prince of Kulu, Michael Saldana, as a modified version of an Edenist habitat, with a number of unique attributes the Prince himself requested. He intended it to act as a base from which the cream of Kulu's xenoc specialists could study the Laymil, and determine what fate had befallen them. It was an action which brought down the considerable wrath of his entire family.

Kulu was a Christian-ethnic culture, and very devout. The King of Kulu was the principal guardian of that faith throughout the kingdom; and because of bitek's synonymous association with Edenists, Adamists (especially good Christian ones) had virtually abandoned that particular branch of technology. Possibly Prince Michael could have got away with bringing Tranquillity into existence; a self-sustaining bitek habitat was a logical solution for an isolated academic research project, and astute propaganda could have smoothed over the scandal. Royalty is no stranger to controversy, if anything it adds to its mystique, especially when relatively harmless.

But the whitewash option never arose; having germinated the habitat, Prince Michael went and compounded his original "crime" (in the eyes of the Church, and more importantly the Privy Council) by having neuron symbionts implanted enabling him to establish an affinity bond with the young Tranquillity.

His final act of defiance, condemned as heretical by Kulu's conclave of bishops, came in 2432, the year his father, King James, died. Michael had a modified affinity gene spliced into his first son, Maurice, so that he too might commune with the kingdom's newest, and most unusual, subject.

Both were excommunicated (Maurice was a three-month-old embryo residing in an exowomb at the time). Michael abdicated before his coronation in favour of his brother, Prince Lukas. And father and son were unceremoniously exiled to Tranquillity, which was granted to them in perpetuity as a duchy.

One of the most ambitious xenoc research projects ever mounted, the unravelling of an entire species from its chromosomes to whatever pinnacles of culture it achieved, virtually collapsed overnight as its royal treasury funds were withdrawn and staff recalled.

And as for Michael: from being the rightful monarch of the seven wealthiest star systems in the Confederation, he became the de facto owner of a half-grown bitek habitat. From commanding a navy of seven hundred warships, the third most powerful military force in existence, he had at his disposal five ex-navy transports, all over twenty-five years old. From having the absolute power of life and death over a population of one and three-quarter billion loyal human subjects, he became an administrator of seventeen thousand abandoned, shit-listed technicians and their families, resentful at their circumstances. From being First Lord of the Treasury dealing in trillion-pound budgets, he was left to write a tax-haven constitution in the hope of attracting the idle rich so he could live off their surplus.

For time evermore, Michael Saldana was known as the Lord of Ruin.

"I am bid three hundred thousand fuseodollars for this excellent plant. Really, ladies and gentlemen, this is a remarkable specimen. There are over five intact leaves, and it is of a type never seen before, completely unclassified." The plant sat in a glass vacuum bubble on the auctioneer's table: a dusty grey stalk, sprouting five long drooping fern-like leaves with frayed edges. The audience gazed at it in unappreciative silence. "Come along now, that protuberance at the top may well be a flower bud. Its cloning will be such a simple matter, and the genome patent will remain exclusively in your hands, an incalculable font of wealth."

Someone datavised another ten thousand fuseodollars.

Joshua Calvert didn't try to see who. This crowd were experts, facial expressions like poker players running downer programs. And they were all here today, packing the room, there wasn't a spare chair to be had. People stood four deep around the walls, spilling down the aisles; the casuals, billionaires looking for a spark of excitement, the serious collectors, consortium bidders, even some industrial company reps hoping for technological templates.

Here because of me.

Barrington Grier's outfit wasn't the largest auction house in Tranquillity, and it dealt in art as much as Laymil artefacts, but it was a tight, polished operation. And Barrington Grier had treated a nineteen-year-old Joshua Calvert who had just returned from his first scavenging flight as an equal, as a professional. With respect. He had used the house ever since.

The bidding room was on the fiftieth floor of the StMary's starscraper, its polyp walls overlaid by dark oak panelling, with velvet burgundy curtains on either side of the entrance arches and thick royal-blue carpets. Elaborate crystal lights cast a bright glow on the proceedings. Joshua could almost imagine himself in some Victorian London establishment. Barrington Grier had told him once that was the effect he wanted, quiet and dignified, fostering an atmosphere of confidence. The broad window behind the auctioneer spoilt the period effect somewhat; stars spun lazily outside, while Falsia, Mirchusko's sixth moon, slowly traversed the panorama, a sliver of aquamarine.

"Three hundred and fifty thousand, once."

Falsia was eclipsed by the auctioneer's chest.

"Three hundred and fifty thousand, twice."

The antique wooden gavel was raised. Falsia reappeared, peeping out over the man's shoulder.

"Final time."

There was a smack as the gavel came down. "Sold to Ms Melissa Strandberg."

The room buzzed with voices as the glass bubble was carried away, excitement and nervousness throttling the air. In his second-row seat, with his nerves alight, Joshua felt it build around him, and shifted round uncomfortably, careful not to knock his legs against those of his neighbours. His feet were still painful if he applied pressure too quickly. Medical nanonic packages had swallowed both legs up to his knees, looking like strange green-leather boots, five sizes too large. The packages had a spongy texture, and he felt as though he was bouncing as he walked.

Three auctioneer's assistants carried a new bubble over to the table, it was a metre and a half high, with a dull gold crown of thermo-dump fins on top, keeping the internal temperature below freezing. A faint patina of condensation misted the glass. The voices in the room chopped off dead.

Joshua caught sight of Barrington Grier standing at the side of the stage, a middle-aged man with chubby red cheeks and a ginger moustache. He wore a sober navy-blue suit with baggy trousers and neck-sealed jacket with flared arms, the faintest of orange lines glowing on the satin material in a spiral pattern. He caught Joshua's eye, and gave him a wink.

"Now, ladies and gentlemen, we come to the final item of the day, lot 127. I think I can safely say that it is unique in my experience; a module stack of Laymil circuitry which has been preserved in ice since the cataclysm. We have identified both processor chips, and a considerable number of solid-state crystal memories inside. All of them in pristine condition. In this one cylinder there are more than five times the number of crystals we have recovered since the discovery of the Ruin Ring itself. I will leave it to you to imagine the sheer wealth of information stored within. This is undoubtedly the greatest find since the first intact Laymil body, over a century ago. And it is my great privilege to open the bidding at the reserve price of two million Edenist fuseodollars."

Joshua had been bracing himself, but there wasn't even a murmur of protest from the crowd.

The bids came in fast and furious, rising in units of fifty thousand fuseodollars. The background level of conversation crept up again. Heads were swivelling around, bidders trying to make eye contact with their opponents, gauge the level of determination.

Joshua gritted his teeth together as the bids rose through four million. Come on, keep going. Four million three hundred thousand. The answer could be stored in there, why the Laymil did it. Four and a half. You'll solve the biggest problem facing science since we cracked the lightspeed barrier. Four million eight hundred thousand. You'll be famous, they'll name the discovery after you, not me. Come on, you bastards. Bid!

"Five million," the auctioneer announced calmly.

Joshua sank back into the chair, a little whimper of relief leaking from his throat. Looking down he saw his fists were clenched, palms sweating.

I've done it. I can start repairing *Lady Mac*, get a crew together. The replacement patterning nodes will have to come from the Sol system. Say a month if I charter a blackhawk to collect them. She could be spaceworthy within ten weeks. Jesus!

He brought his attention back to the auctioneer just as the bidding went through six million. For a second he thought he'd misheard, but no, there was Barrington Grier grinning at him as if he was running wacko stimulant programs through his neural nanonics.

Seven million.

Joshua listened in a waking trance. He could afford more than a simple node replacement and repair job now. *Lady Mac* could have a complete refit, the best systems, no expense spared, new fusion generators, maybe a new spaceplane, no, better than that, an ion-field flyer from Kulu or New California. Yes!

"Seven million, four hundred and fifty thousand for the

first time." The auctioneer looked round expectantly, gavel engulfed by his meaty fist.

Rich. I'm fucking rich!

"Twice."

Joshua closed his eyes.

"For the last time, seven million, four hundred and fifty thousand. Anybody?"

The smack the gavel made was as loud as the big bang. The start of a whole new existence for Joshua Calvert. Independent starship owner captain.

A deep chime sounded. Joshua's eyes snapped open. Everyone had gone silent, staring at the small omnidirectional AV projector on the desk in front of the auctioneer, a slim crystal pillar one metre high. Curlicues of abstract colour swam below the surface. If anything, Barrington Grier's grin had become even wider.

"Tranquillity reserves the right of last bid on lot 127." A mellow male voice sounded throughout the auction room.

"Oh, for fuck's sake—" An angry voice to Joshua's left. The winning bidder? He hadn't caught the name.

The auction room descended into a bedlam of shouting.

Barrington Grier was giving him a manic thumbs-up. The three assistants started to carry the bubble and its precious— seven and a half million!—contents out into the wings.

Joshua waited as the room cleared; a noisy crush of people jostling and gossiping, Tranquillity's right to reserve the last bid their only topic for discussion.

He didn't care, last bid meant the agreed price plus an extra five per cent. The pillar of electronics would go to the Laymil research team now, analysed by the most experienced xenoc experts in the Confederation. He felt quite good about that, virtuous, maybe it was right they should have it.

Michael Saldana had reassembled as much of the team as he could after those first few traumatic years of exile, building it up in tandem with Tranquillity's new economy and rapidly increasing financial strength. There were currently around seven thousand specialists working on the problem, including several xenoc members of the Confederation, providing a welcome alternative viewpoint when it came to interpreting the more baroque artefacts.

Michael had died in 2513, and Maurice had assumed the title of Lord of Ruin with pride, continuing his father's labours. As far as he was concerned, uncovering the reason behind the Laymil cataclysm was Tranquillity's sole reason for existence. And he pursued it vigorously until his own death nine years ago in 2601.

Since then, the project had gone on apparently unabated. Tranquillity said Maurice's heir, the third Lord of Ruin, was running things as before, but chose not to seek a high public profile. There had been a flurry of rumours at the time, saying that the habitat personality had taken over completely, that the Kulu Kingdom was trying to reclaim the habitat, that the Edenists were going to incorporate it into their culture (earlier rumour said Michael stole the habitat seed from Edenists), throwing out the Adamists. They had all come to nothing. Right from the start the habitat personality had acted as both the civil service and police force, using its servitors to preserve order, so nothing changed, taxes were still two per cent, the blackhawks continued their mating flights, commercial enterprise was encouraged, creative finance tolerated. As long as the status quo was maintained, who cared exactly which kind of neurones were running the show, human or bitek?

Joshua felt a hand come down hard on his shoulder as he shuffled towards the exit, the weight pressed through his left leg. "Ouch."

"Joshua, my friend, my very rich friend. This is the day, hey? The day you made it." Barrington Grier beamed rapturously at him. "So what are you going to do with it all? Women? Fancy living?" His eyes lacked focus, he was definitely running a stimulant program. And he was entitled, the auction house was in line for a three per cent cut of the sale price.

Joshua smiled back, almost sheepish. "No, I'm going back into space. See a bit of the Confederation for myself, that kind of thing, the old wanderlust."

"Ah, if I had my youth back I would do the same thing. The good life, it ties you down, and it's a waste, especially for someone your age. Party till you puke every night, I mean what's the point of it all in the end? You should use the money to get out there and accomplish something. Glad to see you've got some sense. So, are you going to buy a black-hawk egg?"

"No, I'm taking the *Lady Mac* back out."

Barrington Grier pursed his lips in rueful admiration. "I remember when your father arrived here. You take after him, some. Same effect on the women, from what I hear."

Joshua raised a wicked smile.

"Come on," Barrington Grier said. "I'll buy you a drink, in fact I'll buy you a whole meal."

"Tomorrow maybe, Barrington, tonight I'm going to party till I puke."

The lakehouse belonged to Dominique's father, who said it used to belong to Michael Saldana, that it was his home in the days before the starscrapers had matured to their full size. It was a series of looping chambers sunk into the side of a cliff above a lake up near the northern endcap. The walls looked as though they had been wind-carved. Inside the decor was simplistic and expensive, a holiday and enter-tainment *pied-à-terre*, not a home; artwork of various eras had been blended perfectly, and big plants from several planets flourished in the corners, chosen for their striking contrasts.

Outside the broad glass window-doors overlooking the huge lake, Tranquillity's axial light-tube was dimming to-wards its usual iridescent twilight. Inside, the party was just beginning to warm up. The eight-piece band was playing twenty-third-century ragas, processor blocks were loaded with *outré* stimulant programs, and the caterers were assem-bling a seafood buffet of freshly imported Atlantis delica-cies.

Joshua lay back on a long couch to one side of the main lounge, dressed in a pair of baggy grey-blue trousers and a green Chinese jacket, receiving and dispensing greetings to strangers and acquaintances alike. Dominique's set were all young, and carefree, and very rich even by Tranquillity's standards. And they certainly knew how to party. He thought he could see the solid raw polyp walls vibrating from the sound they kicked up on the temporary dance-floor.

He took another sip of Norfolk Tears; the clear, light liquid ran down his throat like the lightest chilled wine, punching his gut like boiling whisky. It was glorious. Five hundred fuseodollars a bottle. Jesus!

"Joshua! I just heard. Congratulations." It was Dominique's father, Parris Vasilkovsky, pumping his hand. He had a round face, with a curly beret of glossy silver-grey hair. There were very few lines on his skin, a sure sign of a geneering heritage; he must have been at least ninety. "One of us idle rich now, eh? God, I can hardly remember what it was like right back at the beginning. Let me tell you, the first ten million is always the most difficult. After that . . . no problem."

"Thanks." People had been congratulating him all evening. He was the party's star attraction. The day's novelty. Since his mother had remarried a vice-president of the Brandstad Bank he had dwelt on the fringes of the plutocrat set which occupied the heart of Tranquillity. They were free enough with their hospitality, especially the daughters who liked to think of themselves as bohemian; and his scavenging flights made him notorious enough to enjoy both their patronage and bodies. But he had always been an observer. Until now.

"Dominique tells me you're going into the cargo business," Parris Vasilkovsky said.

"That's right. I'm going to refit *Lady Mac*, Dad's old ship, take her out again."

"Going to undercut me?" Parris Vasilkovsky owned over two hundred and fifty starships, ranging from small clippers up to ten-thousand-tonne bulk freighters, even some colonist-carrier ships. It was the seventh largest private merchant fleet in the Confederation.

Joshua looked him straight in the eye without smiling. "Yes."

Parris nodded, suddenly serious. He had started with nothing seventy years ago. "You'll do all right, Joshua. Come down to the apartment one night before you go, have dinner as my guest. I mean it."

"I'll do that."

"Great." A thick white eyebrow was raised knowingly.

"Dominique will be there. You could do a lot worse, she's one hell of a girl. A little fancy free, but tough underneath."

"Er, yes." Joshua managed a weak smile. Parris Vasilkovsky: matchmaker! And I'm considered suitable for that family? Jesus!

I wonder what he'd think if he knew what his little darling daughter was doing last night? Although knowing this lot, he'd probably want to join in.

Joshua caught sight of Zoe, another sometimes girlfriend, who was on the other side of the room, her sleeveless white gown creating a sharp contrast with her midnight-black skin. She met his eye and smiled, wiggling her glass. He recognized one of the other teenage girls in the group she was with, smaller than her, with short blonde hair, wearing a sea-blue sarong skirt and loose matching blouse. Pretty freckled face, a thinnish nose with a slight downward curve at the end, and deep blue eyes. He had met her once or twice before, a quick hello, friend of a friend. His neural nanonics located her visual image in a file and produced the name: Ione.

Dominique was striding through the throng towards him. He took another gulp of Norfolk Tears in reflex. People seemed to teleport out of her way for fear of heavy bruising should her swaying hips catch them a glancing blow. Dominique was twenty-six, almost as tall as him; sports mad, she had cultivated a splendidly athletic figure, straight blonde hair falling halfway down her back. She was wearing a small purple bikini halter and a split skirt of some shimmering silver fabric.

"Hi, Josh." She plonked herself down on the edge of the couch, and plucked his glass from unresisting fingers, taking a swift sip for herself. "Look what I ran up for us." She held up a processor block. "Twenty-five possibles, all we can manage, taking your poor feet into account. Should be fun. We'll start working through them tonight."

Shadowy images flickered over the surface of the block.

"Fine," Joshua said automatically. He hadn't got a clue what she was talking about.

She patted his thigh, and bounced to her feet. "Don't go away, I'm going to do my rounds here, then I'll be back to collect you later."

"Er, yes." What else was there to say? He still wasn't sure who had seduced who the day after he returned from the Ruin Ring, but he'd spent every night since then in Dominique's big bed, and a lot of the daytime, too. She had the same kind of sexual stamina as Jezzibella, boisterous and frighteningly energetic.

He glanced down at the processor block, datavising a file-title request. It was a program that analysed all the possible free-fall sexual positions where bounceback didn't use the male's feet. The block's screen was showing two humanoid simulacrums running through contortional permutations.

"Hello."

Joshua tipped the processor block screen side down with an incredibly guilty start, datavising a shutdown instruction, and codelocked the file.

Ione was standing next to the couch, head cocked to one side, smiling innocently.

"Er, hello, Ione."

The smile widened. "You remembered my name."

"Hard to forget a girl like you."

She sat in the imprint Dominique had left in the cushions. There was something quirky about her, a suggestion of hidden depth. He experienced that same uncanny thrill he had when he was on the trail of a Laymil artefact, not quite arousal, but close.

"I'm afraid I forgot what you do, though," he said.

"Same as everyone else in here, a rich heiress."

"Not quite everybody."

"No?" Her mouth flickered in an uncertain smile.

"No, there's me, you see. I didn't inherit anything." Joshua let his eyes linger on the outline of her figure below the light blouse. She was nicely proportioned, skin silk-smooth and sun kissed. He wondered what she would look like naked. Very nice, he decided.

"Apart from your ship, the *Lady Macbeth*."

"Now it's my turn to say: you remembered."

She laughed. "No. It's what everyone is talking about. That and your find. Do you know what's in those Laymil memory crystals?"

"No idea. I just find them, I don't understand them."

"Do you ever wonder why they did it? Kill themselves like that? There must have been millions of them, children, babies. I can't believe it was suicide the way everyone says."

"You try not to think about it when you're out in the Ruin Ring. There are just too many ghosts out there. Have you ever been in it?"

She shook her head.

"It's spooky, Ione. Really, people laugh, but sometimes they'll creep in on you out of the shadows if you don't keep your guard up. And there are a lot of shadows out there; sometimes I think it isn't made of anything else."

"Is that why you're leaving?"

"Not really. The Ruin Ring was a means to me, a way to get the money for *Lady Mac*. I've always planned on leaving."

"Is Tranquillity that bad?"

"No. It's more of a pride thing. I want to see *Lady Mac* spaceworthy again. She got damaged quite badly in the rescue attempt. My father barely made it back to Tranquillity alive. The old girl deserves another chance. I could never bring myself to sell her. That's why I started scavenging, despite the risks. I just wish my father could have stayed around to see me succeed."

"A rescue mission?" She sucked in her lower lip, intrigued. It was an endearing action, making her look even younger.

Dominique was nowhere to be seen, and the music was almost painfully loud now, the band just hitting their stride. Ione was clearly hooked on the story, on him. They could find a bedroom and spend a couple of hours screwing each other's brains out. And it was only early evening, this party wouldn't wind down for another five or six hours yet, he could still be back in time for his night with Dominique.

Jesus! What a way to celebrate.

"It's a long story," he said, gesturing round. "Let's find somewhere quieter."

She nodded eagerly. "I know a place."

The trip on the tube carriage wasn't quite what Joshua had in mind. There were plenty of spare bedrooms at the lakehouse which he could codelock. But Ione had been surprisingly adamant, that elusive hint of steel in her personality surfacing as she said: "My apartment is the quietest in Tranquillity, you can tell me everything there, and we'll never be overheard." She paused, eyes teasing. "Or interrupted."

That settled it.

They took the carriage from the little underground station which served all the residences around the lake. The tube trains were a mechanical system, like the lifts in the starscrapers, which were all installed after Tranquillity reached its full size. Bitek was a powerful technology, but even it had limits on the services it could provide; internal transport lay outside the geneticists' ability. The tubes formed a grid network throughout the cylinder, providing access to all sections of the interior. Carriages were independent, taking passengers to whichever station they wanted, a system orchestrated by the habitat personality, which was spliced into processor blocks in every station. There was no private transport in Tranquillity, and everyone from billionaires to the lowest-paid spaceport handler used the tubes to get around.

Joshua and Ione got into a waiting ten-seater carriage, sitting opposite each other. It started off straight away under Ione's command, accelerating smoothly. Joshua offered her a sip from the fresh bottle of Norfolk Tears he'd liberated from Parris Vasilkovsky's bar, and started to tell her about the rescue mission, eyes tracing the line of her legs under the flimsy sarong.

There had been a research starship in orbit around a gas giant, he said, it had suffered a life-support blow-out. His father had got the twenty-five-strong crew out, straining the *Lady Macbeth*'s own life support dangerously close to capacity. And because several of the injured research crew needed treatment urgently they jumped while they were still inside the gas giant's gravity field, which wrecked some of *Lady Macbeth*'s energy-patterning nodes, which in turn put a massive strain on the remaining nodes when the next jump was made. The starship managed the jump into Tranquillity's system, a distance of eight light-years, ruining forty per cent of her remaining nodes in the process.

"He was lucky to make it," Joshua said. "The nodes have a built-in compensation factor in case a few fail, but that distance was really tempting fate."

"I can see why you're so proud of him."

"Yes, well . . ." He shrugged.

The carriage slowed its madcap dash down the length of the habitat, and pulled to a halt. The door slid open. Joshua didn't recognize the station: it was small, barely large enough to hold the length of the carriage, a featureless white bubble of polyp. Broad strips of electrophorescent cells in the ceiling gave off a strong light; a semicircular muscle membrane door was set in the wall at the back of the narrow platform. Certainly not a starscraper lobby.

The carriage door closed, and the grey cylinder slipped noiselessly into the tunnel on its magnetic track. Currents of dry air flapped Ione's sarong as it vanished from sight.

Joshua felt unaccountably chilly. "Where are we?" he asked.

Ione gave him a bright smile. "Home."

Hidden depths. The chill persisted obstinately.

The muscle membrane door opened like a pair of stone curtains being drawn apart, and Joshua gaped at the apartment inside, bad vibes forgotten.

Starscraper apartments were luxurious even without money for elaborate furnishings; given time the polyp would grow into the shapes of any furniture you wanted, but this . . .

It was split level, a wide oblong reception area with an iron rail running along one side opposite the door, overlooking a lounge four metres below. A staircase set in the middle of the railings extended out for three metres, then split into two symmetrically opposed loops that wound down to the lower floor. Every wall was marbled. Up in the reception area it was green and cream; on both sides of the lounge it was purple and ruby; at the back of the lounge it was hazel and sapphire; the stairs were snow white. Recessed alcoves were spaced equidistantly around the whole reception area, bordered in fluted sable-black columns. One of them framed an ancient orange spacesuit, the lettering Russian Cyrillic. The furniture was heavy and ornate, rosewood and teak, polished to a gleam, carved with beautiful intaglio designs, rich with age, the work of master craftsmen from centuries past. A thick living apricot-coloured moss absorbed every footfall.

Joshua walked over to the top of the stairs without a word, trying to take it all in. The wall ahead of him, some thirty metres long and ten high, was a single window. It showed him a seabed.

Tranquillity had a circumfluous salt-water reservoir at its southern end, like all Edenist habitats. In keeping with the size of the habitat, it was some eight kilometres wide, and two hundred metres deep at the centre; more sea than lake. Both coastlines were a mix of sandy coves and high cliffs. An archipelago of islands and atolls ran all the way around it.

Joshua realized the apartment must be at the foot of one of the coastal cliffs. He could see sand stretching into dark blue distance, half-buried boulders smothered beneath crustaceans, long ribbons of red and green fronds waving idly. Shoals of small colourful fish were darting about; caught in the vast spill of light from the window they looked like jewelled ornaments. He thought he saw something large and dark swimming around the boundary of light.

The breath came out of him in an amazed rush. "How did you get this place?"

There was no immediate answer.

He turned to see Ione standing behind him, eyes closed, head tilted back slightly, as if in deep contemplation. She took a deep breath, and slowly opened her eyes to show the deepest ocean-blue irises, an enigmatic smile on her lips. "It's the one Tranquillity assigned me," she said simply.

"I never knew there were any here that you could ask for. And these furnishings—"

Her smile turned mischievous. And she was suddenly all little girlish again. It was her hair, he thought, all the girls he knew in Tranquillity had long, perfectly arranged hair. With her short, shaggy style she looked almost elfin, and supremely sexy.

"I told you I was an heiress," she said.

"Yes, but *this* . . ."

"You like it?"

"I'm afraid of it. I think I've been scavenging in the wrong place."

"Come on." She held out her hand.

He took her proffered fingers in a light grip. "Where are we going?"

"To get what you came for."

"What's that?"

She grinned, pulling him away from the stairs, along the reception area to the wall at the end. Another muscle membrane in one of the alcoves parted.

"Me," she said.

It was a bedroom, circular, with a curving window band looking into the sea, its polyp ceiling hidden by drapes of dark red fabric. In the middle of the floor was a crater filled with perfectly clear jelly and covered by a thin rubbery sheet, silk pillows lining the rim. And Ione was standing very close. They kissed. He could feel her shiver slightly as his arms went round her. Heat began to seep into his body.

"Do you know why I wanted you?" she said.

"No." He was kissing her throat, hands sliding across her blouse to cup her breasts.

"I've watched you," Ione whispered.

"Er—" Joshua broke off fondling her breasts, and stared at her, the dreamy expression.

"You and all those beautiful rich girls. You're an excellent lover, Joshua. Did you know that?"

"Yeah. Thanks." Jesus. She's watched me? When? The night before last had been pretty wild, but he didn't remember anyone else joining them. Although knowing Dominique it was highly possible. Hell, but I must have been smashed out of my skull.

Ione tugged at his jacket's sash, opening the front. "You wait for the girls to climax, you want them to enjoy it. You make them enjoy it." She kissed his sternum, tongue licking the ridges of his pectoral muscles. "That's very rare, very bold."

Her words and deeds were acting like the devil's own stimulant program, sending a sparkling phantom fire shooting down his nerves to invade his groin and send his heart racing. He felt his cock growing incredibly hard as his breathing turned harsh.

Ione's blouse came open easily under his impatient hands, and he pushed it off her shoulders. Her breasts were high and nicely rounded, with large areolae only a shade darker than her tan. He sucked on a nipple, fingers tracing the sleek muscle tone of her abdomen, eliciting indrawn hisses. Hands clutched and clawed at the back of his neck. He heard his name being called, the delight in her voice.

They fell onto the bed together, the jelly-substance under the sheet undulating wildly. The two of them rode the turbulent waves which their own threshing limbs whipped up.

Entering her was sheer perfection. She was delectably responsive, and strong, sinuous. He had to use his neural nanonics to restrain his body, making sure he remained in control. His secret glee. That way he could wait despite her furious pleading shouts. Wait as she strained and twisted sensually against him. Wait, and provoke, and prolong . . . Until the orgasm convulsed her, and a jubilant screech burst out of her mouth. Then he cancelled the artificial prohibitions, allowing his body to spend itself in frenzied bliss, gloating at her wide-eyed incredulity as his semen surged into her in a long exultant consummation.

They watched each other in silence as the bed slowly calmed. There was a moment's silent contemplation, then they were both grinning lazily. "Was I as good as all the others, Joshua?"

He nodded fervently.

"Good enough to make you stay in Tranquillity, knowing I'm available whenever you want?"

"Er—" He rolled onto his side, disquieted by the gleam in her eye. "That's unfair, and you know it."

She giggled. "Yes."

Looking at her, sprawled out on her back, with her arms flung above her head, perspiration slowly drying, he wondered why it should be that girls were always so much more alluring just after they'd had sex. So blatantly rampant, probably. "Are you going to ask me to stay, slap down an ultimatum? You or the *Lady Mac*?"

"Not stay, no." She rolled over onto her side. "But I have other demands."

The second time, Ione insisted on straddling him. It was easier on his feet, and that way he was able to play with her breasts for the whole time she rode him to their twinned climax. For their third encounter, he arranged the cushions into a pile to support her as she went down on all fours, then mounted her from behind.

After the fifth time Joshua really didn't care that he'd missed the party. Dominique would probably have found herself someone else for the night, too.

"When will you leave?" Ione asked.

"It'll take a couple of months to make *Lady Mac* spaceworthy again, maybe three. I placed an order for the patterning nodes right after the auction. A lot depends on how long it takes to deliver them."

"You know Sam Neeves and Octal Sipika haven't returned yet?"

"I know," he said grimly. He had told his story a dozen times a day since he docked, especially among the other scavengers and spaceport crews. The word was out now. He knew they would deny it, maybe even say he attacked them. And he had no proof, it was their word against his. But it was his version which had been told first, his version which was accepted, which carried all the weight. Ultimately, he had money on his side as well now. Tranquillity didn't have a death penalty, but he had filed a charge of attempted murder with the personality as soon as he'd docked; they ought to get twenty years. The personality certainly hadn't challenged his story, which gave his confidence a healthy boost.

"Well, make sure you don't do anything stupid when they do turn up," Ione said. "Leave it to the serjeants."

Tranquillity's serjeants were an addition to the usual habitat servitor genealogy, hulking exoskeleton-clad humanoids that served as a police force.

"Yes," he groused. An unpleasant thought intruded. "You do believe it was them who attacked me, don't you?"

Her cheeks dimpled as she smiled. "Oh, yes, we checked as best we could. There have been eight scavengers lost in the past five years. In six cases, Neeves and Sipika were out in the Ring at the same time, and in each instance they auctioned a larger than usual number of Laymil artefacts after they docked."

Despite the warm weight of her pressing down on him, that eerie chill returned. It was the casual way she said it, the supreme confidence in her tone. "Who checked, Ione? Who's we?"

She giggled again. "Oh, Joshua! Haven't you worked it out yet? Perhaps I was wrong about you, although I admit you have been distracted with other matters since we arrived."

"Worked what out?"

"Me. Who I am, of course."

The intimation of disaster rose through him like a tidal wave. "No," he said hoarsely. "I don't know."

She smiled, and raised herself on her elbows, head held ten centimetres above his, taunting. "I'm the Lord of Ruin."

He laughed, a sort of nervous choke which trailed off. "Jesus, you mean it."

"Absolutely." She rubbed her nose against his. "Look at my nose, Joshua."

He did. It was a thin nose, with a down-turned end. The Saldana nose, that famous trademark which the Kulu royal family had kept through every genetic modification for the last ten generations. Some said the characteristic had deliberately been turned into a dominant gene by the geneticists.

What she said was true, he knew it was. Intuition yammered in his mind, as strong as the day he found the Laymil electronics. "Oh shit."

She kissed him, and sat back, arms folded in her lap, looking smug.

"But why?" he asked.

"Why what?"

"Jesus!" His arms waved about in exasperated agitation. "Why not let people know you're running things? Show them who you are. Why . . . why carry on with this charade of the research project? And your father's dead; who's been looking after you for the last eight years? And why me? What did you mean, being wrong about me?"

"Which order do you want them in? Actually, they're all

connected, but I'll start at the beginning for you. I'm an eighteen-year-old girl, Joshua. I'm also a Saldana, or at least I have their genetic super-heritage, which means I'll live for damn near two centuries, my IQ is way above normal, and I've got the same kind of internal strengthening you have, among other improvements. Oh, we're a breed above, us Saldanas. Just right to rule you common mortals."

"So why don't you? Why spend your time skulking around parties picking up people like me to screw?"

"It's an image thing which makes me a shrinking violet for the moment. Maybe you don't realize just how much authority the habitat personality has in Tranquillity. It is omnipotent, Joshua, it runs the whole shebang, there is no need for a court, for civil servants, it enforces the constitution with perfect impartiality. It provides the most stable political environment in the Confederation outside Edenism and the Kulu Kingdom. That's why it is such a successful haven; not just a tax haven either, but economically and financially. You'll always be safe living in Tranquillity. You can't corrupt it, you can't bribe it, you can't get it to change its laws even through logical argument. *You* can't. I can. It takes orders from me, and only me, the Lord of Ruin. That's the way grandfather Michael wanted it, one ruler, dedicated to one job: government. My father had a lot of children by quite a number of women, and they all had the affinity gene, but they all left to become Edenists. All but me, because I was gestated in a womb-analogue set-up similar to the void-hawks and their captains. We're bonded, you see, little me and a sixty-five-kilometre-long coral-armoured beastie, mind-mated for life."

"Then come forward publicly, let people know you exist. We've been living on rumours for eight years."

"And that was the best thing for you. Like I said, I'm eighteen. Would you trust me to run a nation of three million people? To make alterations to the constitution, tinker with the investment laws, put up the price of the He3 the starships use, which *Lady Macbeth* uses? That's what I can do, change anything I want. You see, unlike Kulu with its court politics, and the Edenists with their communal consensus, I have no one to guide me, or more importantly, to restrain me. What I say goes, and anyone who argues is flung out of an airlock. That's the law, my law."

"Trust," he said, realizing. "Nobody would trust you. Everything works smoothly because we thought the habitat personality was carrying on your father's policies."

"That's right. No billionaire like Parris Vasilkovsky, who has spent seventy years building up his commercial empire, is going to deposit his entire fortune in a nation which has a dizzy teenage girl as absolute ruler. I mean, he's only got to look at the way his daughter behaves, and she's a lot older than I am."

Joshua grinned. "Point taken." He remembered the crack about watching; of course Ione would be able to receive Tranquillity's sensory images through her affinity bond, she could watch anything and anybody she wanted. A slight flush warmed his face. "So that's why you keep on wasting money on the Laymil research project, so people will think it's business as usual. Not that I'm complaining. Jesus! That last bid right you've got, seven and a half million fuseodollars." His smile faded at the expression of disapproval registering on her face.

"You couldn't be further from the truth, Joshua. I consider research into the Laymil to be the single most important issue in my life."

"Oh, come on! I've spent years grubbing round in the Ruin Ring. Sure, it's a mystery. Why did they do it? But don't you see, it doesn't matter. Not to the degree which the research team pursue it. The Laymil are xenocs, for Christ's sake, who cares how weird their psychology was, or that they found some fruitcake death-cult religion."

Ione exhaled, shaking her head in consternation. "Some people refuse to see the problem, I accept that, but I never thought you'd be one of them."

"Refuse to see what problem?"

"It's like that sometimes, something so big, so frightening, staring you right in the face, and you just block it out. Planet dwellers live in earthquake zones and on the side of volcanoes, yet they can't see anything crazy about it, how stupid they're being. The reason is all important, Joshua, vitally important. Why do you think my grandfather did what he did?"

"I haven't got a clue. I thought that was supposed to be the universe's second greatest mystery."

"No, Joshua, no mystery. Michael Saldana established the Laymil research project because he thought it was his duty, not just to the kingdom but to all humanity. He could see just how long a project it would be. That's why he alienated his family and endured the wrath of the Christian Church to grow Tranquillity. So that there would always be someone who shared the need, and had the resources to continue the research. He could have ordered Kulu's xenoc-research institutions to perform the investigation. But how long would that have lasted? His reign, certainly. Maurice's reign, too. Possibly even for that of Maurice's eldest son. But he was worried sick that wouldn't be long enough. It's such a colossal task; you know that more than most. Even the Kings of Kulu couldn't keep a project like this going on a priority budget for more than two or three centuries. He had to be free of his heritage and obligations in order to ensure the most important undertaking in human history wasn't allowed to waste away and die."

Joshua gazed at her levelly, remembering the didactic course he had taken on affinity and Edenist culture. "You talk to him, don't you? Your grandfather. He transferred his memories into the habitat personality, and they leaked into you when you were in the womb-analogue. That's why you spout all this crap. He's contaminated you, Ione."

For a moment Ione looked hurt, then she summoned up a rueful smile. "Wrong again, Joshua. Neither Michael nor Maurice transferred their memories during death. The Saldanas are pretty devout Christians; my Kulu cousins are supposed to rule by divine right, remember?"

"Michael Saldana was excommunicated."

"By the Bishop of Nova Kong, never by the Pope in Rome. It was politics, that's all. His punishment, dished out by the Kulu court. He shocked the family to its odiously complacent core by growing Tranquillity. The whole basis of their sovereignty is that they simply cannot be bribed or corrupted, their wealth and privileges make it totally impossible. They are the ultimate straight arrows, dedicated to service, because they have every physical and material whim catered for. There isn't anything else for them to do but rule. And I have to admit they make quite a good job of it; Kulu is wealthy, strong, independent, with the highest socioeconomic index outside Edenism. The Saldanas and their century-long development projects did that for the Kingdom, a leadership which genuinely considers that its nation's interests are paramount. That's remarkable, bordering on unique. And they are revered for it, there are gods who receive less adulation than the Saldanas. Yet Michael considered an intellectual problem sufficient grounds to lay all that aside. Small wonder the family were terrified, not to mention furious with him. He showed it was possible to suborn a mighty Saldana, to turn their attention from parochial matters. That's why the bishop did what he was ordered to do. But my grandfather remained a Christian until the day he died. And I am too."

"Sorry." Joshua leant over and rummaged round in his pile of clothes until he found the small pear-shaped bottle of Norfolk Tears. He took a swig. "You take some getting used to, Ione."

"I know. Now imagine your reaction magnified three million times. There'd be riots."

Joshua passed her the bottle. It was tipped up daintily, a few drops of the precious imported liquor sliding down past her lips. He admired the way the skin pulled taut over her abdomen as her head went back, the breasts pushed forward. He let a hand slide up the side of her ribs, questing innocently. The initial shock of her identity was fading like a stolen daydream, he wanted the reassurance she was still the same rutty teenager who had turned him on so badly back at the party.

"So if it's not prenatal ideological indoctrination, what convinces you that the research project is worthwhile?" he asked.

Ione lowered the bottle, marshalling her thoughts. Joshua, among his many other faults, could be depressingly cynical. "Proximity. Like I said, Tranquillity and I are bonded. I see what it sees. And the Ruin Ring is always there, just below us. Seventy thousand habitats, not so different from Tranquillity, pulverized into gravel. And it was suicide, Joshua. The research team believes that the living cells in the Laymil habitats underwent some kind of spasm, cracking the outer silicon shell. They would have to be ordered to do it, compelled, probably. I doubt I could get Tranquillity to do it just by asking nicely."

I might, Tranquillity said silently in her mind. **But you would have to give me a very good reason.**

To save me from a fate worse than death?

That would do it.

Name one.

That is something only you can decide.

She grinned and had another nip from the bottle. It was an amazing drink. She could feel its warmth seeping through her. And Joshua's lower torso was cradled between her thighs. The insidious combination was becoming highly arousing.

He was giving her a curious look.

"Tranquillity says it's not very likely," she told him.

"Oh." He took the bottle back. "But this constant awareness of the Ruin Ring is still a kind of unnatural motivation. Tranquillity worries about it, so you do."

"It's more of a gentle reminder, like a crucifix reminds us of what Christ suffered, and why. It means I don't suffer a lack of faith in the work the research team does. I know we have to find the reason."

"Why, though? Why do you and your father, and your grandfather, all consider it so important?"

"Because the Laymil were ordinary." That got through to him, she saw. A frown crinkled his brow below the sticky strands of tawny hair. "Oh, they have a substantially different body chemistry, and three sexes, and monster bodies, but their minds worked along reasonably similar lines to ours. That makes them understandable. It also makes us dangerously similar. And because they were at least equal to us, if not more advanced, technologically. Whatever it was they came up against is something that one day we are also going to encounter. If we know what it is, we can prepare ourselves, maybe even defend ourselves. Provided we have some warning. That's what Michael realized, his revelation. So you see, he never really did abandon his duty and commitment to Kulu. It's just that this was the only possible way he could hope to safeguard the Kingdom in the ultra-long-term. However unconventional, it had to be done."

"And is it being done? Is your precious team any closer to finding out what happened?"

"Not really. Sometimes I get afraid that we are too late, that too much has been lost. We know so much about the Laymil physically, but so little about their culture. That's why we nabbed your electronics. That much stored data might be the breakthrough we need. We wouldn't need much, just a pointer. There's only two real options."

"Which are?"

"They discovered something that made them do it. Their scientists uncovered some fundamental physical truth or law; or a priest group stumbled across an unbearable theological revelation, that death cult you mentioned. The second option is even worse: that something discovered them, something so fearsome that they felt racial death was a preferable alternative to submission. If it was the second, then that menace is still out there, and it's only a matter of time until we encounter it."

"Which do you think it was?"

She squeezed her legs just that fraction tighter against him, welcoming the comfort his physical presence bestowed. As always when she thought about it, the brooding seemed to sap a portion of her will. Racial pride aside, the Laymil were very advanced, and strong . . . "I tend to think it was the second, an external threat. Mainly because of the question over the Laymil's origin. They didn't evolve on any planet in this star system. Nor did they come from any local star. And from the spacecraft fragments we've found we're pretty sure they didn't have our ZTT technology, which leaves a multi-generation interstellar ark as the most likely option. But that's the kind of ship you only use to colonize nearby stars, within fifteen or twenty light-years. And in any case, why travel across interstellar space just to build habitats to live in? There's no need to leave your original star system if that's all you're going to do. No, I think they came a very long way through ordinary space, for a very real reason. They were fleeing. Like the Tyrathca abandoned their homeworld when its star blew up into a red supergiant."

"But this nemesis still found them."

"Yes."

"Has anyone found remnants of an ark ship?"

"No. If the Laymil did travel to Mirchusko in a slower-than-light ship then they must have arrived around seven to eight thousand years ago. To build up a population base of seventy thousand habitats from one, or even ten ships, would take at least three thousand years. Apparently the Laymil didn't have quite our fecundity when it comes to reproduction. Such an ark ship would have been very old by the time it reached Mirchusko. It was probably abandoned. If it was in the same orbit as the habitats when they were destroyed, then the secondary collisions would have broken it apart."

"Pity."

She bent over to kiss him, enjoying the way his hands tightened around her waist. The hazy blue-shadow images she had poached from Tranquillity's sensitive cells, the private cries she had eavesdropped through the affinity bond, had been borne out. Joshua was the most dynamic lover she had ever known. Gentle and domineering; it was a lethal combination. If only he wasn't quite so ruthlessly mechanical about it. A little too much of his pleasure had come from seeing her lose all control. But then that was Joshua, unwilling to share; the life he led—the endless casual sex offered by Dominique and her set, and the false sense of independence incurred from scavenging—left him too hardened for that. Joshua didn't trust people.

"That just leaves me," he said. His breath was hot on her face. "Why me, Ione?"

"Because you're not quite normal."

"What?"

The intimacy shattered.

Ione tried not to laugh. "How many big strikes have you had this year, Joshua?"

"It's been a reasonable year," he said evasively.

"It's been a stupendous year, Joshua. Counting the electronics stack, you found nine artefacts, which netted you a total of over eight million fuseodollars. No other scavenger has ever earned that much in one year in the hundred and eighty years since Tranquillity was germinated. In fact, no other scavenger has ever earned that much, period. I checked. Someone earned six hundred thousand fuseodollars in 2532 for finding an intact Laymil corpse, and she retired straight away. You are either *amazingly* lucky, Joshua, or . . ." She trailed off, leaving the suggestion hanging tantalizingly in the air.

"Or what?" There was no humour in his tone.

"I think you are psychic."

It was the flash of guilt which convinced her she was right. Later, she made Tranquillity replay the moment countless times, the image from its optically sensitive cells in the mock-marble walls providing her a perfectly focused close up of the flattish planes which made up his face. For a brief second after she said it, Joshua looked fearful and frightened. He rallied beautifully, of course, sneering, laughing.

"Bollocks!" he cried.

"How do you explain it, then? Because believe me, it hasn't gone unnoticed amongst your fellow scavengers, and I don't just mean Messrs Neeves and Sipika."

"You said it: amazingly lucky. It's sheer probability. If I went out into the Ruin Ring again, I wouldn't find a single strike for the next fifty years."

She stroked a single finger along the smooth skin of his chin. He didn't have any stubble, facial hair was another free fall irritant geneering had disposed of. "Bet you would."

He folded his arms behind his head and grinned up at her. "We'll never know now, will we?"

"No."

"And that's what made me irresistible to you? My X-ray sight?"

"Sort of. It would be useful."

"Just: useful?"

"Yes."

"Why, what did you expect me to do for you?"

"Make me pregnant."

This time the fright took longer to fade. *"What?"* He looked almost panic stricken.

"Make me pregnant. Psychic intuition would be a very useful trait for the next Lord of Ruin to have."

"I'm not psychic," he said petulantly.

"So you say. But even if you're not, you would still make a more than satisfactory genetic donor to any child. And I do have a paramount duty to provide the habitat with an heir."

"Careful, you're almost getting romantic."

"You wouldn't be tied down by any parental responsibilities, if that's what bothers you. The zygote would be placed in zero-tau until I'm reaching the end of my life. Tranquillity and the servitor housechimps will bring it up."

"Fine way to treat a kid."

She sat up straight, stretching, and ran her hands up her belly, toying with her breasts. You couldn't be any more unfair to a male, especially when he was naked and trapped below you. "Why? Do you think I turned out badly? Point to the flaw, Joshua."

Joshua reddened. "Jesus."

"Will you do it?" Ione picked up the nearly empty liquor bottle. "If I don't turn you on, there is a clinic in the StAnne starscraper which can perform an in-vitro fertilization." She carefully let a single drop of Norfolk Tears fall onto her erect nipple. It stayed there, glistening softly, and she moved the bottle to her other breast. "You just have to say no, Joshua. Can you do that? Say no. Tell me you've had your fill of me. Go on."

His mouth closed around her left breast, teeth biting almost painfully, and he started sucking.

What do you think? Ione asked Tranquillity hours later, when Joshua had finally sated himself with her. He was sleeping on the bed, ripples of aquamarine light played across him, filtering in through the window. High above the water, the axial light-tube was bringing a bright dawn to the habitat's parkland.

I think the blood supply to your brain got cut off when you were in the womb-analogue organ. The damage is obviously irreparable.

What's wrong with him?

He lies continually, he sponges off his friends, he steals whenever he thinks it won't be noticed, he has used stimulant programs illegal on most Confederation worlds, he shows no respect to the girls he has sexual relations with, he even tried to avoid paying his income tax last year, claiming repairs to his spacecraft were legitimate expenses.

But he found all those artefacts.

I admit that is somewhat puzzling.

Do you think he attacked Neeves and Sipika?

No. Joshua was not in the Ruin Ring when those other scavengers disappeared.

So he must be psychic.

I cannot logically refute the hypothesis. But I don't believe it.

You, acting on a hunch!

Where you are concerned, I act on my feelings. Ione, you grew inside me, I nurtured you. How could I not feel for you?

She smiled dreamily at the ceiling. Well, I do think he's psychic. There's certainly something different about him. He has this sort of radiance, it animates him more than any other person I know.

I haven't seen it.

It's not something you can see.

Even assuming you are correct about him being psychic, why would your child retain the trait? It's not exactly something sequenced into any known gene.

Magic passes down through families the same way as red hair and green eyes.

This isn't an argument I'm going to win, is it?

No. Sorry.

Very well. Would you like me to book you an appointment in the StAnne clinic's administration processor?

What for?

An in-vitro fertilization.

No, the child will be conceived naturally. But I will need the clinic later to take the zygote out and prepare it for storage.

Is there a specific reason for doing it this way? In vitro would be much simpler.

Maybe, but Joshua really is superb in bed. It'll be a lot more fun this way.

Humans!

9

The hot rain falling on Durringham had started shortly after daybreak on Wednesday; it was now noon on Thursday and there had been no let-up. The satellite pictures showed there was at least another five hours' worth of cloud waiting over the ocean. Even the inhabitants, normally unperturbed by mere thunderstorms, had deserted the streets. Scummy water swirled round the stone supports of raised wooden buildings, seeping up through the floorboards. More worryingly, there had been several mudslides on the north-east side of the city. Durringham's civic engineers (all eight of them) were alarmed that an avalanche effect would sweep whole districts into the Juliffe.

Lalonde's Governor, Colin Rexrew, received their datavised report phlegmatically. He couldn't honestly say the prospect of losing half of the capital was an idea which roused any great regret. Pity it wasn't more.

At sixty years old he had reached the penultimate position in his chosen profession. Born in Earth's O'Neill Halo, he had started working for the astroengineering giant Miconia Industrial straight after university, qualifying with a degree in business finance, then diversified into subsidiary management, a highly specialized profession, making sure semi-independent divisions retained their corporate identity even though they were hundreds of light-years from Earth. The company's widespread offices meant he was shunted around the Confederation's inhabited systems in three-year shifts, slowly building an impressive portfolio of experience and qualifications, always putting his personal life second to the company.

Miconia Industrial had taken a ten per cent stake in the Lalonde Development Company, the third largest single investor. And Colin Rexrew had been appointed Governor two years ago. He had another eight years of office to run, after which he'd be in line for a seat on Miconia's board. He would be sixty-eight by then, but some geneering in his heritage gave him a life expectancy of around a hundred and twenty. At sixty-eight he would be just hitting his peak. With a successful governorship under his belt, his chances of nabbing the board seat were good verging on excellent.

Although, as he now knew to his cost, success on Lalonde was a slippery concept to define. After twenty-five years of investment by the LDC, Lalonde wasn't even twenty per cent self-financing. He was beginning to think that if the planet was still here in eight years' time he would have accomplished the impossible.

His office took up the entire third storey of a dumper on the eastern edge of the city. The furniture itself was all made by local carpenters from mayope wood, Lalonde's one really useful resource. He had inherited it from his predecessor, and it was a trifle sturdy for his taste. The thick bright jade carpet of kilian hair had come from Mulbekh, and the computer systems were from Kulu. A glass-fronted drinks cabinet was well stocked, with a good third of the bottles in the chiller containing local wines, which he was acquiring a palate for. Curving windows gave him a view out over the cultivated rural areas beyond the suburb, a sight far more pleasing than the backward mundane city itself. But today even the neat white clapboard houses were afflicted by the downpour, appearing dowdy and beleaguered, the usually green fields covered by vast pools of water. Distressed animals crowded onto the island mounds, bleating pathetically.

Colin sat behind his desk, ignoring the datawork flashing urgently on his screens to watch the deluge through the window. Like everyone on Lalonde he wore shorts, although his were tailored in the London arcology; his pale blue jacket was slung over one of the conference chairs, and the conditioner failed to stop sweat stains from appearing under the arms of his pale lemon silk shirt.

There was no such thing as a gym on the whole planet, and he could never bring himself to jog from his official residence to the office in the morning, so he was starting to put on weight at a disappointing rate. His already round face now had accentuated jowls, and a third chin was developing; a smattering of freckles had expanded under Lalonde's sunlight to cover both cheeks and his forehead. Once hale ginger hair was thinning and fading towards silver. Whatever ancestor had paid for the geneered metabolic improvements which increased his life expectancy had obviously stinted on the cosmetic side.

More lightning bolts stabbed down out of the smothering cloud blanket. He counted to four before he heard the thunder. If this goes on much longer even the puddles will develop puddles, he thought bleakly.

There was a bleep from the door, and it slid open. His neural nanonics told him it was his executive aide, Terrance Smith.

Colin swivelled his chair back round to the desk. Terrance Smith was thirty-five, a tall, elegant man with thick black hair and a firm jaw; today he was dressed in knee-length grey shorts and a green short-sleeved shirt. His weight was never anything less than optimum. The rumour around Colin's staff said Smith had bedded half of the women in the administration office.

"Meteorology say we're due for a dry week after this passes over," Terrance said as he sat in the chair in front of Colin's desk.

Colin grunted. "Meteorology didn't say this lot was expected."

"True." Terrance consulted a file in his neural nanonics. "The geological engineers up at Kenyon have finished their preliminary survey. They are ready to move on to more extensive drilling for the biosphere cavern." He datavised the report over to Colin.

Kenyon was the twelve-kilometre-diameter stony iron asteroid that had been knocked into orbit a hundred and twelve thousand kilometres above Lalonde by a series of nuclear explosions. When Lalonde's first stage of development was complete, and the planetary economy was up and functioning without requiring any additional investment, the LDC wanted to progress to developing a space industry station cluster. That was where the real money lay, fully industrial worlds. And the first essential for any zero-gee industrial stations was an abundant supply of cheap raw material, which the asteroid would provide. The mining crews would tunnel out the ores, literally carving themselves a habitable biosphere in the process.

Unfortunately, now Kenyon was finally in place after its fifteen-year journey from the system's asteroid belt, Colin doubted he had the budget even to maintain the geological engineering team, let alone pay for exploratory drilling. Transporting new colonists into the continental interior was absorbing funds at a frightening rate, and the first thing an asteroid settlement needed was a reliable home market as a financial foundation before it could start competing on the interstellar market.

"I'll look into it later," he told Terrance. "But I'm not making any promises. Somebody jumped the gun on that one by about twenty years. The asteroid industry project looks good on our yearly reports. Moving it into orbit is something you can point to and show the board how progressive you're being. They know it doesn't make a dollar while it's underway. But as soon as it's here in orbit they expect it to be instantly profitable. So I'm lumbered with the bloody thing while my cretinous predecessor is drawing his standard pension plus a nice fat bonus for being so dynamic while he was in office. The auditors should have caught this, you know. It's going to be another fifty years before these mud farmers can scrape together enough capital to support high-technology industries. There's no demand here."

Terrance nodded, handsome features composed into a grave expression. "We've authorized start-up loans for another eight engineering companies in the last two months. Power bike sales are healthy in the city, and we should have an indigenous four-wheel-drive jeep within another five years. But I agree, large-scale consumer manufacturing is still a long way off."

"Ah, never mind," Colin sighed. "You weren't the one who authorized Kenyon. If they'd just stop sending us colonists for six months, allow us to catch our breath. A ship every twenty days is too much, and the passage fees the colonists pay don't cover half of the cost of sending them upriver. Once the starship's been paid for the board doesn't care. But what I wouldn't give for some extra funds to spend on basic infrastructure, instead of subsidizing the river-boats. It's not as if the captains don't make enough."

"That was something else I wanted to bring up. I've just finished accessing the latest schedules flek from the board; they're going to send us five colonist-carrier starships over the next seventy days."

"Typical." Colin couldn't even be bothered with a token protest.

"I was thinking we might ask the river-boat captains to take more passengers each trip. They could easily cram another fifty on board if they rigged up some awnings over the open decks. It wouldn't be any different from the transients' dormitories, really."

"You think they'd go for that?"

"Why not? We pay their livelihood, after all. And it's only temporary. If they don't want to take them, then they can sit in harbour and lose money. The paddle-boats can hardly be used for bulk cargo. Once we've repossessed the boats, we'll give them to captains who are more flexible."

"Unless they all band together; those captains are a clannish lot. Remember that fuss over Crompton's accident? He rams a log, and blames us for sending him off into an uncharted tributary. We had to pay for the repairs. The last thing we need right now is an outbreak of trade unionism."

"What shall I do, then? The transients' dormitories can't hold more than seven thousand at once."

"Ah, to hell with it. Tell the captains they're taking more heads per trip and that's final. I don't want the transients in Durringham a moment longer than necessary." He tried not to think what would ever happen if one of the paddle-boats capsized in the Juliffe. Lalonde had no organized emergency services; there were five or six ambulances working out of the church hospital for casualties in the city, but a disaster a thousand kilometres upriver . . . And the colonists were nearly all arcology dwellers, half of them couldn't swim. "But after this we'll have to see about increasing the number of boats. Because as sure as pigs shit, we won't ever get a reduction in the number of colonists they send us. I heard on the grapevine Earth's population is creeping up again, the number of illegal births rose three per cent last year. And that's just the official illegals."

"If you want more boats, that will mean more mortgage loans," Terrance observed.

"I can do basic arithmetic, thank you. Tell the comptroller to shrink some other budgets to compensate."

Terrance wanted to ask which divisions, every administration department was chronically underfunded. The look on Colin Rexrew's face stopped him. "Right, I'll get onto it." He loaded a note in his neural nanonics general business file.

"It wouldn't be a bad idea to look into safety on those paddle-boats some time. Make them carry lifebelts."

"Nobody in Durringham makes lifebelts."

"So that's a fresh business opportunity for some smart entrepreneur. And yes I know it would need another loan to establish. Hell, do we have a cork-analogue tree here? They could carve them, everything else on this bloody planet is made out of wood."

"Or mud."

"God, don't remind me." Colin glanced out of the window again. The clouds had descended until they were only about four hundred metres above the ground. Dante got it all wrong, he thought, hell isn't about searing heat, it's about being permanently wet. "Anything else?"

"Yes. The marshal you sent up to Schuster County has filed his report. I didn't want to load it into the office datanet."

"Good thinking." Colin knew the CNIS team monitored their satellite communications. There was also Ralph Hiltch sitting snugly over in the Kulu Embassy, like a landbound octopus with its tentacles plugged into damn near every administration office, siphoning out information. Although God alone knew why Kulu bothered, maybe paranoia was a trait the Saldanas had geneered into their super genes. He had also heard a strictly unofficial whisper that the Edenists had an active intelligence team on the planet, which was pushing credulity beyond any sane limits.

"What was the summary?" he asked Terrance.

"He drew a complete blank."

"Nothing?"

"Four families have definitely gone missing, just like the sheriff said. All of them lived out on the savannah a fair distance away from Schuster town itself. He visited their homesteads, and said it was like they walked out one morning and never came back. All their gear had been looted by the time he arrived, of course, but he asked around, apparently there was even food laid out ready for a meal in one home. No sign of a struggle, no sayce or kroclion attack. Nothing. It really spooked the other colonists."

"Strange. Have we had any reports of bandit gangs operating up there?"

"No. In any case, bandits wouldn't stop after just a few families. They'd keep going until they were caught. Those families disappeared nine weeks ago now, and there have been no reports of any repetition. Whatever did happen, it looks like a one off."

"And bandits would have stripped the homesteads of every remotely useful piece of gear, anyway," Colin mused out loud. "What about the Tyrathca farmers? Do they know anything?"

"The marshal rode out to their territory. They claim they've had no contact with humans since they left Durringham. He's pretty sure they're telling the truth. There was certainly no sign of any humans ever being in their houses. His affinity-bonded dog had a good scout round."

Colin stopped himself from making the sign of the cross; his Halo asteroid upbringing had been pretty formal. Supervisors and sheriffs using affinity was something he could never get used to.

"The families all had daughters; some teenagers, a couple in their early twenties," Terrance said. "I checked their registration files."

"So?"

"Several of the girls were quite pretty. They could have moved downriver to one of the larger towns, set up a brothel. It wouldn't be the first time. And from what we know, conditions in Schuster are fairly dire."

"Then why not take their gear with them?"

"I don't know. That was the only explanation I could think of."

"Ah, forget it. If there aren't any more disappearances, and the situation isn't developing into an insurrection, I'm not interested. Write it down to an animal carrying them off for nest food, and call the marshal back. Those colonists know the risks of alien frontiers before they start out. If they're mad enough to go and live out in the jungle and play at being cavemen, let them. I've got enough real problems to deal with at this end of the river."

Quinn Dexter had heard of the disappearances, it was all round the Aberdale village camp the day a party from Schuster made their official welcome visit to Group Seven. Four complete families, seventeen people flying off into thin air. It interested him, especially the rumours. Bandits, xenocs (especially the Tyrathca farmers over in the foothills), secret metamorph aborigines, they had all been advanced as theories, and all found wanting. But the metamorph stories fascinated Quinn. One of Schuster's Ivets told him there had been several sightings when they had first arrived a year ago.

"I saw one myself," Sean Pallas told him. Sean was a couple of years older than Quinn, and could have passed for thirty. His face was gaunt, his ribs were starkly outlined. Fingers and arms were covered in red weals, and pocked sores where insects had bitten him. "Out in the jungle. It was just like a man, only completely black. It was horrible."

"Hey," Scott Williams complained. He was the only Afro-Caribbean among Aberdale's eighteen Ivets. "Ain't nothing wrong with that."

"No, man, you don't understand. It didn't have any face, just black skin, there was no mouth or eyes; nothing like that."

"You sure?" Jackson Gael asked.

"Yeah. I was twenty metres from it. I know what I saw. I

shouted out and pointed, and it just vanished, ducked down behind a bush or something. And when we got there—"

"The cupboard was bare," Quinn said.

The others laughed.

"It's not funny, man," Sean said hotly. "It was there, I swear. There was no way it could have got away without us seeing. It changed shape, turned into a tree or something. And there's more just like it. They are out there in the jungle, man, and they're angry with us for stealing their planet."

"If they're that primitive, how do they know we've stolen their planet?" Scott Williams asked. "How do they know we're not the true aboriginals?"

"It's no joke, man. You won't be laughing when one of them morphs out of the trees and grabs you. They'll drag you underground where they live in big cave cities. Then you'll be sorry."

Quinn and the others had talked about Sean and what he said that night. They agreed that he was badly undernourished, probably hysterical, certainly suffering from sun dreams. The visitors from Schuster had cast a tangible gloom on the mood of all Aberdale's residents, an all too physical reminder of how close failure lurked. There hadn't been much contact between the two groups since the *Swithland* departed.

But Quinn had thought a lot about what Sean said, and the talk he picked up around the village. A black humanoid, without a face, who could disappear into the jungle without a trace (more than one, judging by the number of sightings). Quinn was pretty sure he knew what that was: someone wearing a chameleon camouflage suit. Nobody else in Aberdale had guessed, their minds just weren't thinking along those lines, because it would be totally ridiculous to expect someone to be hiding out in the hinterlands of the greatest shit-hole planet in the Confederation. Which, when Quinn considered it, was the really interesting part. To hide away on Lalonde, where *nobody* would ever look, you must be the most desperate wanted criminal in the universe. Group of criminals, he corrected himself; well organized, well equipped. Conceivably, with their own spacecraft.

Later he discovered all the families who had disappeared had been living in savannah homesteads to the south-east of Schuster. Aberdale was east of Schuster.

Could a retinal implant operating in the infrared spectrum spot a chameleon suit?

The options opening up were amazing.

A fortnight after the *Swithland* left Group Seven at their new home on the Quallheim, the voidhawk *Niobe* emerged above Lalonde. With the Edenists having a five per cent stake in the LDC a visit from Jovian Bank officials was a regular occurrence. The visiting voidhawks also brought supplies and fresh personnel to the station in orbit around Murora, the largest of the system's five gas giants. They were there to supervise Aethra, a bitek habitat that had been germinated in 2602 as part of the Edenist contribution to developing the Lalonde system.

Darcy requested the *Niobe*'s captain perform a detailed scan of Schuster County as soon as the voidhawk slipped into equatorial orbit. *Niobe* altered its orbital track to take it over Schuster at an altitude of two hundred kilometres. The verdant, undulating quilt of jungle rolled past below the voidhawk's sensor blisters, and it concentrated every spare neural cell on analysing the images. Resolution was ten centimetres, enough to distinguish individual humans.

After five daylight passes *Niobe* reported that there were no unauthorized human buildings within a one-hundred-kilometre radius of Schuster town, and all humans observed within that area were listed in the immigrant file Lori and Darcy had built up. Aboriginal-animal density was within expected parameters, which suggested than even if a group had concealed themselves in caves or stealth-cloaked structures, they weren't hunting for food. It found no trace of the missing seventeen people.

After six months Aberdale was looking more like a village and less like a lumberyard with each passing day. Group Seven had waded ashore that first day, armed with fission saws from their gear, and single-minded resolution. They had felled the mayope trees nearest the water, trimmed the

trunks to form sturdy pillars which they had driven deep
into the shingly riverbed, then sliced out thick planks from
the boughs to make a solid walkway. Fission blades made
easy work of the timber, ripping through the compacted cel-
lulose like a laser through ice. They sawed like
mechanoids, and sweated the cuts into place, and hammered away until an hour before the sun set. By then they
had a jetty three metres wide that extended twenty-five metres out into the river, with piles that could moor a half-
dozen paddle-craft securely against the current.

The next day they had formed a human chain to unload
their cargo-pods and cases as the paddle-boats docked one
by one. Will-power and camaraderie made light of the task.
And when the paddle-boats had set off back down the river
the next day, they stood on the sloping bank and sang their
hymn: "Onward, Christian Soldiers". Loud, proud voices
carrying a long way down the twisting Quallheim.

The clearing which formed over the next fortnight was a
broad semicircle, stretching a kilometre along the waterfront with the jetty at its centre. But unlike Schuster, Aberdale trimmed each tree as it came down, carrying the
trunks and usable boughs to a neat stack, and flinging the
smaller leftover branches into a firewood pile.

They built a community hall first, a smaller wooden version of the transients' dormitory with a wooden slat roof
and woven palm walls a metre high. Everyone helped, and
everyone learnt the more practical aspects of gussets and
joists and tenons and rabbet grooves that a didactic carpentry course could never impart. Food came from frequent
hunting trips into the jungle where lasers and electromagnetic rifles would bring down a variety of game. Then there
were wild cherry-oak trees with their edible nutty-tasting
fruit and acillus vines with small clusters of apple-analogue
fruit. The children would be sent on foraging expeditions
each day, scouring the fringes of the clearing for the succu-
lent globes. And there was also the river with its shoals of
brownspines that tasted similar to trout, and bottom-cling-
ing mousecrabs. It was a bland diet to start with, often sup-
plemented with chocolate and freeze-dried stocks taken

from the cargo-pods, but they never fell anywhere near Schuster's iron regimen.

They had to learn how to cook for batches of a hundred on open fires, mastering the technique of building clay ovens which didn't collapse, and binding up carcasses of sayce and danderil (a gazelle-analogue) to be spit-roasted. How to boil water in twenty-five-litre containers.

There were stinging insects to recognize, and thorny plants, and poisonous berries, nearly all of which somehow managed to look different from their didactic memory images. There were ways of lashing wood together; and firing clay so that it didn't crack. Some fronds were good for weaving and some shredded immediately; vines could be dried and used for string and nets. How to dig latrines that nobody fell into (the Ivets were given that task). A long, long list of practicalities which had to be grasped, the essential and the merely convenient. And, by and large, they managed.

After the hall came the houses, springing up in a crescent just inside the perimeter of the clearing. Two-room shacks with overhanging veranda roofs, standing half a metre off the ground thanks to astute management of the tree stumps. They were designed to be added to, a room at a time extending out of the gable walls.

Out of the two hundred and eighteen family groups, forty-two elected to live away from the village, out on the savannah which began south of the river where the jungle eventually faded away to scrub then finally grassland, a sea of rippling green stalks stretching away to the foothills of the distant mountain range, its uniformity broken only by occasional lonely trees and the far-off silver glimmer of narrow watercourses. They were the families who had brought calves and lambs and goat kids and foals, geneered to withstand months of hibernation; pumped full of drugs, and transported in marsupium shells. All the animals were female, so that they could be inseminated from the stock of frozen sperm that had accompanied them across three hundred light-years from Earth.

The Skibbows and the Kavas were among the families who had visions of filling the vast, empty savannah with huge herds of meat-laden beasts. They slept in a tent on the edge of the jungle for five weeks while Gerald and Frank assembled their new home, a four-room log cabin with a stone fireplace, and solar panels nailed on the roof to power lights and a fridge. Outside, they built a small lean-to barn and a stockade; then dammed the little nearby stream with grey stones to form a pool they could wash and bathe in.

Four months and three days after the *Swithland* departed, they split open their seventeen marsupium shells (three had been stolen at the spaceport). The animals were curled up in a form-fitting sponge, almost as though they were in wombs, with tubes and cables inserted in every orifice. Fifteen made it through the revival process: three shire-horse foals, three calves, one bison, three goats, four lambs, and an Alsatian pup. It was a healthy percentage, but Gerald found himself wishing he could have afforded zero-tau pods for them.

All five family members spent the day helping the groggy animals stand and walk, feeding them a special vitamin-rich milk to speed recovery. Marie, who had never even patted a living animal before let alone nursed one, was bitten, peed on, butted, and had the yellowy milk spewed up over her dungarees. At nightfall she rolled into bed and cried herself to sleep; it was her eighteenth birthday, and no one had remembered.

Rai Molvi made his way across the clearing towards the jetty where the tramp trader boat was waiting, exchanging greetings with several adults. He felt a surge of pride at what he saw, the sturdy buildings, neat stacks of timber, fish smoking over open fires, danderil hides pegged out on frames to dry in the sun. A well-ordered community chasing a common goal. The LDC could use Aberdale in its promotional campaign without any falsehood, it was exemplary.

A second wave of tree felling had been underway for a month now, cutting rectangular gashes deep into the jungle around the perimeter of the clearing. From the air the village resembled a gear cog with exceptionally long teeth. The colonists were starting to cultivate the new fields, digging out the tree stumps, ploughing the soil with rotovators that charged from solar cells, planting their vegetable plots and fruit groves. Lines of small green shoots were already visible, pushing up through the rich black soil, and the farmers had to organize a bird patrol to scare off the hungry flocks perched waiting in the surrounding trees.

Not all of the Earth seeds had germinated successfully, which was surprising because they were geneered for Lalonde's environment. But Rai had every confidence the village would triumph. Today's fields would become tomorrow's estates. In six months they had accomplished more than Schuster had in eighteen. It was down to effective organization, he felt. His council was acknowledged as a stroke of salutary foresight, organizing them into an effective interactive work unit even back in the transients' dormitory.

He passed the community hall and stood to one side to let a group of children march by, carrying braces of fat polot birds they had caught in their traps. Their skin was scratched from thorns, and their legs were coated in mud, but they were smiling and laughing. Yes, Rai Molvi felt very good indeed.

He reached the jetty and walked its length. A couple of Ivets were in the river, Irley and Scott, hauling up their creels full of mousecrabs. The creels were adaptations of lobster-pots, one of Quinn's ideas.

Rai waved at the two lads, receiving a grinning thumbs-up. The Ivets were undoubtedly his greatest success. A month after they had arrived, Quinn Dexter had asked to talk to him. "Anything we say to Powel Manani just gets automatically ignored, but we know you'll give us a fair hearing, Mr Molvi."

Which was so true. It was his job to arbitrate, and like it or not, the Ivets were part of Aberdale. He must appear strictly impartial.

"We want to organize ourselves," Quinn had said earnestly. "Right now you have all eighteen of us working for you each day, but you have to feed us and let us live in the hall. It's not the best arrangement, because we just sweat our arses off for you and don't get anything out of it for ourselves, so we don't give a hundred per cent, that's only human nature. None of us asked to come to Aberdale, but we're here now, and we want to make the most of it. We thought that if we had a rota so that thirteen of us are available as a general work team each day, then the remaining five could use the time to build something for ourselves, something to give us a bit of pride. We want to have our own cabin; and we could trap and grow our own food. That way you don't have to support us, and you get a far more enthusiastic work team to help put up your cabins and fell the trees."

"I don't know," Rai had said, although he could see the logic behind the idea. It was just Quinn he was unsettled over; he had encountered waster kids back in the arcology often enough, and Quinn's sinewy frame and assertive mannerisms brought the memories back. But he didn't want to appear prejudicial, and the lad was making an honest appeal which might well be beneficial to the whole community.

"We could try it for three weeks," Quinn suggested. "What have you got to lose? It's only Powel Manani who could say no to you."

"Mr Manani is here to help us," Rai answered stiffly. "If this arrangement is what the town council wants, then he must see that it is implemented."

Powel Manani had indeed objected, which Rai thought was a challenge to his authority and that of the council. In a session to which Powel Manani was not invited, the council decided that they would give the Ivets a trial period to see if they could become self-sufficient.

Now the Ivets had built themselves a long (and very well constructed, Rai grudgingly conceded) A-frame building on the eastern side of the clearing where they all lived. They caught a huge number of mousecrabs in their creels, which they traded for other types of food among the other villagers. They had their own chicken run and vegetable allotments (villagers had chipped in with three chicks and a few seeds from their own stocks). They joined the hunting parties, even being trusted to carry power weapons, although those did have to be handed back at the end of the day. And the daily work team were enthusiastic in the tasks they were given. There was also some kind of still producing a rough drink, which Rai didn't strictly approve of, but could hardly object to now.

It all added up to a lot of credit in Rai Molvi's favour for pushing the idea so hard. And it wouldn't be long before the time was right for Aberdale to think about formally electing a mayor. After that, there was the county itself to consider. Schuster town was hardly flourishing; several of its inhabitants had already asked if they could move to Aberdale. Who knew what a positive, forthright man could aspire to out here where this world's history was being carved?

Rai Molvi came to the end of the jetty flushed with a strong sense of contentment. Which was why he was only slightly put out by a close-up view of the *Coogan*. The boat was twenty metres long, a bizarre combination of raft and catamaran. Flotation came from a pair of big hollowed-out trunks of some fibrous red wood, and a deck of badly planed planks had been laid out above them, supporting a palm-thatched cabin which ran virtually the whole length. The aft section was an engine house, with a small ancient thermal-exchange furnace, and a couple of time-expired electric motors used by the McBoeings in their flap actuators which the captain had salvaged from the spaceport. Forward of that was a raised wheel-house, with a roof made entirely of solar panels, then came the galley and bunk cabin. The rest of the cabin was given over to cargo.

The *Coogan*'s captain was Len Buchannan, a wire-thin man in his mid-fifties, dressed in a pair of worn, faded shorts and a tight-fitting blue cap. Rai suspected he had little geneering; the hair peeking out from his cap was tightly curled and pale grey, dark brown skin showed stringy muscles stretched taut and slightly swollen joints, several teeth had rotted away.

He stood in front of the wheel-house and welcomed Rai on board.

"I need a few supplies," Rai said.

"I ain't interested in barter," he said straight away, cheeks puffing out for emphasis. "Not unless it's powered equipment you're offering. I've had my fill of pickled vegetables and fruit preserves and cured hides. And don't even think about saying fish. They're coming out my ears. I can't sell anything like that downriver. Nobody's interested."

Rai fished a roll of plastic Lalonde francs out of his pocket. Buchannan was the third trader captain to appear at Aberdale recently. All of them wanted cash for their goods, and none had bought much of Aberdale's produce in return. "I understand. I'm looking for cloth. Cotton mainly, but I'll take denim or canvas."

"Cost you a lot of francs. You got anything harder?"

"I might have," Rai said, with a grey inevitability. Didn't anybody use Lalonde francs? "Let's see what you've got first."

Gail Buchannan was sitting in the wheel-house, wearing a coolie hat and a shapeless khaki dress. An obese fifty-year-old with long, straggly dark hair, her legs were like water-filled sacks of skin; when she walked it was with a painful waddle. Most of her life was spent sitting on the *Coogan*'s deck watching the world go by. She looked up from the clothes she was sewing to give Rai a friendly nod. "Cloth you wanted, is it, lovie?"

"That's right."

"Plenty of cloth, we've got. All woven in Durringham. Dyed, too. Won't find better anywhere."

"I'm sure."

"No patterns yet. But that'll come."

"Yes."

"Does your wife know how to sew, then?"

"I . . . Yes, I suppose so." Rai hadn't thought about it. Arcology synthetics came perfectly tailored; load your size into the commercial circuit and they arrived within six hours. If they started to wear, throw them into the recycler. Waster kids dressed in patched and frayed garments, but not decent people.

"If she doesn't, you send her to me."

"Thank you."

"Knitting too. None of the women that come here know how to knit. I give lessons. Best lessons east of Durringham. Know why, lovie?"

"No," Rai said helplessly.

"Because they're the only ones." Gail Buchannan slapped her leg and laughed, rolls of flesh quivering.

Rai gave her a sickly smile and fled into the cargo hold, wondering how many times that joke had been cracked over the years.

Len Buchannan had everything a farmstead could ever possibly want stacked up on his long shelves. Rai Molvi shuffled down the tiny aisle, staring round in awe and envy. There were power tools still in their boxes, solar cells (half of Rai's had been stolen back in Durringham), fridges, microwaves, cryostats full of frozen animal sperm, MF album flek-players, laser rifles, nanonic medical packages, drugs, and bottle after bottle of liquor. The Lalonde-made products were equally impressive: nails, pots, pans, glass (Rai saw the panes and groaned, what he wouldn't give for a window of glass), drinking glasses, boots, nets, seeds, cakes of dried meat, flour, rice, saws, hammers, and bale after bale of cloth.

"What kind of things would you take downriver?" Rai asked as Len unrolled some of the cotton for him.

Len pulled his cap off, and scratched his largely bald head. "Truth to tell, not much. What you produce up here, food and the like. People need it. But it's the transport costs, see? I couldn't take fruit more than a hundred kilometres and make a profit."

"Small and valuable then?"

"Yes, that's your best bet."

"Meat?"

"Could do. There's some villages not doing as well as you. They want the food, but how are they going to pay for it? If they spend all their money buying food, it's going to run out fast, then they won't be able to buy in new stocks of what they really need like seed and animals. I seen that happen before. Bad business."

"Oh?"

"The Arklow Counties, a tributary over in the northern territory. All the villages failed about six or seven years back. No food, no money left to buy any in. They started marching downriver towards villages that did have food."

"What happened?"

"Governor sent in the marshals, plus a few boosted mercenaries from offplanet if you believe what people say. Them starving villagers took a right pounding. Some escaped into the jungle, still there by all accounts, lot of bandit reports in the north. Most got themselves killed. The rest got a twenty-year work-time sentence; the Governor parcelled them out to other villages to work, just like Ivets. Families broken up, children never see their parents." He sucked his cheeks in, scowling. "Yes, bad business." Rai sorted out the cloth he wanted, and on impulse bought a packet of sweetcorn seed for Skyba, his wife. He offered the Lalonde notes again.

"Cost you double, that way," Len Buchannan said. "The LDC people at the spaceport, they don't give you anything like the proper exchange rate."

Rai made one last attempt. "How about chickens?"

Len pointed to a shelf given over to cryostats, their tiny green LEDs twinkling brightly in the gloomy cabin. "See that? Two of those chambers are crammed full of eggs. There's chickens, ducks, geese, pheasants, emus, and turkeys stored in there; I've even got three swans. I don't need live chickens crapping on my deck."

"OK." Rai gave up; he dug into his inside pocket and offered his Jovian Bank disk, feeling a little bit shabby. People should believe in their own planet's currency. If—when—Schuster County became an important commercial region, he would make damn sure every transaction was made in Lalonde francs. Patriotism like that would be very popular with the voters.

Len stood beside his wife as Rai walked back down the jetty. "Ten thousand born every second," he murmured.

Gail chuckled. "Aye, and all of them come to live here."

From their vantage point in the river shallows, Irley and Scott gave Rai a cheery wave as he carried his cloth ashore. Another who had a Jovian Bank credit disk, that made seventy-eight known residents now. Quinn would be pleased with them.

Rai reached the end of the jetty just as Marie Skibbow arrived carrying a bulky shoulder-bag. She gave him an uninterested glance and hurried on towards the *Coogan*.

What's she come to pick up? Rai wondered. Gerald's place was one of the prime savannah homesteads. Although the man himself was a complete self-righteous pain in the arse.

Horst Elwes stood at the base of the church's wooden corner stanchion, holding the cloth bag full of nails, and still managing to feel completely useless. Leslie didn't need anyone to hold the nails ready. But Horst could hardly let the Ivet work team assemble the church without being there, without at least the pretence of being involved.

The church was one of the last of Aberdale's buildings to be put up. He didn't mind that at all. These people had toiled hard to build their village and clear their fields. They couldn't spare the time on a structure that would only be used once or twice a week (though he liked to think there would be more services eventually). Nor was it right they should do so. Horst could never forget how the cathedrals of medieval Europe had risen like stone palaces out of the mouldering, stinking wooden slums. How the Church demanded the people of that time give and give and give. How fear was rooted in every soul and carefully nurtured. And because we were so arrogant, as aloof as God Himself, we suffered a terrible price in later centuries. Which again was right. Such a crime deserved a penance that lasted for so long.

So he held his services in the hall, and never complained when only thirty or forty people turned up. The church must be a focal point for unity, a place where people could come together and share their faith, not a baron demanding tribute.

And now the fields had been rotovated, the first batch of crops planted, and the animals brought out of hibernation, Aberdale had a moment of time to spare. Three Ivets had been assigned to him for a fortnight. They had built a long raftlike floor supported half a metre off the ground by old tree stumps, then put up four-metre-high stanchions to hold up the sloping roof.

At the moment it looked like a skeleton of some boxy dinosaur. Leslie Atcliffe was busy hammering the trusses into place, while Daniel held them steady. Ann was busy cutting slates from the sheets of qualtook bark they had stripped off the felled trunks. The church itself would occupy a third of the structure, with a small infirmary at the rear, and Horst's room sandwiched between the two.

It was all going very well, and would probably go better if Horst wasn't there asking what he could do to help the whole time.

The church was going to be a fine building, second only to the Ivets' own A-frame. And how that structure had shown up the hall and the other houses. Horst had joined Rai Molvi in urging the council to allow the Ivets some independence and dignity. Now Quinn was the one who had really worked miracles in Aberdale. Since the long bark-slate covered A-frame had gone up the other residents had taken to quietly improving the structure of their own homes, adding corner braces, putting up shutters. *And none of us will use an A-frame design,* Horst thought. *Oh, foolish pride! Everyone was captured by the quaint white-painted cottages we saw on the first days of the voyage upriver, we thought if we could emulate the look we would have the life that went with it. Now the most practical method of construction is a monopoly. Because using it would mean the Ivets knew best. And I can't even build the church that way, the sensible way, because people would be offended. Not out loud, but they would see and in their hearts they would object. But at least I can use the bark slates rather than slats that will warp and let in the rain like the houses which were built first.*

Leslie climbed down the ladder, a rangy twenty-two-year-old wearing shorts sewn together from an old jump suit. A specially made belt had loops to hold all his carpentry tools. To start with Powel Manani had issued the tools on a daily basis, and demanded their return at night; now the Ivets kept them permanently. Several of them had developed into highly skilled carpenters; Leslie was one of them.

"We'll fetch the last two transverse frames now, Father," Leslie said. "They'll be up by lunch, then we can start with the lathing and the slates. You know, I think we will be finished by the end of the fortnight after all. It's just those pew benches I'm worried about, cutting that many dovetail joints in time is going to be tricky, even with fission blades."

"Don't pay it a second thought," Horst said. "I don't get enough of a congregation to fill every pew. A roof over our heads is more than enough. The rest can wait. The Lord understands that the farms must come first." He smiled, keenly aware of how shabby he was in his stained ochre shirt and oversize knee-length shorts. So much at variance from these uniformly trim young men.

"Yes, Father."

Horst felt a pang of regret. The Ivets were so insular, yet they did more work than most. Aberdale's success was in no small part due to their efforts. And Powel Manani still grumbled about the liberties they were shown. It didn't happen in other settlements, he complained. But then other settlements didn't have Quinn Dexter. It was a thought Horst couldn't be quite as grateful for as he should be. Quinn was a very cold fish. Horst knew waster kids, their motivations, their shallow wishes. But what went on behind those chilling bright eyes was an utter mystery, one he was afraid to probe.

"I shall be holding a consecration service once the roof's on," he said to the two Ivets. "I hope you'll all come to it."

"We'll think about it," Leslie said with smooth politeness. "Thank you for asking, Father."

"I notice that not many of you come to my services. Everybody is welcome. Even Mr Manani, although I don't think he's particularly impressed with me." He tried to make it sound jovial, but their expressions never flickered.

"We're not very religious," Leslie said.

"I'd be happy to explain the broader ramifications of Christianity to anybody. Ignorance isn't a crime, only a misfortune. If nothing else we could have a good argument about it, you needn't worry about shocking me there. Why, I remember some debates from my novice years, we really gave the bishop a roasting." Now he knew he'd lost them. Their earlier magnanimity had turned to stiff-backed formality, faces hard, sparks of resentment agleam in their eyes. And once more he was aware of how ominous these young men could appear.

"We have the Light Brother—" Daniel began. He broke off at a furious look from Leslie.

"Light Brother?" Horst asked mildly. He was sure he'd heard that phrase before.

"Was there anything else, Father?" Leslie said. "We'd like to collect the transverse frames now."

Horst knew when to push, and this wasn't the time. "Yes, of course. What would you like me to do? Help you fetch them?"

Leslie looked around the church impatiently. "We could do with the slates stacking round the floor ready for when we get the lathing up," he said grudgingly. "Piles of twenty by each stanchion."

"Jolly good, I'll start doing that then."

He walked over to where Ann was standing beside a workbench, slicing up the bark with a fission jigsaw. She was wearing a pair of hand-stitched shorts and a halter top, both made from grey jump suit fabric. There was a huge pile of the slates on the ground around her. Her long face was crunched up in an expression of furious concentration, dark auburn hair hanging in damp tassels.

"We don't need the slates that urgently," Horst said lightly. "And I'm certainly not going to complain to Mr Manani if you slacken off a bit."

Ann's hand moved with mechanical precision, guiding the slender blade in a rectangular pattern through the big sheet of glossy ginger-coloured qualtook bark. She never bothered to mark out the shape, but each one came out more or less identical.

"Stops me thinking," she said.

Horst started to pick up some of the slates. "I was sent here to encourage people to think. It's good for you."

"Not me. I've got Irley tonight. I don't want to think about it."

Irley was one of the Ivets; Horst knew him as a thin-faced lad, who was quiet even by their standards.

"What do you mean, you've got him?"

"It's his turn."

"Turn?"

Ann suddenly looked up, her face a mask of cold rage, most of it directed at Horst. "He's going to fuck me. It's his turn tonight. Do you want it in writing, Father?"

"I . . ." Horst knew his face was reddening. "I didn't know."

"What the hell do you think we do in that big hut at night? Basket weaving? There are three girls, and fifteen boys. And the boys all need it pretty bad, banging their fists each night isn't enough, so they take it in turns with us, those that aren't AC/DC. Quinn draws up a nice little impartial list, and we stick to it. He makes sure it's dished out fairly, and he makes sure nobody spoils the merchandise. But Irley knows how to make it hurt without making it painful, without it showing. Do you want to know how, Father? You want the details? The tricks he's got."

"Oh, my child. This must stop, at once. I'll speak to Powel and the council."

Ann surprised him. She burst into shrill contemptuous laughter. "God's Brother. I can see why they dumped you out here, Father. You'd be bloody useless back on Earth. You're going to stop the boys from screwing me and Jemima and Kay, are you? Then where are they going to go for it? Huh? Lotsa your good parishioners got daughters. You think they want Ivets prowling round at night? And how about you, Father, do you want Leslie and Douglas giving your sweet little friend Jay the eye? Do you? Because they will if they can't get it from me. Get real, Father." She turned back to the sheet of bark. A dismissal that was frightening in its finality. Nothing Horst could offer was of the remotest use. Nothing.

It was there, right at the bottom of his pack where it had lain for six and a half months. Untouched, *unneeded*, because the world was full of worthy challenges, and the sun shone, and the village grew, and the plants blossomed, and the children danced and laughed.

Horst took out the bottle, and poured a long measure. Scotch, though this thick amber liquid had never rested in oak barrels in the Highlands. It had come straight out of a molecular filter programmed with the taste of a long-lost ideal. But it burnt as it went down, and slowly lit up his belly and his skull, which was all he wanted from it.

How stupid. How blind to think the serpent hadn't come with them to this fresh world. How obtuse that he, a priest, hadn't thought to look below the shining surface of achievement, to see the sewer beneath.

He poured another measure of Scotch. Breath coming in hot bursts between gulps. God, but it felt good, to abandon mortal failings for a few brief hours. To hide in this warm, silent, forgiving place of sanctuary.

God's Brother, she had said. And she was right. Satan is here amongst us, piercing our very heart.

Horst filled his glass to the very top, staring at it in abject dread. Satan: Lucifer, the light bringer. The Light Brother.

"Oh no," he whispered. Tears filled his eyes. "Not that, not that here. Not the sects spreading over this world's purity. I can't, dear Lord. I can't fight that. *Look at me.* I'm here because I can't." He trailed off into sobs.

Now as always, the Lord answered only with silence. Faith alone wasn't enough for Horst Elwes. But then he'd always known that.

The bird was back again, thirty centimetres long, its plumage a tawny brown flecked with gold. It hovered twenty metres above Quinn, half hidden by the jungle's curving branches, its wings blurring in an intricate pattern as it maintained position.

He watched it out of the corner of his eye. It wasn't like any other bird he'd seen on Lalonde; their feathers were almost like membrane scales. When he scanned it with his retinal implant on high magnification he could see it had real feathers, Earth genealogy feathers.

He gave the hand signal, and they advanced steadily through the bush, Jackson Gael on one side of him, Lawrence Dillon on the other. Lawrence was the youngest Ivet, seventeen, with a slim figure, skinny limbs, and sandy blond hair. Lawrence was a gift from God's Brother. It had taken Quinn a month to break him. There had been the favouritism, the extra food, the smiles and making sure he wasn't bullied by the others. Then there had been the drugs Quinn had bought from Baxter, the gentle lifts which removed Aberdale and all its squalor and endless toil, blurring away the edges until life was easier again. The midnight rape performed in the middle of the A-frame with everybody watching; Lawrence tied to the floor with a pentagon drawn around him in danderil blood, his mind blown out of his skull by the drugs. Now Lawrence belonged to him, his sweet arse, the golden length of his dick, and his mind. Lawrence's devotion to Quinn had evolved to a form of worship.

Sex showed the others the power Quinn had. It showed them how in touch with God's Brother he was. It showed them the glory of freeing the serpent beast that was trapped in every man's heart. It showed them what would happen if they failed him.

He had given them hope and power. All he demanded in return was obedience.

Demanded and received.

The big spongy leaves of the vines which shrouded the trees brushed lightly against Quinn's damp skin as he advanced on his prey. After months of working under the brilliant sun he was a rich all-over brown, wearing just a pair of shorts cut from his jump suit, and the boots he'd stolen in Durringham. He'd eaten well since the Ivets started fending for themselves, and put on muscle weight from the work he'd done around the homesteads.

Creepers were hung between the trunks like a net the jungle had woven to catch its smaller denizens. They crackled annoyingly as he waded through them, booted feet crunching on the spindly mosslike grass that grew deep in the jungle. Birds clucked and squawked as they arrowed through the latticework of branches. He could see the distant movement of vennals high overhead, spiralling round trunks and branches like three-dimensional shadows.

The light filtering down through the leaf canopy was growing darker. He spotted an increasing number of young giganteas interspaced with the usual trees. They resembled elongated cones, with an outer coating of mauve-brown fibrous hair rather than a true bark. Their boughs emerged in rings from the trunk, spaced regularly up the entire length; they all sloped downwards at a fifty-degree angle, supporting fanlike arrangements of twigs, densely packed as birds' nests. Leaves grew on the upper surface like a dark green fur.

The first time Quinn had seen a mature gigantea he thought he must have been tripping. It stood two hundred and thirty metres high, with a base forty-five metres in diameter, rearing out of the jungle like a misplaced mountain. Creepers and vines had wrapped themselves around its lower branches, adding a colourful speckle of multi-coloured flowers to its uninspiring leaden-green leaves. But even the vigorous vines couldn't hope to challenge a gigantea.

Jackson clicked his fingers, and pointed ahead. Quinn risked raising his head above the shoulder-high rall bushes and spindly light-starved saplings.

The sayce they had been tracking was padding through the skimpy undergrowth ten metres away. It was a big specimen, a buck, its black hide scarred and flecked with blue spots, ears chewed down to stubs. It had been in a lot of fights, and won them.

Quinn smiled happily, and signalled Lawrence forwards. Jackson stayed where he was, sighting the laser rifle on the sayce's head. Back-up, in case their attack went wrong.

The hunt had taken a while to set up. There were thirty of Aberdale's residents spread out through the jungle today, but they were all nearer to the river. Quinn, Jackson, and Lawrence had made off south-west into the deeper jungle as soon as they could, away from the river and its humidity, into the country where the sayce lurked. Powel Manani had ridden off at dawn to help one of the savannah homesteads track down the sheep that had wandered off after their stockade had failed. Most importantly, he'd taken Vorix with him to find the scent. Irley had arranged for the stockade fence to fail last night.

Quinn put down the pump-action shotgun he'd bought from Baxter, and took the bolas from his belt. He started spinning it above his head, letting out a fearsome yell. To his right Lawrence was running towards the sayce, his bolas whirling frantically. Nobody knew the Ivets used bolas. The weapon was simple enough to build, all they needed was the dried vine to link the three stones with. They could carry the vine lengths about quite openly, using them as belts.

The sayce turned, its jaws hinging wide to let out its peculiar keening cry. It charged straight at Lawrence. The boy let the bolas fly, yelling with adrenalin intoxication, and it caught the sayce on its forelegs, stones twisting in evershorter arcs with incredible speed. Quinn's whirled around the animal's right flank a second later, tangling one of the hind legs. The sayce fell, skidding through the grass and loam, its body bucking in epileptic frenzy.

Quinn ran forward, tugging the lasso off his shoulder. The sayce was thrashing about, howling, trying to get its razor-sharp teeth into the infuriating vine strands binding its legs. He twisted the lasso, working up a good speed, studying the sayce's movements, then threw.

The sayce's jaws shut between cries, and the lasso's loop slipped over the muzzle. He jerked back with all his strength. The jaws strained to open, but the loop held; it was silicon fibre, stolen from one of the homesteads. All three Ivets could hear the furious and increasingly frantic cries, muted to a harsh sneezing sound.

Lawrence landed heavily on the writhing sayce, struggling to shove its kicking hind legs into his own loop of rope. Quinn joined him, hugging the sayce's thick gnarled hide as he fought to coil another length of rope round the forelegs.

It took another three minutes to subdue and bind the sayce completely. Quinn and Lawrence wrestled with it on the ground, getting covered in scratches and mud. But eventually they stood, bruised and shaking from the effort, looking down at their trussed victim lying helplessly on its side. Its green-tinted eye glared back up at them.

"Stage two," said Quinn.

It was Jay who found Horst late in the afternoon. He was sitting slumped against a qualtook tree in the light drizzle, virtually comatose. She giggled at how silly he was being and shook him by the shoulder. Horst mumbled incoherently then told her to piss off.

Jay stared at him for a mortified second, her lower lip trembling, then rushed to get her mother.

"Ho boy, look at you," Ruth said when she arrived.

Horst burped.

"Come on, get up. I'll help you get home."

The weight of him nearly cracked her spine as he leant against her. With a solemn-faced Jay following a couple of paces behind they staggered across the clearing to the little cabin Horst used.

Ruth let him fall onto his cot, and watched impassively as he tried to vomit onto the duckboard floor. All that came out of his mouth was a few beads of sour yellow stomach juices.

Jay stood in a corner and clutched at Drusilla, her white rabbit. The doe squirmed around in agitation. "Is he going to be all right?"

"Yes," Ruth said.

"I thought it was a heart attack."

"No. He's been drinking."

"But he's a priest," the girl insisted.

Ruth stroked her daughter's hair. "I know, darling. But that doesn't mean they're saints."

Jay nodded wisely. "I see. I won't tell anyone."

Ruth turned and stared at Horst. "Why did you do it, Horst? Why now? You'd been doing so well."

Bloodshot eyes blinked at her. "Evil," he groaned. "They're evil."

"Who are?"

"Ivets. All of them. Devil's children. Burn down the church. Can't consecrate it now. They built it. Evil built it. Herit— here— heretical. Burn it to cinders."

"Horst, you're not setting fire to anything."

"Evil!" he slurred.

"See if there's enough charge in his electron matrix cells to power the microwave," Ruth told Jay. "We'll boil some water." She started to rummage through Horst's gear looking for his silver-foil sachets of coffee.

Right up until the moment the electric motors began to thrum, Marie Skibbow hadn't believed it was actually happening. But here it was, bubbles rising from the *Coogan*'s propeller, the gap between the boat and the jetty growing.

"I've done it," she said under her breath.

The ramshackle boat began to chug its way out into the middle of the Quallheim, the prow pointing downriver, gradually picking up speed. She stopped dropping logs into the thermal-exchange furnace's square hopper-funnel and started to laugh. "Screw you," she told the village as it began to slide astern. "Screw all of you. And good fucking riddance. You won't ever see me again." She shook her fist at them. Nobody was looking, not even the Ivet lads in the water. "Never ever."

Aberdale disappeared from sight as they steered round a curve. Her laughter became suspiciously similar to weeping. She heard someone making their way aft from the wheel-house, and started lobbing logs into the hopper again.

It was Gail Buchannan, who barely fitted on the narrow strip of decking between the cabin and the half-metre-high gunwale. She wheezed heavily for a moment, leaning against the cabin wall, her face red and sweating below her coolie hat. "Happier now, lovie?"

"Much!" Marie beamed a sunlight smile.

"It's not the kind of place a girlie like you should be living in. You'll be much better off downriver."

"You don't have to tell me. God, it was awful. I hated it. I hate animals, I hate vegetables, I hate fruit trees, I hate the jungle. I hate wood!"

"You're not going to be trouble for us are you, lovie?"

"Oh no, I promise. I never signed a settlement contract with the LDC, I was still legally a minor when we left Earth. But I'm over eighteen now, so I can leave home any time I want to."

A nonplussed frown creased the folds of spare flesh on Gail's gibbous face for a second. "Aye, well you can stop loading the hopper now, there's enough logs in there to last the rest of today. We're only sailing for a couple of hours. Lennie'll moor somewhere below Schuster for the night."

"Right." Marie stood up straight, hands pressed against her side. Her heart was racing, pounding away against her ribs. I did it!

"You can start preparing supper in a while," Gail said.

"Yes, of course."

"I expect you'd like a shower first, lovie. Get cleaned up a bit."

"A shower?" Marie thought she'd misheard.

She hadn't. It was in the cabin between the galley and the bunks, an alcove with a curtain across the front, broad enough to fit Gail. When she looked down, Marie could see the river through the gaps between the deck boards. The pump and the heater ran off electricity from the thermal-exchange furnace, producing a weak warm spray from the copper nozzle. To Marie it was more luxurious than a sybarite's jacuzzi. She hadn't had a shower since her last day on Earth. Dirt was something you lived with in Aberdale and the savannah homesteads. It got into the pores, under nails, scaled your hair. And it never came out, not completely. Not in cold stream water, not without decent soap and gels.

The first sluice of water from the nozzle disgusted her as it drained away. It was *filthy*. But Gail had given her a bar of unperfumed green soap, and a bottle of liquid soap for her hair. Marie started scrubbing with a vengeance, singing at the top of her voice.

Gwyn Lawes never even knew the Ivets were there until the club smashed into the small of his back. He blacked out for a while from the pain. Certainly he didn't remember falling. One minute he was lining up his electromagnetic rifle on a danderil, anticipating the praise he would earn from the rest of the hunting party. And the next thing he knew was that there was loam in his mouth, he could barely breathe, and his spine was sheer agony. All he could do was retch weakly.

Hands grabbed his shoulders, and he was turned over. Another blast of fire shot up his spine. The world shuddered nauseously.

Quinn, Lawrence, and Jackson were standing above him,

grinning broadly. They were smothered in mud, hair hanging in soiled dreadlocks, spittle saturating their tufty beards, scratches bleeding, dribbles of red blood curdling with the mud. They were savages reincarnated out of Earth's dawn times. He whimpered in fright.

Jackson bent down, teeth bared with venomous joy. A ball of cloth was thrust into Gwyn's mouth, tied into place with a gag. Breathing became even harder, his nose flaring, sucking down precious oxygen. Then he was turned again, face pressed into the wet ground. All he could see was muddy grass. He could feel thin, hard cord binding his wrists and ankles. Hands began to search him, sliding into every pocket, patting the fabric. There was a hesitant fumble when fingers found the inside leg pouch on his dungarees trousers, tracing the shape of his precious Jovian Bank credit disk.

"Got it, Quinn," Lawrence's voice called triumphantly.

Fingers gripped Gwyn's right thumb, bending it back.

"Pattern copied," Quinn said. "Let's see what he's got." There was a short pause, then a whistle. "Four thousand three hundred fuseodollars. Hey, Gwyn, where's your faith in your new planet?"

Cruel laughter followed.

"OK, it's transferred. Lawrence, put it back where you found it. They can't activate it once he's dead, they'll never know it's been emptied."

Dead. The word cut through Gwyn's sluggish thoughts. He groaned, trying to lift himself. A boot slammed into his ribs. He screamed, or tried to. The gag was virtually suffocating him.

"He's got some handy gear here, Quinn," Lawrence said. "Fission knife, firelighter, and that's a personal guido block. Spare power mags for the rifle, too."

"Leave it," Quinn ordered. "If anything's missing when they find him, they might get suspicious. We can't afford that, not yet. It will all belong to us in the end."

They lifted Gwyn, carrying him on their shoulders like some kind of trophy. He kept drifting in and out of consciousness as he jounced about, twigs and vines slapping against him.

The light was darker when they finally slung him down. Gwyn looked about, and saw the smooth ebony trunk of an old deirar tree twenty metres away, its single giant umbrella-leaf casting a wide circular shadow. A sayce had been tethered to it, straining at the unbreakable silicon-fibre rope, forelegs scrabbling at the loam as it tried to reach its captors, its snapping jaws dripping long chains of saliva. Gwyn suddenly knew what was going to happen next. His bladder gave out.

"Get it riled good and proper," Quinn ordered.

Jackson and Lawrence started throwing stones at the sayce. It keened in torment, its body jacking about as though an electric current was being run through it.

Gwyn saw a pair of boots appear twenty centimetres from his nose. Quinn squatted down. "Know what's going to happen afterwards, Gwyn? We're going to be assigned to help out your widow. Everyone else is busy with their own little plots of heaven. So it'll be the Ivets who get dumped on. Once again. I'm going to be one of them, Gwyn. I'm going to be a regular visitor to poor, grieving Rachel. She'll like me, I'll make sure of that. Just like you and all the others, you want to believe that everything's so perfect on this planet. You convinced yourselves we're just a bunch of regular lads who got a bad break in life. Anything else would have cracked your dream open and made you face reality. Illusion is easy. Illusion is the loser's way out. Your way. You and all the others grubbing round in the dirt and the rain. In a couple of months I'll be in the bed you made, under the roof you sweated over, and I'll have my dick rammed up inside Rachel making her squeal like a pig in heat. I hope you hate that idea, Gwyn. I hope it makes you sick inside. Because that's not the worst. Oh, no. Once I'm through with her, I'll have Jason. Your shiny-eyed beautiful son. I'll be his new father. I'll be his lover. I'll be his owner. He'll be joining us, Gwyn, me and the Ivets. I'll bind him to the Night, I'll show him where his serpent beast is hidden within. He's not going to be a dickhead loser like his old man. You're only the first, Gwyn. One by one I will come to you all, and very few will be given the chance to follow me into darkness. Inside of six months this whole

village, the only hope for a future you ever had, will belong
to God's Brother.

"Do you despise me, Gwyn? I want you to. I want you to
hate me as much as I hate you and all you stand for. Then
you will understand that I'm speaking the truth. You will go
to your pitiful Lord Jesus weeping in terror. And you will
find no comfort there, because the Light Bringer will be the
ultimate victor. You will lose in death, as you have lost in
life. You made the wrong choice in life, Gwyn. My path is
the one you should have walked. And now it's too late."

Gwyn strained and wheezed against the gag until he
thought his lungs would burst from the effort. It made no
difference, the shriek of hatred and all the threats, the
curses condemning Quinn to an eternity of damnation, were
left jailed inside his skull.

Quinn's hands curled round the lapels of Gwyn's shirt,
hauling him upright. Jackson took his feet, and the two of
them swung him back and forth, building momentum. They
let go, and Gwyn's tumbling body flew in a shallow trajectory right over the top of the berserk sayce. He hit the loam
with a dull thud, face contorted with insane dread. The
sayce leapt.

Quinn put his arms round the shoulders of Lawrence and
Jackson as the three of them watched the sayce mauling the
man, its teeth tearing out great strips of flesh. The power to
bring death was equal to that of bringing about life. He felt
enraptured as the hot scarlet blood flowed into the soil.

"After life, death," he chanted. "After darkness, light."

He looked up, and stared round until he found the brown
bird. It was perched up in a cherry oak's branches, head
cocked on one side, observing the carnage.

"You've seen what we are," Quinn called out. "You've
seen us naked. You've seen we're not afraid. We should
talk. I think we have a lot to offer each other. What have
you got to lose?"

The bird blinked as if in surprise, and launched itself into
the air.

Laton let the kestrel's wonderfully clear sensorium fade
from his mind. The sensation of air flowing over wings re-

mained for several minutes. Flying the predator via affinity was always an experience he enjoyed, the freedom granted to creatures of the air was unsurpassed.

The ordinary world rushed back in on him.

He was in his study, sitting in the lotus position on a black velvet cushion. It was an unusual room, an ovoid, five metres high, its curving walls a smooth polished wood. A cluster of electrophorescent cells were fitted flush with the apex, supplying a glimmer of jade light. The single cushion on the cup of the floor was the only thing to break the symmetry; even the door was hard to see, its lines blending with the grain.

The study possessed a unifying simplicity, freeing his mind of distractions. In here, his body motionless, his affinity expanding his consciousness through bitek processors and incorporated brains, his mentality was raised by an order of magnitude. It was a hint of what could be. A pale shadow of the goal he chased before his exile.

Laton remained sitting, thinking about Quinn Dexter and the atrocity he had perpetrated. There had been a lurid flash of gratification in Dexter's eyes as that helpless colonist had been thrown to the sayce. Yet he must be more than a brainless sadistic brute. The fact that he had recognized the kestrel for what it was, and worked out what it represented, was proof of that.

Who is God's Brother? Laton asked the house's subsentient bitek processor network.

Satan. The Christian devil.

Is this a term in wide use?

The term is common among Earth's waster population. Most arcologies have sects built up around the worship of this deity. Their priest/acolyte hierarchy is a simple variant on that of the more standard officer/soldier criminal organization. Those at the top control those at the bottom through a quasi-religious doctrine, and status is enforced by initiation rituals. Their theology states that after Armageddon has been fought, and the universe abandoned to lost souls, Satan will return bringing light. The sects are unusual only in the degree of violence involved to maintain discipline among the

ranks. Because of the level of devotion involved, the authorities have been generally unsuccessful in eradicating the sects.

That explains Quinn, then, Laton thought to himself. But why did he want the money in the colonist's Jovian Bank credit disk? If he was successful in taking over Aberdale no trading boat would ever stop there; he couldn't buy anything. In fact, the Governor would be more than likely to send in a posse of sheriffs and deputies to stamp out any Ivet rebellion as soon as word leaked out. Quinn must know that, he wasn't stupid.

The last thing Laton wanted was for the outside world to show an interest in Schuster County. One marshal digging around was an acceptable risk, he'd known that when he took the colonists from their homesteads. But a whole team of them scouting through the jungle in search of renegade Devil worshippers was totally out of the question.

He had to know more of Quinn Dexter's plans. They would have to meet, just like Quinn had suggested. Somehow the idea of agreeing to his proposition was vaguely disturbing.

The *Coogan* was moored against a small sandy spit an hour's sailing downriver from Schuster town. Two silicon-fibre ropes had been fastened to trees on the shore, holding the tramp trader secure against the current.

Marie Skibbow sat on the prow, letting the warm evening air dry the last traces of water from her hair. Even the humidity had fallen off. Rennison, Lalonde's largest moon, was rising slowly above the dusky-grey treetops, adding a glimmering oyster light to the gloaming. She sat back against the flimsy cabin wall and watched it contentedly.

Water lapped gently against the *Coogan*'s twin hulls. Fish made occasional ripples on the glass-smooth surface.

They've probably realized I've gone by now. Mother will cry, and Father will explode; Frank won't care, and Paula will be sad. They'll all worry about how it will affect them and the animals not having an extra hand at their beck and call all day long. Not one of them will think about what I want, what's good for me.

She heard Gail Buchannan calling, and made her way back to the wheel-house.

"We thought you'd fallen overboard, lovie," Gail said. A splash of light from the galley shone out, showing the sweat beading on her blubbery arms. At supper she had eaten more than half of all the food Marie prepared for the three of them.

"No. I was watching the moon come up."

Gail gave her a lopsided wink. "Very romantic. Get you in the mood."

Marie felt the hairs on the nape of her neck rising. She was cold despite the jungle's breath.

"I've got your night clothes ready," Gail said.

"Night clothes?"

"Very pretty. I did the lacework myself. Len likes his brides to have frills. You won't find better this side of Durringham," she said generously. "That T-shirt's nice and tight. But it hardly flatters your figure, now does it?"

"I paid you," Marie said in a frail voice. "All the way to Durringham."

"That won't cover our costs, lovie. We told you, it's expensive travelling this river. You have to work your passage."

"No."

There was nothing of the bumptious nature left in the huge woman. "We can put you off. Right here."

Marie shook her head. "I can't."

"Course you can. Pretty girl like you." Gail wrapped a weighty hand around Marie's forearm. "Come on, lovie," she coaxed. "Old Lennie, he knows how to treat his brides right."

Marie put one foot forward.

"That's it, lovie. Down you come. It's all laid out here, look."

There was a white cotton negligee on the galley table. Gail led her over to it. "You just slip this on. And don't let's hear any more silly talk about can't." She held it up against Marie. "Oh, you're going to look a picture in this, aren't you?"

She glanced down numbly at it.

"Aren't you?" Gail Buchannan repeated.

"Yes."

"Good girl. Now put it on."

"Where?"

"Here, lovie. Right here."

Marie turned her back to the gross woman, and began to pull her T-shirt off over her head.

Gail chortled thickly. "Oh, you're a one, lovie, you really are. This is going to be a chuckle."

The negligée's hem barely came below Marie's buttocks, but if she tried to pull it down any further her breasts would fall out of the top. She had felt cleaner when she was covered in dirt from the jungle.

Still chortling, and giving her little nudges in her back, Gail followed her into the cabin where Len was waiting dressed in an amber towelling robe. A single electric lamp hanging on the ceiling cast a halo of yellow light. Len's mouth split in a jagged smile as he took in the sight of her.

Gail sank down onto a sturdy stool by the door, puffing in relief. "There now, don't you worry about me, lovie, I only ever watch."

Marie thought that perhaps with the sound of the lapping water and the close wooden walls she could pretend it was Karl and the *Swithland* again.

She couldn't.

The Ly-cilph had been travelling for over five billion years when it arrived at the galaxy which was home to the Confederation, although at that time it was the dinosaurs which were Earth's premier life-form. Half of its existence had been spent traversing intergalactic space. It knew how to slip through the wormhole interstices; a creature of energy, the physical structure of the cosmos was no mystery to it. But its nature was to observe and record, so it sped along at a velocity just short of lightspeed, extending its perceptive field around the outcast hydrogen atoms on their aeons-long fall towards the bright, distant star whorls. Each one was unique, an existence to be treasured, extending the knowledge base, its history placed in the transdimensional storage lattice which provided the Ly-cilph with its identity focus. The Ly-cilph was the section of space through which it passed with less disturbance than a neutrino. Like a quantum black hole, it had almost no physical size, yet within was an entire universe. A carefully patterned universe of pure data.

After it arrived at the rim stars it spent millions of years drifting among them, categorizing the life-forms which rose and fell on their planets, indexing the physical parameters of the multitudinous solar systems. It witnessed interstellar empires that bloomed and failed, and planet-bound civilizations that were lost to the final night as their stars cooled to frozen iron. Saint-like cultures and the most bestial savagery; all clicking neatly into place within its infinite interior.

It progressed inwards on a loose line towards the scintillating glow of the galactic core. And in doing so, arrived at the volume of space populated by the Confederation. Lalonde, freshly discovered, and on the edge of the territory, was the first human world it encountered.

The Ly-cilph arrived at the star's Oort cloud in 2610. After it passed through the band of circling, sleeping comets, occasional laser and microwave emissions impinged on its perception field boundary. They were weak, random fragments of overspill from the communication beams of starships entering orbit above Lalonde.

A preliminary survey showed the Ly-cilph two centres of sentient life in the solar system: Lalonde itself with the human and Tyrathca settlers, and Aethra, the young Edenist habitat in its solitary orbit above Murora.

As always in cases of life discovery, it first performed analytical sweeps of the barren planets. The four inner worlds: sunblasted Calcott and the colossal Gatley with its immense lethal atmosphere, then skipping past Lalonde to review airless Plewis and the icy Mars-like Coum. The five gas giants followed, Murora, Bullus, Achillea, Tol, and distant Puschk with its strange cryochemistry. All of them had their own moon systems and individual milieux requiring examination. The Ly-cilph took fifteen months to classify their composition and environment, then swooped in towards Lalonde.

The search through the jungle took eight hours. Three-quarters of Aberdale's adult population turned out to help. They found Gwyn Lawes fifteen minutes after Rennison had set below the horizon. Most of him.

Because it was a sayce which had killed him; because the ropes had been taken off his wrists and ankles, and the gag removed from his mouth; because his electromagnetic rifle and all his other possessions were accounted for, everyone accepted it was a natural, if horrible, death.

It was the Ivets who were assigned to dig the grave.

10

The *Udat* slid over the surface of Tranquillity's non-rotating spaceport as though it was running on an invisible wire. A honeycomb of deep docking-bays flashed past below the blue and purple hull; the spherical fuselages of Adamist starships nested inside, glinting dully under the rim floodlights. Meyer watched through the blackhawk's sensors as a fifty-five-metre-diameter clipper-class starship manoeuvred itself onto a cradle that had risen out of a bay, orange balls of chemical flame spitting out of its vernier nozzles. He could see the ubiquitous intersecting violet and green loops of the Vasilkovsky Line bold across the forward quarter. It touched the cradle, and pistonlike latches engaged, slipping into sockets around the hull. Umbilical gantries swung round, plugging it into the spaceport's coolant and environmental circuits. The starship's thermo-dump panels retracted, and the cradle started to descend into the bay.

So much effort just to arrive, *Udat* observed.

Quiet down, you'll hurt people's feelings, Meyer told it fondly.

I wish there were more ships like me. Your race should stop clinging to the past. These mechanical ships belong in a museum.

My race, is it? There are human chromosomes in you, don't forget.

Are you sure?

I think I accessed it in a memory core somewhere. There are in voidhawks.

Oh. Them.

Meyer grinned at the overtone of disparagement. **I thought you liked voidhawks.**

Some of them are all right. But they think like their captains.

And how do voidhawk captains think?

They don't like blackhawks. They think we're trouble.

We have been known.

Only when money is short, *Udat* said, gently reproachful.

And if there were more blackhawks and fewer Adamist starships, money would be even tighter. I have wages to pay.

At least we've paid off the mortgage you took out to buy me.

Yes. And there's money to save to buy another when you're gone. But he didn't let that thought filter out of his mind. *Udat* was fifty-seven now; seventy-five to eighty was the usual blackhawk lifespan. Meyer wasn't at all convinced he would want another ship after *Udat*. But there was a quarter of a century of togetherness to look forward to yet, and money wasn't such a problem these days. There was only life-support-section maintenance and the four crew members to pay for. He could afford to pick and choose his charters now. Not like the first twenty years. Now those had been wild days. Fortunately the power compressed into the big asymmetric teardrop shape of *Udat*'s hull gave them a terrific speed and agility. They had needed it on occasion. Some of the more covert missions had been hazardous in the extreme. Not all their colleagues had returned.

I'd still like more of my own kind to talk to, *Udat* said.

Do you talk to Tranquillity?

Oh, yes, all the time. We're good friends.

What do you talk about?

I show it places we visit. And it shows me its interior, what humans get up to.

Really?

Yes, it's interesting. This Joshua Calvert who chartered us, Tranquillity says he's a recidivist of the worst kind.

Tranquillity is absolutely right. That's why I like Joshua so much. He reminds me of me at that age.

No. You were never that bad.

Udat's nose turned slightly, gliding delicately between two designated traffic streams congested with He3 tankers and personnel commuters. The bays in this section of the mammoth spaceport disk were larger, it was where the repairs and maintenance work was carried out. Only half of them were occupied.

The big blackhawk came to a halt directly over bay MB 0-330, then slowly rotated around its long axis so that its upper hull was pointing down over the rim. Unlike voidhawks, with their separate lower hull cargo hold and upper hull crew toroid, *Udat* had all its mechanical sections contained in a horseshoe which embraced its dorsal bulge. The bridge and individual crew cabins were at the front, with the two cargo holds occupying the wings, and an ion-field flyer stored in a small hangar on the port side.

Cherri Barnes walked into the bridge compartment. She was *Udat*'s cargo officer, doubling as a systems generalist: forty-five years old, with light coffee skin and a wide face prone to contemplative pouts. She had been with Meyer for three years.

She datavised a series of orders into her console processors, receiving images fed from the electronic sensors mounted on the hull. The three-dimensional picture which built up in her mind showed her *Udat* hanging poised thirty metres over the repair bay, holding its position steady.

"Over to you," Meyer said.

"Thanks." She opened a channel to the bay's datanet. "MB 0-330, this is *Udat*. We have your cargo paid for and waiting. Ready for your unload instructions. How do you want to handle it, Joshua? Time is money."

"Cherri, is that you?" Joshua datavised back.

"No one else on board will lower themselves to talk to you."

"I wasn't expecting you for another week, you've made good time."

Meyer datavised an access order into his console. "You hire the best ship, you get the best time."

"I'll remember that," Joshua told him. "Next time I have some money I'll make sure I go for a decent ship."

"We can always take our nodes elsewhere, Mr Hotshot Starship Captain who's never been outside the Ruin Ring."

"My nodes, genetic throwback who's too scared to go in the Ruin Ring and earn a living."

"It's not the Ruin Ring which worries me, it's what the Lord of Ruin does to people who skip outsystem before they register their finds in Tranquillity."

There was an unusually long pause. Meyer and Cherri shared a bemused glance.

"I'll send Ashly out with the *Lady Mac*'s MSV to pick up the nodes," Joshua said. "And you're all invited to the party tonight."

"So this is the famous *Lady Macbeth*?" Meyer asked a couple of hours later. He was in bay 0–330's cramped control centre with Joshua, his left foot anchored by a stikpad, looking out through the glass bubble wall into the bay itself. The fifty-seven-metre ship resting on the cradle in the middle of the floor was naked to space. Its hull plates had been stripped off, exposing the systems and tanks and engines, fantastically complex silver and white entrails. They were all contained inside a hexagonal-lattice stress structure. Jump nodes were positioned over each junction. Red and green striped superconductor cabling wormed inwards from each node, plugged directly into the ship's fusion generators. Meyer hadn't thought about it before, but the lenticular nodes were almost identical to the voidhawk profile.

Engineers wearing black SII suits and manoeuvring packs were propelling themselves over the open stress structure, running tests and replacing components. Others rode platforms on the end of multi-segment arms which were fitted out with heavy tools to handle the larger systems. Yellow strobes flashed on all the bay's mobile equipment, sending sharp-edged amber circles slicing over every surface in crazy gyrating patterns.

Hundreds of data cables were stretched between the ship and the five interface couplings around the base of the cradle. It was almost as though *Lady Macbeth* was being tethered down by a net of optical fibres. A two-metre-diameter airlock tube had concertinaed out from the bay wall, just below the control centre, giving the maintenance team access to the life-support capsules buried at the core of the ship. Brackets on the bay walls held various systems waiting to be installed. Meyer couldn't see where they could possibly fit. *Lady Macbeth*'s spaceplane clung to one wall like a giant supersonic moth, wings in their forward-sweep position. The additional tanks and power cells Joshua had strapped on for flights to the Ruin Ring were gone; a couple of suited figures and a cyberdrone were trying to remove the thick foam from the fuselage with a solvent spray. Crumbling grey flakes were flying off in all directions.

"What were you expecting?" Joshua asked. "A Saturn V?" He was strapped into a restraint web behind a cyberdrone operations console. The boxy drones ran along the rails which spiralled up the bay walls, giving them access to any part of the docked ship. Three of them were currently clustered round an auxiliary fusion generator, which was being eased into its mountings at the end of long white waldo arms. Engineers floated around it, supervising the cyberdrones which were performing the installation, mating cables, coolant lines, and fuel hoses. Joshua monitored their progress through the omnidirectional AV projectors arrayed around his console.

"More like a battle cruiser," Meyer said. "I saw the power ratings on those nodes, Joshua. You could jump fifteen light-years with those brutes fully charged."

"Something like that," he said absently.

Meyer grunted, and turned back to the starship. The MSV was returning from another trip to *Udat*, a pale green oblong box three metres long with small spherical tanks bunched together on the base, and three segmented waldo arms ending in complex manipulators sprouting from the mid-fuselage section. It was carrying a packaged node, coasting down towards one of the engineering shop airlocks.

Cherri Barnes frowned, peering forwards into the bay. "How many reaction drives has she got?" she asked. There seemed an inordinate number of unbilicals jacked into the *Lady Macbeth*'s rear quarter. She could see a pair of fusion tubes resting in the wall brackets, fat ten-metre cylinders swathed with magnetic coils, ion-beam injectors, and molecular-binding initiators.

Joshua turned his head fractionally, switching AV projectors. The new pillar shot a barrage of photons along his optical nerves, giving him a different angle on the auxiliary fusion generator. He studied it for a while, then datavised an instruction into one of the cyberdrones. "Four main drives."

"Four?" Adamist ships usually had one fusion drive, with a couple of induction engines running off the generator as an emergency back-up.

"Yeah. Three fusion tubes, and an antimatter drive."

"You can't be serious," Cherri Barnes exclaimed. "That's a capital offence!"

"Wrong!"

Joshua and Meyer both grinned at her, infuriatingly superior. There were smiles from the other five console operators in the control centre.

"It's a capital offence to *possess* antimatter," Joshua said. "But there's nothing in the Confederation space law about possessing an engine which uses antimatter. As long as you don't fill up the confinement chambers and use it, you're fine."

"Bloody hell."

"It makes you very popular when there's a war on. You can write your own ticket. Or so I'm told."

"I bet you've got a real powerful communication maser as well. One that can punch a message clean through another starship's hull."

"No, actually. *Lady Mac* has eight. Dad was a real stickler for multiple redundancy."

Harkey's Bar was on the thirty-first floor of the StMartha starscraper. There was a real band on the tiny stage, churning out scarr jazz, fractured melodies with wailing trumpets. A fifteen-metre bar made from real oak that Harkey swore blind came from a twenty-second-century Paris brothel, serving thirty-eight kinds of beer, and three times that number of spirits, including Norfolk Tears for those who could afford it. It had wall booths that could be screened from casual observation, a dance floor, long party tables, lighting globes emitting photons right down at the bottom of the yellow spectrum. And Harkey prided himself on its food, prepared by a chef who claimed he had worked in the royal kitchens of Kulu's Jerez Principality. The waitresses were young, pretty, and wore revealing black dresses.

With its ritzy atmosphere, and not too expensive drinks, it attracted a lot of the crews from ships docked at Tranquillity's port. Most nights saw a good crowd. Joshua had always used it. First when he was a cocky teenager looking for his nightly fix of spaceflight tales, then when he was scavenging, lying about how much he made and the unbelievable find that had just slipped from his fingers, and now as one of the super-elite, a starship owner-captain, one of the youngest ever.

"I don't know what kind of crap that foam is which you sprayed on the spaceplane, Joshua, but the bloody stuff just won't come off," Warlow complained bitterly.

When Warlow spoke everybody listened. You couldn't avoid it, not within an eight-metre radius. He was a cosmonik, born on an industrial asteroid settlement. He had spent over sixty-five per cent of his seventy-two years in free fall, and he didn't have the kind of geneering bequeathed to Joshua and the Edenists by their ancestors. After a while his organs had begun to degenerate, depleted calcium levels had reduced his bones to brittle porcelain sticks, muscles had atrophied, and fluid bloated his tissues, impairing his lungs, degrading his lymphatic system. He had used drugs and nanonic supplements to compensate at first, then supplements became replacements, with bones exchanged for carbon-fibre struts. Electrical consumption supplanted food intake. The final transition was his skin, replacing the eczema-ridden epidermis with a smooth ochre silicon membrane. Warlow didn't need a spacesuit to work in the vacuum, he could survive for over three weeks without a power and oxygen recharge. His facial features had become purely cosmetic, a crude mannequin-like caricature of human physiognomy, although there was an inlet valve at the back of his throat for fluid intake. There was no hair, and he certainly didn't bother with clothes. Sex was something he lost in his fifties.

Although some cosmoniks had metamorphosed into little more than free-flying maintenance craft with a brain at the centre, Warlow had kept his humanoid shape. The only noticeable adaptation was his arms; they forked at each elbow, giving him two pairs of forearms. One set retained the basic hand and finger layout, the other set ended in titanium sockets, capable of accepting a variety of rigger tools.

Joshua grinned and raised his champagne glass at the sleek-skinned two-metre-tall gargoyle dominating the table. "That's why I put you on it. If anybody can scrape it off, you can." He counted himself lucky to get Warlow on his crew. Some captains rejected him for his age, Joshua welcomed him for his experience.

"You should get Ashly to fly it on a bypass trajectory that grazes Mirchusko's atmosphere. Burn it off like an ablative. One zip and it's all gone." Warlow's primary left forearm came down, palm slapping the table. Glasses and bottles juddered.

"Alternatively, you could plug a pump in your belly, and use your arse as a vacuum cleaner," Ashly Hanson said. "Suck it off." His cheeks caved in as he made a slurping sound.

The pilot was a tall sixty-seven-year-old, whom geneering had given a compact frame, floppy brown hair, and a ten-year-old's wonderstruck smile. The whole universe was a constant delight for him. He lived for his skill, moving tonnes of metal through any atmosphere with avian grace. His Confederation Astronautics Board licence said he was qualified for both air and space operations, but it was three hundred and twenty years out of date. Ashly Hanson was temporally displaced; born into reasonable wealth, he had signed over his trust fund to the Jovian Bank in 2229 in exchange for a secure zero-tau pod maintenance contract (even then the Edenists had been the obvious choice as custodians). He alternated fifty years in entropy-free stasis, and five years "bumming round" the Confederation.

"I'm a futurologist," he told Joshua the first time they met. "On a one-way ride to eternity. I just get out of my time machine for a look round every now and then."

Joshua had signed him on as much for the tales he could tell as his piloting ability.

"We'll just remove the foam according to the manual, thanks," he told the bickering pair.

The vocal synthesizer diaphragm protruding from Warlow's chest, just above his air-inlet gills, let out a metallic sigh. He shoved his squeezy bulb into his mouth and squirted some champagne into the valve. Drink was one thing he wasn't giving up, although with his blood filters he could sober up with astonishing speed if he had to.

Meyer leant across the table. "Any word on Neeves and Sipika yet?" he asked Joshua quietly.

"Yeah. I forgot, you wouldn't know. They arrived back in port a couple of days after you left for Earth. They bloody nearly got lynched. The serjeants had to rescue them. They're in jail, waiting judicial pronouncement."

Meyer frowned. "Why the wait? I thought Tranquillity processed the charges right away?"

"There's a lot of bereaved relatives of scavengers who never came back who are claiming Neeves and Sipika are responsible. Then there's the question of compensation. The *Madeeir* is still worth a million and a half fuseodollars even after my axe work. I waived my claim, but I suppose the families are entitled."

Meyer took another sip. "Nasty business."

"There's talk about fitting emergency beacons to all the scavenger craft, making it an official requirement."

"They'll never go for that, they're too independent."

"Yeah, well, I'm out of it now."

"Too true," Kelly Tirrel said. She was sitting pressed up next to Joshua, one leg hooked over his, arm draped around his shoulders.

It was a position he found extremely comfortable. Kelly was wearing an amethyst dress with a broad square-cut neckline which showed off her figure, especially from his angle. She was twenty-four, slightly shorter than medium build, with red-brown hair and a delicate face. For the last couple of years she had been a rover correspondent for Tranquillity's office of the Collins news group.

They had met eighteen months earlier when she was

doing a piece on scavengers for distribution across the Confederation. He liked her for her independence, and the fact that she wasn't born rich.

"Nice to know you worry about me," he said.

"I don't, it's the dataloss when you detonate your brain across the cosmos in that relic you're flying, that's what I'm concerned over." She turned to Meyer. "Do you know he won't give me the coordinates for this castle he found?"

"What castle?" Meyer asked.

"Where he found the Laymil electronics stack."

A smile spread across Meyer's whole face. "A castle. You didn't tell me that, Joshua. Did it have knights and wizards in it?"

"No," Joshua said firmly. "It was a big cube structure. I called it a castle because of the weapons systems. It was tough work getting in, one wrong move and . . ." Grave lines scored his face.

Kelly squirmed a fraction closer.

"It was operational?" Meyer was enjoying himself.

"No."

"So why was it dangerous?"

"Some of the systems still had power in their storage cells. So given how much molecular decay they've suffered out there in the Ring, just brushing against them could have triggered off a short circuit. They would have blown like a chain reaction."

"Electronic stacks, *and* functional power cells. That really was a terrific find, Joshua."

Joshua glared at him.

"And he won't tell me where it is," Kelly complained. "Just think, something that big which survived the suicide could well hold the key to the whole Laymil secret. If I could capture that on a sensevise, I'd be made. I could pick my own office with Collins, then. Hell, I'd be in charge of my own office."

"I'll sell you where it is," Joshua said, "it's all up here." He tapped his head. "My neural nanonics have got its orbital parameters down to a metre. I can locate it any time in the next ten years for you."

"How much are you asking?" Meyer asked.

"Ten million fuseodollars."

"Thanks, I'll pass."

"Doesn't it bother you, standing in the way of progress?" Kelly asked.

"No. Besides, what happens if the answer turns out to be something we don't particularly like?"

"Good point." Meyer raised his glass.

"Joshua! People have a right to know. They are quite capable of making up their own minds, they don't need to be protected from facts by people like you. Secrets seed oppression."

Joshua rolled his eyes. "Jesus. You just like to think reporters have a God-given right to stuff their noses in anywhere they want."

Kelly tipped a glass to his lips, encouraging him to sip the champagne. "But we do."

"You'll get it bitten off one day, you see. In any case, we will know what happened to the Laymil. With the size of the research team Tranquillity employs, results are inevitable."

"That's you, Joshua, the eternal optimist. Only an optimist would even think about going anywhere in that ship of yours."

"There's nothing wrong with the *Lady Mac*," Joshua bridled. "You ask Meyer, those systems are the finest money can buy."

Kelly fluttered long dark lashes enquiringly at Meyer.

"Oh, absolutely," he said.

"I still don't want you to go," she said quietly. She kissed Joshua's cheek. "They were good systems when your father was flying her, and they were newer then. Look what happened to him."

"That's different. Those orphans on the hospital station would never have made it back here without the *Lady Mac*. Dad had to jump while he was too close to that neutron star."

Meyer let out a distressed groan, and drained his glass.

Joshua was up at the bar when the woman approached him. He didn't even see her until she spoke, his attention was elsewhere. The barmaid's name was Helen Vanham, she was nineteen, with a dress cut lower than Harkey's normal, and she seemed eager to serve Joshua Calvert, the starship captain. She said she finished work at two in the morning.

"Captain Calvert?"

He turned from the pleasing display of cleavage and thigh. Jesus, but that title felt good. "You got me."

The woman was black, very black. There couldn't have been much geneering in her family, he decided, although he was suspicious about that deep pigmentation; she was fifty centimetres shorter than him, and her short beret of hair was frosted with strands of silver. He reckoned she was about sixty years old, and ageing naturally.

"I'm Dr Alkad Mzu," she said.

"Good evening, Doctor."

"I understand you have a ship you're fitting out?"

"That's right, the *Lady Macbeth*. Finest independent trader this side of the Kulu Kingdom. Are you interested in chartering her?"

"I may be."

Joshua skipped a beat. He took another look at the small woman. Alkad Mzu was dressed in a suit of grey fabric, a slim collar turned up around her neck. She seemed very serious, her features composed in a permanent expression of resignation. And right at the back of his mind there was a faint tingle of warning.

You're being oversensitive, he told himself, just because she doesn't smile doesn't mean she's a threat. Nothing is a threat in Tranquillity, that's the beauty of this place.

"Medicine must pay very well these days," he said.

"It's a physics doctorate."

"Oh, sorry. Physics must pay very well."

"Not really. I'm a member of the team researching Laymil artefacts."

"Yeah? You must have heard of me, then, I found the electronics stack."

"Yes, I heard, although memory crystals aren't my field. I mainly study their fusion drives."

"Really? Can I get you a drink?"

Alkad Mzu blinked, then slowly looked about. "Yes, this is a bar, isn't it. I'll just have a white wine, then, thank you."

Joshua signalled to Helen Vanham for a wine. Receiving a very friendly smile in return.

"What exactly was the charter?" he asked.

"I need to visit a star system."

Definitely weird, Joshua thought. "That's what *Lady Mac* does best. Which star system?"

"Garissa."

Joshua frowned, he thought he knew most star systems. He consulted his neural nanonics cosmology file. That was when his humour really started to deflate. "Garissa was abandoned thirty years ago."

Alkad Mzu received her slim glass from the barmaid, and tasted the wine. "It wasn't abandoned, Captain. It was annihilated. Ninety-five million people were slaughtered by the Omutan government. The Confederation Navy managed to get some off after the planet-buster strike, about seven hundred thousand. They used marine transports and colonist-carrier ships." Her eyes clouded over. "They abandoned the rescue effort after a month. There wasn't a lot of point. The radiation fallout had reached everyone who survived the blasts and tsunamis and earthquakes and superstorms. Seven hundred thousand out of ninety-five million."

"I'm sorry, I didn't know."

Her lips twitched around the rim of the glass. "Why should you? An obscure little planet that died before you were born; for politics that never made any sense even then. Why should anybody remember?"

Joshua shot the fuseodollars from his Jovian Bank credit card into the bar's accounts block as the barmaid delivered his tray of champagne bottles. There was an oriental man at the far end of the bar who was keeping an unobtrusive watch on himself and Dr Mzu over his beer mug. Joshua forced himself not to stare in return. He smiled at Helen Vanham and added a generous tip. "Dr Mzu, I have to be honest. I can take you to the Garissan system, but a landing given those circumstances is out of the question."

"I understand, Captain. And I appreciate your honesty. I don't wish to land, simply to visit."

"Ah, er, good. Garissa was your homeworld?"

"Yes."

"I'm sorry."

"That's the third time you've said that to me."

"One of those evenings, I guess."

"How much would it cost me?"

"For a single passenger, there and back; you're looking at about five hundred thousand fuseodollars. I know it's a lot, but the fuel expenditure will be the same for one person as a full cargo hold. And the crew time is the same as well, they all need paying."

"I doubt I can raise your full charter fee in advance. My research position is a comfortable one, but not that comfortable. However, I can assure you that once we reach our destination adequate funds will be available. Does that interest you?"

Joshua gripped the tray tighter, interested despite himself. "It may be possible to come to an arrangement, subject to a suitable deposit. And my rates are quite reasonable, you won't find any cheaper."

"Thank you, Captain. Can I have a copy of your ship's handling parameters and cargo capacity? I need to know whether the *Lady Macbeth* can fulfil my requirements, they are rather specialized."

Jesus, if she needs to know how big the cargo hold is, just what is she planning on bringing back? Whatever it is, it must have been hidden for thirty years.

His neural nanonics reported she had opened a channel. "Sure." He datavised over the *Lady Mac*'s performance tables.

"I'll be in touch, Captain. Thank you for the drink."

"My pleasure."

At the other end of the bar, Onku Noi, First Lieutenant serving in the Oshanko Imperial Navy, and assigned to the C5 Intelligence arm (Foreign Observation Division), finished his beer and paid the bill. The audio discrimination program in his neural nanonics had filtered out the bar's chatter and background music, allowing him to record the conversation between Alkad Mzu and the handsome young starship captain. He stood up and opened a channel into Tranquillity's communication net, requesting access to the spaceport's standard commercial reference memory core.

The file on the *Lady Macbeth* and Joshua Calvert was datavised into his neural nanonics. What he accessed caused an involuntary twitch in his jaw muscle. *Lady Macbeth* was a combat-capable starship, complete with antimatter drive and combat-wasp launch-rails, and she was being capaciously refurbished. Pausing only to confirm Joshua Calvert's visual profile was filed correctly in his neural nanonics memory cell, he followed Dr Mzu out of Harkey's Bar, keeping an unobtrusive thirty seconds behind her.

Joshua, interested before, was now outright fascinated as he surreptitiously watched the three men trailing after the diminutive Dr Mzu almost collide in the doorway. His intuition had been right again.

Jesus, who is she?

Tranquillity would know. But then Tranquillity would know she was being tailed as well, and who the tails were. Which meant that Ione would know.

He still hadn't resolved his feelings about Ione. There couldn't be anyone in the universe who was better at sex, but knowing that Tranquillity was looking at him out of those enchanting sea-blue eyes, that all those fluffy girlish mannerisms were wrapped around thought processes cooler than solid helium, was more than a little disconcerting. Though never inhibiting. She had been quite right about that, he simply couldn't say no. Not to her.

He returned to her every day, as instinctively as a migrating bird to an equatorial continent. It was exciting screwing the Lord of Ruin, a Saldana. And the feel of her body pressed against his was supremely erotic.

The male ego, he often reflected these days, was a puppet master with a very black sense of humour.

Joshua didn't have any time to ponder the puzzle of Dr Mzu before someone else hailed him. He turned with a slightly pained expression on his face.

A thirty-year-old man in a slightly worn navy-blue ship's one-piece was pushing through the throng, waving hopefully. He was just a few centimetres shorter than Joshua with the kind of regular features below short black hair that suggested a good deal of geneering. There was a smile on his face, apprehensive and keen at the same time.

"Yes?" Joshua asked wearily, he was only halfway back to his table.

"Captain Calvert? I'm Erick Thakrar, a ship's general systems engineer, grade five."

"Ah," Joshua said.

Warlow's thousand-decibel laugh blasted out, silencing the bar for an instant.

"Grade ratings are mostly down to logged flight hours," Erick said. "I did a lot of time in port maintenance. I'm up to grade three level in practice, if not more."

"And you're looking for a berth?"

"That's right."

Joshua hesitated, He still had a couple of berths to fill, and one of them was for a systems generalist. But that itchy sensation of discomfort had returned, much stronger than it had been with Dr Mzu.

Jesus, what's this one, a serial killer?

"I see," he said.

"I would be a bargain, I'm only asking grade five pay."

"I prefer to make flight pay a percentage of the charter fee, or a percentage of profits if we trade our own cargo."

"Sounds pretty good to me."

Joshua couldn't fault his attitude. Youthful, enthusiastic, no doubt a good worker, obviously willing to accept the rule bending necessary to keep independent ships flying. Ordinarily, a man you'd want at your back. But that intimation of *wrongness* wouldn't leave.

"OK, let me have your CV file, and I'll look it over," he said. "But not tonight, I'm in no fit state to make command judgements tonight."

In the end he invited Erick Thakrar back to the table to see how he got on with the other three crew members. He shared their sense of humour, had some good stories of his own, drank a lot, but not excessively.

Joshua watched it happen through the increasingly rosy glow fostered by the champagne, occasionally having to push Kelly to one side for a proper view of the table. Warlow liked him, Ashly Hanson liked him, Melvyn Ducharme, the *Lady Mac*'s fusion specialist, liked him, even Meyer and the *Udat* crew liked him. He was one of them.

And that, Joshua decided, was the problem. Erick fitted into his role a little too perfectly.

At quarter past two in the morning, feeling very smug, Joshua managed to give Kelly the slip, and sneaked out of Harkey's Bar with Helen Vanham. She lived by herself in an apartment a couple of floors below Harkey's. It was sparsely furnished, the walls of the lounge were bare white polyp; big brightly coloured cushions had been scattered around on a topaz moss floor, several aluminium cargo-pods served as tables with bottles and glasses, a giant AV projector pillar occupied one corner. The archways into different rooms all had folding silk screens for doors. Someone had been painting outlines of animals on them, there were paint pots and brushes lying on one of the pods. Joshua saw new tumours of polyp pushing up through the moss like rock mushrooms: furniture buds starting the slow growth into the form Helen wanted.

There was a food secretion panel on the wall opposite the window; a row of teats, like small yellow-brown rubber sacks, were standing proud, indicating regular use. It had been a long time since Joshua had used a panel for food, though a few years ago when money was tight they had been a godsend.

Every apartment in Tranquillity had one. The teats secreted edible pastes and fruit juices synthesized by a series of glands in the wall behind. There was nothing wrong with the taste, the pastes were indistinguishable from real chicken, and beef, and pork, and lamb, even the colours were reasonable. It was the constituency, like viscid grease, which always put Joshua off.

The glands ingested a nutrient fluid from a habitatwide network of veins which were fed from Tranquillity's mineral digestion organs in the southern endcap. There was also a degree of recycling, human wastes and organic scraps being broken down in specialist organs at the bottom of each starscraper. Porous sections of the shell vented toxic chemicals, preventing any dangerous build-up in the habitat's closed biosphere.

There was no such thing as starvation in bitek habitats, though both Edenists and Tranquillity's residents imported vast quantities of delicacies and wines from across the Confederation. They could afford it. But Helen obviously couldn't. Despite its size, the full teats and absence of materialism marked the apartment down as student digs.

"Help yourself to a drink," Helen said. "I'm getting out of this customer-friendly dress." She walked through an archway into the bedroom, leaving the screen folded back.

"What else do you do apart from serve bar at Harkey's?" he asked.

"I'm studying art," she called back. "Harkey's is just for funtime money."

Joshua broke off from examining the bottles and gave the screens with their animals a more appraising look. "Are you any good?"

"I might be eventually. My tutor says I have a good feel for form. But it's a five-year course, we're still on basic sketching and painting. We don't even get to AV technology until next year, and mood synthesis is another year after that. It's a drag, but you need to know the fundamentals."

"So how long have you been at Harkey's?"

"A couple of months. It's not bad work, you space industry people tip well, and you're not a pain like the finance mob. I worked at a bar over in the StPelham for a week. Crapoodle!"

"Have you ever seen Erick Thakrar before? He was sitting at my table, thirtyish, in a blue ship-suit."

"Yes. He's been in most nights for a fortnight or so. He's another good tipper."

"Do you know where he's been working?"

"Out in the dock; the Lowndes company, I think. He started a couple of days after he arrived."

"Which ship did he arrive on?"

"The *Shah of Kai*."

Joshua opened a channel into Tranquillity's communication net, and datavised a search request into the Lloyd's office. The *Shah of Kai* was a cargo vessel registered to a holding company in the New Californian system. It was an ex-navy transport ship, with a six-gee fusion drive; one hold was equipped with zero-tau pods for a company of marines, and it had proximity-range defence lasers. An asteroid assault craft.

Gotcha, Joshua thought.

"Did you ever meet any of the crew?" he asked.

Helen reappeared in the bedroom archway. She was wearing a long-sleeved net body-stocking, and white suede boots which came halfway up her thighs.

"Tell you later," she said.

Joshua gave his lips an involuntary lick. "I've got a great location file to match that costume, if you want to try it."

She took a step into the room. "Sure."

He accessed the sensenviron file, and ordered his neural nanonics to open a channel to Helen. A subliminal flicker crossed his optic nerves. Her sparse apartment gave way to the silk walls of a magnificent desert pavilion. There were tall ferns in brass urns around the entrance, a banquet table along one side was laid out with golden plates and jewelled goblets, and exotic, intricate drapes swung slowly in the warm, dry breeze that blew in from the crimson desert outside. Behind Helen was a curtained-off section, with the silk drawn apart just enough to show them a huge bed with purple sheets and a satin canopy which rose behind the scarlet-tasselled pillows like a sunrise sculpted from fabric.

"Nice," she said, glancing round.

"It's where Lawrence of Arabia pleasured his harem back in the eighteenth century. He was some sort of sheik king who fought the Roman Empire. Absolutely guaranteed genuine sensevise recording from old Earth. I got it from a starship captain friend of mine who visited the museum."

"Really?"

"Yeah. Old Lawrence had about a hundred and fifty wives, so they say."

"Wow. And he pleasured all of them himself?"

"Oh, yeah, he had to, there was an army of eunuchs to protect them. No other men could get in."

"Does the magic linger?"

"Wanna find out?"

Ione's mind encompassed the entirety of Helen Vanham's bedroom, the photosensitive cells in the bare polyp walls, floor, and ceiling giving her a complete visualization. It was a thousand times more detailed than an AV projection. She could move through the bedroom as if she was there, which in a way she was.

The bed was simply a plump mattress on the floor. Helen lay across it, with a naked Joshua straddling her. He was slowly and deliberately tearing the body-stocking off her.

Interesting, Ione observed.

If you say so, Tranquillity replied coolly.

Helen's long booted legs kicked the air behind his back. She was giggling and squealing as more and more strips of her stocking were ripped away.

I don't mean the sex, though judging by the way he's turned on I'll have to try wearing something like that for him myself one day. I was thinking of the way he latched on to Erick Thakrar.

His alleged psychic ability again?

He has had twelve applicants for the post of ship's general systems engineer so far. All of them legitimate. Yet the minute Erick asked for the berth, he was suspicious. Are you going to maintain it was nothing but luck?

I acknowledge Joshua's actions do indicate a degree of prescience on his part.

At last! Thank you.

This means you will be going ahead with the zygote extraction, then?

Yes. Unless you have an objection.

I would never object to receiving your child into me, no matter who was the father. It will be our child, too.

And I'll never know him, she said sadly, **not really, just for a few years of his childhood, like I saw Daddy. Sometimes I think our way is too harsh.**

I will love him. I will tell him of you when he asks.

Thank you. I shall have other children, though. And I'll know them.

With Joshua?

Possibly.

What are you going to do about him and Dr Mzu?

Ione sighed in exasperation. The image of Helen's bedroom rippled away. She glanced round her own study; it was cluttered with dark wooden furniture, centuries old, brought from Kulu by her grandfather. Her whole environment was steeped in history, reminding her who she was, her responsibilities. It was a depressing burden, one which she'd managed to avoid for a long time. But even that would have to end soon.

I'm not going to say anything to him, not now, anyway. Joshua is the seventh captain Mzu has approached in the last five months, she's just testing the water, seeing what sort of reaction she generates.

She is giving all the Intelligence operatives a bad case of the jitters.

I know. That's partly my fault. They don't know what will happen if she tries to leave. There isn't a Lord of Ruin they can ask, all they have is Daddy's promise.

And that holds true?

Yes, of course it does. She cannot be allowed to leave. The serjeants must be used to restrain her if she ever attempts it. And if she does get into a ship, you're going to have to use the strategic defence weapons.

Even if that ship is the *Lady Macbeth*?

Joshua wouldn't try to take her out, especially if I asked him not to.

But if he does?

Ione's fingers curled about the small silver crucifix round her neck. Then you shoot her out of space.

I'm sorry. I can feel the pain in you.

It's a null situation. He won't do it. I trust Joshua. Money isn't his prime motivation. He could have told people I exist. That reporter woman, Kelly Tirrel, she would have paid him a fortune for a scoop like that.

I don't think he will accept Dr Mzu's charter, either.

Good. All this is making me think. People do need some kind of reassurance that there is an authority figure behind you. Do you think I'm old enough to start making public appearances yet?

Mentally, you have been mature enough for years. Physically, possibly; you are old enough to face motherhood, after all. Although I think a more suitable mode of

attire would help. Image is the paramount issue in your case.

Ione glanced down. She was wearing a pink bikini and a small green beach jacket, ideal for the swim in the cove she took each evening.

I think you may have a point there.

Tranquillity had no blackhawk docking-ledges on its southern endcap. The polyp which made up that hemisphere was twice the usual thickness of the shell so that it could incorporate the massive mineral-digestion organs, as well as several lake-sized hydrocarbon reservoirs. These were the organs which produced the various nutrient fluids circulating in the shell's vast network of ducts, sustaining the mitosis layer which regenerated the polyp, the starscraper apartment food-secretion glands, the ledge pedestals which fed the visiting blackhawks and voidhawks, as well as various specialist organs responsible for environmental maintenance. Access passages to the outer shell would have been difficult to route through such a tightly packed grouping of titanic viscera.

There was no non-rotational spaceport either. The external hub was taken up by a craterlike maw, fifteen hundred metres in diameter. Its inner surface was lined with tubular cilia, hundred-metre spikes that impaled the asteroidal rubble which ships boosted out of Mirchusko's inner ring. Once in the maw, the rocks were coated by enzymes ejected from the cilia and broken down into dust and gravel, more manageable chunks which could be ingested and consumed with ease.

The lack of any spaceport outside the endcap, plus the circumfluous salt-water sea lapping around the base on the inside, meant that there was little activity on its curving slopes. The first two kilometres above the coves were terraced like an ancient hill farm, planted with flowering bushes and orchards tended by agronomy servitors. Above the terraces a claggy soil clung to the ever-steepening polyp wall, a vast annular meadow land of thick grasses, whose roots strove to counteract gravity and keep the soil in place. Both grass and soil stopped short three kilometres from the hub, where the polyp was virtually a vertical cliff. Right at the axis, the light-tube emerged, running the entire length of the massive habitat: a cylindrical mesh of organic conductors, their powerful magnetic field containing the fluorescent plasma which brought light and heat to the interior.

Michael Saldana had decided that the quiet, semi-secluded southern endcap would be an ideal site for the research project into the Laymil. Its offices and laboratories now sprawled over two square kilometres of the lower terraces, the largest cluster of buildings inside the habitat, resembling the campus of some wealthy private university.

The project director's office was on the top floor of the five-storey administration building, a squat, circular pillar of copper-mirror glass ringed with grey stone colonnaded balconies. It sat on the terrace at the back of the campus, five hundred metres above the circumfluous sea, giving it an unsurpassed view of the cycloramic sub-tropical parkland stretching away into misty distance.

The view was something Parker Higgens was immensely proud of, easily the finest in Tranquillity, another fitting perk due to the research project's eighth director—along with the scrumptious office itself, with its deep-burgundy coloured ossalwood furniture that had come from Kulu in the days before the abdication crisis. Parker Higgens was eighty-five. His appointment had come nine years ago, almost the last act of the Lord of Ruin, and by the grace of God (plus an ancestor wealthy enough to afford some decent geneering) he would keep the post for another nine. He had left actual research behind twenty years ago to concentrate on administration. It was a field he excelled in; building the right teams, massaging mercurial egos, knowing when to push, when to ease off. Genuinely effective scientific administrators were rare, and under his leadership the project had functioned reasonably smoothly, everyone acknowledged that. Parker Higgens liked to keep his world neat and tidy, it was one of his formulas for success, which was why he was particularly shocked to come into work one morning and find a young blonde-haired girl lounging in the deep cushioning of *his* straight-backed chair behind *his* desk.

"Who the bloody hell are you?" he shouted. Then he saw the five serjeants standing to attention around the room.

Tranquillity's serjeants were the habitat's sole police force, sub-sentient bitek servitors controlled via affinity by the personality, enforcing the law with scrupulous impartiality. They were (intentionally) intimidating humanoids, two metres tall, with a reddish-brown exoskeleton, limb joints encased by segmented rings permitting full articulation. The heads had a sculpted appearance, with eyes concealed in a deep horizontal crease. Their hands were their most human characteristic, with leathery skin replacing the exoskeleton. It meant they could use any artefact built for a human, with emphasis on weapons. Each of them carried a laser pistol and a cortical jammer on their belts, along with restraint cuffs. The belt was their sole article of clothing.

Parker Higgens glanced round dumbly at the serjeants, then back at the girl. She was wearing a very expensive pale blue suit, and her ice-blue eyes conveyed an unnerving impression of depth. Her nose . . . Parker Higgens might have been a bureaucrat, but he wasn't stupid. "You?" he whispered incredulously.

Ione gave him a faint smile and stood up, extending her hand. "Yes, Mr Director. Me, I'm afraid. Ione Saldana."

He shook the hand weakly, it was very small and cool in his. There was a signet ring on her finger, a red ruby carved with the Saldana crest: the crowned phoenix. It was the Kulu Crown Prince's ring, Michael hadn't bothered to return it to the keeper of the crown jewellery when he was sent into exile. Parker Higgens had last seen it on Maurice Saldana's finger.

"I'm honoured, ma'am," Parker Higgens said; he had come very close to blurting: *but you're a girl.* "I knew your father, he was an inspiring man."

"Thank you." There was no trace of humour on Ione's face. "I appreciate you're busy, Mr Director, but I'd like to inspect the project's major facilities this morning. Then I shall require each division's senior staff to assemble summaries of their work for a presentation in two days' time. I have tried to keep abreast of the findings, but remote viewing through Tranquillity's senses and having them explained in person are two different things."

Parker Higgens's whole universe trembled. A review, and like it or not this slip of a girl held the purse strings, the *life* strings of the research project. What if . . . "Of course, ma'am, I'll show you round myself."

Ione started to walk round the desk.

"Ma'am? May I ask what your policy towards the Laymil research project is? Previous Lords of Ruin have been very—"

"Relax, Mr Director. My ancestors were quite right: unravelling the Laymil mystery should be given the highest priority."

The prospect of imminent disaster retreated from his view, like rain-clouds rolling away to reveal the sun. It was going to be all right after all. Almost. A girl! Saldana heirs were always male. "Yes, ma'am!"

The serjeants lined up into an escort squad around Ione. "Come along," she said, and swept out of the office.

Parker Higgens found his legs racing in an undignified manner to catch up. He wished he could make people jump obediently like that.

There *is* a third Lord of Ruin.

The news broke thirty-seven seconds after Ione and Parker Higgens walked into the laboratory block housing the Laymil Plant Genetics Division. Everybody who worked for the project was fitted with neural nanonics. So once the instinctive flash of guilt and the accompanying shock of having the director and five serjeants walk in unannounced ten minutes into the working day had worn off, and the introductions began, professors and technicians alike opened channels into the habitat's communication net. Nearly every datavise began: You're not going to believe this—

Ione was shown AV projections of Laymil plant genes, sealed propagators with seed shoots worming their way up through the soil, and large fern-analogue plants with scarlet fronds growing in pots, and given small shrivelled black fruits to taste.

After friends, relatives, and colleagues were brought up to speed, it took another fifteen seconds before anyone thought of contacting the news company offices.

Ione and Parker Higgens walked on from the plant genetics laboratory to the Laymil Habitat Structure Analysis office. People were lining the stone path, trampling on the shrubs. Applause and cheers followed her like a wave effect, wolf-whistles were flung boisterously. The serjeants had to gently push aside the more enthusiastic spectators. Ione started to shake hands and wave.

There were five major Confederationwide news companies who maintained offices in Tranquillity, and all of them had been told about Ione's arrival at the research project campus within ninety seconds of her tour beginning. The disbelieving assistant editor at Collins immediately asked the habitat personality if it was true.

"Yes," Tranquillity said simply.

The scheduled morning programmes were immediately interrupted to carry the news. Reporters sprinted for tube carriages. Editors frantically opened channels to their contacts in the Laymil project staff, seeking immediate on-the-ground coverage. Datavises became sensevises, relaying optical and auditory nerve inputs directly to the studio. After twelve minutes, eighty per cent of Tranquillity's residents were hooked in, either watching Ione's impromptu walkabout on the AV broadcasts, or receiving the sensevise direct through neural nanonics.

It's a girl, the Lord of Ruin is a girl. God, the Royal Saldanas will go mad over that, there's not a chance of reconciliation with the Kingdom now.

There were two Kiint working in the physiology laboratory; one of them came into the glass-walled lobby to greet Ione. It was an impressive and moving sight, the slight human girl standing in front of the huge xenoc.

The Kiint was an adult female, icy-white hide glimmering softly in the bright morning light, almost as if she was wearing a halo. She had an oval cross-section body nine metres long, three wide, standing on eight fat elephantlike legs. Her head was as long as Ione was tall, which was slightly intimidating as it reminded her of a primitive shield; a bony, slightly convex, downward pointing triangle with a central vertical ridge which gave it two distinct planes. There were a pair of limpid eyes halfway up, just above a series of six breathing vents, each of which had a furry fringe that undulated with every breath. The pointed base of the head served as her beak, with two smaller hinged sections behind.

Two arm-appendages emerged from the base of her neck, curving round the lower half of her head. They looked almost like featureless tentacles. Then tractamorphic muscles rippled below the skin, and the end of the right arm shaped itself into a human hand.

You are much welcome here, Ione Saldana, the Kiint spoke into her mind.

Kiint could always use the human affinity band, but Edenists had found it almost impossible to sense any form of private Kiint communication. Perhaps they had a true telepathic ability? It was one of the lesser mysteries about the enigmatic xenocs.

Your interest in this research venture does you credit, the Kiint continued.

My thanks to you for assisting us, Ione replied. **I'm told the analysis instruments you have made available here have been an immeasurable help.**

How could we refuse your grandfather's invitation? Foresight such as his is a rare quality among your race.

I would like to speak with you about that sometime.

Of course. But now you must complete your grand progress. There was a note of lofty amusement behind the thought.

The Kiint extended her new-formed hand, and they touched palms briefly. She inclined her massive head in a bow. Murmurs of surprise rippled round the others in the lobby.

Hell, look at that, even the Kiint's bowled over by her.

After the tour Ione stood alone in one of the orchards outside the campus, surrounded by trees rigorously pruned into mushroom shapes, their branches congested with a fleece of blossom. Petals swirled slowly through the air about her, sprinkling the ankle-length grass with a snowy mantle. She had her back to the habitat, so that the entire interior appeared to curve around her like a pair of emerald waves, their peaks clashing in a long, straight flame of scintillating white light far overhead.

"I want to tell you of the faith I have in everybody who lives in Tranquillity," she began. "Out of nothing a hundred and seventy-five years ago we have built a society that is respected throughout the Confederation. We are independent, we are virtually crime free, and we are wealthy, both collectively and individually. We can be justifiably proud in that achievement. It was not given to us, it was bought with hard work and sacrifices. And it will continue only by encouraging the industry and enterprise that has generated this wealth. My father and grandfather gave their wholehearted support to the business community, in creating an environment where trade and industry enrich our lives, and allow us to aspire for our children. In Tranquillity, dreams are given a greater than average chance to become real. That you will continue to pursue your dreams is the faith I have in you. To this end I pledge that my reign will be devoted to maintaining the economic, legal, and political environs which have brought us to the enviable position we find ourselves in today and enable us to look forward to the future with courage."

The image and voice faded from the news studios, along with the aromatic scent of blossom. But not the shy half-smile, that lingered for a long time.

Christ: young, pretty, rich, and smart. How about that!

By the end of the day, Tranquillity had received eighty-four thousand invitations for Ione. She was wanted at parties and dinners, she was asked to give speeches and present prizes, her name was wanted on the board of interstellar companies, designers offered their entire portfolio for her to wear, charities begged her to become their patron. Old friends treated her as though she was a reincarnated messiah. Everyone wanted to be her new friend. And Joshua—Joshua got very grumpy when she spent the first evening reviewing Tranquillity's summaries of the incredible public reaction rather than spending it in bed with him.

He was also none too happy that *Lady Macbeth*'s refit was still a fortnight short of completion. Over the next twenty hours, seventy-five charter flights were organized to carry recordings of Ione around the Confederation. The news company offices were engaged in a ferocious ratings war; they were desperate to break the scoop on as many worlds as possible, as soon as possible. Starship captains cursed their earlier binding contracts to deliver mundane cargoes, and some even broke them. Those that didn't have immediate contracts named wholly unreasonable prices to the news companies, which were paid without question.

Right across the Confederation, the sensation-hungry devoured Ione, rekindling an avid interest in the black sheep branch of the Saldana family; and even briefly pushing the old Laymil enigma into the limelight again.

Merchants became extremely wealthy on Ione fashions and Ione accessories. Bluesense directors remodelled their female meat to look and feel like her. Mood Fantasy bands composed tracks about her. Even Jezzibella announced she looked cute, and said she'd like to fuck her one day.

The news agencies on Kulu and its Principality worlds treated her appearance as a minor footnote. The royal family didn't believe in censoring the press, but the court certainly didn't see her appearance as anything to celebrate. Black-market sensevise recordings of her sold for an absolute fortune right across the Kingdom.

It was one of the abandoned cargo contracts which brought Joshua his first charter two days later.

Roland Frampton was a merchant friend of Barrington Grier, which was how he heard of the *Lady Macbeth* and how she would be ready to depart in fourteen days.

"When I get my hands on that bastard Captain McDonald I'll have him broken up for transplant meat," Roland said angrily. "The *Corum Sister* won't get another cargo contract this side of Jupiter, that I do promise." Joshua sipped his mineral water and nodded sympathetically. Harkey's Bar didn't have the same appeal by day, although the term was ambiguous in a starscraper. But people's biorhythms were in tune with the habitat light-tube; his body knew this was mid-morning.

"I paid good rates, you know, not like I was ripping him

off. It was a regular run. Now this bloody girl comes along, and everyone goes berserk."

"Hey, I'm glad we've got a Saldana back running things," Barrington Grier protested. "If she's half as good as the last two Lords, this place is going to be swinging."

"Yeah, well, I haven't got no quarrel with her," Roland Frampton said hurriedly. "But the way people react." He shook his head in bemusement. "Did you hear what the news companies were offering captains for the Avon run?"

"Yeah. Meyer and the *Udat* got the Time Universe charter to Avon," Joshua said with a grin.

"The point is, Joshua, I'm up shit creek," Roland Frampton said. "I've got my clients screaming for those nanonic medical supplements. There are a lot of wealthy old people in Tranquillity, the medical industry here is big business."

"I'm sure we can come to an arrangement."

"Cards on the table, Joshua, I'll pay you three hundred and fifty thousand fuseodollars for the flight, with an extra seventy thousand bonus if you can get them back here in five weeks from today. After that, I can offer you a regular contract, a flight to Rosenheim every six months. Not to be sneered at, Joshua."

Joshua glanced at Melvyn Ducharme, who was stirring his coffee idly. He had come to rely a lot on his fusion engineer during *Lady Mac*'s refit; he was forty-eight, with over twenty years' solid starflight experience behind him. The dark-skinned little man gave a small nod.

"OK," Joshua said. "But you know the score, Roland, the *Lady Mac* doesn't leave that bay until I'm happy she's integrated properly. I'm not rushing it and botching it just for the sake of a seventy-thousand-dollar bonus."

Roland Frampton gave him an unhappy look. "Sure, Joshua, I appreciate that."

They shook on it and started to work out details.

Kelly Tirrel arrived twenty minutes later, dropped her bag on the carpet, and sat down with an exaggerated sigh. She called a waitress over and ordered a coffee, then gave Joshua a perfunctory kiss.

"Have you got your contract?" she asked.

"We're working on it." He gave the bar a quick scan. Helen Vanham wasn't anywhere to be seen.

"Good for you. God what a day! My editor's been having kittens."

"Ione caught you all on the hop, did she?" Barrington Grier asked.

"And then some," Kelly admitted. "I've been researching for the last fifteen hours without a break, going through the Saldana family history. We're putting together an hour-long documentary for tonight. Those royals are one bunch of weird people."

"Are you going to present it?" Joshua asked.

"No chance. Kirstie McShane got it. Bitch. She's sleeping with the current affairs editor, you know, that's why. I'll probably wind up as fashion correspondent or something. If only we'd had some advance warning, I could have prepared, found an angle."

"Ione wasn't sure about the timing herself," he said. "She's only been thinking about public appearances for the last fortnight."

There was a murderous silence as Kelly's head slowly turned to focus on Joshua. "What?"

"Er . . ." He felt as though he'd suddenly been dumped into free fall.

"You know her? You've known who she is?"

"Well, sort of, in a way, I suppose, yes. She did mention it."

Kelly stood up fast, the motion nearly toppling her chair. "Mention it! You SHIT, Joshua Calvert! Ione Saldana is the biggest story to hit the whole Confederation for three years, and you KNEW about it, and you didn't tell me! You selfish, egotistical, mean-minded, xenoc-buggering bastard! I was sleeping with you, I cared . . ." She clamped her mouth shut and snatched her bag up. "Didn't that mean anything to you?"

"Of course. It was . . ." He accessed his neural nanonics' thesaurus file. "Stupendous?"

"Bastard!" She took two paces towards the door then turned round. "And you're shit-useless in bed, too," she shouted.

Everyone in Harkey's Bar was staring at him. He could see a lot of grins forming. He closed his eyes for a moment and let out a resigned sigh. "Women." He swivelled round in his chair to face Roland Frampton. "About the insurance rates . . ."

The cavern wasn't like anything Joshua had seen in Tranquillity before. It was roughly hemispherical, about twenty metres across, with the usual level white polyp floor. But the walls' regularity was broken up by organic protuberances, great cauliflower growths that quivered occasionally as he watched; there were also the tight doughnuts of sphincter muscles. Equipment cabinets, with a medical look, were fused into the polyp; as though they were being extruded, or osmotically absorbed. He couldn't tell which.

The whole place was so *biological*. It made him want to squirm.

"What is it?" he asked Ione.

"A clone womb centre." She pointed to one of the sphincters. "We gestate the servitor housechimps in these ones. All of the habitat's servitors are sexless, you see, they don't mate. So Tranquillity has to grow them. We've got several varieties of chimps, and the serjeants, of course, then there are some specialist constructs for things like tract repair and light-tube maintenance. There are forty-three separate species in all."

"Ah. Good."

"The wombs are plumbed directly into the nutrient ducts, there's very little hardware needed."

"Right."

"I was gestated in here."

Joshua's nose wrinkled up. He didn't like to think about it.

Ione walked over to a waist-high, steel-grey equipment stack standing on the floor. Green and amber LEDs winked at her. There was a cylindrical zero-tau pod recessed into the top, twenty centimetres long, ten wide; its surface resembled a badly tarnished mirror. She used her affinity to load an order into the stack's bitek processors, and the pod hinged open.

Joshua watched silently as she placed the little sustentator globe inside. His son. Part of him wanted to put a stop to this right now, to have the child born properly, to know him, watch him grow up.

"It is customary to name the child now," Ione said. "If you want to."

"Marcus." His father's name. He didn't even have to think about that.

Her sapphire eyes were damp, reflecting the soft pearl light from the electrophorescent strips in the ceiling. "Of course. Marcus Saldana it is, then."

Joshua's mouth opened to protest. "Thank you," he said meekly.

The pod closed and the surface turned black. It didn't look solid, more like a fissure which had opened into space. He stared at it for a long time. You just can't say no to Ione.

She slipped her arm through his and steered him out of the clone womb centre into the corridor outside. "How's the *Lady Macbeth* coming along?"

"Not so bad. The Confederation Astronautics Board inspectors have cleared our systems integration. We're starting to reassemble the hull now, it should be finished in another three days. One final inspection for the spaceworthiness certificate, and we're away. I've got a contract with Roland Frampton to collect some cargo from Rosenheim."

"That's good news. So I've got you to myself for another four nights."

He pulled her a bit closer. "Yeah, if you can fit me in between engagements."

"Oh, I think I might manage to grant you a couple of hours. I've got a charity dinner tonight, but I'll be finished before eleven. Promise."

"Great. You've done beautifully, Ione, really, you just blew them away. They love you out there."

"And nobody's packed up and left yet, none of the major companies, nor the plutocrats. That's my real success."

"It was that speech you made. Jesus, if there were elections tomorrow you'd be president."

They reached the tube carriage waiting in the little station. Two serjeants stood aside as the door opened.

Joshua looked at them, then looked into the ten-seater carriage. "Can they wait out here?" he asked innocently.

"Why?"

He leered.

She clung to him tightly afterwards, trembling slightly, their bodies hot and sweaty. He was sitting right on the edge of one of the seats, with her as the clinging vine, legs bent up behind his back. The carriage's air-conditioning fans made a loud whirring sound as they recycled the unusually humid air.

"Joshua?"

"Uh huh." He kissed her neck, hands stroking her buttocks.

"I can't protect you once you leave."

"I know."

"Don't do anything stupid. Don't try to beat anything your father did."

His nose nuzzled the base of her chin. "I won't. I'm no death wisher."

"Joshua?"

"What?"

She pulled her head back and looked straight into his eyes, trying to make him believe. "Trust your instincts."

"Hey, I do."

"Please, Joshua. Not just about objects, people too. Be careful of people."

"Yes."

"Promise me."

"I promise."

He rose up, with Ione still wrapped round his torso. She could feel him getting hard again.

"See those hand hoops?" he asked.

She glanced up. "Yes."

"Catch hold, and don't let go."

She reached up with both hands and gripped a pair of the steel loops on the ceiling. Joshua let go of her, and she yelped. Her toes didn't quite reach the floor. He stood in front of her, grinning, and gave her a small shove, starting her swinging.

"Joshua!" Ione forked her legs at the top of the arc.

He moved forward, laughing.

Erick Thakrar floated into bay MB 0-330's control centre towing his bag. He stopped himself with an expert nudge against a grab loop. There was an unusually large number of people grouped round the observation bubble. He recognized all of them, engineers who had worked on the *Lady Macbeth*'s refit. All of them had been working long shifts together for the last couple of weeks.

Erick didn't mind the work, it meant he had won his place on the *Lady Macbeth*'s crew. A stiff back and perpetual tiredness was a price worth paying for that. And in another two hours he would be on his way.

The buzz of voices faded away as people became aware of him. A vacant slot around the observation bubble materialized. He steadied himself and looked out.

The cradle had telescoped up out of the bay, taking the *Lady Macbeth* with it. As he watched, the starship's thermodump panels unfolded from their recesses in the lustreless grey hull. Cradle umbilical couplings withdrew from the rear quarter.

"You are cleared for disconnection," the bay supervisor datavised. "*Bon voyage*, Joshua. Take care."

Orange candle-flames ignited around the *Lady Macbeth*'s equator, and the chemical verniers lifted her clear of the cradle with a dexterity only a master pilot could ever achieve.

The engineering team whooped and cheered.

"Erick?"

He looked round at the supervisor.

"Joshua says to say sorry, but the Lord of Ruin thinks you're an arsehole."

Erick turned back to the empty bay. The cradle was sinking slowly back towards the floor. Blue light washed down as the *Lady Macbeth*'s ion thrusters took over from the verniers.

"Son of a bitch," he muttered numbly.

There were four separate life-support capsules in the *Lady Macbeth*, twelve-metre spheres grouped together in a pyramid shape at the very heart of the ship. With the expense of fitting them out coming to a minute fraction of the starship's overall cost, they were well appointed.

Capsules B, C, and D, the lower spheres, were split into four decks apiece, with the two middle levels following a basic layout of cabins, a lounge, galley, and bathroom. The other decks were variously storage compartments, maintenance shops, equipment bays, and airlock chambers for the spaceplane and MSV hangars.

Capsule A housed the bridge, taking up half of the upper middle deck, with consoles and acceleration couches for all six crew-members. Because neural nanonics could interface with the flight computer from anywhere in the ship, it was more of a management office than the traditional command centre, with console screens and AV projectors providing specialist systems displays to back up datavised information.

Lady Macbeth was licensed to carry up to thirty active passengers, or if the cabin bunks were removed and zero-tau pods installed, eighty people travelling in stasis. With only Joshua and five crew on board, there was a luxurious amount of space available. Joshua's cabin was the largest, taking up a quarter of the bridge deck. He refused to change it from the layout Marcus Calvert had chosen. The chairs were from some luxury passenger ship decommissioned over half a century ago, hinged black-foam sculptures which looked like giant seashells in their folded positions. A bookcase held acceleration-reinforced leather-bound volumes of ancient star charts. An Apollo command module guidance computer (of dubious provenance) was displayed in a transparent bubble. But the major feature, from his point of view, was the free-fall-sex cage, a mesh globe of rubberized struts which deployed from the ceiling. You could bounce around happily inside that without any danger of crashing into inconvenient (and sharp) pieces of furniture or decking. He intended to get into full practice with Sarha Mitcham, the twenty-four-year-old general systems engineer who had taken Erick Thakrar's place.

Everyone was strapped in their bridge couch when Joshua lifted the *Lady Macbeth* off bay 0–330's cradle. He did it with instinctive ease, he did it like a chrysalis opening its wings to the sun, he did it knowing this was what his spiralling DNA had been reconfigured to do.

Flight vectors from the spaceport traffic control centre insinuated their way into his mind, and ion thrusters rolled the ship lazily. He took them out over the edge of the giant disk of girders using the secondary reaction drive, then powered up the three primary fusion drives. The gee-force built rapidly, and they headed up out of Mirchusko's gravity well towards the green crescent of Falsia, seven hundred thousand kilometres away.

The shakedown flight lasted for fifteen hours. Test programs ran systems checks; the fusion drives were pushed up to producing a brief period of seven-gee thrust, and their plasma was scanned for instabilities; life-support capacity was tested in each capsule. The guidance systems, the sensors, fuel tank slosh baffles, thermal insulation, power circuits, generators . . . the million components that went into making up the starship structure.

Joshua inserted *Lady Mac* into orbit two hundred kilometres above the craterous lifeless moon while they took a rest for ninety minutes. After a final, formal report confirming overall performance efficiency matched the Confederation Astronautics Board's requirements, he powered up the fusion drives again, and accelerated back in towards the hazy ochre gas giant.

Adamist starships lacked the flexibility of voidhawks not only in manoeuvrability, but also in their respective methods of faster than light translation. While the bitek craft could tailor their wormholes to produce a terminus at the required location irrespective of their orbit and acceleration vector, ships like the *Lady Macbeth* jumped along their orbital track without any leeway at all. It was that limitation which cost captains a great deal of time between jumps. The starship had to align itself directly on its target star. In interstellar space it wasn't so difficult, simply a question of adjusting for natural error. But the initial jump out of a star system had to be as accurate as humanly possible to prevent emergence point inaccuracies from growing out of hand. If a starship was departing an asteroid that was heading away from its next port of call, the captain could spend days reversing his orbit, and the cost in delta-V reserve was horrendous. Most captains simply employed the nearest available planet, giving them the choice of jumping towards any star in the galaxy once every orbit.

Lady Macbeth fell into a circular orbit a hundred and eighty-five thousand kilometres above Mirchusko, a ten-thousand-kilometre safety margin. Gravity distortion prohibited Adamist starships from jumping within a hundred and seventy-five thousand kilometres of gas giants.

The flight computer datavised the vector lines into Joshua's mind. He saw the vast curved bulk of quarrelling storm bands below, the black cave-lip of the terminator creeping towards him. *Lady Mac*'s trajectory was a tube of green neon rings stretching out ahead until they merged into a single thread which looped round behind Mirchusko's darkside. The green rings swept past the hull at a dizzying velocity.

Rosenheim showed as an insignificant point of white light, bracketed by red graphics, rising above the gas giant.

"Generators on line," Melvyn Ducharme reported.

"Dahybi?" Joshua asked.

"Patterning circuits are stable," Dahybi Yadev, their node specialist, said in a calm voice.

"OK, looks like we're go for a jump." He ordered the nodes to power up, feeding the generators' full output into the patterning circuits. Rosenheim was rising higher and higher above the gas giant as *Lady Mac* raced round her orbit.

Jesus, an actual jump.

According to his neural nanonics physiological monitor program his heart rate was up to a hundred beats a minute and rising. It had been known for some first-time crewmembers to panic when the actual moment came, terrified by the thought of the energy loci being desynchronized. All it took was one glitch, one failed monitor program.

Not me! Not this ship.

He datavised the flight computer to pull in the thermo-dump panels and the sensor clusters.

"Nodes fully charged," Dahybi Yadev said. "She's all yours, Joshua."

He had to grin at that. She always had been.

Ion thrusters flickered briefly, fine tuning their trajectory. Rosenheim slid across the vector of green rings, right into the centre. Decimals spun down to zero, tens of seconds, hundredths, thousandths.

Joshua's command flashed through the patterning nodes at lightspeed. Energy flowed, its density racing to achieve infinity.

An event horizon rose from nowhere to cloak the *Lady Macbeth*'s hull. Within five milliseconds it had shrunk to nothing, taking the starship with it.

Erick Thakrar took the StMichelle starscraper's lift down to the forty-third floor, then got out and walked down two flights of stairs. There was nobody about on the forty-fifth floor vestibule. This was office country, half of them unoccupied; and it was nineteen hundred hours local time.

He walked into the Confederation Navy bureau.

Commander Olsen Neale looked up in surprise when Erick entered his office. "What the hell are you doing here? I thought the *Lady Macbeth* had departed."

Erick sat down heavily in the chair in front of Neale's desk. "She has." He explained what happened.

Commander Neale rested his head in his hands, frowning. Erick Thakrar was one of half a dozen agents the CNIS was operating in Tranquillity, trying to insert them on independent traders (especially those with antimatter drives) and blackhawks in the hope of getting a lead on pirate activity and antimatter production stations.

"The Lord of Ruin warned Calvert?" Commander Neale asked in a puzzled tone.

"That's what the maintenance bay supervisor said."

"Good God, that's all we need, this Ione girl turning Tranquillity into some kind of anarchistic pirate nation. It might be a blackhawk base, but the Lords of Ruin have always supported the Confederation before." Commander Neale glanced round the polyp walls, then stared at the AV pillar sticking out of his desk's processor block, half expecting the personality to contact him and deny the accusation. "Do you think your cover's blown?"

"I don't know. The refit team thought it was all a big joke. Apparently Joshua Calvert signed on some girl to replace me. They said she was rather attractive."

"Well, it certainly fits what we know about him; he could very easily have dumped you for a doxy and a quick leg-over."

"Then why the reference to the Lord of Ruin?"

"God knows." He let out a long breath. "I want you to keep trying for a berth on a ship; you'll find out soon enough if you have been blown. I'm going to put all this on the diplomatic report flek, and let Admiral Aleksandrovich worry about it."

"Yes, sir." Erick Thakrar saluted and left.

Commander Neale sat in his chair for a long time, watching the starfield rotate past the window. The prospect of Tranquillity going renegade was horrifying, especially given the one particular status quo it had maintained for twenty-seven years. Eventually he accessed his neural nanonics file on Dr Mzu, and started to check through the circumstances under which he was authorized to have her assassinated.

11

Some of the more superstitious amongst Aberdale's population were heard to say that Marie Skibbow had taken the village's luck with her when she departed. There was no change in their physical circumstances, but they seemed to suffer a veritable plague of depressing and unfortunate incidents.

Marie had been right about her family's reaction. After the truth was finally established (Rai Molvi confirmed she boarded the *Coogan*, Scott Williams confirmed she was loading the thermal furnace when it cast off) Gerald Skibbow's reaction to what he thought of as his daughter's betrayal was pure fury. He demanded Powel Manani either chase after the tramp trader on his horse, or use his communication block to have the county sheriff arrest her when the *Coogan* sailed past Schuster.

Powel politely explained that Marie was now legally an adult, and didn't have a settlement contract with the LDC, and was therefore free to do as she pleased. Gerald, with Loren weeping quietly at his side, raged at the injustice, then went on to complain bitterly of the incompetence of the LDC's local representatives. At which point the Ivet supervisor, exhausted from leading the search for Gwyn Lawes after a full day spent in the saddle rounding up stray animals on the savannah, came very close to punching Gerald Skibbow's lights out. Rai Molvi, Horst Elwes, and Leslie Atcliffe had to pull them apart.

Marie Skibbow's name was never mentioned again.

The fields and plantations carved out of the jungle at the rear of Aberdale's clearing were now so large that the vigorous ground creepers which invaded the rotovated soil were growing back almost as fast as they could be chopped up. It was a wearisome task, taxing even the disciplined Ivets. Any further expansion was clearly out of the question until the first batch of crops was firmly established. The more delicate varieties of terrestrial vegetables were struggling laboriously under the never-ending assault from the rain. Even with their geneering, tomatoes, courgettes, lettuce, kale, celeriac, and aubergines laboured upwards, their leaves bent and drooping, yellowing round the edges. One violent storm which left the jungle shrouded in mist for days afterwards scattered half of the village's chickens, few of which were ever found.

A fortnight after the *Coogan* departed, another tramp trader, the *Louis Leonid*, arrived. There was almost a riot at the prices the captain charged; he cast off hurriedly, swearing to warn every boat in the Juliffe basin to avoid the Quallheim tributary in future.

And there were the deaths as well. After Gwyn Lawes there was Roger Chadwick, drowned in the Quallheim, his body discovered a kilometre downriver. Then the terrible tragedy of the Hoffman family: Donnie and Judy, along with their two young teenage children, Angie and Thomas, burnt to death in their savannah homestead one night. It wasn't until morning when Frank Kava saw the thin pyre of smoke rising from the ashes that the alarm was raised. The bodies were charred beyond recognition. Even a well-equipped pathology lab would have been hard pressed to realize that they had all died from having a hunting laser fired through their eyes at a five-centimetre range.

Horst Elwes pushed the sharpened bottom of the cross thirty centimetres into the sodden black loam, and started to press it in with his boot. He had made the cross himself from mayope wood, not as good as anything Leslie could make, of course, but untainted. He felt that was important for little Angie.

"There's no proof," he said as he looked down at the pathetically small oblong mound of earth.

"Ha!" Ruth Hilton said as she handed him Thomas's cross.

They went over to the boy's grave. Horst found it very hard to visualize Thomas's face now. The boy had been thirteen, all smiles, always running everywhere. The cross went in the ground with a sucking sound.

"You said yourself they are Satanists," Ruth insisted. "And we damn well know those three colonists were murdered back in Durringham."

"Mugged," Horst said. "They were mugged."

"They were murdered."

The cross had Thomas's name burnt in crudely with a fission blade. I could have done better than that, Horst thought, it wouldn't have been much to ask for the poor boy, staying sober while I carved his headmarker.

"Murdered, mugged, it happened in a different world, Ruth. Was there ever really such a place as Earth? They say the past is only a memory. I find it very hard to remember Earth now. Does that mean it's gone, do you think?"

She looked at him with real concern. He was unshaven, and probably hadn't been eating properly. The vegetable garden he kept was choked with weeds and vine tendrils. His beefy figure had thinned down considerably. Most people in Aberdale had lost weight since they'd arrived, but they'd built muscle to compensate. Horst's flesh was starting to hang in folds below his chin. She suspected he'd found another supply of drink since she stood on the end of the jetty and emptied his last three bottles of Scotch into the Quallheim. "Where was Jesus born, Horst? Where did he die for our mortal sins?"

"Oh, very good. Yes, very good indeed. I could train you up as a lay preacher in no time if you'd let me."

"I have a field to tend. I have chickens and a goat to feed. I have Jay to look after. What are we going to do about the Ivets?"

"Let he who has not sinned cast the first stone."

"Horst!"

"I'm sorry." He looked mournfully at the cross she was holding.

Ruth thrust it into his hand. "I don't want them living here. Hell, have you seen the way that little Jason Lawes trots around after Quinn Dexter? He's like a puppy on a leash."

"How many of us stop by to look after Rachel and Jason? Oh, we were all such fine neighbours to her for the first week after Gwyn died, ten days even. But now . . . To keep on and on for weeks without end when you have your own family to nurture. People can't do it, they lack the tenacity. Of course they designate the Ivets to help Rachel. Something is done, and conscience is saved. But I attach no blame for that. This place drains us, Ruth. It turns us inwards, we only have time for ourselves."

Ruth bit back on what she had heard about Rachel and Quinn Dexter. Hell, poor Gwyn had only been gone five weeks, couldn't the damn woman wait a little longer? "Where is it going to stop, Horst? Who's next? Do you know what I dream about? I dream of Jay running round after that super-macho Jackson Gael, or Lawrence Dillon with his pretty face and his dead smile. That's what I dream. Are you going to tell me I have nothing to worry about, that I'm just paranoid? Six deaths in five weeks. Six *accidents* in five weeks. We have to do something."

"I know!" Horst jabbed Judy Hoffman's cross into the ground. Water oozed up around the edge of the wood. Like blood, he thought, filthy blood.

The jungle steamed softly. It had rained less than an hour ago, and every trunk and leaf was still slick with water. One thick stratum of swan-white mist had formed at waist height. It meant the four Ivets tramping down the animal track could barely see their feet. Fingers of sunlight probing down through the screen of overhead leaves shone out like solid strands of gold in the ultra-humid air. Away in the distance was the tremulous gobbling and cooing of the birds, the chorus they had long since learnt to filter out.

The ground here was rough, distorted by meandering hummocks twice the height of a man. Trees grew out of their sides at slapdash angles, curving upwards, supported by vast buttress roots. Their ash-grey trunks were slender in relation to their height, seldom more than thirty centimetres wide, yet they were all over twenty metres high, crowned by interlaced umbrellas of emerald foliage. Nothing grew on the trunks below. Even the vines and scrub plants around the triangular roots lacked their usual vigour.

"There's no game here," Scott Williams said after half an hour of scrambling over interminable hummocks and splashing through the water that pooled around them. "It's the wrong sort of country."

"That's right," Quinn Dexter said. "No reason for anyone to come this way." They had started out early that morning, marching down the well-worn path towards the savannah homesteads to the south of Aberdale, a legitimate hunting party, with four borrowed laser rifles and one electromagnetic rifle. Quinn had led them straight down the path for five kilometres, then broke off into the jungle towards the west. He made one sweep each week, the guido block he'd taken from the Hoffmans' homestead making sure a different area was searched each time.

They had done well from the Hoffmans that night a fortnight ago. Donnie had come to Lalonde well prepared for the rigours of pioneering life. There had been freeze-dried food, tools, medical supplies, several rifles, and two Jovian Bank credit disks. The six Ivets he had led on the night-time mission to the homestead had feasted well before he turned them loose on Judy and the two children.

That had been the first time Quinn had conducted the full ceremony, the dark mass of dedication to God's Brother. Binding the others to him with the shared corruption. Before that it had been fear which made them obey. Now he owned their souls.

Two of them had been the weakest of the Ivet group, Irley and Scott, disbelievers until lovely Angie was offered to them. The serpent beast had awoken in each of them, as it always did, inflamed by the heat, and chanting, and orange torchlight shining on naked skin. God's Brother had whispered into their hearts, and shown them the true way of the flesh, the animal way. Temptation had triumphed yet again, and Angie's cries had carried far across the savannah in the still night air. Since the ceremony they had become Quinn's most trusted comrades.

It was something Banneth had shown him; the ceremonies were more than simple worship, they had a purpose. If you lived through them, if you committed the rituals, you became part of the sect for ever. There was nobody else after that. You were a pariah, irredeemable; loathed, hated, and rejected by decent society, by the followers of Jesus and Allah.

Soon there would be more ceremonies, and all the Ivets would undergo their initiation.

The ground began to flatten out. The trees were growing closer together now, with thicker undergrowth. Quinn plodded through another stream, boots crunching on the pebbles. He was wearing knee-length green denim shorts and a sleeveless vest of the same material, just right to protect his skin from thorns and twigs. They used to belong to Gwyn Lawes; Rachel had given all his clothes to the Ivets as a thank you for keeping her field free of weeds and creepers. Poor Rachel Lawes was not a well woman these days, she had become very brittle since her husband's death. She talked to herself and heard the voices of saints. But at night she listened to what Quinn wanted, and did it. Rachel hated Lalonde as much as he did, and she wasn't alone in the village. Quinn took note of the names she confessed, and ordered the Ivets to ingratiate themselves with the disaffected.

Lawrence Dillon let out an exuberant whoop, and fired off his borrowed laser rifle. Quinn looked up in time to see a vennal shooting through the tops of the trees, the little lizardlike animal flowing like liquid along the high branches, its paws barely touching the bark.

Lawrence fired again. A puff of smoke squirted from a branch where the vennal had been an instant before. "Sheech, but it's fast."

"Leave it," Quinn said. "You'll only have to carry it the rest of the day. We'll bag some meat on the way back."

"OK, Quinn," Lawrence Dillon said doubtfully. His head was cranked back, shifting from side to side as he squinted upwards. "I've lost it, anyway."

Quinn looked up at where the vennal had been. The nimble tree-dwelling creatures had a blue-green hide which was nearly impossible to distinguish from more than fifteen metres. He switched to infrared, and scanned the treetops of the shadowless red and pink world his retinal implant revealed. The vennal was a bright salmon-pink corona, lying prone along the top of a thick bough, triangular head peering down nervously at them. Quinn turned a complete circle.

"I want you to put your weapons down," he said.

The others gave him puzzled glances. "Quinn—"

"Now." He unslung his laser rifle, and laid it on the wet grass. It was a tribute to his authority that the others did as they were told without any further protest.

Quinn spread his hands, palms open. "Satisfied?" he demanded.

The chameleon suit lost its bark pattern, reverting to a dark grey.

Lawrence Dillon took a pace backwards in surprise. "Shit. I never saw him."

Quinn only laughed.

The man was standing with his back pressed against a qualtook tree eight metres away. He pulled the hood back revealing a round forty-year-old face with a steep chin and light grey eyes.

"Morning," Quinn said in a jaunty tone. He had been expecting someone different, someone with Banneth's brand of lashed-up mania; this man seemed to have no presence at all. "You've taken my advice, then? Very wise."

"Tell me why you should not be eliminated," the man said.

Quinn thought his voice sounded as though it had been synthesized by a processor block, completely neutral. "Because you don't know who I've told, or what I've told them. That makes me safe. If you could go around snuffing out entire villages whenever your security had been compromised, you wouldn't be stashed away here. Now would you?"

"What do you want to talk about?"

"I won't know that until I see what you've got. For a start, who are you?"

"This body's name is Clive Jenson."

"What have you done to him, put in a persona sequestrator nanonic?"

"Not quite, but the situation is similar."

"So, are you ready to talk now?"

"I will listen." The man beckoned. "You will come with me, the others will remain here."

"Hey, no way," Jackson Gael said.

Quinn held his hands up. "It's OK, it's cool. Stay here for three hours, then go back to Aberdale whether I'm back or not." He checked the coordinate on the guido block, and started walking after the man in the chameleon suit whose name used to be Clive Jenson.

After six weeks' travelling and trading the *Coogan* was approaching the end of its voyage. Marie Skibbow knew they were within days of Durringham even though Len Buchannan had said nothing. She recognized the lying villages again; the white-painted slat walls of the trim houses, neat gardens, the pastoral fantasy. The Juliffe was coffee brown again, running eagerly towards the freedom of the ocean that couldn't be far away now. She could see the Hultain Marsh squatting on the north shore when the wavelets weren't riding too high, a dismal snarl of mouldy vegetation sending out eye-smarting streamers of brimstone gases. Big paddle-craft similar to the *Swithland* were churning their way up-river, leaving a foamy wake behind them. Fresh colonists gazed out at the shoreline with wonder and desire animating their faces, and children raced round the decks laughing and giggling.

Fools. All of them, utter fools.

The *Coogan* was stopping at fewer and fewer jetties now. Their original stocks were almost depleted, the tramp trader riding half a metre higher in the water. The balance in Len Buchannan's Jovian Bank credit disk had grown in proportion. Now he was buying cured meat to sell in the city.

"Stop loading," Len shouted at her from the wheel-house. "We're putting ashore here."

The *Coogan*'s blunt prow turned a couple of degrees, aiming for a jetty below a row of large wooden warehouses. There were several cylindrical grain silos to one side. Power bikes bumped along the dirt tracks winding round the houses. The village was a wealthy one. The kind Marie thought Group Seven was heading for, the kind that had tricked her.

She abandoned the logs she was loading into the hopper, and straightened her back. Weeks spent cutting up timber with a fission saw then feeding the hopper in all weathers had given her the kind of muscles she'd never got from the gym at the arcology's day centre. She had lost almost two centimetres from her waist, her old shorts didn't cling anything like the way they used to.

Thin smoke from the furnace's leaky iron stack made her eyes water. She blinked furiously, staring at the village they were approaching, then ahead to the west. She made up her mind, and walked forward.

Gail Buchannan was sitting at the side of the wheelhouse, her scraggly hair tied back, coolie hat casting a shadow over her knitting needles. She had knitted and sewed her way down the whole length of the river from Aberdale.

"Where do you think you're going, lovie?" the huge woman asked.

"My cabin."

"Well, you make sure you get back out here in time to help my Lennie with the mooring. I'm not having you slacking off while he has work to do. I've never known anyone as lazy as you. My poor husband works like a mechanoid to keep us afloat."

Marie ignored the obloquy and brushed past her, ducking down into the cabin. She had turned a corner of the cargo hold into a little nest of her own, sleeping on a length of shelving at nights after Len had finished with her. The wood was hard, and she'd repeatedly knocked her head on the frame during the first week until she got used to the confined space; but there was no way she was going to spend the night lying in his embrace.

She stripped off the colourless dungarees she used on deck, and pulled a clean bra and a T-shirt from her bag where they had lain throughout the voyage. Feeling the smooth synthetic fabric snug against her skin brought back memories of Earth and the arcology. Her world, where there was life and a future, where Govcentral gave away didactic courses, and people had proper jobs, and went to clubs, and had a thousand sensevise entertainment channels to choose from, and the vac trains could take you to the other side of the planet in six hours. Black tropical-weave jeans with a leathery look finished the change. It was like wearing civilization. She picked up the shoulder-bag, and went forwards.

Gail Buchannan was hollering for her as she slid the bolt on the toilet door. The toilet itself was just a wooden box (built from mayope so it could take Gail's weight) with a hole in the top; there was a stack of big vine leaves to wipe with. Marie knelt down and prised the bottom plank off the front of the box. The river gurgled by a metre below. Her two packets were hanging below the decking, tied into place with silicon-fibre fishing-line. She cut the fibre with a pocket fission blade and stuffed the two polythene-wrapped bundles into her shoulder-bag. They were mostly medical nanonic packages, the highest value-for-weight-ratio items the *Coogan* carried; she'd also included some personal MF players, a couple of processor blocks, small power tools. A hoard that had been steadily built up over the voyage. The shoulder-bag's seal barely closed around them.

Gail's voice was reaching hysteria pitch by the time Marie got back to the galley and gave a last look round the wooden cell where she had spent an eternity cooking and cleaning. She took down the big brown clay pot of mixed herbs, and tugged out a thick wad of Lalonde francs. It was only one of the various bundles Gail had secreted around the tramp trader. She stuffed the crisp plastic notes into a rear pocket, then, on impulse, picked up a match before she went out on deck.

The *Coogan* had already pulled up next to the jetty and Len Buchannan was busy tying one of the cables to a bollard. Gail's face had turned a thunderous purple below her coolie hat.

She took in Marie's appearance with one flabbergasted look. "What the hell do you think you're doing dressed like that, you little strumpet? You've got to give Lennie a hand loading the meat. My poor Lennie can't shift all those heavy carcasses by himself. And where the hell do you think you're going with that bag? And what have you got in it?"

Marie smiled her lazy smile, the one her father always

called intolerably indolent. She struck the match on the cabin wall.

Both of them watched the phosphorus tip splutter into life, the yellow flame biting into the splinter of wood, eating its way along towards her fingers. Gail's mouth dropped open as realization dawned.

"Goodbye," she said brightly. "It's been so nice knowing you." She dropped the match into the sewing box at Gail's feet.

Gail screeched in panic as the match disappeared under her scraps of cotton and lace. Bright orange flames licked upwards.

Marie marched off down the jetty. Len was standing by the bollard ahead of her, a length of silicon-fibre rope coiled in his hands.

"You're leaving," he said.

Gail was shouting a tirade of obscenities and threats after her. There was a loud splash as the precious sewing box hit the water.

Marie couldn't manage the blasé expression she wanted. Not in front of him. There was a curious look of dismay on the skinny old man's face.

"Don't go," he said. It was a plea, she'd never heard his voice so whiny before.

"Why? Was there something you didn't have? Something you forgot to try out?" Her voice came close to breaking.

"I'll get rid of her," he said desperately.

"For me?"

"You're beautiful, Marie."

"Is that it? All you've got to say to me?"

"Yes. I thought . . . I never hurt you. Never once."

"And you want it to go on? Is that what you want, Len? The two of us sailing up and down the Juliffe for the rest of our days?"

"Please, Marie. I hate her. I want you, not her."

She stood ten centimetres away from him, smelling the fruit he'd eaten that morning on his breath. "Is that so?"

"I have money. You would live like a princess, I promise."

"Money is nothing. I would have to be loved. I could give

everything of myself to a man who loved me. Do you love me, Len? Do you really love me?"

"I do, Marie. God, I do. Please. Come with me!"

She ran a finger along his chin. Tears were welling up in his eyes.

"Then kill yourself, Len," she whispered thickly. "For she is all you have. She is all you'll ever have. For the rest of your life, Len, you're going to live with the knowledge that I am always beyond you."

She waited until his tragi-hopeful face crumpled in utter mortification, then laughed. It was so much more satisfactory than kneeing him in the balls.

There was a wagon loaded with silage trundling along the main dirt track, heading west. A fourteen-year-old boy in dungarees was driving it, giving occasional flicks on the big shire-horse's reins. Marie stuck out her thumb, and he nodded eagerly, overawed eyes goggling at her. She clambered aboard while it was still moving.

"How far to Durringham?" she asked.

"Fifty kilometres. But I'm not going that far, just to Mepal."

"That'll do for a start." She sat back on the hard wooden plank seat, the jolting wheels rocking her gently from side to side. The sun was boiling, the swaying was uncomfortable, the horse stank. She felt wonderful.

The gigantea was over seven thousand years old when Laton and his small band of followers arrived on Lalonde. It was set on a small rise in the land, which pushed its three-hundred-metre-plus length even further above the surrounding jungle. Storms had frayed and broken the tip, resulting in a bulbous knot of snarled twigs with tufts of leaves sticking out at odd angles. Birds had turned this malformed pinnacle into a voluminous eyrie, pecking away at it over the centuries until it was riddled with a warren of holes.

When it rained, water would clog in the gigantea's thick fuzzy leaves, their weight pushing the downward-sloping boughs even closer towards the fat bole. Then for hours afterwards droplets would sprinkle down, drying the gigantea out from the top, the boughs slowly rising again. Standing on the ground below was like standing under a small, powerful waterfall. The last traces of soil had been washed away from under the boughs several millennia ago. All that remained was a solid undulating tangle of roots, extending outwards for a hundred metres, slimed like seaside rocks at low tide.

Laton's blackhawk had brought him to Lalonde in 2575. At that time there were less than a hundred people on the planet, a caretaker squad looking after the landing site camp. The ecological assessment team had completed their analysis and left; the Confederation inspection team wasn't due for another year. He had obtained a classified copy of the company report; the planet was habitable, it would gain the Confederation's certification. There would be colonists eventually; dirt poor, ignorant, without any advanced technology. Given his own particular designs on the future, it would be a perfect culture to infiltrate.

They had landed in the mountains on Amarisk's eastern side, twenty humans and seven landcruisers loaded with enough luxuries to make exile bearable, along with more essential stocks: small cybernetic manufacturing systems, and his genetics equipment. He also had the blackhawk's nine eggs, removed from its ovaries and stored in zero-tau. The blackhawk was sent to oblivion in the fierce blue-white star; and the little convoy started to batter its way through the jungle. It took them two days to reach the tributary river which would one day be called the Quallheim. Three days' sailing (the landcruisers had amphibious fuselages) brought them to Schuster County, a territory where the soil was deep enough to support the giganteas. Jungle again, and half a day later he found what must surely be the largest gigantea specimen on the continent.

"This will do," he told his fellowship. "In fact, I think it is rather appropriate."

The branches were still shedding their weight of water from the earlier rain when Clive Jenson led Quinn Dexter onto the slippery coils of the gigantea's roots. There was a perpetual twilight under the huge shaggy boughs. Water pattered down, forming runnels that gurgled and sucked their way around the intestinal tangle below his feet.

Quinn resisted the impulse to hunch his shoulders against the big drops splashing on his head. Spores or sap—something organic—had curdled with the water, making it tacky. It was cool in the shade, the coolest he'd ever been on Lalonde.

They neared the colossal bole. The roots began to curve up to the vertical, wooden waves crashing against a wooden cliff. Between the thick cords were dark anfractuous clefts five times his height, tapering away to knife-thin fissures. Clive Jenson stepped into one. Quinn watched him disappear round a curve, then shrugged and followed him in.

After five metres the floor became level and the walls widened out to a couple of metres, the coarse mat of fibre which passed for the gigantea's bark giving way to smooth bare wood. Carved, he realized. God's Brother, he's cut his home into the tree. How much effort has gone into this?

There was a glimmer of light up ahead. He walked round an S-bend, and into a brightly lit room. It was fifteen metres long, ten wide, perfectly ordinary except for the lack of windows. Pegs on one wall held a row of dark green cagoules. Gigantea wood was a pale walnut colour, with a widely spaced grain, making it look as though the walls were built from exceptionally broad planks. There was a desk, like a long bar, running down one side, that had been carved from a single block. A woman stood at the far end of it, watching him impassively.

Quinn broke into a slow grin. She looked about twenty-five, taller than him, with black skin and long chestnut hair, a petite button nose. Her sleeveless amber blouse and white culottes showed off a full figure.

A flicker of distaste crossed her face. "Don't be disgusting, Dexter."

"What? I never said a word."

"You didn't have to. I'd sooner screw a servitor housechimp."

"Do I get to watch?"

Her expression intensified. "Stand still, don't move, or

I'll have Clive dissect you." She picked a sensor wand off the desk.

Still grinning, Quinn lifted his arms out, and let her run the wand around him. Clive stood to attention a couple of metres away, perfectly still, as if he was a mechanoid construct that had been switched off. Quinn tried not to let it show how much that bothered him.

"So how long have you been here?" he asked.

"Long enough."

"What do I call you?"

"Camilla."

"OK, Camilla, that's cool. So what's the story here?"

"I'll let Laton tell you." Her tongue was pushed into her cheek. "That's if he doesn't just decide to incorporate you like Clive here."

Quinn threw a glance at the stationary man. "One of the colonists from the Schuster homesteads?"

"That's right."

"Ah."

"Your heart rate is high, Dexter. Worried about something?"

"No. Are you?"

She put the wand back on the desk. "You can see Laton now. You're no danger; two implants and a whole load of attitude."

He flinched at the mention of implants. There went his last advantage, tiny though it had been. "Got me this far, hasn't it?"

Camilla started to walk towards the door. "Getting in is the easy part."

There was a broad spiral staircase leading up through the bole. Quinn caught glimpses of corridors and rooms. A whole level was given over to a large pool-cum-spa. Steam was thick in the air, men and women were lounging about in the water or on various ledges; one was lying flat on a slab being given a massage by a middle-aged woman with an empty expression he was beginning to recognize. He realized what was missing: some people were laughing, but nobody was talking. Servitor housechimps scurried down corridors on mysterious errands; they were about a metre and a half tall, walking with an almost human gait, their golden fur well groomed. When he looked closely he saw they had proper feet rather than the paws of their Earth-jungle ancestors.

God's Brother, those are Edenist constructs. What the fuck is this?

Camilla took him down a corridor that looked no different to any other. A door opened soundlessly, a thick wooden rectangle with some kind of synthetic muscle as a hinge.

"Lion's den, Dexter; in you go."

The door closed as silently as it had opened. Inside was a large circular space with a vaulted ceiling. The furniture was a severe minimalist style: a glass-topped desk with metal legs, a dining table, also glass topped, two settees facing each other; every piece arranged to put a maximum amount of distance between them. One section of the wall was a vast holographic screen with a view of the jungle outside. The camera was well above the treetops, showing an unbroken expanse of leaves; steamy scraps of cloud drifted in meandering patterns. An iron perch, three metres high, stood in the centre of the room. On it was the kestrel, watching him intently. Two people were waiting, a man seated behind the desk and a young girl standing beside the settees.

Laton rose from behind the desk. He was one of the tallest men Quinn had ever seen; well muscled, with cinnamon-coloured skin, looking like a tan rather than natural pigmentation, a handsome, vaguely Asian face with deep-set grey-green eyes and a neat beard, ebony hair tied back in a small pony-tail. He wore a simple green silk robe, belted at the waist. His age was indeterminable, over thirty, less than a hundred. That he was the product of geneering was in no doubt.

This was the presence Quinn had looked for when Clive Jenson had pulled off his chameleon-suit hood. The invincible self-assurance, a man who inspired devotion.

"Quinn Dexter, you've caused quite a stir among my colleagues. We have very few visitors, as you can imagine. Do sit down." Laton gestured to a royal-purple settee where the girl was waiting. "Can we get you anything while you're here? A decent drink? A proper meal, perhaps? Dear old Aberdale isn't exactly flowing with milk and honey yet."

Quinn's instinct was to refuse, but the offer was too tempting. So bollocks if it made him look grasping and inferior. "A steak, medium rare, with chips and a side salad, no mustard. And a glass of milk. Never thought I'd miss milk." He gave Laton what he hoped was a phlegmatic smile as the big man sat down on the settee opposite. Out-cooling him was going to be a major problem.

"Certainly, I think we can manage that. We use starscraper food-secretion glands, modified to work from the gigantea's sap. The taste is quite passable." Laton raised his voice a degree. "Anname, see to that, would you, please."

The girl gave a slight, uncertain bow. She must have been about twelve or thirteen, Quinn thought, with thick blonde hair coming down below her shoulders and pale Nordic skin; her lashes were almost invisible. Her light blue eyes put Quinn in mind of Gwyn Lawes in the moments before his death. Anname was one very badly frightened little girl.

"Another member of the missing homestead families?" Quinn guessed.

"Indeed."

"And you haven't incorporated her?"

"She's given me no reason to. The adult males are useful for various labour-intensive tasks, which is why I kept them on; but the young boys I had no requirement for at all, so they were stored for transplant material."

"And what were your requirements?"

"Ovaries, basically. I didn't have a sufficient quantity for the next stage of my project. It was a situation which the homestead females were fortunately able to rectify for me. We have enough suspension tanks here to maintain their Fallopian tubes in a fully functional state, thus ensuring they keep dropping their precious little gifts into my palm each month. Anname hasn't quite matured enough for that yet. And seeing as how organs never really prosper in tanks, we allow her to run around the place until she's ready. Some of my companions have become quite fond of her. I even confess to finding her moderately tolerable myself."

Anname flashed him a glance of pure terror before the door opened and let her out.

"There's a lot of bitek at work here," Quinn said. "If I didn't know better, I'd say you were an Edenist."

Laton frowned. "Oh dear. My name doesn't register amongst your memories, then?"

"No. Should it?"

"Alas, such is fame. Fleeting at best. Of course, I did achieve my notoriety a considerable number of years before you were born, so I suppose it's to be expected."

"What did you do?"

"There was an irregularity concerning a quantity of antimatter, and a proteanic virus which damaged my habitat's personality rather badly. I'm afraid I released it before the replicant code RNA transfer was perfected."

"Your habitat? Then you are an Edenist?"

"Wrong tense. I was an Edenist, yes."

"But you're all affinity bonded. None of you breaks the law. You can't."

"Ah, there, I'm afraid, my young friend, you are a victim of popular prejudice, not to mention some rather sickly propaganda on Jupiter's behalf. There aren't many of us; but believe me, not everybody born an Edenist dies an Edenist. Some of us rebel, we shut off that cacophony of nobility and unity that vomits into our minds every living second. We regain our individuality, and our mental freedom. And more often than not, we choose to pursue our independent course through life. Our ex-peers refer to us as Serpents." He gave an ironic smile. "Naturally they don't like to admit we exist. In fact they go to rather tedious lengths to track us down. Hence my current position."

"Serpents," Quinn whispered. "That's what all men are. That's what God's Brother teaches us. Everyone is a beast in their heart, it is the strongest part of us, and so we fear it the most. But if you find the courage to let it rule, you can never be beaten. I just never thought an Edenist could free his beast."

"Interesting linguistic coincidence," Laton murmured.

Quinn leaned forwards. "Don't you see, we're the same, you and me. We both walk the same path. We are brothers."

"Quinn Dexter, you and I share certain qualities; but understand this, you became a waster kid, and from that a Light Brother sect member, because of social conditions. That sect was your only route away from mediocrity. I chose to be what I am only after a careful review of the alternatives. And the one thing I retain from my Edenist past is complete atheism."

"That's it! You said it. Shit, both of us told ordinary life to go fuck itself. We follow God's Brother in our own way, but we both follow him."

Laton raised an exasperated eyebrow. "I can see this is a pointless argument. What did you want to talk to me about?"

"I want your help to subdue Aberdale."

"Why should I want to do that?"

"Because I'll turn it over to you afterwards."

Laton looked blank for a second, then inclined his head in understanding. "Of course, the money. I wondered what you wanted the money for. You don't want to be Aberdale's feudal lord, you intend to leave Lalonde altogether."

"Yeah, on the first starship I can buy passage on. If I can get down to Durringham before any alarm gets out, then I can use one of the villagers' Jovian Bank credit disks without any trouble. And with you in charge back here there wouldn't be no alarm."

"What about your Ivet friends, the ones you seem to be busy baptizing in blood?"

"Fuck 'em. I want out. I got business back on Earth, serious business."

"I'm sure you have."

"How about it? We could work it together. Me and the Ivets could round up the women and children during the day when the men are out hunting and farming, use 'em as hostages. Get 'em all into the hall and take their guns away. Once the men are disarmed, it'll be no problem for you to incorporate 'em all. Then you just make 'em live like they do now. Anyone turns up later, Aberdale is just another crappy colonist village full of arse scratchers. I get what I want, which is *out of here*, and you get plenty of warm bods; plus there's no more security risk of someone stumbling on this wood palace and shouting to Durringham about it."

"I think you're overestimating my ability."

"No way. Not now I've seen what you've got. This incorporation gimmick has got to be like persona sequestration. You could run a whole arcology with that technology."

"Yes, but the bitek regulators we implant would have to be grown first. I don't have them in store, certainly not five hundred and fifty of them. It all takes time."

"So? I ain't going anywhere."

"No, indeed. And of course, were I to agree, you would make no mention of me once you returned to Earth?"

"I'm no squeal. One of the reasons I'm here."

Laton eased back onto his settee and gave Quinn a long thoughtful look. "Very well. Now let me make you an offer. Leave Aberdale and join me. I can always use someone with your nerve."

Quinn let his gaze wander round the big vacuous room. "How long have you been here?"

"In the region of thirty-five years."

"I figured something like that; you couldn't have landed after the colonists arrived, not if you're as well known as you say you are. Thirty-five years living in a tree without any windows, I gotta tell you, it ain't me. In any case, I ain't no Edenist, I don't have this affinity trick to control the bitek."

"That can be rectified, you can use neuron symbionts just like your friend Powel Manani. More than a third of my colleagues are Adamists, the rest are my children. You'd fit in. You see, I can give you what you want most."

"I want Banneth, and she's three hundred light-years away. You ain't got her to give."

"I meant, Quinn Dexter, what you really want. What all of us want."

"Oh, yeah? What?"

"A form of immortality."

"Bullshit. Even I know that ain't on. The best the Saldanas can do is a couple of centuries, and that's with all their money and genetic research teams."

"That's because they are going about it the wrong way. The Adamist way."

Quinn hated the way he was being drawn into this conversation. It wasn't what he wanted, he'd seen himself making his pitch on how to subdue Aberdale, and the boss-man seeing the sense of it. Now he was having to think about freaky ideas like living for ever, and trying to make up an excuse why he didn't want to. Which was stupid because he did. But Laton couldn't possibly have it to offer anyway. Except this was a very high-technology operation, and he was using the girls for some kind of biological experiment. God's Brother, but Laton was a smooth one. "So what's your way?" he asked reluctantly.

"A combination of affinity and parallel thought-processes. You know Edenists transfer their memories into their habitat's neural cells when they die?"

"I'd heard about it, yeah."

"That's a form of immortality, although I consider it somewhat unsatisfactory. Identity fades after a few centuries. The will to live, if you like, is lost. Understandable, really, there are no human activities to maintain the spark of vitality which goads us on, all that's left is observation, living your life through your descendants' achievements. Hardly inspiring. So I began to explore the option of simply transferring my memories into a fresh body. There are several immediate problems which prevent a direct transfer. Firstly you require an empty brain capable of storing an adult's memories. An infant brain would be empty, but the capacity to retain an adult personality, the century and a half of accumulated memories that go towards making us who we are, that simply isn't there. So I began looking at the neuron structure to see if it could be improved. It's not an area that's been well researched. Brain size has been increased to provide a memory capacity capable of seeing you through a century and a half, and IQ has been raised a few points, but the actual structure is something the geneticists have left alone. I started to examine the idea of human parallel thought-processing, just like the Edenist habitats. They can hold a million conversations at once, as well as regulating their environment, acting as an administrative executive, and a thousand other functions, although they have only the one consciousness. Yet we poor mortal humans can only ever think about or do one thing at a time. I sought to reprofile a neural network so that it could conduct several operations simultaneously. That was the key. I realized that as there was no limit to the number of operations which could be conducted, you could even have multiple independent units, bonded by affinity, and sharing a single identity. That way, when one dies, there is no identity loss, the consciousness remains intact and a new unit is grown to replace it."

"Unit?" Quinn said heavily. "You mean a person?"

"I mean a human body with a modified brain, bonded to any number of cloned replicas via affinity. That is the project to which I have devoted my energies here in this exile. With some considerable degree of success, I might add, despite the difficulties of isolation. A parallel-processing brain has been designed, and my colleagues are currently sequencing it into my germ plasm's DNA. After that, my clones will be grown in exowombs. Our thoughts will be linked right from the moment of conception, they will feel what I feel, see what I see. My personality will reside in each of us equally, a homogenized presence. Ultimately, this original body will wither away to nothing, but I shall remain. Death shall become a thing of the past for me. Death will die. I intend to spread out through this world until its resources belong to me, its industries and its population. Then a new form of human society will take shape, one which is not governed by the blind overwhelming biological imperative to reproduce. We shall be more ordered, more deliberate. Ultimately I envisage incorporating bitek constructs into myself; as well as human bodies I will be starships and habitats. Life without temporal limit nor physical restriction. I shall transcend, Quinn; isn't that a dream worth chasing? And now I offer it to you. The homestead girls can provide enough ova for all of us to be cloned. Modifying your DNA is a simple matter, and each of your clones will breed true. You can join us, Quinn, you can live for ever. You can even deal with this Banneth person; ten of you, twenty, an army of your mirrorselves can descend on her arcology to effect your revenge. Now doesn't that appeal, Quinn? Hasn't that got more style than rushing round a jungle at night carving people's guts out for a few thousand fuseodollars?"

Sheer willpower kept Quinn's face composed into an indifferent mask. He wished he had never come, wished he had never figured out the kestrel. God's Brother, how he wished. Banneth was nothing compared to this crazo, Banneth was pure reasoned sanity. Yet all the shit Laton sprouted had a terrible logic, drawing him in like the dance of the black widow. Telling him he could be immortal was the same trick he had used against the Ivets, but with such demonic panache, blooding him in conspiracy, making sure there was no turning back. He knew Laton would never let him get to Durringham's spaceport, let alone reach an orbiting starship. Not now, not with him knowing. The only way out of this tree—this room!—with his brain still his own was by agreeing. And it was going to have to be the most convincing agreement he had ever made in his life.

"This spreading your mind around gimmick, would I have to give up my belief?" he asked.

Laton gave him a thin smile. "Your belief would be amplified, safeguarded against loss in your multiple units, and carried down the centuries. You could even step out of the shadows to exhort your belief. What difference would it make if individual units were flung in jail or executed? The you that is you would remain."

"And sex, I'd still have sex, wouldn't I?"

"Yes, with one small difference, every gene would be dominant. Every child you sired would be another of your units."

"How far along are you with this parallel-processor brain? Have you actually grown one to see if it works?"

"A numerical simulacrum has been run through a bitek processor array. The analysis program proved its validity. It's a standard technique; the one Edenist geneticists used to design the voidhawks. They work, don't they?"

"Sure. Look, I'm interested. I can hardly deny that. God's Brother, living for ever, who wouldn't want it? Tell you what, I won't make any move to get back to Earth until after these clones of yours have popped out the exowombs. If they check out as good as you say, I'll be with you like a shot. If not, we'll review where we stand. Fuck, I don't mind waiting around a few years if that's what it takes to perfect it."

"Commendable prudence," Laton purred.

"Meantime, it'd be a good idea to bugger up Supervisor Manani's communicator block. For both our sakes. However it turns out, neither of us wants the villagers shouting to the capital for help. Can you let me have a flek loaded with some kind of processor-buster virus? If I just smash it, he's gonna know it's me."

Anname walked in carrying a tray with Quinn's steak, and a half-litre glass of milk. She put it down on Quinn's lap, and glanced hesitantly at Laton.

"No, my dear," Laton told her. "This is definitely not St George come to spirit you away from my fire-breathing self."

She sniffed hard, cheeks reddening.

Quinn grinned wolfishly at her round a mouthful of steak.

"I think I can live with that arrangement," Laton said. "I'll have one of my people prepare a flek for you before you go."

Quinn slurped some of his milk, and wiped his mouth with the back of his hand. "Great."

There was something wrong with Aberdale's church. Only half of the pews had ever been built and installed, though Horst Elwes occasionally worked on the planks of planed wood the Ivets had cut ready for the remainder. He doubted the three pews he had already assembled in the occasional bouts of shame-induced activity would take the weight of more than four people. But the roof didn't leak, there was the familiarity of hymn books and vestments, the paraphernalia of worship, and he had a vast collection of devotional music on fleks which the audio-player block projected across the building. For all its deviant inception, it still symbolized a form of hope. Of late, it had become his refuge. Hallowed ground or not, and Horst wasn't stupid enough to think that was any form of protection, the Ivets never came inside.

But something had.

Horst stood in front of the bench which served as an altar, hair on his arms pricked up as though he was standing in some kind of massive static stream. There was a presence in the church, ethereal yet with an almost brutal strength. He could feel it watching him. He could feel age almost beyond comprehension. The first time Horst had seen a gigantea he had spent over an hour just looking up at it in stupefaction, a living thing that had been old when Christ walked the Earth. But the gigantea was nothing compared to this, the tree was a mere infant. Age, real age, was a fearful thing.

Horst didn't believe in ghosts. Besides, the presence was too real for that. It enervated the church, absorbing what scant ration of divinity had once existed.

"What are you?" he whispered to the gentle breeze. Night was falling outside, waving treetops cast a jagged sable-black silhouette against the gold-pink sky. The men were returning from the fields, sweaty and tired, but smiling. Voices carried through the clearing. Aberdale was so peaceful, it looked like everything he had wanted when he left Earth.

"What are you?" Horst demanded. "This is a church, a house of God. I will have no sacrilege committed here. Only those who truly repent are welcome."

For a giddy moment his thoughts were rushing headlong through empty space. The velocity was terrifying. He yelled in shock, there was nothing around him, no body, no stars. This was what he imagined the null-dimension that existed outside a starship would look like while it jumped.

Abruptly, he was back in the church. A small ruby star burnt in the air a couple of metres in front of him.

He stared at it in shock, then giggled. "Twinkle twinkle, little star. How I wonder what you are."

The star vanished.

His laughter turned to a strangled pule. He fled out into the dusky clearing, stumbling through the soft loam of his vegetable garden, heedless of the shabby plants he trampled.

It was his singing which drew the villagers a few hours later. He was sitting on the jetty with a bottle of home-brew vodka. The group that had gathered looked down at him with contempt.

"Demons!" Horst shouted when Powel Manani and a couple of the others pulled him to his feet. "They've only gone and summoned bloody demons here."

Ruth gave him one disgusted glance, and stalked off back to her cabin.

Horst was dragged back to his cot, where they administered one of his own tranquillizers. He fell asleep still mumbling warnings.

The Ly-cilph was interested in humans. Out of the hundred and seventy million sentient species it had encountered, only three hundred thousand had been able to perceive it, either by technology or their own mentalities.

The priest had clearly been aware of its identity focus, although not understanding the nature. Humans obviously had a rudimentary attunement to their energistic environment. It searched through the records it had compiled by accessing the few processor blocks and memory fleks available in Aberdale, which mostly comprised the educational texts owned by Ruth Hilton. The so-called psychic ability was largely dismissed as hallucinatory or fraud committed for financial gain. However the race had a vast history of incidents and myths in its past. And its strong continuing religious beliefs were an indication of how widespread the faculty was, granting the "supernatural" events a respectable orthodoxy. There was obviously a great deal of potential for energistic perception development, which was inhibited by the rational mentality. The conflict was a familiar one to the Ly-cilph, although it had no record of a race in which the two opposing natures were quite so antagonistic.

What do you think? Laton asked his colleagues when the door closed behind Quinn Dexter.

He's a psychopathic little shit, with a nasty steak of sadism thrown in, said Waldsey, the group's chief viral technologist.

Dexter is certainly unstable, Camilla said. **I don't think you can trust him to keep any agreement. His revenge obsession with this Banneth person is the dominant motivator. Our immortality scheme is unlikely to replace it; too cerebral.**

I say we should eliminate him, Salkid said.

I'm inclined to agree, Laton said. **Pity. It's rather like watching a miniature version of one's self.**

You were never that gratuitous, Father, Camilla said.

Given the circumstances, I might have been. However, that is an irrelevant speculation. Our immediate problem is our own security. One can reasonably assume Quinn Dexter has informed most, if not all, of his fellow Ivets that something wicked lurks in the woods. That is going to make life difficult.

So? We just take out all of them, Salkid said. Out of all the exiles, the ex-blackhawk captain found the decades of inactivity hardest to handle. **I'll lead the incorporated. It'll be a pleasure.**

Salkid, stop acting the oaf, Laton said. **We can't possibly eliminate all the Ivets ourselves. The attention such an overt action would generate would be quite intolerable coming so soon after the homesteads.**

What, then?

Firstly we shall wait until Quinn Dexter incapacitates Supervisor Manani's communicator, then we shall have to get the villagers to eliminate the Ivets for us.

How? Waldsey asked.

The priest already knows the Ivets are Devil worshippers. We shall simply make the knowledge available to everyone else in a fashion they cannot possibly ignore.

12

Idria traced a slightly elliptical orbit through the Lyll asteroid belt in the New Californian system, with a median distance of a hundred and seventy million kilometres from the G5 primary star. It was a stony-iron rock, which looked like a bruised, flaking swede, measuring seventeen kilometres across at its broadest and eleven down the short spin axis. A ring formation of thirty-two industrial stations hung over the crinkled black rock, insatiable recipients of a never-ending flow of raw material ferried out from Idria's non-rotating spaceport.

It was the variety of those compounds which justified the considerable investment made in the rock. Idria's combination of resources was rare, and rarity always attracts money.

In 2402 a survey craft found long veins of minerals smeared like a diseased rainbow through the ordinary metal ores, their chemistry a curious mixture of sulphurs, alumina, and silicas. A planetside board meeting deemed that the particular concentration of crystalline strata was valuable enough to warrant an extraction operation; and the miners and their heavy digging machinery began chewing shafts into the interior in 2408. Industrial stations followed, refining and processing the ores on site. Population began to creep upwards, caverns were expanded, biospheres started. By 2450 the central cavern was five kilometres long and four wide, Idria's rotation was increased to give it a half-standard gravity on the floor. There were ninety thousand people living in it by then, forming a community which was self-sufficient in most areas. It was declared independent, and earned a seat in the system assembly. But it was a company town, the company being Lassen Interstellar.

Lassen was into mining, and shipping, and finance, and

starship components, and military systems, amongst other endeavours. It was a typical New Californian outfit, a product of innumerable mergers and takeovers; a linear extension of its old Earth predecessors which had thrived on America's western seaboard. Its management worshipped the super-capitalist ethic, expanding aggressively, milking governments for development contracts, pressuring the assembly for ever more convenient tax breaks, spreading subsidiaries across the Confederation, shafting the opposition at every opportunity.

There were thousands of companies like it based on New California. Corporate tigers whose spoils elevated the standard of living right across the system. The nature of their competition was fierce and confrontational. The Confederation assembly had passed several censure motions on their dubious exports, and held inquiries into individual supply contracts. New California's level of technology was high, its military products were in great demand. Companies were indifferent to the use they would ultimately be put to: once the buyer was identified, the pitch made, the finance organized, nothing would be allowed to stop the sale. Not the Government Export Licence office, and certainly not the meddlesome Confederation inspectors. With this in mind, shipping could be a problem, especially the trickier contracts to star systems operating unreasonable embargoes. Captains who took on those contracts could expect high rewards. And the challenge always attracted a certain type of individual.

The *Lady Macbeth* was resting on a docking cradle in one of the thirty-odd industrial stations coasting in a loose orbit around Idria. Both of her circular cargo hold doors on the forward hull were open, each showing a metallic cave of bracing struts coiled by power and data cables, load clamps, and environmental regulation interface sockets; all of it wrapped in tarnished gold foil and badly illuminated to boot.

The docking bay was a seventy-five-metre crater of carbotanium and composite, ribbed by various conduits and pipes. Spotlights around the curving walls shone stark white beams on the starship's leaden hull, compensating for the pallid slivers of sunlight falling on the station while it was in Idria's penumbra. Several storage frames stood around the rim of the bay, looking much like scaffold towers left over from the station's construction. Each of them was equipped with a long quadruple-jointed waldo arm to load and unload cargo from ships. The arms were operated from a console inside small transparent bubbles protruding from the carbotanium surface like polished barnacles.

Joshua Calvert hung on a grab hoop inside the cargo supervisor's compartment, his face centimetres from the curving radiation-shielded glass, watching the waldo arm raising another cargo-pod out of its storage frame. The pods were two metres long, pressurized cylinders with slightly domed ends; a thick white silicon-composite shell protected them from the wider temperature shifts encountered in space. They were stamped with Lassen's geometric eagle logo, and line after line of red stencil lettering. According to the code they were high-density magnetic-compression coils for tokamaks. And ninety per cent of the pods did indeed contain what they said; the other ten per cent held smaller, more compact coils which produced an even stronger magnetic field, suitable for antimatter confinement.

The waldo arm lowered the pod into *Lady Mac*'s hold, and a set of load clamps closed around it. Joshua felt a considerable twinge of apprehension. Inside the New Californian system the coils were a legitimate cargo, no matter the misleading coding. In interstellar space their legality was extremely ambiguous, although a decent lawyer should be able to quash any charges. And in the Puerto de Santa Maria system where he was going they spelt deep shit in capital letters ten metres high.

Sarha Mitcham's hand tightened around his. "Do we really need this?" she asked in a murmur. She had left her padded skullcap off in the transparent hemisphere, letting her short hazel hair wave around lethargically in free fall. Her lips were drawn together in concern.

" 'Fraid so." He tickled her palm with a finger, a private signal they often used on board *Lady Mac*. Sarha was a spirited lover, they had spent long hours experimenting in his cabin's cage; but this time it didn't break her mood.

It wasn't that the *Lady Macbeth* didn't make money: in

the eight months since Roland Frampton's first charter they had landed seven cargoes and one passenger group, some bacteriology specialists on their way to join an ecology review team on Northway. But *Lady Macbeth* also consumed money at a colossal rate: there was fuel and consumables each time they docked; an endless list of component spares, there wasn't a flight which went by without some kind of burn-out or a mandatory time-expiry replacement; the crew's wages had to be met; and then there were spaceport charges and customs and immigration fees. Joshua hadn't quite realized the sheer expense involved in operating the *Lady Macbeth*. Somehow Marcus Calvert had glossed over that part. Profits were slim verging on non-existent, and he couldn't afford to bump his rates up any higher, he wouldn't land a single charter. He'd made more money while he was scavenging.

So now he knew the truth behind the captains' talk in Harkey's Bar, and its countless equivalents across the Confederation. Like him they all said how well they were doing, how they only kept flying for the life it offered rather than financial necessity. Lies, all of it a magnificent, artistic construct of lies. Banks sat back and made money, everyone else worked for a living.

"There's no shame in it," Hasan Rawand had told him a fortnight ago. "Everyone's in the same grind. Hell, Joshua, you're a lot better off than most of us. You haven't got a mortgage to pay off."

Hasan Rawand was the captain of the *Dechal*, an independent trader smaller than the *Lady Mac*. He was in his mid-seventies, and he'd been flying for fifty years, the last fifteen as an owner-captain.

"The real money isn't in cargo charters," he explained. "Not for people like us. That's just makework to tide us over. The big lines have got all the really profitable routes tied up. They operate vacuum-sealed cartels the likes of you and I aren't going to break in."

They were drinking in a club in the dormitory section of an industrial station orbiting Baydon, a two-kilometre alithium wheel spinning to produce a two-thirds standard gravity around the rim. Joshua leant against the bar, and watched the planet's nightside sliding past the huge window. Sparkles of light from cities and towns sketched strange curves across the darkness.

"Where is the money, then?" Joshua asked. He'd been drinking for three solid hours, long enough to sluice enough alcohol past his enhanced organs and into his brain, giving the universe a snug aura.

"Flights which use that fancy fourth drive tube the *Lady Mac*'s fitted out with."

"Forget it, I'm not that anxious to make money."

"All right, OK," Hasan Rawand gestured extravagantly, beer slopping over his glass, drops falling in a slight curve. "I'm just saying that's the nature of it: combat and sanctions busting. That kind of thing is what the independents like you and me were put in this galaxy for. Everybody makes one of those trips every now and then. Some of us, like me, more often than most. That's what keeps the hull intact, and the radiation outside the baffles."

"You make a lot of runs?" Joshua asked, staring into his glass morosely.

"Some. Not a lot. That's where us owner-captains' bad-boy reputation comes from. People think we do it all the time. We don't. But they don't hear about that, about the mundane flights we make for fifty weeks a year. They only hear about us when we get caught, and the news agencies blitz the networks with the arrest. We're the perpetual victims of bad publicity. We should sue."

"But you don't get caught?"

"Haven't yet. There's a method I use, virtually foolproof, but it needs two ships."

"Ah." Joshua must have been drunker than he realized, because the next thing he heard himself saying was: "Tell me more."

And now two weeks later he was starting to regret listening. Although, he had to admit, it damn near was foolproof. Those two weeks had been spent in furious preparation. In a way, he supposed having Hasan Rawand consider him for any kind of partner was an oblique compliment, since only the very best captains could hope to pull it off. And the ultimate risk wasn't his, not this run. He was the junior partner.

But still, twenty per cent wasn't to be sneered at, not when it came to a straight eight hundred thousand fuseodollars, half in advance.

The last pod of magnetic coils was secured in the *Lady Mac*'s cargo hold. Sarha Mitcham let out a soft, rueful sigh as the waldo arm folded down on its cradle. This flight worried her, but she had agreed, along with the rest of the crew when Joshua explained what it entailed. And their money situation was becoming uncomfortably shaky. Even the fleks of MF-band albums the crew always hawked around ports to the bootleg distributors were fetching minimal prices. A lot of her private stock was getting obsolete, official company distribution was catching up on her. Here on Idria she had actually bought more albums than she'd sold. At least New California was a hot system for MF culture, she ought to be able to sell the fresh recordings for another six months yet, especially on the kind of backworld ports *Lady Macbeth* flew to.

The money would go into the crew's pooled account so they could finance their own cargo in a couple of months' time. It was their one bright dream, which made the mundane tolerable. Norfolk was reaching conjunction soon, a cargo of Tears would make some real profit for them if they owned it rather than simply carried it for someone else. And then just maybe they wouldn't have to do this kind of flight again for a long time.

"All loaded, and not a scratch on your hull," the woman operating the waldo arm said cheerfully.

Joshua looked back over his shoulder and smiled at her. She was slender, and a bit tall for his taste, but her one-piece uniform showed a nice collection of curves below its emerald fabric. "Yeah, good work, thanks." He datavised her console, loading in his personal code to confirm the cargo had been transferred on board the *Lady Mac*.

She checked the data, and handed him his manifest flek. "*Bon voyage*, Captain."

Joshua and Sarha glided out of the compartment, negotiating the maze of narrow corridors down to the telescoping airlock tube that linked the *Lady Mac*'s life-support capsules to the station.

The waldo operator waited for a minute after they left, then closed her eyes. **The cargo pods are all loaded.** *Lady Macbeth* **is scheduled to disengage from the station in eighteen minutes.**

Thank you, *Oenone* replied.

Tranquillity's senses perceived the gravitational disturbance caused by the wormhole terminus opening in a designated emergence zone a hundred and fifteen thousand kilometres away from the habitat itself. Against Mirchusko's mud-yellow immensity the terminus was a neutral two-dimensional disk. Yet observing it through an optical sensor on one of the strategic-defence platforms ringing the zone, Tranquillity received an inordinately powerful intimation of *depth*.

Ilex flew out of the wormhole. A voidhawk with a hull that was more grey than the usual blue. It slipped smoothly away from the rapidly shrinking terminus, yawing gracefully as it orientated itself.

Ilex, **Confederation Navy ship ALV-90100, requesting approach and docking permission,** it said formally.

Granted, Tranquillity replied.

The voidhawk accelerated in towards the habitat, building up to three gees almost immediately.

You're very welcome, Tranquillity said. **I don't get many voidhawks visiting me.**

Thank you. Though this is not a privilege I was expecting. Up until three days ago we were assigned to fleet patrol duties in the Ellas sector. Now we've been switched to diplomatic courier duty. My captain, Auster, is experiencing a mild notion of displeasure, he says we didn't sign on to be used as a taxi service.

Oh, this sounds interesting.

I believe the circumstances are exceptional. And in connection with this, my captain has another request. He asks that Ione Saldana receive a special envoy from First Admiral Samual Aleksandrovich: one Captain Maynard Khanna.

You have come directly from Avon to bring this captain?

Yes.

The Lord of Ruin is honoured to accept the Admiral's envoy, and she invites Captain Auster and his crew to dinner this evening.

My captain accepts. He is curious about Ione Saldana, the news agencies have been most effusive on her behalf.

I could tell you a tale or two about her.

Really?

And I'd be interested to hear about the Ellas sector. Are there many pirates there?

The tube carriage slid to a halt and Captain Khanna stepped out onto the small station's platform. He was thirty-eight years old, with crew-cut sandy red hair, pale skin given to freckles if he was caught by the sun, regular features, and dark brown eyes. His body was kept in trim by a stiff forty-minute navy-approved workout each morning without fail. Out of his academy class of one hundred and fifteen officer cadets he had finished third; it would have been first but the computer psychological assessment said his flexibility wasn't all that it could be, he was "doctrine orientated".

He had been on the First Admiral's executive staff for eighteen months, and in that time hadn't made a single mistake. This was his first independent assignment, and he was frankly terrified. Tactics and command decisions he could handle, even Admiralty office politics; but a semi-reclusive universally revered black sheep Saldana teenage girl affinity-bonded to a non-Edenist bitek habitat was another matter. How the hell did you prepare motivation-analysis profiles on such a creature?

"You'll do all right," Admiral Aleksandrovich had said in his final briefing. "Young enough not to alienate her, smart enough not to insult her intelligence. And all the girls love a uniform." The old man had winked and given him a companionable pat on the back.

Maynard Khanna pulled the jacket of his immaculate deep-blue dress uniform straight, placed his peaked cap firmly on his head, squared his shoulders, and marched up the stairs out of the station. He came out onto a courtyard of flagstones, lined with troughs full of colourful begonias and fuchsias. Paths led off from all sides into the surrounding sub-tropical parkland. He could see some sort of building a hundred metres away; but it was given only a fleeting glance as he stared round in astonishment. After coming through the airlock from the docking-ledge he had climbed straight into the waiting tube carriage, he hadn't seen anything of the interior until now. The sheer size of Tranquillity was awesome, big enough to put a couple of standard Edenist habitats inside and shake them around like dice in a cup. A blinding light-tube glared hotly overhead, white candyfloss clouds trailed slowly through the air. A panorama of forests and meadows flecked with silver lakes and long watercourses rose up on either side of him like the walls of God's own valley. And there was a sea about eight kilometres away—it couldn't be called anything else with its sparkling wavelets and picturesque islands. He followed the arch of it rising up and up, his neck tilting back until his cap threatened to fall off. Millions of tonnes of water were poised above him ready to crash down in a flood which would have defeated Noah.

He brought his head down hurriedly, trying to remember how he had got rid of the giddiness when he visited the Edenist habitats orbiting Jupiter.

"Don't look outside the horizontal, and always remember the poor sod above you thinks you're going to fall on him," his crusty old guide had said.

Knowing he had been defeated before he even started, Maynard Khanna walked along the yellow-brown stone path towards the building that resembled a Hellenic temple. It was a long basilica which had one end opening out into a circular area with a domed roof of some jet-black material supported by white pillars, the gaps between them filled by sheets of blue-mirror glass.

The path took him to the opposite end of the basilica, where a pair of serjeants stood guard duty like nightmare goblin statues on either side of the entrance arch.

"Captain Khanna?" one asked. The voice was mild and friendly, completely at odds with its appearance.

"Yes."

"The Lord of Ruin is expecting you, please follow my servitor." The serjeant turned and led him into the building. They walked down a central nave with large gilt-framed pictures hanging on the brown and white marble walls.

Maynard Khanna assumed they were holograms at first, then he realized they were two-dimensional, and a more detailed look revealed that they were oil paintings. There were a lot of countryside scenes where people wore elaborate, if baroque, costumes, riding on horses or gathered in ostentatious groups. Scenes from old Earth, pre-industrial age. And a Saldana would never make do with copies. They must be genuine. His mind balked at how much they must be worth; you could buy a battle cruiser with the money just one of them would fetch.

At the far end of the nave a Vostok capsule was resting on a cradle under a protective glass dome. Maynard stopped and looked at the battered old sphere with a mixture of trepidation and admiration. It was so small, so *crude*, yet for a few brief years it had represented the pinnacle of human technology. What ever would the cosmonaut who rode it into space think of Tranquillity?

"Which one is it?" he asked the serjeant in a hushed tone.

"Vostok 6, it carried Valentina Tereshkova into orbit in 1963. She was the first woman in space."

Ione Saldana was waiting for him in the large circular audience chamber at the end of the nave. She sat behind a crescent-shaped wooden desk positioned in the centre; thick planes of light streamed in through the giant sheets of glass set between the pillars, turning the air into a platinum haze.

The white polyp floor was etched with a giant crowned phoenix emblem in scarlet and blue. It took an eternity for him to cover the distance from the door to the desk; the sound of his boot heels clicking against the polished surface echoed drily in the huge empty space.

Intended to intimidate, he thought. You know how alone you are when you confront her.

He snapped a perfect salute when he reached the desk. She was a head of state, after all; the Admiral's protocol office had been most insistent about that, and how he should treat her.

Ione was wearing a simple sea-green summer dress with long sleeves. The intense lighting made her short gold-blonde hair glimmer softly.

She was just as lovely as all the AV recordings he'd studied.

"Do take a seat, Captain Khanna," she said, smiling. "You look most uncomfortable standing up like that."

"Thank you, ma'am." There were two high-backed chairs on his side of the desk; he sat in one, still keeping his pose rigid.

"I understand you've come all the way from the First Fleet headquarters at Avon just to see me?"

"Yes, ma'am."

"In a voidhawk?"

"Yes, ma'am."

"Owing to the somewhat unusual nature of this worldlet, we don't have a diplomatic corps, nor a civil service," she said airily. A delicate hand waved around at the audience chamber. "The habitat personality handles all the administrative functions quite effectively. But the Lords of Ruin employ a legal firm on Avon to represent Tranquillity's interests in the Confederation Assembly chamber. If there's a matter of urgency arising, you only have to consult them. I have met the senior partners, and I have a lot of confidence in them."

"Yes, ma'am—"

"Maynard, please. Stop calling me ma'am. This is a private meeting, and you're making me sound like a day-club governess for junior aristocrats."

"Yes, Ione."

She smiled brightly. The effect was devastating. Her eyes were an enchanting shade of blue, he noticed.

"That's better," she said. "Now what have you come to talk about?"

"Dr Alkad Mzu."

"Ah."

"Are you familiar with the name?"

"The name and most of the circumstances."

"Admiral Aleksandrovich felt this was not a matter to take to your legal representatives on Avon. It is his opinion that the fewer people who are aware of the situation, the better."

Her smile turned speculative. "Fewer people? Maynard, there are eight different Intelligence agencies who have set up shop in Tranquillity; and all of them run surveillance operations on poor Dr Mzu. There are times when their pursuit becomes dangerously close to a slapstick routine. Even the Kulu ESA have posted a team here. I imagine that must be a real thorn in my cousin Alastair's regal pride."

"I think what the Admiral meant was: fewer people outside high government office."

"Yes, of course, the people *most* able to deal with the situation."

The irony in her tone made Maynard Khanna give an inward flinch. "In view of the fact that Dr Mzu is now contacting a number of starship captains, and the Omutan sanctions are about to expire, the Admiral would be extremely grateful if we could be told of your policy regarding Dr Mzu," he said formally.

"Are you recording this for the Admiral?"

"Yes, a full sensevise."

Ione stared straight into his eyes, speaking in a clear precise diction. "My father promised Admiral Aleksandrovich's predecessor that Dr Alkad Mzu would never be allowed to leave Tranquillity, and I repeat that promise to the Admiral. She will not be permitted to leave, nor will I countenance any attempt to sell or hand over the information she presumably holds to anybody, including the Confederation Navy. Upon her death, she will be cremated in order to destroy her neural nanonics. And I hope to God that sees the end of the threat."

"Thank you," Maynard Khanna said.

Ione relaxed a little. "I hadn't even been gestated when she arrived here twenty-six years ago, so tell me, I'm curious. Has Fleet Intelligence discovered yet how she survived Garissa's destruction?"

"No. She can't have been on the planet. The Confederation Navy was in charge of the evacuation, and we have no record of carrying her on any of our ships. Nor was she listed as being in any of the asteroid settlements. The only logical conclusion is that she was outsystem on some kind of clandestine military mission when Omuta bombed Garissa."

"Deploying the Alchemist?"

"Who knows? The device certainly wasn't used; so either it didn't work or they were intercepted. The general staff favours the interception scenario."

"And if she survived, so did the Alchemist," Ione concluded.

"If it was ever built."

She raised an eyebrow. "After all this time, I thought that was taken for granted."

"The thinking goes that after all this time, we should have heard something other than rumours. If it does exist, why haven't the Garissan survivors tried to use it against Omuta?"

"When it comes to Doomsday machines, rumours are all I want to hear."

"Yes."

"You know, I've watched her sometimes while she's been working over in the Laymil project's physics centre. She's a good physicist, her colleagues respect her. But she's nothing exceptional, not mentally."

"One idea in a lifetime is all it takes."

"You're right. Clever of her to come here, really. The one place where her security is guaranteed, and at the same time the one mini-nation which everybody knows is no military threat to other Confederation members."

"So may I say you have no objection to our maintaining our observation team?"

"You can, providing you don't flaunt the privilege. But please reassure yourselves. I don't think she's received much geneering, if any. She can't last more than another thirty years, forty at the outside. Then it will all be over."

"Excellent." He leant forward a few millimetres, lips moving upwards into a slight awkward smile. "There was one other matter."

Ione's eyes widened with innocent anticipation. "Yes?"

"An independent trader captain called Joshua Calvert mentioned your name in connection with one of our agents."

She squinted up at the ceiling as if lost in a particularly difficult feat of recall. "Oh, yes, Joshua. I remember him, he caused quite a stir at the start of the year. Found a big chunk of Laymil electronics in the Ruin Ring. I met him at a party once. A nice young man."

"Yes," Maynard Khanna said gingerly. "So you didn't warn him about Erick Thakrar being one of our deep-cover operatives?"

"Erick Thakrar's name never passed my lips. Actually, Thakrar has just been accepted by Captain André Duchamp for a berth on the *Villeneuve's Revenge*, that's an Adamist ship with an antimatter drive fitted. I'm sure Commander Olsen Neale will confirm that for you. Erick Thakrar's cover is completely intact, I can assure you that André Duchamp doesn't suspect a thing."

"Well, that's a great relief, the Admiral will be pleased."

"I'm glad to hear it. And please don't concern yourself over Joshua Calvert, I'm sure he'd never do anything illegal, he's really an exemplary citizen."

The *Lady Macbeth* is preparing to jump insystem, *Oenone* warned the crew. They were two light-weeks from Puerto de Santa Maria's star, which cast a barely perceptible shadow on the voidhawk's foam-encased hull. The *Nephele* was drifting eight hundred kilometres over the upper hull, yet *Oenone*'s optical sensors were unable to see it.

Twenty-eight thousand kilometres further in towards the faint star, the *Lady Macbeth*'s sensor clusters and thermodump panels were folding with the neatness of an alighting eagle.

If only everything about the Adamist starship's flight was that neat, Syrinx wished. This Captain Calvert was a born incompetent. It had taken them six days to get here from New California, a distance of fifty-three light-years. The manoeuvres which *Lady Macbeth* performed every time she reached a jump coordinate were appallingly sloppy, they went on for hours at a time. Time was money in the cargo business. And if this was the way Calvert navigated on every voyage it was no wonder he needed the money so desperately.

"Stand by," Syrinx told Larry Kouritz. "He's lined up on the Ciudad asteroid."

"Roger," the marine captain acknowledged.

"The Ciudad," Eileen Carouch muttered as she accessed the Puerto de Santa Maria file in her neural nanonics. "There are several insurrectionist cells based there, according to the planetary government's Intelligence agency. They are pushing hard for independence."

Attention everybody, Syrinx broadcast, **I want us out of stealth mode the moment we emerge. This *Lady Macbeth* is fitted with maser cannons, so let's not have any mistakes. Chi, you have fire-control authority as of now. If they make one smartarse move, slice them in two. *Nephele*, you keep a sharp watch for approaching ships. If these insurrectionists are desperate enough to try and obtain antimatter-confinement technology they may be dumb enough to try and assist their courier.**

We'll cover you, Targard, the *Nephele*'s captain, replied.

Syrinx returned her attention to *Oenone*'s sensor inputs. The *Lady Macbeth* had reverted to a perfect sphere. Blue ion flames shrank away to nothing. There was a sharp twist in space's uniformity.

Go, she commanded.

Oenone erupted out of the wormhole terminus seventeen hundred kilometres distant from the *Lady Macbeth*. A blizzard of foam flakes swirled away as electronic sensors and thermo-dump panels were uncovered around the crew toroid. Fusion generators in the lower hull combat systems toroid powered up. X-ray lasers deployed. Gravity returned to the crew toroid. The distortion field swelled outwards, accelerating the voidhawk up to seven gees. It chased a sharp curve round to align on the *Lady Macbeth*. Two hundred kilometres away the *Nephele* was shaking off its stealth cloak.

Ciudad was a distant lacklustre speck, with a small constellation of industrial stations wrapped around it. Strategic defence sensor radiation raked across the *Oenone*.

Syrinx was aware of a curious secondary oscillation in the distortion field. Foam was streaming away from all across the hull.

That's better, *Oenone* sighed almost subliminally.

Syrinx didn't have time to form a rebuke. A transmitter dish unfolded from the lower hull toroid, swinging round to focus on the *Lady Macbeth*.

"Starship *Lady Macbeth*," she relayed through the transmitter's bitek processors. "This is Confederation Navy ship *Oenone*. You are ordered to hold your position. Do not activate your reaction drive, do not attempt to jump away. Stand by for rendezvous and boarding."

Oenone's distortion field reached out to engulf the Adamist starship.

Syrinx could hear Tula communicating with Ciudad's defence control centre, informing them of the interception.

"Hi there, *Oenone*," Joshua Calvert's voice came cheerfully out of the bridge's AV pillars. "Are you in some kind of trouble? How can we assist?"

Lying prone on her couch, her teeth gritted against the four-gee acceleration, Syrinx could only glance at the offending pillar in disconcerted amazement.

Oenone covered the last five kilometres cautiously, every sensor and weapon trained on the *Lady Macbeth*, alert for the slightest hint of treachery. At a hundred and fifty metres' distance, the voidhawk rotated slowly, presenting its upper hull towards the Adamist starship. The two extended airlock tubes, then touched and sealed. Larry Kouritz led his squad into the *Lady Macbeth*'s life-support capsules, executing the penetration and securement procedures with textbook precision.

Syrinx watched through *Oenone*'s sensor blisters as the crew toroid's clamshell hangar doors hinged apart. Oxley piloted their small boxy multifunction service vehicle out into space, yellow-orange chemical flames propelling it round towards *Lady Macbeth*'s open cargo hatch.

Joshua Calvert was marched into the bridge by two marines in dark carbotanium armour suits. He grinned round affably at the members of Syrinx's crew, with an even wider display of teeth when his eyes found her.

She shifted uncomfortably under the handsome young

man's attention. This was not how the interception was supposed to be going.

We've been had, Ruben told her abruptly.

Syrinx flicked a glance at her lover. He was sitting behind his console, an expression of glum resignation settling on his features. He combed his fingers back through his beret of curly white hair.

What do you mean? she asked.

Oh, just look at him, Syrinx. Does that look like a man facing a forty-year sentence for smuggling?

We were on the *Lady Macbeth* for the whole flight, she never rendezvoused with anybody.

Ruben simply raised an ironic eyebrow.

She returned her attention to the tall captain. She was annoyed at the way his gaze seemed to be fastened on her breasts.

"Captain Syrinx," he said warmly. "I must congratulate you and your ship. That was a superb piece of flying, really quite superb. Jesus, you scared the crap out of some of my crew the way you jumped us like that. We thought you were a pair of blackhawks." He stuck his hand out. "It's a pleasure to meet a captain who is so obviously talented. And I hope you don't take offence, but an extremely attractive captain as well."

Yes, we've definitely been had.

Syrinx ignored the offered hand. "Captain Calvert, we have reason to suspect you are involved with importing proscribed technology into this star system. I am therefore cautioning you that your ship will be searched under the powers invested in me by the Confederation Assembly. Any refusal to permit our search is a violation of Confederation space regulatory code which permits lawful officers full access to all systems and records once a request has been made by said officers. I am now making that request. Do you understand?"

"Well, gosh, yes," Joshua said earnestly. A note of doubt crept in. "I hate to ask, but are you quite sure you've got the right ship?"

"Perfectly sure," Syrinx said icily.

"Oh, well of course I'll cooperate in any way I can. I think you navy people do a great job. It's always reassuring for us commercial vessels to know we can always rely on you to maintain interstellar order."

"Please. Don't spoil the effect now, son," Ruben said wearily. "You've been doing so well."

"I'm just a citizen happy to oblige," Joshua said.

"A citizen who owns a ship that has an antimatter drive," Syrinx said sharply.

Joshua's gaze refocused on the front of her pale blue ship-tunic. "I didn't design it. That's the way it was built. Actually it was built by the Ferring Astronautics company in Earth's O'Neill Halo. I understand Earth is the greatest Edenist ally in the Confederation? That's what my didactic history courses say, anyway."

"We have a common viewpoint," Syrinx said reluctantly, anything else would have sounded like an admission of guilt.

"Couldn't you have the drive taken out?" Ruben asked.

Joshua managed an appropriately concerned expression. "I wish I could afford to. But there was a lot of damage when my father saved those Edenists from the pirates. The refit took all the money I had."

"Saved which Edenists?" Cacus blurted.

Idiot, Syrinx and Ruben told him together. The life-support engineer spread his hands helplessly.

"It was an aid convoy to Anglade," Joshua said. "There was a bacteriological plague there several years ago. My father joined the relief effort, of course; what are commercial needs compared to saving human life? They were taking viral-processing equipment to the planet to manufacture an antidote. Unfortunately they were attacked by blackhawks who wanted to steal the cargo, that kind of equipment is expensive. Jesus, I mean some people are really low, you know? There was a fight, and one of the escort voidhawks was wounded. The blackhawks were closing in for the kill, but my father waited until the crew got out. He jumped with a blackhawk's distortion field locked on. It was the only chance they had, they were badly damaged, but the old *Lady Mac*, she got them out alive." Joshua closed his eyes, remembering old pain. "Father didn't like to mention it much."

No kidding? Ruben asked heavily.

Was there ever a plague on Anglade? Tula asked.

Yes, *Oenone* said. **Twenty-three years ago. I don't have any record of an attack on an aid convoy, though.**

You do surprise me, Syrinx said.

This captain seems to be a nice young man, *Oenone* said. **He's obviously very taken with you.**

I'd sooner join an Adamist nunnery. And just leave the psychological analysis to us humans, please.

The silence in her mind was reproachful.

"Yes, well, that was the past," Syrinx said awkwardly to Joshua Calvert. "Your problem is here in the present."

Syrinx? Oxley called.

The cautious mental tone warned her. **Yes?**

We've opened two of their cargo-pods. They both contain the tokamak coils listed in the manifest. No antimatter-confinement technology in sight.

What? They can't have tokamak coils. She looked through Oxley's eyes into the MSV's tiny cabin. Eileen Carouch was strapped in a web next to him; several screens were covered in complicated multi-coloured graphics. The liaison officer wore a worried frown as she studied the displays. Outside the port, Syrinx could see one of the *Lady Macbeth*'s cargo-pods gripped in the MSV's heavy-duty waldo arm. It had been opened, and the tokamak coils had been removed by some of the mandible-like manipulator waldos.

Eileen Carouch turned to face Oxley. "It doesn't look good. According to our information both of these pods should contain the confinement coils."

We've been had, Ruben said.

Will you stop saying that, Syrinx demanded.

What do you want us to do? Oxley asked.

Examine every pod supposed to hold the antimatter-confinement coils.

OK.

"Everything all right?" Joshua asked.

Syrinx opened her eyes, and manufactured a killer-sweet smile. "Just fine, thank you."

Eileen Carouch and Oxley opened all eighteen cargo-pods supposed to contain the illegal coils. In every one they found neatly packaged tokamak coils.

Syrinx ordered them to open another five pods at random. They contained tokamak coils.

Syrinx gave up. Ruben was right, they'd been had.

That night she lay on her bunk, unable to sleep even though the body tensions due to ten days of enforced stealth routine had almost abated. Ruben was asleep beside her. There had been no prospect of sex when they came off duty, her mood was too black. He seemed to accept their defeat with a phlegmatism which she found annoying.

Where did we go wrong? she asked *Oenone*. **That ratty old ship was never out of your sight. You followed them superbly. I was more worried about the *Nephele* keeping up. Its spacial orientation isn't a patch on yours.**

Perhaps it was the operatives at Idria who lost track of the coils?

They were very certain the coils had been put on board. I could accept Calvert hiding one set in the ship, there's a lot of cubic volume there, but not eighteen.

There must have been a switch.

But how?

I don't know. I'm sorry.

Hey, it's not your fault. You did everything you were asked to, even when you were coated in foam.

I hate that stuff.

I know. Well, we've only got another two months to go. We'll be civilians after that.

Great!

Syrinx smiled in the cabin's half light. **I thought you liked military duty.**

I do.

But?

But it's lonely, all those patrols. When we're on commercial runs we'll meet lots of other voidhawks and habitats. It'll be fun.

Yes, I suppose it will. It's just that I would have liked to finish on a high note.

Joshua Calvert?

Yes! He was laughing at us.

I thought he was nice. Young and carefree, roaming the universe. Very romantic.

Please! He won't be roaming it for much longer. Not with an ego like that. He'll make a mistake soon enough, that sheer arrogance of his will force him into it. I'm only sorry we won't be there when he does. She put an arm over Ruben so that he would know she wasn't angry with him when he woke. But when she closed her eyes the normal vista of starfields that accompanied her into sleep had been replaced by a roguish smile and a rugged face that was all angles.

13

His name was Carter McBride, and he was ten years old; an only child, the pride of his parents Dimitri and Victoria, who spoilt him as best their circumstances would allow. Like most of Aberdale's younger generation he enjoyed the jungle and the river; Lalonde was much more fun than the cheerless dry concrete, steel, and composite caves of Earth's arcologies. The opportunities for games in his new land were limitless. He had his own little garden in the corner of his father's field, which he kept chock-full of strawberry plants, geneered so that the big scarlet fruits didn't rot in the rain and humidity. He had a cocker spaniel called Chomper that was always getting underfoot and making off with clothes from the McBride cabin. He was receiving didactic courses from Ruth Hilton, who said he was absorbing the agronomy data at a satisfactory rate, and would make a promising farmer one day. And because he was almost eleven his parents trusted him to play unsupervised, saying he was responsible enough not to wander too far into the jungle.

The morning after Horst Elwes encountered the Ly-cilph in the church, Carter was down by the river where he and the other kids were building a raft from scraps of timber left over from one of the adults' construction projects. He realized that he hadn't seen Chomper for about fifteen minutes, and looked around the clearing. A flash of ginger fur in the trees behind the community hall made him shout in exasperation at the silly animal. There was no immediate response, so he set off in vigorous pursuit, boots kicking up a splash in the thin layer of mud. By the time he reached the boundary of the jungle he could hear Chomper barking excitedly somewhere inside the crush of trees and creepers. He waved at Mr Travis, who was hoeing the soil around his baby pineapple plants, and plunged into the jungle after his dog.

Chomper seemed intent on leading him directly away from the village. Carter called and called until his throat felt raw. He was hot and sticky and his fraying T-shirt was smeared in long streaks of green-yellow sap from the broken creepers. He was also very angry with Chomper, who was going to be put on a choker lead as soon as they got home. And after that there would be the proper obedience-training classes that Mr Manani had promised him.

The chase finally came to an end in a small glade of tall qualtook trees, whose thick canopy of foliage didn't let much sunlight through. Spindly blades of grass grew up to Carter's knees, vines with a mass of lemon-coloured berries foamed up around the glossy trunks. Chomper was standing in the middle of the glade, his hackles raised, growling at a tree.

Carter grabbed hold of his neck, yelling out exactly what he thought of dogs at that moment. The spaniel resisted the pulling and urging, yapping frantically.

"What's the matter with you?" he demanded in exasperation.

Then the tall black lady appeared. One second there was only a qualtook tree in front of him, the next she was standing five metres away, dressed in a grey jump suit, and pulling her hood off. Long chestnut hair tumbled down.

Chomper had fallen silent. Carter clung to him, gazing at the lady with his mouth open, too surprised to say anything. She winked and beckoned. Carter smiled up at her trustingly, and trotted over.

Got him, Camilla said. **He's very sweet.**

So is my neck, Laton replied curtly. **Just make sure you leave him where they can find him without too much trouble.**

"Horst, this can't go on," Ruth said.

The priest just groaned with immense self-pity. He was lying on the cot where he'd been dumped the night before, crumpled olive-green blankets wound tightly round his legs. Sometime during the night he'd been sick again. A congealing puddle of waxy vomit lay on the floorboards below his pillow.

"Go away," he mumbled.

"Stop feeling so bloody sorry for yourself, and get up."

He rolled over slowly. She could see he'd been crying, his eyes were red rimmed, the lashes sticky. "I mean it, Ruth. Go away, right away. Take Jay with you, and leave. Find a boat, pay whatever it costs, get yourself back to Durringham, then get off this planet. Just leave."

"Stop talking like an idiot. Aberdale isn't that bad. We'll find a way to deal with the Ivets. I'm going to have Rai Molvi call a town meeting tonight, I'm going to tell people what I think is going on." She took a breath. "I want you to back me up, Horst."

"No. You mustn't. Don't antagonize the Ivets. Please, for your own safety, Ruth. Don't do it. There's still time for you to get away."

"For God's sake, Horst—"

"Ha! God is dead," he said bitterly. "Or at least He's banished this planet from His kingdom long ago." He beckoned her down with an agitated hand signal, glancing furtively at the open door.

Ruth took a reluctant step closer to the cot, wrinkling her nose up at the smell.

"I saw it," Horst said in a throaty whisper. "Last night. It was there in the church."

"What was there?"

"It. The demon they've summoned. I saw it, Ruth. Red, gleaming red, blinding red. The light of hell. Satan's eye opened and stared right at me. This is his world, Ruth. Not our lord Christ's. We should never have come here. Never."

"Oh, shit," she murmured under her breath. A whole host of practical problems ran through her mind: how to get him back to Durringham, whether there was even a psychiatrist on the planet, who could take over the little clinic he ran for the village. She scratched at the back of her sweaty hair, looking down at him as if he was some kind of elaborate riddle she was supposed to solve.

Rai Molvi ran up the wooden steps to the door and barged in. "Ruth," he said breathlessly. "I thought I'd find you here. Carter McBride is missing; kid's been gone a couple of hours now. Someone said they saw him chasing that damn nuisance dog of his into the jungle. I'm organizing a search party. Are you in?" Rai Molvi didn't even seem to have noticed Horst.

"Yes," she said. "I'll get someone to watch Jay."

"Mrs Cranthorp is taking care of that, she'll get the kids into a group and give them some lunch. We're assembling by the hall in ten minutes." He turned to go.

"I'll help," Horst said.

"As you like," Rai said, and hurried out.

"Well, you made a big impression on him," Ruth said.

"Please, Ruth, you must leave this place."

"We'll see after tonight. Right now I've got a child to help find." She paused. "Damn, Carter's about the same age as Jay."

The drawn-out whistle brought them all running. Arnold Travis was sitting slumped against the foot of a mayope tree. He just stared brokenly at the ground, silver whistle hanging from a corner of his mouth.

The villagers arrived in pairs, crashing through the vines and scrub bushes, sending hordes of birds screeching into the baking sky. When they did stumble into the little glade the sight which greeted them seemed to suck the strength from their limbs. A semicircle formed round the big cherry oak tree, stricken faces staring at its grisly burden.

Powel Manani was one of the last to arrive. Vorix was with him, loping easily through the lush undergrowth. Canine senses bubbled into Powel's mind, the monochrome images, the sharp sounds, and the vast range of smells. There was an overpowering scent of blood in the air.

He pushed and elbowed his way to the front of the shocked crowd, caught sight of the cherry oak tree— "Jesus!" His hand came up to cover his mouth. Something deep inside wanted to let loose a primaeval wail, just to shout and shout until all the pain was disgorged.

Carter McBride was hanging upside-down against the tree. His feet had been bound to the trunk with dried vine cords, making it look as though he was standing on his head. Both arms were spread wide, held parallel to the ground by a pair of stakes at each wrist. The long wounds were no longer bleeding. Tiny insects wriggled through the saturated grass below his head, gorging on the bounty.

Dimitri McBride took two tottering steps towards his son, then sank down to his knees as though in prayer. He looked round at the circle of ashen faces with a faintly bewildered expression. "I don't understand. Carter was ten years old. Who did this? I don't understand. Please tell me." He saw his own pain reflected in the weeping eyes surrounding him. "Why this? Why do this?"

"The Ivets," Horst said. Little Carter's scarlet eyeballs were staring right into him, urging him to speak. "This is the inverted cross," he said pedantically. It was important to be right in a matter like this, he felt, important that they should all fully comprehend. "The opposite of the crucifix. They worship the Light Brother, you see. The Light Brother is diametrically opposed to our lord Jesus, so the sects perform this sacrifice as a mockery. It's very logical, really." Horst found his breath was hard to come by, as if he'd been running a long distance.

Dimitri McBride crashed into him with the force of a jackhammer. He was flung backwards, Dimitri riding him down. "You knew! You knew!" he cried. Metal fingers closed round Horst's throat, clawing. "That was my son. And you knew!" Horst's head was yanked up, then slammed down into the spongy loam. "He'd still be alive if you'd told us. You killed him! You killed him! You!"

Horst's world was turning black around the edges. He tried to speak, to explain. That was what he had been trained for, to make people accept the world the way it was. But all he could see was Dimitri McBride's open screaming mouth.

"Get him off," Ruth told Powel Manani.

The supervisor gave her a dark look, then nodded reluctantly. He signalled to a couple of the villagers, and between them they prised Dimitri's fingers from Horst's throat. The priest lay as he was left, sucking air down like a cardiac victim.

Dimitri McBride collapsed into a limp, sobbing bundle.

Three of the villagers cut little Carter down, wrapping him in a coat.

"What do I tell Victoria?" Dimitri McBride asked vacantly. "What do I tell her?" The reassuring hands found his shoulders again, patting, offering their pathetically inadequate sympathy. A hip-flask was pressed to his lips. He spluttered as the acidic brew went down his gullet.

Powel Manani stood over Horst Elwes. I'm as guilty as the priest, he thought. I knew that little ratprick Quinn was trouble. But dear God, *this*. The Ivets, they're not human. Somebody who could do this could do anything.

Anything. The thought struck him like a twister of gelid wind. It cleared away even the remotest feeling of pity for the wretched drunken priest. He nudged Horst with the toe of his boot. "You? Can you hear me?"

Horst gurgled, his eyes rolling around.

Powel let his full fury vent into Vorix's mind. The dog lurched towards Horst, snarling in rage.

Horst saw it coming, and scrabbled feebly on all fours, cringing from the hound's ferocity. Vorix barked loudly, his muzzle centimetres away from his face.

"Hey!" Ruth protested.

"Shut up," Powel said, not even looking at her. "You. Priest. Are you listening to me?"

Vorix growled.

Everybody was watching the tableau now, even Dimitri McBride.

"It's what they are," Horst said. "The balance of nature. Black and white, good and evil. God's kingdom of heaven, and hell. Earth and Lalonde. Do you see?" He smiled up at Powel.

"The Ivets didn't all come from the same arcology," Powel said with a dangerously level voice. "They'd never even met each other before they came here. That means Quinn did this since we arrived, turned them into what they are now. You know about this doctrine of theirs. You know all about it. How long have they been a part of this sect movement? Before Gwyn Lawes? Were they, priest? Were they all involved before his odd, unseen, bloody death out here in the jungle? *Were they?*"

Several of the watchers gasped. Powel heard someone moaning: "Oh, God, please no."

Horst's mad smile was still directed up at the supervisor.

"Is that when it started, priest?" Powel asked. "Quinn had months to turn them, to break them, to control them. Didn't he? That's what he was doing all the time inside that fancy A-frame hut of theirs. Then when he'd got them all whipped into line, they started to come after us." His finger lined up on Horst. He wanted it to be a hunting rifle, to blow this failed wreckage of a man to pieces. "Those muggings back in Durringham, Gwyn Lawes, Roger Chadwick, the Hoffmans. My God, what did they do to the Hoffmans that they had to incinerate them afterwards so we wouldn't see? And all because you didn't tell us. How are you going to explain that to your God when you face him, priest? Tell me that."

"I wasn't sure," Horst wailed. "You're as bad as them. You're a savage, you love it out here. The only difference between you and an Ivet is that you get paid for what you do. You would have gone berserk if I even hinted that they had turned to the sect instead of me."

"When did you know?" Powel screamed at him.

Horst's shoulders quaked, he hugged his chest, curling up. "The day Gwyn died."

Powel threw his head back, fists thrust into the sky. "QUINN!" he bellowed. "I'll have you. I'll have every fucking one of you. Do you hear me, Quinn? You're dead." Vorix was howling defiance into the heavens.

He looked round at the numb expressions centred on him, seeing the cracks opening into their fear, and the anger that was beginning to spark inside. He knew people, and these were with him now. At long last, every one of them. There would be no rest now until the Ivets had been tracked down and exterminated.

"We can't just assume the Ivets are guilty like this," Rai

Molvi said. "Not on his word." He glanced scathingly down at Horst. That was how Vorix took him unawares. The hound landed on his chest, bowling him over. Rai Molvi yelped in terror as Vorix barked, long fangs snapping centimetres from his nose.

"You," Powel Manani said. It was spat out like an allegation. "You, lawyer man! You are the one who wanted me to ease off them. You let them have their A-frame. You wanted them walking round free. If we had done this by the book, kept those dickheads in the filth where they belong, none of this would have happened." He called Vorix off from the panting, badly scared man. "But you're right. We don't *know* the Ivets had anything to do with Gwyn or Roger or the Hoffmans. We can't prove that, can we, counsel for the defence? So all we've got is Carter. Do you know anyone else out here that is going to rip apart a ten-year-old child? Do you? Because if you do, I think we'd all like to hear who."

Rai Molvi shook his head, teeth clamped together in anguish.

"Right then," Powel said. "So what do you say, Dimitri? Carter was your boy. What do you think we should do to the people who did this to your son?"

"Kill them," Dimitri said from the centre of the little knot of people who were trying to comfort him. "Kill every last one of them."

High above the treetops, the kestrel wheeled and turned in an agile aerial dance, using the fast streams of hot, moist air to stay aloft with minimum effort. Laton always allowed the bird's natural instincts to take over on such occasions, contenting himself simply to direct. Down below, under the almost impenetrable barrier of leaves, people were moving. Little flecks of colour were visible through the minute gaps, the distinctive pattern of a particular shirt, grubby, sweaty skin. The kestrel's predator instincts amplified each motion, building up a comprehensive picture.

Four men carried the body of the boy on a makeshift stretcher. They moved slowly, picking their way over roots and small gullies, all of them labouring under an air of reluctance.

Ahead of them was the main body of men, led by Supervisor Manani. They walked with a bold stride. Men who had a purpose. Laton could see it in the stern, hate-filled faces, the grim determination. Those that didn't have laser rifles had acquired clubs or stout sticks.

Trailing way behind everyone else the kestrel saw Ruth Hilton and Rai Molvi. Weak, dejected figures who never said a word. Both lost in their own private guilt.

Horst Elwes was left by himself in the small clearing. He was still curled up on the ground, shivering quite violently. Every now and then he would let out a loud cry, as if something had bitten him. Laton suspected his mind had gone completely. It didn't matter, he had fulfilled his role beautifully.

Leslie Atcliffe broke surface ten metres away from the end of Aberdale's jetty, a creel full of mousecrabs clamped between his hands. He rolled onto his back, and began to kick towards the shore, towing the creel. Rifts of gun-metal cloud were starting to slash the western horizon. It would rain in another thirty minutes, he reckoned.

Kay was sitting on the shore just above the water, opening a creel and tipping the still wriggling mousecrabs into a box ready for filleting. She was wearing a pair of faded shorts, halter made out of a cut-up T-shirt, boots with blue socks rolled down, and a scrappy dried-grass hat she had woven herself. Leslie enjoyed the look of her lean body, a rich nut-brown after all these months in the sun. It was another three days until they would have a night together. And he liked to think Kay enjoyed screwing with him more than the others. She certainly talked to him the rest of the time, like a friend.

His feet found the shingle and he stood up. "Another lot for you," he called. The mousecrabs slithered and squirmed round each other in the creel, ten at least; narrow flat bodies with twelve spindly legs apiece, brown scales that did resemble wet fur, and a pointed head ending in a black tip like a rodent nose.

Kay grinned, and waved at him, her filleting knife gripped in her hand, steel blade glinting in the sun. That grin made his whole day worthwhile.

The search party emerged from the jungle forty metres away from the quay. Leslie knew something was wrong straight away. They were walking too fast, the way angry men walk. And they were heading towards the jetty, all of them, fifty or more. Leslie stared uncertainly. It wasn't the jetty, they were heading for him!

"God's Brother," he murmured. They looked like a lynch mob. Quinn! It had be something Quinn had done. Quinn who was always so smart he never got caught.

Kay twisted round at the sound of the low rumble of voices, shielding her eyes from the sun. Tony had just surfaced with a full creel; he was watching the approaching crowd in confusion.

Leslie looked behind him, over the river. The far shore with its muddy bank and wall of creeper-bound trees was a hundred and forty metres away. It suddenly looked very tempting, he had become a strong swimmer over the last few months. They wouldn't catch him if he started straight away.

The first members of the crowd reached Kay where she was sitting. She was punched full in the face without the slightest warning. Leslie saw who did it, Mr Garlworth, a forty-five-year-old oenophile who was determined to establish his own vineyard. A quiet, peaceable man who was fairly reclusive. Now his face was flushed, berserker exhilaration lighting his features. He grunted in triumph as his knuckles connected with Kay's jaw.

She cried out in pain and toppled over, a bead of blood spurting from her mouth. Men clustered round, kicking at her with a fierceness that rivalled a sayce's blood-lust.

"Fuck you!" Leslie yelled. He slung the creel away and drove his legs through the knee-high water towards the shore, sending up long tails of spray. Kay was screaming, lost behind the flurry of kicking legs. Leslie saw the filleting knife slash once. One of the men fell, clutching at his shin. Then a club was raised high.

Leslie never heard nor saw if it fell on the battered girl.

He cannoned into the band of villagers who were racing down the slope at him. Powel Manani was one of them, a big fist cocked back. Leslie's world disintegrated into a chaos where instinct ruled. Fists slammed into him from all directions. He lashed out with blind violence. Men shouted and roared. His hair was gripped by a meaty hand, strands making a terrible ripping sound as they were torn slowly out of his scalp. A torrent of foam raged around him, almost as though he was fighting under a waterfall. Fangs clamped around his wrist, dragging his arm down. There was snarling, the snap of splintering bone that went on interminably. Pain was everything now, flooding down every nerve. Somehow it didn't bother him nearly as much as it should. He couldn't strike back the way he wanted to now. His arms didn't respond. He found he was on his knees, vision fading away into pink-grey streaks. The muddy river water was boiling scarlet.

There was a moment when nothing happened. He was being held prone by invincible hands. Powel Manani towered in front of him, his thick black beard soaked and straggly, grinning savagely as he lined himself up. In the silent pause, Leslie could hear a child wailing frantically somewhere off in the distance. Then Powel's heavy boot smashed into his balls with all the force the brawny supervisor could summon.

The pulse of agony knocked out every other thread of awareness. Leslie was cut off from life at the centre of a dense red neon mist, feeling or hearing nothing from outside. There was only the sickening pain.

Red turned to black. Twinges of sensation oozed back in on him. His face was being crushed into cold gravel. That was important, but he couldn't think why. His lungs ached abominably. With his jaw shattered and useless, Leslie tried to suck air through his mashed nose. The Quallheim's grubby, blood-stained water rushed into his lungs.

Lawrence Dillon was running for his life, running away from the insanity that had claimed the inhabitants of Aberdale. He and Douglas had been working in the allotments behind the A-frame when the villagers arrived back from the search. The tall bean canes and flourishing sweetcorn plants had partially hidden them from view as the men attacked Kay and Leslie and Tony down by the river Lawrence had never seen such a display of wanton violence before. Even Quinn wasn't that rabid, Quinn's violence was directed and purposeful.

Both he and Douglas stood mesmerized as their fellow Ivets disappeared beneath the blows. Only when Powel Manani came wading out of the river did they think to flee.

"Split up," Lawrence Dillon yelled at Douglas as they crashed into the jungle. "We'll stand more chance that way." He heard that monster hound, Vorix, barking loudly behind them, caught a glimpse of it racing across the village clearing in pursuit. "Get to Quinn. Warn him." Then they peeled apart, tearing through the undergrowth as if it was made from tissue paper.

Lawrence found a small animal path a minute later. It was becoming overgrown, deserted by the danderil ever since the village had been built. But it was good enough to give him an extra burst of speed. His tatty shoes were falling apart, and he only had shorts on. Creepers and branches tore at him with needle-sharp claws. Irrelevant. Living was all that mattered, building distance from the village.

Then Vorix went after Douglas. Lawrence threw a wordless cry of thanks to the Light Brother for sparing him, and slackened off his pace a fraction, scanning the ground for suitable stones. The hound would find him as soon as it had dispatched Douglas. The hound could pick up scents even in the damp jungle. The hound would lead the villagers to any hidden Ivet. He must do something about it if any of them were to have the slightest chance of surviving this day. And that bastard supervisor didn't know just how big a menace those who followed the Light Brother could be to any who stood in their way. The thought lifted his spirit, enabling him to throw off some of the panic. He had Quinn to thank for that. Quinn had shown him there was no fear in true release. Quinn had helped him find his own inner strength, showing him how to embrace the serpent beast. Quinn who featured so powerfully in his dreams, a dark fantasy figure crowned in searing orange flames.

Grimacing at the multitude of scratches he had picked up during his mad flight, Lawrence looked around with a determined gaze.

Powel Manani was used to seeing the world through Vorix's eyes. It was a prospect of blues and greys, as if every structure was bonded together from layers of shadow. Trees stretched far overhead until they vanished into an almost hazy veil of sky and the bushes and undergrowth of the jungle loomed in oppressively, black leaves flicking aside like cards snapped down by an expert dealer.

The robust dog was chasing down an old animal track after Lawrence Dillon. The young Ivet's scent was everywhere. It lay like an oily mist in the footprints left behind in the soft loam, it wafted down from the leaves he had brushed against. Occasional spots of blood from lacerated feet were soaking into the spongy loam. Vorix didn't even have to press his nose to the ground.

Sensations flowed into Powel's mind, the tireless bands of muscle pumping in his haunches, tongue lolling over his jaw, hot breath flaring in his nostrils. They were a duality, Vorix's body, Powel's mind, working in perfect fusion. Just like they had when the dog caught up with Douglas. Animal attack reflexes and human skill combined into a synergistic engine of destruction, knowing exactly where to strike to cause the maximum damage. Powel could still feel the soft flesh giving beneath hardened paws, the taste of blood lingered long after fangs had punctured the lad's throat, severing the carotid. Sometimes the rustling breeze seemed to carry Douglas's gurgling cries.

But that was just a foretaste. Soon it would be Quinn who faced the dog. Quinn who would scream in fright. Just like little Carter must have done. The thought spurred both of them on, Vorix's heart thudding gleefully.

The scent trail petered out. Vorix lumbered on for a few paces then stopped and raised his blunt head, sniffing intently. Powel knew a frown would be crinkling his own face. There was a touch of rain in the air, but not nearly

enough to wash away such a strong trace. He had almost
caught up with Lawrence, the Ivet couldn't be far away.

There was a soft thud behind the dog. Vorix whipped
round with electric speed. Lawrence Dillon stood on the
track seven metres away, crouched on bloody feet as
though he was about to spring at the dog, a fission blade in
one hand, some kind of vine loop in the other.

The lad must have backtracked and scampered up one of
the trees. Cunning little shit. But it wouldn't do him any
good, not against Vorix. His only chance had been to drop
on the dog and plunge the knife in before either of them realized what was happening. And he'd blown it.

Powel laughed as the dog started its run. Lawrence
twirled the length of vine around. Too late Powel realized
it was weighted with oval stones. Vorix was already leaping as the supervisor's mind bawled its warning. Lawrence
let go of the bolas.

Insidious coils of vine snagged Vorix's forelegs with a
barely audible *whirr*, the spinning cord biting sharply into
his fur. One of the stones knocked heavily against his cra-
nium, sending a shower of pain stars down the affinity link
to daze Powel. Vorix crashed into the ground, slightly
groggy. He flexed round trying to reach the vine with his
teeth. An incredibly heavy mass landed hard on his back,
nearly snapping his spine. His breath was knocked out of
his lungs, winding him. Several ribs cracked. Hind legs
scrabbled frantically for purchase to try and buck the Ivet
off.

An excruciating lance of pain fired into Powel Manani's
brain. He yelled out loud, stumbling around. He felt one
knee give out, and pitched over. For a moment the affinity
link wavered, and he saw a ring of villagers gazing down
in dismay. Hands reached out to steady him.

Vorix had frozen in pain and shock. There was no feeling at all from one of his hind legs. The dog squirmed
round on the rucked loam. His leg was lying on the bloody
grass, twitching and jerking.

Lawrence cut the second hind leg off with his fission
knife. Blood hissed and steamed as it bubbled over the radiant yellow blade.

Both of Powel's legs were being squeezed by tourniquets made from bands of ice. He fell leadenly to sit on his rump, breath wheezing out of parched lips. His thigh muscles were spasming uncontrollably.

The fission blade penetrated Vorix's left mandible joint, skewering through muscle, bone, and gristle. Its tip emerged into the back of his mouth, severing a large portion of the tongue.

Powel started to gag, fighting for breath. His whole body was shaking wildly. He vomited weakly down his beard.

Vorix was emitting a harrowing whining from his ruined jaw. Sallow eyes rolled round, glazed with pain, trying to find his tormentor. Lawrence aimed a blow at each of his forelegs, slicing clean through the knees, leaving the dog with stumps.

At the far end of a murky whorled tunnel, Powel saw the sandy-haired teenager walk round in front of the dog. He spat on Vorix's squat muzzle. "Not so fucking smart now, are you?" Lawrence shouted. Powel could barely hear him, his voice sounded as though it was coming from the bottom of a deep rocky shaft. "Want to play chase again, doggy?" Lawrence did a little jig, laughing. Vorix's stumps knocked feebly against the soil in a parody of walking. The sight sent him off into another bout of laughter. "Walkies! Come on, walkies!"

Powel groaned with helpless fury. The affinity bond was weakening, stretching the dog's pain-lashed thoughts to a tenuous thread. He coughed some of the bile out of his mouth.

"I know you can hear me, Manani, you superfuck," Lawrence called. "And I hope your heart's bleeding out through these cuts. I'm not going to kill your hound, not all quick and clean and neat. No, I'm going to leave him here rolling round in his own shit and piss and blood. That way you'll feel him dying the whole time, however long it takes. I like that idea, cos you really loved this dog. God's Brother always takes his retribution on those who displease him. Vorix is kind of like an omen, see? I did this to a dog, think what Quinn's gonna do to you."

It was raining steadily when Jay led Sango, Powel Manani's beige horse, from the lean-to at the back of the supervisor's cabin which served as a stable. Mr Manani had been true to his word back on the *Swithland*, he had let her groom Sango, and help feed him, and take him for exercise. Two months ago, when the frantic urgency which governed Aberdale while the cabins were going up and the fields were being levelled had abated, he had taught her how to ride.

Aberdale wasn't quite the dreamy rural existence she had expected, but it was pretty nice in its own fashion. And Sango played a huge part in making it right. Jay knew one thing, she didn't want to go back to any arcology.

Or at least she hadn't before today.

Something had happened out in the jungle this morning that none of the adults would talk about. She and all the other kids knew that Carter was dead, they'd been told that much. But there had been the awful fight down by the jetty, and a lot of the women had cried, the men too though they tried to hide it. Then twenty minutes ago Mr Manani had some kind of dreadful drawn-out fit, howling and panting as he keeled about.

Things had quietened down after that. There had been a meeting in the hall, and afterwards people had gone back to their cabins. Now though she could see them congregating in the centre of the village again; they were all dressed like they did when they went hunting. Everyone seemed to be carrying a weapon.

She knocked on the front stanchion of Mr Manani's cabin. He came out dressed in navy-blue jeans, a green and blue check shirt, and a fawn waistcoat that held a lot of cylindrical power magazines for laser rifles. He carried a couple of slate-grey tubes fifty centimetres long, with pistol grips at one end. She had never seen them before, but she knew they were weapons.

Their eyes met for a moment, then Jay looked at the muddy ground.

"Jay?"

She glanced up.

"Listen, honey. The Ivets have been bad, very bad. They're all funny in their heads."

"Like waster kids in the arcologies, you mean?"

A sad smile flickered on his lips at the bright curiosity in her voice. "Something like that. They killed Carter McBride."

"We thought so," she admitted.

"So we're going to have to catch them and stop them from doing anything like it again."

"I understand."

He slotted the maser carbines into their saddle holsters. "It's for the best, honey, really it is. Listen, Aberdale's not going to be very nice for a couple of weeks, but afterwards it'll get better. I promise. Before you know it, we'll be the best village on the whole tributary. I've seen it happen before."

She nodded. "Be careful, Mr Manani. Please."

He kissed the top of her head. Her hair was sprinkled with tiny drops of water.

"I will be," he said. "And thank you for saddling up Sango. Now go and find your mum, she's a bit upset about what happened this morning."

"I haven't seen Father Elwes for hours. Will he be coming back?"

He stiffened his back, unable to look at the girl. "Only to pick up his things. He won't be staying in Aberdale any longer. His work's done here."

Powel rode Sango over to the waiting hunters, hoofs splattering in the mud. Most of them were wearing waterproof ponchos, slick with rain. They looked more worried than angry now. The initial heat of Carter's death had abated, and the shock of killing the three Ivets was percolating through their minds. They were more scared for their families and their own skin than they were bothered about vengeance. But the end product was the same. Their fear of Quinn would compel them until the job was done.

He saw Rai Molvi standing among them, clutching a laser rifle beneath his poncho. It wasn't worth making an issue over. He leaned forward from the saddle to address them. "First thing you should know is that my communication block is out. I haven't been able to tell Schuster's sheriff what's been happening here, or the Governor's office in Durringham. Now those communication blocks are more or less solid chunks of circuitry with all kinds of redundancy built in, I've never heard of one failing before. The LED lights up, so it's not a simple power loss. It was working when I made my routine report three days ago. I'll leave it to you to work out the significance of it failing today."

"Christ, just what are we up against?" someone asked.

"We're up against waster kids," Powel said. "Vicious and frightened. That's all they are. This sect crap is just an excuse for Quinn to order them about."

"They've got guns."

"They have eight laser rifles, and no spare power magazines. Now I can see about a hundred and twenty rifles just from here. They aren't going to be any problem. Shoot to kill, and don't give any warning. That's all we have to do. We don't have courts, we don't have time for courts, not out here. I sure as hell know they're guilty. And I want to make damn sure that the rest of your kids can walk about this village without looking over their shoulders for the rest of their lives. That's what you came here for, isn't it? To get away from all this shit Earth kept flinging at you. Well, a little bit got carried here with you. But today we finish it. After today there won't be any more Carter McBrides."

Determination returned to the gathering; men nodded and exchanged bolstering glances with their neighbours, rifles were gripped just that fraction harder at the mention of Carter's name. It was a collective building up of nerve, absolving them of any guilt in advance.

Powel Manani watched it accumulate with satisfaction. They were his again, just like the day they came off the *Swithland*, before that dickhead Molvi started interfering. "OK, the Ivets got split into three work parties this morning. There's two out helping the savannah homesteads, and one lot with the hunting party to the east. We'll split into two groups. Arnold Travis, you know the eastern jungle pretty well, you take fifty men with you and try and find the hunting party. I'm going to ride out to the homesteads to try and warn them. I expect that's where Lawrence Dillon is headed, because that's where Quinn is. The rest of you follow after me as fast as you can, and for Christ's sake don't get spread out. Once you get to the homesteads, we'll decide what to do next. OK, let's go."

Enlarging the Skibbow homestead's stockade was hard work; the wood for the fence had to be pre-cut in the jungle, a kilometre away, then hauled all the way back. The ground was difficult to prepare for the posts, with a vast accumulation of dead matted grass to scrape away before the hard, sandy soil was uncovered. Loren Skibbow's lunch had been cold chikrow meat and some kind of flaccid tasteless stewed vegetable which most of the Ivets had left. And on top of all that, Gerald Skibbow was off on the savannah somewhere looking for a lost sheep, which left Frank Kava in charge, who was a bossy little shit.

By midafternoon Quinn had already decided that the Skibbows and Kavas were going to be playing a very prominent role in his next black mass ceremony.

The lengths of wood they had cut that morning were laid out across the grass, marking out a square of land thirty-five metres a side next to the existing stockade. Quinn and Jackson Gael were working together, taking it in turns to hammer the upright posts into the ground. The other four Ivets in the work party were busy nailing the horizontal beams into place behind them. They had already completed one side, and were three posts along the next. It had rained earlier, but Frank hadn't let them stop work.

"Bastard," Jackson Gael muttered as he took another swing with the sledgehammer. The post shook as it thudded another three centimetres into the soil. "He wants to have this finished by tonight so he can show Gerald what a good keen little boy he's been. Means we're gonna be walking back in the dark."

"Don't worry about it," Quinn said. He was kneeling down, holding the black post upright. The mayope wood was wet, difficult to grip.

"This rain makes everything slippery," Jackson grumbled. "Accidents come easy, and on this planet you get damaged, you stay damaged. That drunken old fart of a priest don't know shit about proper doctoring." The sledgehammer hit the post again.

"Relax. I been thinking, this place would be a good target for us."

"Yeah. You know what really pisses me off? Frank climbs into bed with that Paula every bloody night. I mean, she's not got tits like Marie had, but God's Brother, every night!"

"Will you stop thinking with your dick for one fucking minute. I let you have Rachel, don't I? That's as well as our girls."

"Yeah. Thanks, Quinn. Sorry."

"Right, we'll start working out who we want to bring, and when we're going to do it."

Jackson tightened the scraps of cloth he had wrapped round his palms to give a tighter grip on the sledgehammer's handle. "Tony, maybe. He's pretty easy around the village; talks to the residents. Think he could do with reminding where his loyalties lie."

"Could be."

Jackson swung the sledgehammer again.

Quinn caught a flash of motion out on the vast plain of rippling grass back towards the thin dark green line which marked the start of the jungle. "Hold it." He upped his retinal implant to full magnification. The running figure resolved. "It's Lawrence. God's Brother, he looks about dead." He scanned the land behind the youth, looking for a sayce or a kroclion. Something must be making him run like that. "Come on." He started trotting towards the floundering teenager.

Jackson dropped the sledgehammer and followed Quinn.

Frank Kava was measuring out the distance between the posts, setting them up correctly for the Ivets. Not that those idle buggers would appreciate the effort, he thought. You had to watch them the whole time, and they had no initiative, everything had to be explained. He strongly believed most of them were retarded, their sullen silence certainly indicated it.

He leaned in on the spade, tearing out the knobby roots of grass. This stockade was going to be a mighty useful addition to the homestead. The original one was far too cramped now the animals were reaching adult size. They'd need the extra room for the second generation soon. Certainly the sheep would be mature enough to be inseminated in a few more months.

Frank had been faintly dubious about coming to Lalonde. But now he had to admit it was the greatest decision he'd ever made. A man could sit back every evening and see what he'd achieved. It was a tremendous feeling.

And there was Paula, too. She hadn't said anything yet. But Frank had his suspicions. She looked so *vital* of late.

The sounds made him look up—something wrong. Four of the Ivets were still hammering away at the horizontal bars, but there was no one using the sledgehammer. He cursed under his breath. Quinn Dexter and the stalwart Jackson Gael were a hundred metres away, running through the grass. Unbelievable. He cupped his hands to his mouth and shouted, but they either didn't hear him, or they just ignored him. Probably the latter, knowing them. Then he saw the figure running in from the jungle, the erratic stumbling gait of a desperate man on his last legs. As he watched, the figure fell, arms windmilling; Quinn and Jackson increased their pace. Frowning, Frank started towards them.

The voices led Frank for the last twenty metres. All three of them were crouched below the wispy grass.

It was another Ivet, the young one. He was lying on his back, sucking down air in huge gulps, trying to talk in a high-pitched choking voice. His feet were reduced to bloody meat. Quinn and Jackson were kneeling beside him.

"What's going on here?" Frank asked.

Quinn glanced back over his shoulder. "Take him out," he said calmly.

Frank took a pace backwards as Jackson rose. "Wait—"

* * *

Paula and Loren were in the homestead's living-room, waiting for their freshly prepared elwisie jam to boil. The elwisie was one of the local edible fruits, a dark purple sphere ten centimetres in diameter. A whole cluster of the small, wizened trees grew on the fringe of the jungle; they'd had a long picking session yesterday. Sugar was going to be the main problem; several people grew cane in the village, but the few kilos they'd traded weren't particularly high quality.

It would get better though, Loren thought. Everything about Aberdale was slowly getting better. That was part of the joy of living here.

Paula took the clay jars from the oven where they'd been warming.

"Could do with a minute longer," Loren said. She was stirring the mixture that was bubbling away inside the big pan.

Paula put the tray of jars down, and looked out through the open door. A party of people were coming round the corner of the stockade. Jackson Gael was carrying someone in his arms, a teenage boy whose feet were dripping blood. Another two Ivets were carrying the unmistakable figure of Frank.

"Mother!" Paula charged out of the door.

Frank's face was terribly battered, his nose squashed almost flat, lips torn, eyes and cheeks swollen and bruised. He groaned weakly.

"Oh my God!" Paula's hands came up to press against her face. "What happened to him?"

"We did," said Quinn.

Loren Skibbow almost made it. There was something about Quinn Dexter which had always made her uncomfortable, and the sight of Frank had set every mental alarm ringing. Without hesitating she turned and raced back into the house. The laser hunting rifles were hung up on the living-room wall. Five of them, one each. Gerald had taken his with him this morning. She reached for the next one, the one that used to be Marie's.

Quinn punched her in the kidneys. The blow slammed her into the wall. She rebounded, and Quinn kicked her on the back of the knee. She collapsed onto the floorboards, moaning at the pain. The rifle clattered down beside her.

"I'll take that, thank you," Quinn said.

Loren's vision was blurred by tears. She heard Paula screaming, and managed to turn her head. Jackson Gael had dragged her inside, holding her under one arm while her legs kicked wildly.

"Irley, Malcolm; I want the guns and every spare power magazine, any medical gear, and all their freeze-dried food. Get to it," Quinn ordered as the other Ivets piled in. "Ann, take watch outside. Manani will be coming out here on his horse, and keep an eye out for Gerald as well." He threw the rifle to her. She caught it and nodded crisply.

Irley and Malcolm started to ransack the shelves.

"Shut up," Quinn yelled at Paula.

She broke off screaming, staring at him with huge, terrified eyes. Jackson Gael shoved her into a corner, and she shrank down, hugging herself.

"That's better," Quinn said. "Imran, put Lawrence down in the chair, then search out the boots in this house, as many pairs as you can find. We're gonna need 'em. Got a long way to go."

Loren saw the young Ivet with the ruined feet being lowered into one of the chairs around the square kitchen table. His face was grey, sweating profusely.

"You just find me some bandages and some boots, I'll be all right," Lawrence said. "Really, Quinn, I'll be fine."

Quinn caressed his forehead, fingers teasing back the damp strands of blond hair. "I know. That was a hell of a run out here. You did great, Lawrence. Really. You're the best."

Loren saw Lawrence look up at Quinn, reverence in the lad's eyes. She saw Quinn slide a fission blade from his shorts. She tried to say something as the blade came alive in a burst of yellow light, but only a gurgle emerged from her throat.

Quinn sank the blade into the nape of Lawrence's neck, angling it upwards so it penetrated the brain. "The very best," he whispered. "God's Brother will welcome you into the Night."

Paula opened her mouth in a silent wail as Lawrence's body slid down onto the floor. Loren started to sob quietly.

"Shit, Quinn!" Irley protested.

"What? We've got to get out of here, yesterday. You saw his feet; he would have held us up. That way we all get caught. That what you want?"

"No," Irley mumbled lamely.

"It was quicker than what they would have done to him," Quinn said half to himself.

"You did the right thing," Jackson Gael said. He turned back to Paula and grinned broadly. She whimpered, trying to push herself further back into the corner. He grabbed her hair and pulled her up.

"We don't have time," Quinn said mildly.

"Sure we do. I won't be long."

Loren tried to pick herself off the floor as Paula's screams began again.

"Naughty," Quinn said. His boot caught her on the side of the temple. She flopped onto her back like a broken mechanoid, incapable of movement. Her vision was fuzzy, shapes were obscured behind blotches of grey. But she saw Quinn take Paula's rifle off the wall, calmly check the power level, and shoot Frank. He turned round, and aimed the barrel at her.

The recall whistle sounded sharply through the jungle. Scott Williams sighed and picked himself off the ground, brushing dead leaves from his threadbare jump suit.

The arseholes! He was sure that had been a danderil rustling through the undergrowth up ahead. Well, he'd never know now.

"Wonder what's happened?" Alex Fitton said.

"Dunno," Scott replied. He didn't mind Alex too much. The man was twenty-eight, and he was happy enough to talk to an Ivet. He knew some good filthy jokes too. Scott had hunted with him regularly.

The whistle sounded again.

Alex grunted. "Come on."

They trudged towards the sound. Several other pairs of hunters appeared out of the trees, all of them walking towards the insistent whistle. Queries were shouted to and fro. Nobody knew why they were being called in. The whistle was supposed to be for injuries and the end of the day.

Scott was surprised to see a big group of people lined up waiting at the top of a steepish earth mound, there were about forty or fifty of them. They must have come out from the village. He saw Rai Molvi standing in front of them, blowing the whistle for all he was worth. He was very conscious of all those eyes on him as he and Alex Fitton made their way up the incline.

There was a large qualtook tree straddling the brow of the mound. One of its thick lower branches overhung the slope on the other side. Three silicon-fibre ropes had been slung over it.

The group of villagers parted silently, forming an alley towards the tree. Definitely worried now, Scott walked through them and saw what was hanging from the ropes. Jemima had been the last, she was still choking and kicking. Her face was purple, eyes bulging.

He tried to run, but they shot him in the thigh with a laser pulse, and dragged him back. It was Alex Fitton who pulled the noose tight around his neck. Tears ran down his cheeks as he did it, but then Alex had been Roger Chadwick's brother-in-law.

The run back to his homestead had nearly killed Gerald Skibbow. He had been returning anyway when he saw the smoke, tugging the errant sheep along on a leash. Orlando, the Skibbow family's Alsatian, bounded about through the long grass in high spirits. He knew he'd done well following the sheep's scent. Gerald smiled indulgently at his antics. He was almost fully grown now. Oddly enough it was Loren who was the best at training him.

Gerald had traipsed across what had seemed like half of the savannah that morning. He couldn't believe how far the damn sheep had strayed in just a few hours. They had eventually found it bleating at the end of a steep-walled gully about three kilometres from the homestead. He was just grateful that sayce kept to the jungle. They had never had any trouble from the kroclions which were supposed to roam the grassland, a few distant glimpses of sleek bodies in the grass, some night-time roars.

Then when he was a couple of kilometres from home that terrible blue-white streamer of smoke twisted idly into the sky ahead of him, its root hidden beyond the horizon. He stared at it in cold fear. All the other homesteads were kilometres away, and there was only one possible source. It was like watching his own life's blood pouring up into the cloudless azure heavens. The homestead was everything, he'd invested his life in it, there was no other future.

"Loren!" he called. He let go of the sheep's leash and started to run. "Paula!" The laser rifle banged against his side. He slung it away. Orlando barked urgently, picking up on his master's agitation.

It was the grass, the bloody grass. It clung to his pounding legs, hindering him. Rucks and folds in the ground kept tripping him. He fell headlong, grazing his hands, knocking his knee. It didn't matter. He picked himself up and kept on running. Again and again.

The savannah sucked sounds away from him. The slashing of the grass on his dungarees trousers, his laboured panting, the grunts each time he fell. All of them soaked away into the hot, still air as though it fed on them, hungry for the slightest noise.

The last two hundred yards were the worst. He topped a small rise, and the homestead was revealed to him. Only the skeleton remained upright, sturdy black timbers swathed by shooting flames. The slats and roof planks had already burnt through, peeling off like putrid skin to lie in crumbling strips around the base.

The animals had scattered. Panicked by the heat and roaring flames they had butted their way through the stockade fence. They had run for a hundred metres or so until their immediate fear slackened, then wandered about aimlessly. He could see the horse and a couple of pigs over by the pool, drinking unconcernedly. Others were dotted about among the grass.

There was no other movement. No people. He gaped

numbly. Where were Frank and Loren and Paula? And the Ivet work team; they should all be trying to put out the fire.

With legs like weights of dead meat, and breath burning in his lungs, he ran the last length in a daze. A bright golden rain of sparks swirled high into the sky. The homestead's frame gave one harrowed creak, and buckled in on itself with a series of jerks.

Gerald let out a single wretched wail as the last timbers crashed down. He slowed to a halt fifteen metres from the wreckage. "Loren? Paula? Frank? Where are you?" The cry was snatched up with the sparks. Nobody answered. He was too frightened to go over to the remnants of the homestead. Then he heard Orlando whine softly. He walked up to the dog.

It was Paula. Darling Paula, the little girl who would sit on his lap in their apartment back in the arcology and try to pull his nose, giggling wildly. Who grew up into a lovely young woman possessed of a quiet dignified strength. Who had bloomed out here in this venturesome land.

Paula. Eyes staring blindly at the swarm of sparks. A two-centimetre hole in the centre of her forehead, cauterized by the hunting laser.

Gerald Skibbow looked down at his daughter, knuckles jammed into his gaping mouth. His legs gave way, and he slowly folded up onto the trampled grass beside her.

That was how Powel Manani found him when he rode up forty minutes later. The supervisor took in the scene with a single glance. All the anger and hatred that had been building up during the day crystallized into a lethal Zen-like calmness.

He inspected the smouldering ruin of the homestead. There were three scorched bodies inside, which puzzled him for a while until he realized the second male was probably Lawrence Dillon.

Quinn would want to move swiftly, of course. And Lawrence's feet had been in poor shape even back when he killed Vorix. Christ, but Quinn was a cold bastard.

The question was, where would he go?

There were just six Ivets left now. Powel had arrived at the Nicholls' homestead where the second Ivet work team was busy assembling a barn. His maser carbine had picked them off one at a time under the horrified eyes of the Nicholls family. He had explained why afterwards. But they had still looked at him as though he was some kind of monster. He didn't much care. The rest of the villagers would put them right tomorrow.

Powel stared at the band of jungle a kilometre away. Quinn was in there, that much was obvious. But finding him was going to be difficult. Unless . . . Quinn might just head back to the village. He was a true bandit now, he'd need food and weapons, enough supplies to get well clear of Schuster County. A small roving band could elude the sheriffs and even a marshal (assuming the Governor sent one) for a long time out here.

Orlando nosed around his legs and Powel stroked him absently. He missed Vorix more than ever now. Vorix would have tracked Quinn down within an hour.

"Right," he said to the Alsatian. "Back to Aberdale it is." It was his duty to warn the villagers what had happened in any case. Quinn would have taken the homestead's weapons. Thank Christ the colonists were only allowed hunting rifles, no heavy-calibre stuff.

Gerald Skibbow said nothing when Powel covered Paula with a canvas tarpaulin used to keep the pile of hay dry. But he allowed Powel to lead him away, and mounted Sango when he was told.

The two of them rode off across the savannah back to the Nicholls homestead, Orlando racing alongside through the thick grass. Behind them, the abandoned animals began to wander over to the pool to drink, nervous with their new-found freedom.

Jay Hilton was bored. The village felt most peculiar with no one working in the fields and allotments. By late afternoon all the children had been called to their cabins. The whole place looked deserted, although she could see people glancing out of their cabin windows as she wandered aimlessly along the familiar paths.

Her mother didn't want to talk, which was unusual. After she had come back from the search for Carter McBride she had rolled onto her bunk and just stared at the ceiling. She hadn't joined the party which left with Mr Manani to hunt down the Ivets.

Jay walked past the church. Father Elwes wasn't back yet. She knew he'd done something terribly wrong from the way Mr Manani had reacted when she mentioned his name earlier, more than just his drinking. But it still wasn't right for him to be out in the jungle alone with the evening coming in. The sun was already invisible, skulking below the tops of the trees.

Her enthusiastic and imaginative mind filled the blank jungle with all sorts of images. The priest had fallen over and broken an ankle. He was blundering about lost. He was hiding up a tree from a wild sayce.

Jay knew the jungle immediately around the village as though a didactic map had been laser imprinted in her brain. If she was the one who found Father Elwes she'd be a real heroine. She threw a quick glance at her cabin. There was no light on inside, Mother wouldn't notice her missing for half an hour or so. She hurried towards the sombre fence of trees.

It was quiet in the jungle. Even the chikrows had departed. And the shadows were deeper than she was used to. Spires of orange and pink light pierced the rustling leaves, unnaturally bright in the gathering gloom.

After ten minutes she thought that maybe this wasn't such a good idea after all. The well-worn track leading to the savannah homesteads wasn't far off. She cut quickly through the undergrowth, coming out on the path a couple of minutes later.

This was much better, she could see for about seventy metres in each direction. Some of her anxiety evaporated.

"Father?" she called experimentally. Her voice was loud in the hushed ranks of dusky trees looming all around. "Father, it's me, Jay." She turned a complete circle. Nothing moved, nothing made a sound. She wanted the hunting parties to come marching into view so she could walk home with them. Some company would be very welcome.

There was a crackling noise behind her, like someone treading on a twig.

"Father?" Jay turned round, and let out a squeak. At first she thought the black woman's head was hovering in the air all by itself, but when Jay squinted hard she could just make out the silhouette of her body. It was as though light bent round it, leaving a tiny blue and purple ripple effect around the edges.

The woman raised a hand. Leaves and twigs flowed fluidly over her palm, an exact pattern of what was behind her. She put a finger to her lips, then beckoned.

Sango cantered down the track back to Aberdale, keeping to a steady rhythm as darkness began to pool around the base of the trees. Powel Manani ducked occasionally to avoid low hanging branches. The route was one he knew by heart now. He rode automatically as his mind reviewed possibilities.

Everyone would have to stay in the village tomorrow, they could post guards so that work in the fields could continue. Any major interruption to their lives would be a victory for Quinn, and he mustn't allow that to happen. People were already badly shaken up by what had happened, their confidence in themselves had to be built up from scratch again.

He had passed Arnold Travis's group a quarter of an hour ago on their way home. They'd hanged all their Ivets. And the group that had gone out to the homesteads was burying the Ivets he'd shot at the Nicholls place. Tomorrow a gang would trek out to the Skibbow homestead and do what they could.

Which wasn't going to be much, he admitted bitterly. But it could have been worse. Then again, it could have been a whole lot better.

Powel sucked air in through his teeth at the thought of Quinn on the loose. At first light he would ride downriver to Schuster. The sheriff there would contact Durringham, and a proper manhunt could be organized. He knew Schuster's supervisor, Gregor O'Keefe, who had an affinity-bonded Doberman. They could go after Quinn straight away, before the trail went cold. Gregor would understand the need.

None of this was going to look good on his record. Families murdered and Ivets in open revolt. The Land Allocation Office probably wouldn't give him another supervisor contract after this. Well, screw them. Quinn was all that mattered now.

Sango shrieked, rearing up violently. He grabbed the reins hard in reflex. The horse came down, and he realized its legs were collapsing. Momentum carried him forward, his head meeting Sango's neck as it snaked back. Mane hair lashed across his face, and his nose squashed into the bristly beige coat. He tasted blood.

Sango hit the ground, inertia skidding him forwards a couple of metres before he finally rolled onto his side. Powel heard his right leg break with a shockingly loud snap as the horse's full weight came down on it. He blanked out for a moment. When he came to he promptly threw up. His right leg was completely numb below the hip. He felt dangerously light headed. Cold sweat prickled his skin.

The horse's flank had his leg pinned to the ground. He hunched himself up on his elbow, and tried to pull it out. Red-hot pain flared along his nerve paths. He groaned, and slumped back down onto the mossy grass, panting heavily.

The undergrowth swished behind him. There was the sound of footfalls on the loam.

"Hey!" he cried. "Christ, help me. The bloody horse keeled over on me. I can't feel my leg." He craned round. Six figures were walking out of the murky shadows which lined the track.

Quinn Dexter laughed.

Powel made a frantic lunge for the maser carbine in the saddle holster. His fingers curled round the grip.

Ann had been waiting for the move. She fired her laser rifle. The infrared pulse struck the back of Powel's hand, slicing clean through. Skin and muscle vaporized in a five-centimetre crater, veins instantly cauterized, his straining tendons roasted and snapped. Around the edge of the wound skin blackened and flaked away, a huge ring of blisters erupted. Powel let out a guttural snarl, jerking his hand back.

"Bring him," Quinn ordered.

The demon sprite had come back to the church. It was the first thing Horst Elwes discovered when he returned.

Most of the day was lost to him. He must have lain in the little clearing for hours. His shirt and trousers were damp from the rain, and smeared with mud. And Carter McBride's blood-filmed eyes still stared at him.

"Your fault!" Supervisor Manani had shouted in rage. He was right, too.

A sin by omission. The belief that human dignity would triumph. That all he had to do was wait and the Ivets would grow tired of their foolish rituals and genuflecting. That they would realize the Light Brother sect was a charade designed to make them do Quinn's bidding. Then he would be there for them, waiting to forgive and welcome them into the Lord's fold.

Well, now that arrogance had cost a child his life, perhaps others too if the suspicions of Ruth and Manani were correct. Horst wasn't at all sure he wanted to go on living.

He walked back into the village clearing as the penumbra arose from the east and the brighter stars started to shine above the black treetops. A few cabins had yellow lights glimmering inside, but the village was deathly quiet. The life had gone out of it.

The spirit, Horst thought, that is what's missing. Even afterwards, even after they've had their revenge and slaughtered the Ivets, this place will be tainted. They have bitten their apple now, and the knowledge of truth has corrupted their souls. They know what beasts lie in their hearts. Even though they dress it up as honour and civilized justice. They know.

He walked heavily out of the shadows towards the church. That simple little church which symbolized all that was wrong with the village. Built on a lie, home to a fool, laughed at by all. Even here, the most God-forsaken planet in the Confederation, where nothing really matters, I can't get it right. I can't do the one thing I vowed before God that my life was for, I can't give them faith in themselves.

He pushed through the swing door at the rear of the church. Carter McBride was laid out on a pew at the front, draped in a blanket. Someone had lit one of the altar candles.

A dainty red star flickered a metre over the body.

All Horst's anguish returned in a deluge that threatened to extinguish his sanity. He bit his trembling lower lip.

If God the Holy Trinity exists, said the waster sect Satanists, then, *ipso facto*, the Dark One is also real. For Jesus was tempted by Satan, both have touched the Earth, both will return.

Now Horst Elwes looked at the speck of red light and felt the dry weight of aeons press in on his mind again. To have the existence of supernatural divinity proven like this was a hideous travesty. Men were supposed to come to faith, not have it forced upon them.

He dropped to one knee as if pushed down by a giant irresistible hand. "O my Lord, forgive me. Forgive me my weakness. I beg Thee."

The star slid through the air towards him. It didn't seem to cast any light on the pews or floor.

"What are you? What have you come here for? The boy's soul? Did Quinn Dexter summon you for that? How I pity you. That boy was pure in mind no matter what they did to him, no matter what they made him say. Our Lord would not reject him because of your acolytes' inhumanity. Carter will be welcomed into heaven by Gabriel himself."

The star stopped two metres short of Horst.

"Out," Horst said. He stood, the strength of recklessness infusing his limbs. "Get ye gone from this place. You have failed. Doubly you have failed." His face split in a slow grin, a drop of spittle running down his beard. "This old sinner has taken heart again from your presence. And this place you desecrate is holy ground. Now out!" He thrust a rigid forefinger at the gloaming-soaked jungle beyond the door. "Out!"

Footsteps thudded on the steps outside the church, the

swing door banged open. "Father!" Jay yelled at the top of her voice.

Small, thin arms hugged his waist with a strength a full-grown man would be hard put to match. He instinctively cradled her, hands smoothing her knotted white-blonde hair.

"Oh, Father," she sobbed. "It was horrible, they killed Sango. They shot him. He's dead. Sango's dead."

"Who did? Who shot him?"

"Quinn. The Ivets." Her face tilted up to look at him. The skin was blotchy from crying. "She made me hide. They were very close."

"You've seen Quinn Dexter?"

"Yes. He shot Sango. I *hate* him!"

"When was this?"

"Just now."

"Here? In the village?"

"No. We were on the track to the homesteads, about half a kilometre."

"Who was with you?"

Jay sniffled, screwing a fist into her eye. "I don't know her name. She was a black lady. She just came out of the jungle in a funny suit. She said I must be careful because the Ivets were very near. I was frightened. We hid from them behind some bushes. And then Sango came down the track." Her chin began to tremble. "He's dead, Father."

"Where is this woman now?"

"Gone. She walked back to the village with me, then left."

More puzzled than worried, Horst tried to calm his whirling thoughts. "What was funny about her suit?"

"It was like a piece of jungle, you couldn't see her."

"A marshal?" he said under his breath. That didn't make any sense at all. Then he abruptly realized something missing from her story. He took hold of her shoulders, staring down at her intently. "Was Mr Manani riding Sango when Quinn shot him?"

"Yes."

"Is he dead?"

"No. He was shouting cos he was hurt. Then the Ivets carried him away."

"Oh, dear Lord. Was that where the woman was going, back to help Mr Manani?"

Jay's face radiated misery. "Don't think so. She didn't say anything, she just vanished as soon as we reached the fields around the village."

Horst turned to the demon sprite. But it had gone. He started to hustle Jay out of the church. "You are to go straight home to your mother, and I mean straight home. Tell her what you told me, and tell her to get the other villagers organized. They must be warned that the Ivets are near."

Jay nodded, her eyes round and immensely serious.

Horst glanced about the clearing. Night had almost fallen, the trees seemed much nearer, much larger in the dark. He shivered.

"What are you going to do, Father?"

"Just have a look, that's all. Now go on with you." He gave her a gentle push in the direction of Ruth's cabin. "Home."

She scampered off between the rows of cabins, long, slender legs flying in a shaky gait that looked as though she was perpetually about to lose her balance. Then Horst was all by himself. He gave the jungle a grim glance, and set off towards the gap in the trees where the track to the savannah homesteads started.

Sentimental fool, Laton said.

Listen, Father, after what I did today I'm entitled to show some sentiment, Camilla retorted. **Quinn would have ripped her apart. There's no need for that kind of bloodshed any more. We have achieved what we set out to do.**

Well, now this idiot priest is heading out to be a hero. Do you intend to save him as well?

No. He's an adult. He makes his own choices.

Very well. The loss of Supervisor Manani is vexing, though. I was relying on him to eradicate the rest of the Ivets.

Do you want me to shoot them?

No, the hunting party is returning, they will find the horse soon enough, and the trail Quinn Dexter has left. They would wonder what killed them. There must be no hint of our existence. Though Jay—

Nobody will believe her.

Possibly.

So what are you going to do about Dexter? Our original scenario didn't envisage him surviving this long.

Quinn Dexter will come to me now, there is nowhere else he can go. The sheriffs will assume he has run off into the wilderness, never to be seen again. Not quite the perfect solution, but no battle plan survives the opening shot. And Ann's ova will be a welcome addition to our genetic resources.

Is my provocateur duty over now?

Yes, I don't believe the situation requires further intervention on our part. We can monitor events through the servitor scouts.

Good. I'm on my way home; have a bath and a tall drink waiting, it's been a long day.

Quinn looked down at Powel Manani. The naked supervisor had regained consciousness again now they had finished lashing his badly crushed legs to the mayope's trunk. His head hung a few centimetres from the ground; cheeks puffed out from all the fluid that was building up in the facial tissue. They had spread his arms wide, tying his hands to small stakes in the ground. The inverted cross.

Powel Manani moaned dazedly.

Quinn held out his hands for silence. "The Night grows strong. Welcome to our world, Powel."

"Dickhead," Powel grunted.

Quinn flicked on a pocket-sized thermal inducer, and pressed it against Powel's broken shin. He groaned, and jerked about feebly.

"Why did you do it, Powel? Why did you drown Leslie and Tony? Why did you kill Kay? Why did you send Vorix after Douglas?"

"And the others," Powel wheezed. "Don't forget them."

Quinn stiffened. "Others?"

"You're all that's left, Quinn. And tomorrow there won't even be you."

The thermal inducer was applied to his leg again.

"Why?" Quinn asked.

"Carter McBride. Why do you think? You're fucking animals, all of you. Just *animals*. No human could do that to another. He was ten years old!"

Quinn frowned, turning off the thermal inducer. "What happened to Carter McBride?"

"This! You dickhead. You strung him up, you and your Light Brother bastards. You split him in half!"

"Quinn?" Jackson Gael asked uncertainly.

Quinn gestured him quiet with a wave. "We never touched Carter. How could we? We were out at the Skibbow homestead."

Powel pulled at the vines holding his hands. "And Gwyn Lawes, and Roger Chadwick, and the Hoffmans? What about them? You got alibis for them, too?"

"Ah, well now I have to admit, you have a point there. But how did you know we followed the Light Brother?"

"Elwes, he told us."

"Yes, I should have realized a priest would know what was going down. Not that it matters now." He took his fission blade from his dungarees pocket.

"Quinn," Jackson said hotly. "This is weird, man. Who snuffed out Carter if we didn't?"

Quinn held the blade up in front of his face, regarding it in a virtual trance. "What happened after Carter was found?"

"What do you mean?" Jackson yelled. "What are you talking about? Shit, Quinn, snap out of it, man. We're gonna die if we don't move."

"That's right. We're gonna die. We've been set up." The blade came alive, radiating a spectral yellow light that gave his face a phosphene hue. He smiled.

Jackson Gael felt a deadly frost settle around his heart. He hadn't realized how insane Quinn was before this; nutty, sure, a psycho streak thrown in. But this—God's

Brother, Quinn was actually enjoying himself, he believed he was the Night's disciple.

The other Ivets were giving each other very edgy glances.

Quinn didn't notice. He leaned closer to Powel Manani. The supervisor sagged, giving up the struggle.

"We are the princes of the Night," Quinn intoned.

"We are the princes of the Night," the Ivets chanted with numb obedience.

Camilla, get back there now. Eliminate all of them immediately. I'm dispatching the incorporated to help you clear away the bodies. If the hunting party arrive first, use a thermal grenade to obliterate the scene. It's hardly elegant, but it will have to suffice. Quinn Dexter must not be allowed to divulge our existence.

I'm on my way, Father.

The Ly-cilph moved its identity focus between Quinn Dexter and Powel Manani, extending its perception field around all the people in the cramped jungle clearing. It couldn't quite read individual thoughts, not yet, the complexity of human synaptic discharges would take some time to unravel and catalogue, but their brains' emotional content was plain enough.

The emotional polarity between Quinn Dexter and Powel Manani was enormous; one triumphant and elated, life loving; the other defeated and withdrawn, willing death to come quickly. It mirrored their religious traits, the diametric opposition.

Right out on the fringe of awareness, the Ly-cilph could detect a minute transmission of energy from Powel Manani into Quinn Dexter. It came from the basic energistic force which pervaded every living cell. This kind of transference was extraordinarily rare in corporeal entities. And Quinn Dexter seemed to be aware of it at some fundamental level, he possessed an energistic sense far superior to that of the priest. To Quinn Dexter the black mass sacrifices were a lot more than an empty ritual of worship, they generated a weighty expectation in his mind, confirming his belief.

The Ly-cilph watched the sensation growing inside him, and waited with every perceptive faculty extended eagerly to record the phenomenon.

"When the false lord leads his legions away into oblivion, we will be here," Quinn said.

"We will be here," the Ivets repeated.

"When You bring light into the darkness, we will be here."

"We will be here."

"When time ends, and space collapses into itself, we will be here."

"We will be here."

Quinn reached out with the fission blade. He pushed the tip into Powel Manani's groin, just above the root of his penis. Skin sizzled as the blade sank in, pubic hair singed and shrivelled. Powel clenched his teeth, neck muscles bulging out like ropes as he struggled against the scream. Quinn began to saw the blade down through the supervisor's abdomen.

"This is our sacrament to You, Lord," Quinn said. "We have freed our serpents, we are the beast we were made. We are real. Accept this life as a token of our love and devotion." The knife reached Powel's navel, ribbons of blood were pouring out of the wound. Quinn watched the scarlet liquid mat the man's thick body hair, experiencing a fierce delight. "Give us Your strength, Lord, help us defeat Your enemies." The dark joy of the serpent beast had never been so good before; he felt intoxicated. Every cell in his body vibrated with euphoria. "Show us, Lord!" he cried. "Speak to us!"

Powel Manani was dying. The Ly-cilph observed the swirl of energistic patterns raging throughout his body. A small discharge crackled into Quinn, where it was hungrily absorbed, raising the Ivet's mental rapture to greater heights. The remainder of Powel's life energy dwindled, but its dissipation wasn't entirely entropic, a minute fraction flowed away through some kind of arcane dimensional twist. The Ly-cilph was fascinated, this ceremony was releasing an incredible wealth of knowledge; it had never attuned itself to an entity's death so pervasively before in all its terrible length of being.

It inserted itself into the energy flow from Manani's cells, tracing it between the neat folds of quantum reality, and finding itself emerging in a continuum it had no prior conception of: an energistic vacuum. A void as daunting to it as space was to a naked human. Retaining cohesion in such an environment was inordinately difficult, it had to contract its density to prevent flares of self-energy from streaming away like cometary volatiles. Once it had stabilized its internal structure, the Ly-cilph opened its perception field wide. It wasn't alone.

Ill-focused swirls of information raced through this foreign void, similar in nature to the Ly-cilph's own memory facility. They were separate entities, it was sure, though they continually mingled themselves, interpenetrating then diverging. The Ly-cilph observed the alien mentalities cluster around the boundary zone of its identity focus. Delicate wisps of radiation stroked it, bringing a multitude of impossibly jumbled images. It assembled a standardized identity and interpretation message and broadcast it on the same radiation bands they were using. Horrifyingly, instead of responding, the aliens penetrated its boundary.

The Ly-cilph fought to retain its fundamental integrity as its thought routines were violated and subsumed by the incursive alien mentalities. But there were too many of them to block. It started to lose control of its functions; the perception field contracted, access to the vast repository of stored knowledge began to falter, it was unable to move. They began to alter its internal energy structure, opening a wide channel between their empty continuum and spacetime. Patterns started to surge back through the dimensional twist, strands of raw memory using the Ly-cilph as a conduit, seeking a specific physical matrix in which they could operate.

It was a monstrous usurpation, one which contravened the Ly-cilph's most intrinsic nature. The alien mentalities were forcing it to participate in the flux of events which ordered the universe, to interfere. There was only one option left. It stored itself. Thought processes and immediate memory were loaded into the macro-data lattice. The active functions ceased to exist.

The Ly-cilph would hang in stasis between the two variant continua until it was discovered and re-animated by one of its own kind. The chance of that discovery before the universe ended was infinitesimal, but time was of no consequence to a Ly-cilph. It had done all it could.

Thirty metres away from the Ivets and Powel Manani, Horst Elwes crept through the undergrowth, drawn by the low chanting voices. The trail of broken vines and torn leaves leading away from the dead horse had been absurdly easy to follow even in the last flickers of fading sunlight. It was as though Quinn didn't care who found them.

Night had fallen with bewildering suddenness after Horst left the track, and the jungle had constricted ominously around him. Blackness assumed the quality of a thin liquid. He was drowning in it.

Then he heard the grating voices, the truculent incantation. The voices of frightened people.

A spark of yellow light bobbed between the trees ahead of him. He pressed himself against a big qualtook trunk, and peered round. Quinn sank the fission blade into Powel Manani's prostrate body.

Horst gasped, and crossed himself. "Lord, receive Your son—"

The demon sprite flared like a miniature nova between Quinn and Powel, turning the jungle to a lurid crimson all around. It was pulsing in a mockery of organic life. Incandescent webs of vermilion light crawled over Quinn like icy flames.

Horst clung to the tree, beyond both terror and hope. None of the Ivets had even noticed the manifestation. Except for Quinn. Quinn was smiling with orgasmic joy.

When the rapture reached an almost unbearable peak, Quinn heard the voices. They came from inside his head, similar to the fractured whispers which dream chimeras uttered. But these grew louder, entire words rising out of the clamorous babble. He saw light arise before him, a scarlet aureole that cloaked Powel's body. Right at the heart there was a crevice of absolute darkness.

Quinn stretched out his arms towards the empty tear in space. "My Lord! You are come!"

The multitude of voices came together. "Is the darkness what you crave, Quinn?" they asked in unison.

"Yes, oh yes."

"We are of the dark, Quinn. Aeons we have spent here, seeking one such as you."

"I am yours, Lord."

"Welcome us, Quinn."

"I do. Bring me the Night, Lord."

Seething tendrils of spectral two-dimensional lightning burst out of Powel Manani's corpse with an ear-puncturing screech. They reached directly for Quinn like an avaricious succubus. Jackson Gael staggered backwards yelling in shock, shielding his eyes from the blinding purple-white light. Beside him, Ann clung to a slender tree trunk as though caught in the blast of a hurricane, her hair whipping about, eyes squeezed shut. The flat lightning strands were coiling relentlessly around Quinn. His limbs danced about in spastic reflex. Mad shadows flickered across the little clearing. The stench of burning meat filled the air. Powel's body was smouldering.

"You are the chosen one, Quinn," the unified voices called inside his skull.

He felt them emerging out of the shadows, out of Night so profound it was perpetual torment. His heart filled with glory at their presence, they were kindred, serpent beasts. He offered himself to them and they rushed into his mind like a psychic gale. Darkness engulfed him, the world of light and colour falling away at tremendous speed.

Alone in his cherished Night, Quinn Dexter waited for the coming of the Light Brother.

Horst Elwes saw the red demon light wink out. The ungodly lightning blazed in its place, arcing through the air, stray ribbons raking around the clearing. Things seemed to be swimming down the incandescent strands, slender, turbid shadows, like the negative image of a shooting star. Leaves and vine creepers flapped and shook as air rushed by.

The Ivets were screaming, flailing about in panic. Horst

saw Irley being struck by a wild quivering lightning bolt; the lad was flung two metres through the air to land stunned and twitching.

Quinn stood fast at the centre of the storm, his body shaking, yet always remaining upright. An incredulous smile on his face.

The lightning cut off.

He turned slowly, uncertainly, as though he was unacquainted with his own body, testing his musculature. Horst realized he could see him perfectly even though it was now pitch black. The other Ivets were near-invisible shadows. Quinn's beatific gaze swept round them all.

"You as well," he said gently.

Lightning streamed out of him, slender bucking threads that flashed unerringly at his five companions. Screams laced the air.

"Our Father, Who art in Heaven—" Horst said. He was waiting for the lightning to seek him out. "Hallowed be Thy name—" The Ivets' cries were fading. "Forgive us our trespass—"

The terrible surging light vanished. Silence descended.

Horst peeked round the tree. All six Ivets were standing in the clearing. Each had their own nimbus of light.

Like angels, he thought, so handsome with their youthfully splendid bodies. What a cruel deceiver nature is.

As he watched they began to dim. Jackson Gael turned and looked straight at him. Horst's heart froze.

"A priest," Jackson laughed. "How wonderful. Well, we don't require your services, padre. But we do need your body." He took a step forwards.

"Up there," Ann cried. She pointed deeper into the jungle.

Camilla had arrived right at the end of the sacrifice ceremony, just in time to see the lightning writhe around the clearing. She used the chameleon suit's takpads to climb up a big tree, and crouched in the fork of a bough, looking down on them.

I don't know what the hell that lightning is, Laton said. **It can't be electrical, they'd be dead.**

Does it matter? she demanded. Adrenalin was tingling

inside her veins. **Whatever is causing it isn't working for us.**

True. But look how they are staying visible. It's like a holographic effect.

Where's it coming from?

I have no idea. Somebody must be projecting it.

But the scouts haven't seen anything.

Ann called out and pointed. The other Ivets swiveled round.

Camilla knew what fear was for the first time in her life. **Shit, they can see me!** She brought her maser rifle up.

Don't! Laton called.

The chameleon suit ignited. Bright white flame engulfed her completely. She felt her skin burning and screamed. The plastic fabric melted rapidly, flaming droplets raining down out of the tree. She squirmed about, beating at herself frantically with her arms. She fell from her perch, a tumbling fireball, flames streaming out behind her. By then she had no air left in her lungs to scream with. She hit the ground with a dull *whoomp*, flinging out a wreath of flame. The temperature of the internecine fire increased, burning like a magnesium flare, consuming muscles, organs, and bone alike.

The Ivets gathered round as the last flames sputtered and died. All that remained was a blackened outline of scorched earth scattered with glowing clinker-like ashes. They crackled sharply as they cooled.

"What a waste," Jackson Gael said.

They turned as one to look for Horst Elwes. But he had fled long ago.

Ruth Hilton and the other remaining adult villagers were grouped around the community hall in a defensive ring. The children were all inside it. Nobody knew quite what to make of Jay's story, but there was no disputing she had seen Quinn Dexter.

Torchlight sliced round the empty cabins and muddy paths. The wooden slat walls shone a pale grey in the beams. Those whose rifles were equipped with nightsights were scanning the surrounding jungle.

"Christ, how much longer before the hunting party gets back?" Skyba Molvi complained. "They've got enough fire-power to blow out an army of Ivets."

"Won't be long," Ruth muttered tightly.

"I see him!" someone bellowed.

"What?" Ruth spun round, every nerve hotwired.

Targeting lasers stabbed out, forming bright ruby and emerald zigzag patterns in the air. A magnetic rifle trilled. A patch of ground forty metres away bucked as the slugs hit, forming deep narrow craters, and surrounding vegetation caught light.

The firing stopped.

"Bugger; it's a dog."

The breath rushed out of Ruth. Her arms were trembling. Children were shouting from the hall, demanding to know what was happening.

I should be in there with Jay, Ruth thought. Fine mother I am, letting her wander off into the jungle while I'm busy moping. And what the hell did happen out there anyway?

Horst came ploughing out of the jungle, arms spinning madly for balance. His clothes were torn, face and hands scratched and grazed. He saw the beams of light sweeping out from the hall, and shouted at the top of his voice.

Ruth heard someone say: "It's that idiot priest."

"Drunk again."

"That bastard could have saved Carter."

Ruth wanted to shrink up into a little ball that no one could see. She was sure everybody could smell her own guilt.

"Demons," Horst cried as he ran towards the hall. "They've unleashed demons. Lord save us. Flee! Flee!"

"He is drunk."

"It should have been him, not Carter."

Horst staggered to a halt in front of them, his body aching so badly from the exertion he could hardly stand. He saw the disgust and contempt in their faces, and wanted to weep. "For pity's sake. I promise you. Quinn is out there, he killed Powel Manani. Something happened, something came."

There were angry murmurs from the crowd. One of them spat in Horst's direction.

Ruth noticed her torch was dimming. She slapped it.

"Why didn't you help Powel, priest?" someone asked.

"Ruth?" Horst begged. "Please, tell them how evil Quinn is."

"We know."

"Shut up, priest. We don't need a worthless piss-artist telling us about the Ivets. If Quinn shows his face here, he's dead."

Ruth's torch went out.

Alarmed gasps went up from the others as all the torches began to flicker and fade.

"Demons are coming!" Horst yelled.

Fierce orange flames shot out of one of the cabins fifty metres away from the hall; they licked along its base then raced up the stanchions to the roof. Within thirty seconds the whole structure was ablaze. The twisting flames were ten metres high.

"Holy shit," Ruth whispered. Nothing should burn that quickly.

"Mummy!" a child called from the hall.

"Horst, what *happened* out there?" Ruth cried.

Horst shook his head, a bubbling giggle coming from his lips. "Too late, too late. Satan's beasts walk among us now. I told you."

A second cabin began to blaze.

"Get the children out of the hall," Skyba Molvi shouted. There was a general rush for the door. Ruth hesitated, looking at Horst imploringly. Most of the village clearing was now illuminated by erratic amber light. Shadows possessed a life of their own, leaping about at random. A black silhouette fluttered between the cabins in the distance behind the priest.

"They're here," she said. Nobody was listening. "They're here, the Ivets!" She tugged her laser rifle up. The green targeting beam pierced the air, sending relief flooding through her. At least something bloody worked. She pulled the trigger, sending a barrage of infrared pulses after the elusive figure.

The children swept out of the hall like a wave, some of the older ones scaling the flimsy metre-high side walls. Cries and shouts broke out as they tried to run to their parents.

"Jay!" Ruth called.

A line of flame streaked along the roof. It was an unerringly straight line, Ruth could see the wood turning black an instant before the actual flame shot up. Maser!

She worked out roughly where it must be firing from, and brought the laser rifle to bear. Her finger punched down on the trigger stud.

"Mummy," Jay called.

"Here."

The laser rifle bleeped. Ruth ejected the drained power magazine and slammed in a fresh one.

Several other people were firing into the jungle. The neon threads of targeting lasers lashed out, chasing elusive phantoms.

There was a concerted movement away from the hall, everyone crouching low. It was pandemonium, children wailing, adults shouting. The woven palm wall of the hall caught fire.

They could kill every one of us if they wanted to, she realized.

Jay rushed up and flung her arms round her waist. Ruth grabbed her arm. "Come on, this way." She started towards the jetty. Another three cabins were on fire.

She saw Horst a couple of metres away, and jerked her head in a determined gesture. He began to lumber along after them.

A scream sounded across Aberdale, a gruesome drawn-out warbling that could never have come from a human throat. It shocked even the distraught children into silence. Targeting lasers jabbed out in reflex, spearing the gaps between the cabins.

The scream faded to a poignant desperate whimper.

"Jesus God, they're everywhere, all around."

"Where are the hunters? The hunters!"

There seemed to be fewer targeting lasers active now.

The first burning cabin suddenly crumpled up, blowing out ephemeral spires of brilliant sparks.

"Horst, we've got to get Jay away," Ruth said urgently.

"No escape," he mumbled. "Not for the damned. And were we ever anything but?"

"Oh, yeah? Don't you believe it." She began to pull Jay across the stream of people, heading towards the nearest row of cabins. Horst lowered his head and followed.

They reached the cabins just as some kind of commotion started down by the jetty: shouting, the splash of something heavy falling into the river. It meant nobody was paying her much attention.

"Thank Christ for that," Ruth said. She led Jay down the gap between two cabins.

"Where are we going, Mummy?" Jay asked.

"We'll hide out for a couple of hours until that bloody hunting party gets back. God damn Powel for stripping the village."

"He's beyond damnation now," Horst said.

"Look, Horst, just what—"

Jackson Gael stepped around the end of the cabin and planted himself firmly in front of them. "Ruth. Little Jay. Father Horst. Come to me. You are so welcome."

"Bollocks," Ruth snarled. She swung the laser rifle round. There was no targeting beam, even the power-level LEDs were dead. "Shit!"

Jackson Gael took a step towards them. "There is no death any more, Ruth," he said. "There will never be death again."

Ruth thrust Jay towards Horst. It was one of the hardest things she had ever done. "Get her out of here, Horst, get her away."

"Trust me, Ruth, you will not die." Jackson Gael held out his hand. "Come."

"Screw you." She dropped the useless laser rifle, standing between him and Jay.

"There is no sanctuary," Horst mumbled. "Not on this cursed planet."

"Mummy!" Jay wailed.

"Horst, just for once in your fucking pitiful life do

something right; take my daughter and get her out of here. This bastard isn't getting past me."

"I—"

"Do it!"

"God bless you, Ruth." He started to pull a struggling Jay back the way they had come.

"Mummy, please!" she shrieked.

"Go with Horst. I love you." She drew her Bowie knife from its belt scabbard. Good solid dependable steel.

Jackson Gael grinned. Ruth could have sworn she saw fangs.

14

Ione Saldana stood in front of the tube carriage's door, urging it to open.

I can't make it go any faster, Tranquillity grumbled as the backwash of emotion dissipated through the affinity bond.

I know. I'm not blaming you. She clenched her fists, shifting her weight from one foot to the other. The carriage started to slow, and she reached up to hold one of the hand hoops. The memory of Joshua flashed into her mind—she'd never be able to use the carriages without thinking of him again. She smiled.

There was a frisson of disparagement from Tranquillity sounding in her mind.

Jealous, she teased.

Hardly, came the piqued reply.

The carriage door slid open. Ione stepped out on the deserted platform and raced up the stairs, her serjeant bodyguard clumping along behind.

It was a southern endcap cove station, a couple of kilometres away from the Laymil research project campus. The cove was six hundred metres long, a gentle crescent with fine gold-white sands and several outcrops of granite boulders. A rank of ageing coconut trees followed the beach's curve; several had keeled over, pulling up large clods of sand and roots, and three had snapped off halfway up the trunk, adding to the vaguely wild look of the place. At the centre of the cove, sixty metres out from the shore, there was a tiny island with a few tall palm trees, providing an appealing nook for the more enthusiastic swimmers. A shingly bluff planted with coarse reeds rose up from the rear of the sands, blending into the first and widest of the endcap's terraces.

Six low polyp domes, forty metres in diameter, broke the

expanse of grass and silk oak trees behind the bluff, giving the impression of being partially buried. They were the Kiint residences, grown specifically for the eight big xenocs who participated in the Laymil project.

Their involvement had been quite a coup for Michael Saldana. Even though they didn't build ZTT starships (they claimed their psychology meant they had no real interest in space travel), the Kiint remained the most technologically advanced race in the Confederation. Up until Michael's invitation was accepted they had refrained from any joint scientific enterprise with other Confederation members. However, Michael succeeded where countless others had failed, in presenting them with a peaceful challenge which would tax even their capabilities. Their intellect, along with the instrumentation they provided, would inevitably speed up the research. And of course their presence had helped to bolster Tranquillity's kudos in the difficult early days.

Eight was the largest number of Kiint resident on a human world or habitat outside the Confederation capital, Avon. Something else which had given Michael a considerable degree of underhand satisfaction—Kulu only rated the customary pair as ambassadors.

Inside Tranquillity the Kiint were as insular as they were in the Confederation at large. Although cordial with their fellow project staff members, they did not socialize with any of the habitat's population, and Tranquillity guarded their physical privacy quite rigorously. Even Ione had only had a few formal meetings with them, where both sides stuck to small-talk pleasantries. It was just as bad as having to "receive" all those national ambassadors. The hours she'd spent with those semi-senile bores . . .

Ione had never been out to the Kiint buildings before, and probably never would have. But this occasion justified it, she felt, even if they were upset with her breach of etiquette.

She stood on the top of the bluff, and looked down at the bulky white xenocs bathing in the shallows. From her vantage point she could see a lot of splashing going on.

Thirty metres away, there was a wide path of crumbling soil leading to the sands. She started down.

How do they get to the project campus every day? she asked, suddenly curious.

They walk. Only humans demand mechanized transport to move from one room to another.

My, but we are touchy this morning.

I would point out that guaranteed seclusion was part of the original agreement between the Kiint and your grandfather.

Yes, yes, she said impatiently. She reached the bottom of the path, and took her sandals off to walk across the sand. The towelling robe she wore over her bikini flapped loosely.

There were three Kiint in the water, Nang and Lieria, a pair who worked in the Laymil project Physiology Division, and a baby. Tranquillity had reported its appearance as soon as Ione woke up that morning, although the personality refused to show her its own memory of the birth, which had come sometime in the night. **Would you like recordings of your labour pains shown to xenocs simply because they were morbidly curious?** it asked sternly.

She had acquiesced with bad grace.

The baby Kiint was about two metres long, its body more rounded than the adults' and slightly whiter. The legs were a metre high, which brought the top of the head level with Ione's. It was clearly having a rare old time in the water. The tractamorphic arms were formshifting at a frantic rate, first scoops, then paddles slapped about to raise sheets of spray, now bulblike pods which squirted out jets of water. Its beak was flapping open and shut.

The parents were patting and stroking it with their arms as it charged about in circles. Then it caught sight of Ione.

Panic. Alarm. Incredulity. Thing has not enough legs. Topple walk. Fall over not. Why why why? What is it?

Ione blinked against the sudden wash of jumbled emotions and frantic questions that seemed to be shouted into her mind.

That'll teach you to creep up on entities, Tranquillity said drily.

The baby Kiint butted up against Lieria's flank, hiding itself from Ione.

What is it? What is it? Fear strangeness.

Ione caught the briefest exchange of mental images that the adult Kiints directed at the baby, an information stream more complex than anything she'd known before. The speed was bewildering, over almost as it began.

She stopped with her feet in the warm, clear water and gave the adults a small bow. **Nang, Lieria, I came to offer my congratulations on the birth, and to see if your child has any special requirements. My apologies if I intrude.**

Thank you, Ione Saldana, Lieria said. There was a suggestion of lofty amusement behind the mental voice. **Your interest and concern is gratifying, no apology is required. This is Haile, our daughter.**

Welcome to Tranquillity, Haile, Ione told the baby, projecting as much warmth and delight as she could muster. It came easily, the little Kiint was so cute. Very different from the solemn adults.

Haile pushed her head comically round Lieria's neck, huge violet-tinged eyes looked steadily at Ione. **It communicates! Alive think.**

There was another fast mental communiqué from one of the adults. The baby turned to look at Nang, then back at Ione. The tumult of emotions leaking into the affinity band began to slow.

Formal address wrongness. Much sorriness. Greetings ritual observance. The thoughts stopped abruptly, almost like a mental gathering of breath. **Hello Ione Saldana. Rightness?**

Very much.

Human you are?

I am.

I Haile am.

Hello, Haile, I'm pleased to meet you.

Haile squirmed round excitedly, water frothed around her eight feet. **It likes me! Happiness feel much.**

I'm glad.

Human identity query: Part of the all-around?

She means me, Tranquillity said.

No, I'm not part of the all-around. We're just good friends.

Haile surged forward, ploughing the water aside. She still hadn't quite got the hang of walking, and her rear pair of legs almost tripped her up.

This time Ione could understand the adults' warning perfectly. **Careful!**

Haile stopped a metre short of her. Warm breath exhaled from the facial vents smelt slightly spicy, and the tractamorphic arms waved about. She held her hand out, palm facing the baby, fingers spread. Haile tried to imitate the hand; her attempt looked like a melted wax model.

Fail! Sorrowness. Show me how, Ione Saldana.

I can't, mine's always like this.

Haile emitted a burst of shock.

Ione giggled. **It's all right. I'm very happy with the way I am.**

It is rightness?

It is rightness.

There is so much strangeness to life, Haile said wistfully.

You're right there.

Haile bent her neck almost double to look back round at her parents. The fast affinity exchange which followed made Ione feel woefully inadequate.

Are you my friend, Ione Saldana? Haile asked tentatively.

I think I could be, yes.

Will you show me the all-around? It has a vastness. I don't want to go alone. Loneliness fear.

It would be a pleasure, she said, surprised.

Haile's arms hit the water sending up a giant plume of spray. Ione was instantly drenched. She pulled the wet hair from her eyes, sighing ruefully.

You have no liking of water? Haile asked anxiously.

I'll have you know I'm a better swimmer than you.

Much gleeful!

Ione, Tranquillity said. **The *Lady Macbeth* has just emerged from a ZTT jump. Joshua has requested docking permission.**

"Joshua!" Ione shouted. Too late she remembered Kiint did have auditory senses.

Haile's arms writhed in alarm. **Panic. Fright. Joy shared.** She shied back from Ione and promptly fell down.

"Oh, I'm sorry," Ione splashed towards her.

Nang and Lieria came up and slipped their arms under Haile's belly, while the baby Kiint coiled an arm tip around Ione's hand. She tugged.

Query Joshua identity? Haile asked as she regained her feet and stood swaying unsteadily.

He's another friend of mine.

More friends? My friend? I meet him?

Ione opened her mouth—then thought about it. Away at the back of her mind Tranquillity was registering a serene hauteur.

Ione closed her mouth. **I think we'll wait until you understand humans a little better.**

It was almost an infallible rule that to be an Edenist a human must have affinity and live in a habitat; certainly every Edenist returned to a habitat for their death, or had their thoughts transferred to one after death. Physically, the bitek systems integral to their society were capable of sustaining a very high standard of living at little financial cost: the price of steering asteroidal rubble into a habitat maw, the internal mechanical systems like starscraper lifts and the tube carriage network. Culturally though the symbiosis was much more subtle. With the exception of Serpents, there were no psychological problems among the Edenist population; although they displayed a full emotional range, as individuals there were all extremely well adjusted. The knowledge that they would continue as part of the habitat personality after bodily death acted as a tremendous stabilizing influence, banishing a great many common human psychoses. It was a liberation which bestowed them with a universal confidence and poise that Adamists nearly always considered to be unbridled arrogance. The disparity in wealth between the two cultures also contributed to the image of Edenists being humanity's aristocrats.

Edenism, then, was dependent on habitats. And bitek habitats were only to be found orbiting gas giants. They were totally reliant on the vast magnetospheres of such worlds for power. Photosynthesis was a wholly impractical method of supplying a habitat's energy demands; it necessitated the deployment of vast leaf-analogue membranes, and the numerous difficulties inherent in doing so from a rotating structure, as well as being unacceptably susceptible to damage from both particle impact and cosmic radiation. So the Edenists were confined to colonizing the Confederation's gas giants.

However there was one exception, one terracompatible planet which they settled successfully: Atlantis; so named because it was a single giant ocean of salt water. Its sole exports were the seafood delicacies for which it was renowned across the Confederation. The variety of marine life below its waves was so great that even two hundred and forty years after its discovery barely one-third had been classified. A vast number of traders, both independent and corporate, were attracted to it; which was why Syrinx flew *Oenone* there right after their navy duty tour finished.

Syrinx had decided to go straight into the independent trading business once her discharge order came through. The prospect of years spent on He3 deliveries depressed her. A lot of voidhawk captains took on the tanker contracts for the stability they offered, it was exactly what she'd done when *Oenone* started flying, but the last thing she wanted was to wind up in a rigid flight routine again; the navy had given her quite enough of that already, a feeling the rest of the crew heartily shared (apart from Chi, who left along with all the weapons hardware in the lower hull). Although some doubts lingered obstinately in her mind, it was a big step from the precisely ordered navy life she was used to.

On seeing her daughter dithering, Athene pointed out that Norfolk was approaching conjunction, and spent an evening reminiscing on her own flights to collect the planet's fabled Tears. Three days later *Oenone* left the maintenance station dock at Romulus; new cargo cradles fitted, a new civilian registration filed, licensed by the Confederation Astronautics Board to carry freight and up to twenty passengers, crew toroid refurbished, and crew-members in a tigerish frame of mind.

It emerged from its wormhole terminus a hundred and fifteen thousand kilometres above Atlantis, almost directly over the dawn terminator. Syrinx felt the rest of the crew observing the planet through the voidhawk's sensor blisters. There was a collective emission of admiration.

Atlantis was a seamless blue, overlaid with rucked spirals of pure white cloud. There were fewer storms than an ordinary world, where continental and sea winds whipped up high and low air fronts in unceasing turmoil. Most of the storms below were concentrated in the tropical zones, stirred by the Coriolis effect. Both the polar icecaps were nearly identical circles, their edges amazingly regular.

Ruben, who was sitting in Syrinx's day cabin in the shape-moulding couch beside her, gripped her hand a fraction tighter. **This was an excellent choice, darling. A true fresh start to our civilian life. You know, in all my years I've never been here before.**

Syrinx knew she was still too tense after every swallow manoeuvre, alert for hostile ships. True navy paranoia. She let the external image bathe her mind, soothing away the old stress habits. The ocean had a delightful sapphire radiance to it. **Thank you. I think I can smell the salt already.**

As long as you don't try and drink this ocean like you did on Uighur.

She laughed at the memory of the time he had taught her how to wind surf in that beautiful deserted cove on a resort island. Four—no five years ago. Where did the time go?

Oenone descended into a five-hundred-kilometre orbit, complaining all the while. The planet's gravity was exerting its inexorable influence over local space, tugging at the stability of the voidhawk's distortion field, requiring extra power to compensate, a degradation which increased steadily as it approached the surface. When *Oenone* reached the injection point, it could barely generate half a gee acceleration.

There were over six hundred voidhawks (and thirty-eight blackhawks, Syrinx noted with vague disapproval), and close to a thousand Adamist starships, sharing the same standard equatorial orbit. *Oenone*'s mass-sensitivity revealed them to Syrinx's mind like muddy footprints across snow. Every now and then sunlight would flash off a silvered surface betraying their position to the optical sensors. Ground to orbit craft were shuttling constantly between them and the buoyant islands floating far below. She saw that most of them were spaceplanes rather than the newer ion-field craft. There was a quiet background hum in the affinity band as the void-hawks conversed and exchanged astrogation updates.

Can you find Eysk for me? she asked.

Of course, *Oenone* replied. **Pernik Island is just over the horizon, it is midday for them. It would be easier to reach from a higher orbit,** it added with apparent innocence.

No chance. We're only here for a week.

She sensed the affinity link to Eysk opening. They exchanged identity traits. He was fifty-eight years old, a senior in a family business that trawled for fish and harvested various seaweeds then packaged them for transit.

My sister Pomona said I should contact you, Syrinx said.

I'm not sure if that's good or bad, Eysk replied. **We haven't quite recovered from her last visit.**

That's my sister, all right. But I'll let you decide. I'm sitting up here with a tragically empty cargo hold which needs filling. Four hundred tonnes of the classiest, tastiest products you have.

Mental laughter followed. **Heading for Norfolk by any chance?**

How did you guess?

Take a look around you, Syrinx, half the ships in orbit are loading up ready for that flight. And they place contracts a year in advance.

I couldn't do that.

Why not?

We just finished a Confederation Navy duty tour three weeks ago. *Oenone* **has spent the time since then in dock having the combat-wasp launchers removed and standard cargo systems fitted.** She felt his mind close up slightly as he considered her request.

Ruben crossed his fingers and pulled a face.

We might have some surplus, he declared eventually.

Great!

It's not cheap, and it's nowhere near four hundred tonnes.

Money's no problem. She could sense the dismay tweak

of the crew at that blasé statement. They had all pooled their navy severance pay, and taken out a big loan option from the Jovian Bank, in the hope of putting together a cargo deal with a Norfolk roseyard-association merchant. Contrary to the firmly seated Adamist belief, the Jovian Bank did not hand out money to any Edenist on request. Between them, *Oenone*'s crew had only just scraped together enough fuseodollars for a cash collateral.

I should be so lucky, Eysk said. Still, anything to help out an old naval hand. Do you know what you're looking for?

I had some unlin crab once, they were gorgeous. Orangesole, too, if you have some.

Futchi, Cacus chipped in.

And silvereel, Edwin said eagerly.

I think you'd better come down and have a tasting session, Eysk said. Give you a better idea of what we have available.

Right away. And do you know any other families who might have a surplus we can buy up?

I'll ask round. See you for supper.

The affinity link faded.

Syrinx clapped her hands together. Ruben kissed her lightly. "You're a marvel," he told her.

She kissed him back. "This is only half the battle. I'm still relying on your contact once we get to Norfolk."

"Relax, he's a sucker for seafood."

Oxley, she called. Break out the flyer, it looks like we're in business.

Joshua hadn't expected to feel like this. He lived for space, for alien worlds, the hard edge of cargo deals, an unlimited supply of adventurous girls in port cities. But now Tranquillity's drab matt-russet exterior was filling half of the *Lady Mac*'s sensor array visualization, and it looked just *wonderful*. I'm coming home.

A break from Ashly moaning about how much better life was two centuries ago, no more of Warlow's grumpiness, an end to Dahybi's fastidious and perfidious attention to detail. Even Sarha was getting stale, free fall didn't provide an infinite variety of positions after all—and once you'd discounted the sex, there wasn't much else between them.

Yes, a rest was most definitely what he needed. And he could certainly afford one after that Puerto de Santa Maria run. Harkey's Bar was going to resemble a pressure blow-out after he hit it this evening.

The rest of the crew were hooked into the flight computer via their neural nanonics, sharing the view. Joshua guided the ship along the vector spaceport traffic control had datavised to him, keeping the ion-thruster burns to a strict minimum. *Lady Mac*'s mass distribution held no mysteries now, he knew how she would respond to the impact of a single photon.

She settled without a bounce on the cradle, and the hold-down latches clicked home. Joshua joined the rest of them in cheering.

Two serjeants were waiting for him when they came through the rotating pressure seal connecting the spaceport disk with the habitat. He just shrugged lamely at his open-mouthed crew as the bitek servitors hauled him towards a waiting tube carriage, all three of them skip gliding in the ten per cent gravity field, his shoulder-bag with its precious contents trailing in the air like a half-inflated balloon.

"I'll catch up with you tonight," he called over his shoulder as the door slid shut.

Ione was standing on the platform when it opened again. It was the little station outside her cliff-base apartment.

She was wearing a black dress with cut-away sides and a fabulously tight skirt. Her hair was frizzed elaborately.

When he stopped looking at her legs and breasts in anticipation he saw there was a daunting expression on her face.

"Well?" she said.

"Er . . ."

"Where is it?"

"What exactly?"

A black shoe with a sharply pointed toe tapped impatiently on the polyp. "Joshua Calvert, you have spent over eleven months gallivanting around the universe, without, I might point out, sending me a single memory flek to say how you were getting on."

"Yes. Sorry. Busy, you see." Jesus, but he wanted to rip that dress off. She looked ten times more sexy than she did when he replayed the neural nanonic memories. And everywhere he went people were talking about the new young Lord of Ruin. Their fantasy figure was his girl. It just made her all the more desirable.

"So where's my present?"

He almost did it, he almost said: "I'm your present." But even as he started grinning he felt that little spike of anxiety inside. He didn't want anything to foul up this reunion. Besides, she was only a kid, she needed him. So best to leave off the crappy jokes. "Oh, that," he murmured.

Sea-blue eyes hardened. "Joshua!"

He twisted the catch on his shoulder-bag. She pulled it open eagerly. The sailu blinked at the light, looking up at her with eyes that were completely black and stupendously appealing.

They were described as living gnomes by the first people to see them, thirty centimetres fully grown, with black and white fur remarkably similar to a terrestrial panda. On their home world, Oshanko, they were so rare they were kept exclusively in an imperial reserve. Only the Emperor's children were allowed to have them as pets. Cloning and breeding programmes were an anathema to the imperial court, they lived by natural selection alone. No official numbers of their population were given, but strong rumour suggested there were less than two thousand of them left.

Despite the bipedal shape, they had a very different skeleton and musculature to terrestrial anthropoids. There were no elbows or knees, their limbs bent along their whole length, making their movements incredibly ponderous. They were herbivores, and, if official AV recordings of the Emperor's family were to be believed, clingingly affectionate.

Ione covered her mouth with one hand, eyes alight with incredulity. The creature was about twenty centimetres high. "It's a sailu," she said dumbly.

"Yes."

She put a hand into the bag, extending one finger. The sailu reached for it in a graceful slow motion, deliciously silky fur stroked against her knuckle. "But only the Emperor's children are supposed to have these."

"Emperor, Lord—what's the difference? I got it because I thought you'd like it."

The sailu had clambered upright, still holding itself against her finger. Its flat wet nose sniffed her. "How?" she asked.

Joshua gave her a precocious smile.

"No. I don't want to know." She heard a soft crooning, and looked down, only to lose herself in the adoring gaze. "It's very wicked of you, Joshua. But he's quite lovely. Thank you."

"Not sure about the 'him'. I think there are three or four sexes. There's not much on them in any reference library. But it does eat lettuce and strawberries."

"I'll remember." She eased her finger from the sailu's grip.

"So what about my present?" Joshua asked.

Ione struck a pose, tongue licking her lips. "I'm your present."

They didn't make it to the bedroom. Joshua got her dress off just inside the door, and in return Ione tugged at his shipsuit seal so hard it broke. The first time was on one of the alcove tables, after that they used the ornate iron stair railings for support, then it was rolling around on the apricot moss carpet.

The bed did get used eventually, after a shower and a bottle of champagne. Hours later, Joshua knew he'd missed the party in Harkey's Bar, and didn't much care. Outside the window the light filtering through the water had faded to a dusky green, small orange and yellow fish were looking in at him.

Ione was sitting cross-legged on the rubbery transparent sheet with her back resting against some of the silk cushions. The sailu was snuggled up in her hand as she fed it with the crinkled red and green leaves of a lollo lettuce. It munched them daintily, gazing up at her.

Isn't he adorable? she said happily.

The sailu genus exhibit a great many anthropomorphic traits which endear them to humans.

I bet you'd be nicer if it wasn't Joshua who brought him.

Removing the sailu from its home planet is not only in complete contravention of the planetary statutes, it is also a direct personal insult to the Emperor himself. Joshua has put you in an invidious position. A typically thoughtless action on his part.

I won't tell the Emperor if you won't.

I was not proposing to tell the Emperor, nor even the Japanese Imperium's ambassador.

That old fart.

Ione, please, Ambassador Ng is a very senior diplomat. His appointment here is a mark of the Emperor's respect towards you.

I know. She tickled the sailu under its tiny chin. Face and body were both flattish ovals, joined by a short neck. Its legs curved slowly, pressing the torso against her finger.

"I'm going to call him Augustine," she announced. "That's a noble name."

"Great," Joshua said. He leant over to the side of the bed and pulled the champagne bottle out of its ice bucket. "Flat," he said, after he tipped some into his glass.

"Proves you have staying power," she said coyly.

He reached for her left breast, smiling.

"No, don't," she moved out of the way. "Augustine's still feeding. You'll upset him."

He lay back, disgruntled.

"Joshua, how long are you staying this time?"

"Couple of weeks. I need to get a contract with Roland Frampton sorted out. Distribution, not a charter. We're going for a Norfolk run, Ione. We raised a lot of capital on some of our contracts; put that together with what I had left over from scavenging, and we'll have enough for a cargo of Norfolk Tears. Imagine that! A hold full of the stuff."

"Really? That's wonderful, Joshua."

"Yeah, if I can swing it. Distribution isn't the problem. Acquisition is. I've been talking to some of the other captains. Those Norfolk roseyard-association merchants are tough nuts to crack. They won't allow a futures market, which is pretty smart of them actually. It would be dominated by offworld finance houses. You have to show up with a ship and the cash, and even then it's not a certainty you'll get any bottles. You need a pretty reliable contact in the trade."

"But you've never been there, you don't have any contacts."

"I know. First-time captains need a cargo to sell, a part-exchange deal. You've got to have something the merchants can't do without, that way you can get a foot in the door."

"What sort of cargo?"

"Ah, now that's the real problem. Norfolk is constitutionally a pastoral world, there's hardly any high technology they'll allow you to import. Most captains take cordon bleu food, or works of antique art, fancy fabrics, stuff like that."

Ione put Augustine down carefully on the other side of the silk pillows, and rolled onto her side facing him. "But you've got something else, haven't you? I know that tone, Joshua Calvert. You're feeling smug."

He smiled up at the ceiling. "I was thinking about it: something essential, and new, but not synthetic. Something all those Stone Age towns and farms are going to want."

"Which is?"

"Wood."

"You're kidding? Wood as in timber?"

"Yeah."

"But they have wood on Norfolk. It's heavily forested."

"I know. That's the beauty of it, they use it for everything. I've studied some sensevise recordings of the place; they make their buildings with it, their bridges, their boats, Jesus they even make carts out of it. Carpentry is a major industry there. But what I'm going to take them is a hard wood, and I mean really hard, like metal. They can use it in their furniture, or for their tool handles, their windmill cogs even, anything that's used every day, or rots or wears out. It's not high technology, yet it'll be a real cost-effective upgrade. That ought to get me in with the merchants."

"Hauling wood across interstellar space!" She shook her head in amazement. Only Joshua could come up with an idea so wonderfully crazy.

"Yep, *Lady Mac* should be able to carry almost a thousand tonnes if we really pack the stuff in."

"What sort of wood?"

"I checked in a botanical reference library file when I was in the New California system. The hardest known wood in the Confederation is mayope, it comes from a new colony planet called Lalonde."

Oenone's flyer was a flattened egg-shape, eleven metres long, with a fuselage that gleamed like purple chrome. It was built by the Brasov Dynamics company on Kulu, who had been heavily involved with the Kulu Corporation (owned by the Crown) in pioneering the ion-field technology which had sent panic waves through the rest of the Confederation's astroengineering companies. Spaceplanes were on their way out, and Kulu was using its technological prowess to devastating political effect, granting preferential licence production to the companies of allied star systems.

Standard ion thrusters lifted it out of *Oenone*'s little hangar and pushed it into an elliptical orbit that grazed Atlantis's upper atmosphere. When the first wisps of molecular fog began to thicken outside the fuselage, Oxley activated the coherent magnetic field. The flyer was immediately surrounded by a bubble of golden haze, moderating the flow of gas streaking around the fuselage. Oxley used the flux lines to grab at the mesosphere, braking the flyer's velocity, and they dropped in a steep curve towards the ocean far below.

Syrinx settled back in her deeply cushioned seat in the cabin along with Ruben, Tula, and the newest member of the crew, Serina, a crew toroid generalist who had replaced Chi. All of them were gazing keenly out of the single curving transparency around the front of the cabin. The flyer had been customized by an industrial station at Jupiter, replacing Brasov's original silicon flight-control circuits with a bitek processor array; but the image from the sensors had a poor resolution compared to *Oenone*'s sensor blisters. Eyes were almost as good.

There was absolutely no way of judging scale, no reference points. Unless she consulted the flyer's processors, Syrinx didn't know what their altitude was. The ocean rolled past below, seemingly without end.

After forty minutes Pernik Island appeared on the horizon. It was a circle of verdant green that was so obviously vegetation. The islands which Edenists had used to colonize Atlantis were a variant of habitat bitek. They were circular disks, two kilometres in diameter when they matured, made from polyp that was foamed like a sponge for buoyancy. A kilometre-wide park straddled the centre, with five accommodation towers spaced equidistantly around it, along with a host of civic buildings and light industry domes. The outer edge bristled with floating quays for the boats.

Like habitat starscrapers, the tower apartments had basic food-synthesis glands, though they were primarily for fruit juices and milk—there simply wasn't any need to supply food when you were floating on what was virtually a protein-packed soup. An island had two sources of energy to power its biological functions. There was photosynthesis, from the thick moss which grew over every outside surface including the tower walls, and triplicated digestive tracts which were fed from the tonnes of krill-analogues captured by baleen scoops around the rim. The krill also provided the raw material for the polyp, as well as nutrient fluids. Electricity for industry came from thermal potential cables; complex organic conductors trailing kilometres below the island, exploiting the difference in temperature between the cool deep waters and the sun-heated surface layer to generate a current.

There was no propulsion system. Islands drifted where they would, carried by sluggish currents. So far six hundred and fifty had been germinated. The chances of collision were minute; for two to approach within visible range of each other was an event.

Oxley circled Pernik once. The water in the immediate vicinity was host to a flotilla of boats. Pernik Island's trawlers and harvesters produced a crisscross of large V-shaped wakes as they departed for their fishing fields. Pleasure craft bobbed about behind them, small dinghies and yachts with their verdant green membrane sails fully extended.

The flyer darted in towards one of the landing pads between the towers and the rim. Eysk himself and three members of his family walked over as soon as the haze of ionized air around the flyer dissolved, grounding out through the metal grid.

Syrinx came down the stairs that had folded out of the air-lock, breathing in a humid, salty, and strangely silent air. She greeted the reception party, exchanging identity traits: Alto and Kilda, a married couple in their thirties who supervised the preparation of the family's catches, and Mosul, who was Eysk's son, a broad-shouldered twenty-four-year-old with dark hair curling gypsy-style below his shoulders, wearing a pair of blue canvas shorts. He skippered one of the fishing boats.

A fellow captain, Syrinx said appreciatively.

It's not quite the same, he replied courteously as they all started to walk towards the nearest tower. **Our boats have a few bitek items grafted in, but they are basically me-chanical. I sail across waves, you sail across light-years.**

To each their own, she replied playfully. There was an al-most audible buzz as their thoughts meshed at a deeper, more intense, level. For a moment she felt the sun on his bare torso, the strength in his figure, a sense of balance which was the equal to her spacial orientation. And the physical admira-tion, which was mutual.

Do you mind if I go to bed with him? she asked Ruben on singular engagement. **He is rather gorgeous.**

I never stand in the way of the inevitable, he replied, and winked.

Eysk had an apartment on the tower's fifteenth floor, a large one which doubled as an entertainment suite for visit-ing traders. He had chosen a rich style, combining modernist crystal furniture with a multi-ethnic, multi-era blend of art-work from across the Confederation.

The reception room had a transparent wall with archways leading out onto a broad balcony. A long table of sculpted blue crystals flecked with firefly sparks sat in the middle of the room, laid with a scrumptious buffet of Atlantean seafood.

Ruben glanced round at the collection of ornaments and pictures, pulling his lower lip thoughtfully. **The seafood trade must be pretty good.**

Don't let Eysk's dragon hoard fool you, Kilda said, bringing him a goblet of pale rose wine. **His grandfather, Gadra, started it a hundred and eighty years ago. Pernik**

is one of the older islands. Our family could have its own island by now if we didn't suffer from these "investments". Pieces lose their relevance so fast these days.

Ignore the woman, Ruben, Gadra spoke out of the island's multiplicity. A lot of this stuff is worth double what it was bought for. And all of it retains its beauty providing you view it in context. That's the trouble with young people, they take no time to appreciate life's finer qualities.

Syrinx allowed Eysk to lead her along the table. There was an enormous range of dishes arrayed, white meats arranged on leaves, fish steaks in sauces, some wild-looking things that were all legs and antenna and didn't even seem to have been cooked. He handed her a silver fork and a goblet of carbonated water.

The art is to taste then flush the mouth with a sip, he told her.

Like a wine tasting?

Yes, but with so much more to savour. Wines are simply variants on a theme. Here we have diversity that defies even the island personalities to catalogue. We'll start with unlin crab, you said you remembered it.

She pushed her fork into the pâté-like slab he indicated. It melted like fudge in her mouth. Oh! This is just as good as I remember. How much do you have?

They started to discuss details as they moved round the table. Everybody joined in good-naturedly, advising and arguing over individual dishes, but the final agreements were always between Syrinx and Eysk. The Jovian Bank segment of the island's personality was brought in to record the transactions as they were finalized.

They wound up with a complicated arrangement whereby Syrinx agreed to sell ten per cent of any cargo of Norfolk Tears back to Eysk's family in return for preferential treatment to obtain the seafood she wanted. The ten per cent would be sold at just three per cent above the transport cost, to allow Eysk to make a decent profit distributing it to the rest of the island. Syrinx wasn't entirely happy, but she had come into the Norfolk run too late to make heavy demands to her only supplier. Besides, ninety per cent was still a lot of drink, and *Oenone* could transport it right across the Confederation. The price was always set in relation to the distance from Norfolk it had travelled, and a voidhawk's costs were minimal compared to an Adamist starship's.

After two hours negotiating Syrinx stepped out onto the balcony with Serina and Mosul. Ruben, Tula, and Alto had gathered on one of the reception room's low settees to polish off some of the wine.

They were on a corner of the tower which gave them a view over both the park and the ocean. A gentle moist breeze ruffled Syrinx's hair as she leaned on the railing, a glass of honey wine held loosely in her hand.

I'm not going to eat for days after that, she told the other two, giving away a sense of rumbling pressure inside her belly. **I'm bloated.**

I often think we named this planet wrong, Mosul said. **It should have been Bounty.**

You're right, Serina said. **No Norfolk merchant is going to be able to resist this cargo.** She was twenty-two, the only crew-member younger than Syrinx, slightly shorter than the Edenist norm, with black skin and a delicate face. She was watching Syrinx and Mosul with quiet amusement, enjoying the vaguely erotic overspill of their growing rapport.

Syrinx was delighted with her company, it was nice to have someone so unashamedly girlish on board. She'd chosen her original crew for their experience, and they were highly professional, but it was nice to have someone she could really let her hair down with. Serina added a sparkle to shipboard life which had been absent before.

We're a pretty common choice, Mosul said. **But none the less successful for that. Nearly every first-time captain takes some of our produce. That's if they've got any sense. You know, even the Saldanas send a ship here every couple of months to supply the palace kitchens.**

Does Ione Saldana send one as well? Serina asked interestedly.

I don't think so.

Tranquillity doesn't own any starships, Syrinx said.

Have you been there? Mosul asked.

Certainly not, it's a blackhawk base.

Ah.

Serina looked up suddenly, her head swivelling round. **At last! I've just worked out what's missing.**

What? Syrinx asked.

Birds. There are always birds by the shore on normal terracompatible worlds. That's why it's so quiet here.

One of the larger cargo spaceplanes chose that moment to lift from its pad. The vertical-lift engines produced a strident metallic whine until it was a hundred metres in the air. It banked to starboard and slid off over the ocean, picking up speed rapidly.

Serina started laughing. **Almost quiet!**

Be a friend, Syrinx said in singular engagement. **Vanish!**

She pulled a wry face, and drained her wineglass. "Refill time. I'll leave you two alone for a moment." She sauntered off into the reception room with a suspicious wiggle.

Syrinx grinned. **My loyal crew,** she told Mosul in singular engagement.

Your attractive crew, he replied on the same mode.

I'll tell her you said that. Once we're safely outsystem.

He came over and put his arm round her shoulder.

I have a small confession, she said. **This isn't all pleasure.**

It looks that way to me.

I want to hire a boat and visit the whales. I'd also need someone who can navigate properly to take me. Is that possible?

Alone on a boat with you? That's not merely possible, that's a guaranteed certainty.

Are there any schools near here, or do we have to go from a different island? I've only got a week.

There was a school of blues a hundred kilometres south of here a day ago. Hang on, I'll ask the dolphins if they're still there.

Dolphins?

Yes. We use dolphins to help with the fishing.

I didn't know you had servitor dolphins.

We don't. They're just plain ordinary dolphins with an affinity gene spliced in.

She followed his mind as he called. The answer was

strange, more of a tune than phrases or emotions. A gentle harmony that quietened the soul. Accompanying senses flooded in. She was barrelling through solid greyness, seeing little, receiving sharp outlines of sound. Shapes moved around her like a galaxy of dark stars. She reached the surface and flashed through the ephemeral mirror into the dazzle and the emptiness where she hung with tingling skin stretched taut.

She felt her own body stretch luxuriously in tandem. The affinity link faded away, and she sighed in regret.

Dolphins are fun, *Oenone* said. **They make you feel good. And they rejoice in their freedom.**

Like voidhawks in water, you mean?

No! Well, yes. A bit.

Happy with being able to tease *Oenone* successfully, Syrinx turned to Mosul. **It was very beautiful, but I didn't understand any of it.**

Roughly translated from the scherzo, it means the whales are still within range. It'll take a day's sailing if we use my boat. Good enough?

Excellent. Can your family spare you?

Yes. This is a slow month coming up. We've been working our arses off for the last nine weeks preparing for the Norfolk trade, I'm entitled to a rest.

So you think you're going to get some rest on that boat, do you?

I sincerely hope not. Although you didn't strike me as someone who'd do the tourist routine. Not that the whales aren't worth a look.

Syrinx turned to face the ocean again, squinting at the white cloud stripe where the sky merged with the water. **It's a memory for someone else.** "My brother."

Mosul sensed the pain integral with the thought, and didn't pry.

Alkad Mzu walked up the stairs from her first-floor apartment in the St Pelham starscraper, coming out into the circular foyer with its high, wave-curved ceiling and tall transparent walls looking out across the habitat parkland. A dozen or so other early risers were moving around the foyer, waiting for the lifts in the central pillar, or heading for the broad stairs around the rim which led down to the starscraper's tube stations. It was an hour after the axial light-tube had brought a timid rosy dawn to Tranquillity's interior; patches of fine mist were still lurking amid the deeper tracts of undergrowth. The parkland around each of the starscraper foyers was maintained as open meadow dotted with small copses of ornate trees and clumps of flowering bushes. She stepped out through the sliding doors into damp air flush with the perfume of midnight-blooming nicotiana. Colourful birds arrowed through the air, trilling loudly.

She set off down the raked sand path towards a lake two hundred metres away, with only the slightest hint of a limp in her walk. Flamingos were wading through the shallows between the thick clusters of white and blue lilies. Scarlet avian lizards floated among them; the xenoc creatures were smaller than the terrestrial birds, with brilliant turquoise eyes, holding themselves very still before suddenly diving below the glass-smooth surface. Both species began to move towards the shore as she walked past. Alkad reached into her jacket pocket and pulled out some stale biscuits, throwing the crumbs. The birds and lizard-things (she never had bothered to learn their name) gobbled them up hungrily. They were old friends, she had fed them every morning for the last twenty-six years.

Alkad found Tranquillity's interior tremendously relaxing, its sheer size went a long way to suggesting invulnerability. She wished she could find an apartment which was above the surface. Naked space outside the starscraper apartment window still made her shiver even after all this time. But repeated requests to be re-allocated inside were always politely refused by the habitat personality who said there were none. So she made do with the first-floor apartment which was close to the security of the shell, and spent long hours hiking or horse riding through the parkland during her spare time. Partly for her own frame of mind, and partly because it made life very difficult for the Intelligence agency watchers.

A couple of metres from the path a gardener servitor was ambling round an old tree stump which was now hidden beneath the shaggy coat of a stephanotis creeper. It was a heavily geneered tortoise, with a shell diameter of a metre. As well as enlarging the body, geneticists had added a secondary digestive system that turned dead vegetation into small pellets of nitrogen-rich compost which it excreted. It had also been given a pair of stumpy scaled arms which emerged from holes on either side of its neck, ending in pincerlike claws. As she watched it started to clip off the shrivelled tubular flowers and put them into its mouth.

"Happy eating," she told it as she walked on.

Her destination was Glover's, a restaurant right on the edge of the lake. It was built out of bare wood, and the architect had given it a distinct Caribbean ancestry. The roof was a steep thatch, and there was a veranda on stilts actually over the water, wide enough for ten tables. Inside it had the same raw-cut appearance, with thirty tables, and a long counter running along the back where the chefs prepared the food over glowstone grills. During the evening it took three chefs to keep up with the orders; Glover's was popular with tourists and middle-management corporate executives.

When Alkad Mzu walked in there were ten people sitting eating. The usual breakfast crowd, bachelor types who couldn't be bothered to cook for themselves. An AV projection pillar stood on the counter between the tea urn and the coffee percolator, throwing off a weak moire glow. Vincent raised a hand in acknowledgement from behind the counter where he was whisking some eggs. He had been the morning cook for the last fifteen years. Alkad waved back, nodded to a regular couple she knew, then pointedly ignored the Edenist Intelligence operative, a ninety-seven-year-old called Samuel, who in turn pretended she didn't exist. Her table was in the corner, giving her a prime view out over the lake. It was set for one.

Sharleene, the waitress, came over with her iced orange juice and a bowl of bran. "Eggs or pancakes today?"

Alkad poured some milk onto the bran. "Pancakes, thanks."

"New face this morning," Sharleene said in a quiet voice. "Right nob-case." She gave Alkad a secret little smile and went back to the bar.

Alkad ate a few spoonfuls of the bran, then sipped her orange, which gave her a chance to look round.

Lady Tessa Moncrieff was sitting by herself at a table near the bar where the smell of frying bacon and bubbling coffee was strongest. She was forty-six, a major in the Kulu ESA, and head of station in Tranquillity. She had a thin, tired face, and fading blonde hair cut into a not very stylish bob; her white blouse and grey skirt gave the impression of an office worker stuck in the promotion groove. Which was almost true. The Tranquillity assignment was one she had accepted with relish two years ago when she'd been briefed on the nature of the observation duty and the underlying reason. It was a hellish responsibility, which meant she'd finally been accepted in her rank. Reverse snobbery was a fact of life in all branches of the Kulu services, and anyone with a hereditary title had to work twice as hard as normal to prove themselves.

Tranquillity had turned out to be a quiet duty, which meant maintaining discipline was difficult. Dr Alkad Mzu was very much a creature of habit, and very boring habit at that. If it hadn't been for her frequent rambles over the parkland, which presented a challenge to the observation team, morale might have gone to pot long ago.

In fact the biggest upset since Lady Moncrieff arrived hadn't been Dr Mzu at all, but rather the sudden appearance of Ione Saldana almost a year ago. Lady Moncrieff had to compile a huge flek report on the girl for Alastair II himself. Interesting to think the royal family shared the same intense thirst for details as the general public.

Lady Moncrieff made sure she was munching her toast impassively as Dr Mzu's glance took her in. This was only the third time she had seen Mzu in the flesh. But this morning wasn't something she could entrust to the team, she wanted to observe the doctor's reactions first hand. Today could well be the beginning of the end of the ESA's twenty-three-year observation duty.

Alkad Mzu ran a visual identity search through her neural nanonics, but drew a blank. The woman could be a new operative, or even a genuine customer. Somehow Alkad didn't think it was the latter; Sharleene was right, there was a refined air about her. She loaded the visual image in the already large neural nanonics file labelled *adversary*.

When she finished her bran and orange, Alkad sat back and looked straight at the AV pillar on the bar. It was relaying the Collins morning news programme. A sparkle of monochrome green light shot down her optic nerve, and the news studio materialized in front of her. Kelly Tirrel was introducing the items, dressed in a green suit and lace tie, hair fastened up in a tight turban. Her rigidly professional appearance added ten years to her age.

She had done local items on finance and trade, a charity dinner Ione had attended the previous evening. Regional items followed, the politics of nearby star systems. An update on Confederation Assembly debates. Military stories:

"This report comes from Omuta, filed nine days ago by Tim Beard." The image changed from the studio to a terra-compatible planet seen from space. "The Confederation imposed a thirty-year sanction against Omuta for its part in the Garissan holocaust of 2581, prohibiting both trade and travel to the star system. Since then, the 7th Fleet has been responsible for enforcing this sanction. Nine days ago, that duty officially ended."

Alkad opened a channel into Tranquillity's communication net, and accessed the Collins sensevise programme directly. She looked out of Tim Beard's eyes, listening through his ears. And finally her feet were pressed against the ground of Omuta as she filled her lungs with the world's mild pine-scented air.

What a wretched irony, she thought.

Tim Beard was standing on the concrete desert apron of some vast spaceport. Away to one side were the grey and blue walls of composite hangars, faded with age, stained by streaks of rust from the panel pins. Five large swept-delta Sukhoi SuAS-686 spaceplanes were lined up ahead of him, pearl-grey fuselages gleaming in the warm mid-morning sunlight. A military band stood to rigid attention just in front of their bullet-shaped noses. On one side a temporary seating stand had been erected, holding a couple of hundred people. Omuta's twenty-strong cabinet were standing on the red carpet at the front, fourteen men, six women, dressed in smart formal grey-blue suits.

"You join me in the last minutes of Omuta's isolation," Tim Beard said. "We are now awaiting the arrival of Rear-Admiral Meredith Saldana, who commands a squadron of the 7th Fleet on detachment here in the Omutan system."

In the western sky a glowing golden speck appeared, expanding rapidly. Tim Beard's retinal implant zoomed in to reveal a navy ion-field flyer. It was a neutral-grey wedge-shape forty metres long, which hovered lightly over the concrete for a moment while the landing struts deployed. The scintillating cloud of ionized air molecules popped like a soap bubble after it touched down.

"This is actually the first ion-field flyer to be seen on Omuta," Tim Beard said, filling in as the Foreign Minister greeted the Rear-Admiral. Meredith Saldana was as tall and imposing as his royal cousins, with that same distinctive nose. "Although the press cadre received special dispensation to come down last night, we had to use Omuta's own spaceplanes, some of which are now fifty years old with spare parts hard to come by. That's an indication of just how hard the sanctions have hit this world; it has fallen behind both industrially and economically. But most of all, it lacks investment. It's a situation the cabinet is keen to remedy; we've been briefed that establishing trade missions will be a priority."

The Rear-Admiral and his retinue were escorted over to the President of Omuta, a smiling, silver-haired man a hundred and ten years old. The two shook hands.

"There's some irony in this situation," Tim Beard said. Alkad could feel his facial muscles shifting into a small smile. "The last time a squadron commander of the Confederation Navy's 7th Fleet met the Omutan planetary president was thirty years ago, when the entire cabinet were executed for their part in the Garissan holocaust. Today things are a little different." His retinal implants provided a close-up of the Rear-Admiral handing a scroll to the President. "That is the official invitation from the President of the Confederation Assembly for Omuta to take up its seat again. And now you can see the President handing over the acceptance."

Alkad Mzu cancelled the channel to Collins, and looked away from the counter. She poured some thick lemon syrup over her pancakes, and used a fork to cut them up, chewing thoughtfully. The AV pillar next to the tea urn buzzed softly as Kelly Tirrel nattered away.

The date was seared into Alkad's brain, of course, she'd known it was coming. But even so her neural nanonics had to send a deluge of overrides through her nervous system to prevent her tears from falling and her jaw from quaking.

Knowing and seeing were two very different things, she discovered painfully. And that ridiculous ceremony, almost designed to reopen the wound in her soul. A handshake and an exchange of symbolic letters, and all was forgiven. Ninety-five million people. Dear Mother Mary!

A single tear leaked out of her left eye despite the best efforts of her neural nanonics. She wiped it away with a paper tissue, then paid for her breakfast leaving the usual tip. She walked slowly back to the StPelham foyer to catch a tube carriage to work.

Lady Moncrieff and Samuel watched her go, her left leg trailing slightly on the gravel path. They exchanged a mildly embarrassed glance.

The tableau hung in Ione's mind as she stirred her morning tea. **That poor, poor woman.**

I think her reaction was admirably restrained, Tranquillity said.

Only on the outside, Ione said glumly. She had a hangover from the charity dinner party of the previous night. It was a mistake to sit next to Dominique Vasilkovsky all evening; Dominique was a good friend, and hadn't exploited that friendship either, which was refreshing—but heavens how the girl drank.

Ione watched as Lady Moncrieff paid her bill and left Glover's. **I wish those agency operatives would leave Mzu alone, that kind of perpetual reminder can't make her life any easier.**

You can always expel them.

She sipped her tea, pondering the option as the housechimp cleared away her breakfast dishes. Augustine was sitting on top of the oranges in the silver fruit bowl, trying to pull a grape from the cluster. He didn't have the strength.

Better the devil we know, she said in resignation. Sometimes I wish she'd never come here. Then again, I'd hate anyone else to have her expertise at their disposal.

I imagine there are several governments who feel the same with respect to you and me. Human nature.

Maybe, maybe not. None of them has volunteered for the job.

They are probably worried about instigating a conflict over possessing her. If one made an approach to you, they would all have to. Such a wrangle would be impossible to keep under wraps. In that respect, the First Admiral is quite correct, the fewer people who know about her the better. Public reaction to super-doomsday weapons would not be favourable.

Yes, I suppose so. That Rear-Admiral Meredith Saldana, I take it he's a relative of mine?

Indeed. He is the son of the last Prince of Nesko, which makes him an earl in his own right. But he chose to become a Confederation fleet career officer, which couldn't be easy, with his name acting against him.

Did he turn his back on Kulu like my grandfather?

No, the fifth son of a principality ruler is not naturally destined for high office. Meredith Saldana decided to achieve what he could on his own merit; had he remained on Nesko such an action could well have brought him into conflict with the new prince. So he left to pursue an independent course; given his position, it was the act of a loyal subject. The family are proud of his accomplishment.

He'll never make First Admiral, then?

No, given his heritage it would be politically impossible, but he might manage 7th Fleet commander. He is a highly competent and popular officer.

Nice to know we're not totally decadent yet. She picked Augustine off the oranges, putting him down beside her side plate, then cut a grape open for him. He hummed contentedly and lifted a segment to his mouth in the dawdling fashion that so bewitched her. As always, her mind wandered to Joshua. He must be halfway to Lalonde by now.

I have two messages for you.

You're trying to distract me, she accused.

Yes. You know I don't like it when you are upset. It is my failure as well.

No, it isn't. I'm a big girl now, I knew exactly what I was getting into with Joshua. So what are the messages?

Haile wants to know when you are coming for a swim. Ione brightened. **Tell her I'll see her in an hour.**

Very well. Secondly, Parker Higgens requests you visit him today, as soon as possible, in fact. He was rather insistent.

Why?

I believe the team analysing Joshua's Laymil electronics stack have made a breakthrough.

Pernik's fishing boats were halfway to the horizon by the time Syrinx emerged from the base of the tower on the morning she was due to visit the whales. The cool dawn sun had coloured the island's covering of moss a matt black. She breathed in the salty air, relishing the cleanliness.

I never really thought of our air as anything exceptional, Mosul said. He was walking beside her, holding a big box full of supplies for the voyage.

It isn't once the humidity gets up. But don't forget, over ninety per cent of my life is spent in a perfectly regulated environment. This is an exhilarating change.

Oh, thank you! *Oenone* said tartly.

Syrinx grinned.

We're in luck, Mosul said. **I've checked with the dolphins, and the whales are actually closer today. We should be there by late afternoon.**

Great.

Mosul led her along the broad avenue down to the rim quays. Water slapped lazily against the polyp. Pernik could have been a genuine island rooted in the planet's crust for all the motion it made.

Sometimes a real storm rocks us a degree or so.

Ah, right. Her grin faded. **I'm sorry, I didn't realize I was**

leaking so much. It's very rude of me. Preoccupied, I guess.

No problem. Do you want Ruben to come with us? Perhaps he would make you feel easier.

Syrinx thought of him curled up in the bed where she'd left him half an hour ago. There was no response to her half-hearted query. He had gone back to sleep. No. I'm never alone, I have Oenone.

She watched a frown form on Mosul's handsome sea-browned face. How old is Ruben? the semi-apologetic thought came.

She told him and had to stifle a laugh as the surprise and faint disapproval spilled out of his mind despite a frantic effort to cover them up. Gets them every time.

You shouldn't tease people so, Oenone said. He's a nice young man, I like him.

You always say that.

I only voice what you feel.

The quay was balanced on big cylindrical flotation drums which rode the swell in long undulations. Thick purple-red tubes ran along the edge, carrying nutrient fluid out to the boats. Leaky couplings dribbled the dark syrupy fluid into the water.

Syrinx stood to one side as a couple of servitor chimps carrying boxes passed by. They were wildly different from the standard habitat housechimps, with a scaled reptilian skin a mild blue-green in colour. Their feet were broad, with long webbed toes.

The boat that waited for them was called the *Spiros*, a seventeen-metre sailing craft with a white composite hull. Bitek units were blended into the structure with a skill that went far beyond mechanical practicality, it was almost artistry. The digestive organs and nutrient-reserve bladders were in the bilges, supporting the sub-sentient processor array and the mainsail membrane, as well as various ancillary systems. Her cabin fittings were all wooden, the timber coming from trees grown in the island's central park. She was used by Mosul's whole family for recreation. Which explained why the cabin was in a bit of a mess when they came on board.

Mosul stood in the galley clutching his box of supplies and

looking round darkly at the discarded wrappers, unwashed pans, and crusty stains on the work surface. He muttered under his breath. **My younger cousins had her out a couple of days ago,** he apologized.

Well, don't be too hard on them, youth is a time to be treasured.

They're not that young. And it's not as though they couldn't have detailed a housechimp to clean up afterwards. No damn thought for others. There were more curses when he went forward and found the bunks in the same state.

Syrinx overheard a furious affinity conversation with the juvenile offenders. Smiling to herself she started stowing supplies.

Mosul unplugged the quay's nutrient-feed veins from their couplings on the *Spiros*'s aft deck, then cast off. Leaning over the taffrail Syrinx watched the five-metre-long silver-grey eel-derived tail wriggling energetically just below the surface, nudging the boat away from the quay. The tightly whorled sail membrane began to unfurl from its twenty-metre-high mast. When it was fully open it was a triangle the colour of spring-fresh beech leaves, reinforced with a rubbery hexagonal web of muscle cells.

It caught the morning breeze, filling out. A small white wake arose, curling around the bow. The tail straightened out, giving just the occasional tempestuous flick to maintain the course Mosul had loaded into the processor array.

Syrinx made her way forward carefully. The decking was damp below her rubber-soled plimsolls, and they had already picked up a surprising turn of speed. She leaned contentedly on the rail, letting the wind bathe her face. Mosul came up and put his arm round her shoulder.

You know, I think I'm finding this ocean more daunting than space, Syrinx said as Pernik fell astern rapidly. **I know space is infinite, and that doesn't bother me in the slightest, but Atlantis *looks* infinite. Thousands of kilometres of empty ocean conjures up a more readily accessible concept for the human mind than all those light-years.**

To your mind, Mosul said. **I was born here, to me it doesn't seem infinite at all, I could never be lost. But**

space, that's something else. In space you can set out in a straight line and never return. That's scary.

They spent the morning talking, exchanging the memories of particularly intense or moving or treasured incidents from their respective lives. Syrinx found herself feeling slightly envious of his simplistic life of fishing and sailing, realizing that was the instinctive attraction she had felt at their first meeting. Mosul was so wonderfully uncomplicated. In turn he was almost in awe of her sophistication, the worlds she'd seen, people she'd met, the arduous naval duty.

Once the sun had risen high enough to be felt on her skin, Syrinx stripped off and rubbed on a healthy dose of screening cream.

That's another difference, she said as Mosul ran his hands over her back, between her shoulder blades where she couldn't reach. Look at the contrast, I'm like an albino compared to you.

I like it, he told her. All the girls here are coffee coloured or darker, how are we supposed to tell if we're African-ethnic or not?

She sighed and stretched out on a towel on the cabin's roof, forward of the sail membrane. It doesn't matter. All our ethnic ancestors disowned us long ago.

There's a lot of resentment in that thought. I don't know why. The Adamists we get here are pleasant enough.

Of course they are, they want your foodstuffs.

And we want their money.

The sail creaked and fluttered gently as the day wore on. Syrinx found the rhythm of the boat lulling her, and coupled with the warmth of the sun she almost went to sleep.

I can see you, *Oenone* whispered on that unique section of affinity which was theirs alone.

Without conscious thought she knew its orbit was taking it over the *Spiros*. She opened her eyes and looked into boundless azure sky. My eyes aren't as good as your sensor blisters. Sorry.

I like seeing you. It doesn't happen often.

She waved inanely. And behind the velvet blueness she saw herself prone on the little ship, waving. The boat dropped away, becoming a speck, then vanishing. Both universes were solid blue.

Hurry back, *Oenone* said. **I'm crippled this close to a planet.**

I will. Soon, I promise.

They sighted the whales that afternoon.

Black mountains were leaping out of the water. Syrinx saw them in the distance. Huge curved bodies sliding out of the waves in defiance of gravity, crashing down amid breakers of boiling surf. Fountain plumes of vapour rocketing into the sky from their blow-holes.

Syrinx couldn't help it, she jumped up and down on the deck, pointing. "Look, look!"

I see them, Mosul said, amusement and a strange pride mingling in his thoughts. **They are blue whales, a big school, I reckon there's about a hundred or more.**

Can you see? Syrinx demanded.

I can see, *Oenone* reassured her. **I can feel too. You are happy. I am happy. The whales look happy too, they are smiling.**

Yes! Syrinx laughed. Their mouths were upturned, smiling. A perpetual smile. And why not? Such creatures' existing was cause to smile.

Mosul angled *Spiros* in closer, ordering the edges of the sail to furl. The noise of the school rolled over the boat. The smack of those huge bodies as they jumped and splashed, a deep gullet-shaking whistle from the blow-holes. She tried to work out how big they were as the *Spiros* approached the school's fringes. Some, the big adult bulls, must have been thirty metres long.

A calf came swimming over to the *Spiros*; over ten metres long, spurting from his blow-hole. His mother followed him closely, the two of them bumping together and sliding against each other. Huge forked tails churned up and down, flukes slapping the water, while flippers beat like shrunken wings. Syrinx watched in utter fascination as the two passed within fifty metres of the boat, rocking it alarmingly in their pounding wake. But she hardly noticed the pitching, the calf was feeding, suckling from its mother as she rolled onto her side.

"That is the most stupendous, miraculous sight," she said, spellbound. Her hands were gripping the rail, knuckles whitening. "And they're not even xenocs. They're ours. Earth's."

"Not any more." Mosul was at her side, as mesmerized as she.

Thank Providence we had the sense to preserve the genes. Although I'm still staggered the Confederation Assembly allowed you to bring them here.

The whales don't interfere with the food chain, they stand outside it. This ocean can easily spare a million tonnes of krill a day. And nothing analogous could ever possibly evolve on Atlantis, so they're not competing with anything. The whales are mammals, after all, they need land for part of their development. No, the largest thing Atlantis has produced is the redshark, and that's only six metres long.

Syrinx curled her arm round his, and pressed against him. **I meant, it's pretty staggering for the Assembly to show this much common sense. It would have been a monumental crime to allow these creatures to die out.**

What a cynical old soul you are.

She kissed him lightly. **A foretaste of what's to come.** Then rested her head against him, and returned her entire attention to the whales, gathering up every nuance and committing it lovingly to memory.

They followed the school for the rest of the afternoon as the giant animals played and wallowed in the ocean. Then when dusk fell, Mosul turned the *Spiros*'s bow away. The last she saw of the school was their massive dark bodies arching gracefully against the golden red skyline, whilst the roar of the blow-holes faded away into the ocean's swell.

That night twisters of phosphenic radiance wriggled through the water around the hull, casting a wan diamond-blue light over the half-reefed sail membrane. Syrinx and Mosul brought cushions out onto the deck, and made love under the stars. Several times *Oenone* gazed down on their entwined bodies, its presence contributing to the wondrous sense of fulfilment in Syrinx's mind. She didn't tell Mosul.

The Laymil project's Electronics Division was housed in a three-storey octagonal building near the middle of the campus. The walls were a soft white polyp with large oval windows, and climbing hydrangeas had reached the bottom of the second-storey windows. Chuantawa trees from Raouil were planted around the outside, forty-metre-high specimens, their rubbery bark and long tongue-shaped leaves a bright purple, clusters of bronze berries dangling from every branch.

Ione walked towards it down the amaranthus-lined path from the nearest of the campus's five tube stations, three serjeant bodyguards in tow. Her hair was still slightly damp from her swim with Haile, and the ends brushed against the collar of her formal green-silk suit jacket. She drew wide-eyed stares and cautious smiles from the few project staff wandering around the campus.

Parker Higgens was waiting just outside the main entrance, dressed as ever in his hazel-coloured suit with red spirals on the flared arms. The trousers were fashionably baggy, but he was filling out the jacket quite comfortably. His mop of white hair hung down over his forehead in some disarray.

Ione forbade a smile as they shook hands. The director was always so nervous around her. He was good at his job, but they certainly didn't share the same sense of humour. He would think teasing was a personal insult.

She greeted Oski Katsura, the head of the Electronics Division. She had taken over from the former head six months ago; her appointment had been the first Ione had confirmed. A seventy-year-old, taller than Ione, with a distinguished willowy beauty, wearing an ordinary white lab smock.

"You have some good news for me, then?" Ione asked as they went inside and started walking down the central corridor.

"Yes, ma'am," Parker Higgens said.

"Most of the stack's circuitry was composed of memory crystals," Oski Katsura said. "The processors were subsidiary elements to facilitate access and recording. Basically it was a memory core."

"I see. And had the ice preserved it like we hoped?" Ione asked. "It looked intact when I saw it."

"Oh, yes. It was almost completely intact, the chips and crystals encased in ice functioned perfectly after they had been removed and cleaned. The reason it has taken us so long to decrypt the data stored in the crystals is that it is non-standard." They came to a set of wide double doors, and Oski Katsura datavised a security code to open them, gesturing Ione through.

The Electronics Division always reminded her of a cyber-factory: rows of identical clean rooms illuminated by harsh white lighting, all of them filled with enigmatic blocks of equipment trailing wires and cables everywhere. This room was no different, broad benches ran round the walls, with another down the centre, cluttered with customized electronics cabinets and test rigs. The far end was a glass wall partitioning off six workshop cubicles. Several researchers were inside, using robot precision-assembly cells to fabricate various units. At the opposite end of the room to the cubicles a stainless steel pedestal sat on the floor, supporting a big sphere made up of tough transparent composite. Thick environmental-support hoses snaked away from the lower quarter of the sphere, plugging into bulky conditioning units. Ione saw the Laymil electronics stack in the middle of the sphere, with power leads and fibre-optic cables radiating out of its base. More surprisingly, Lieria was standing in front of the long bench in the middle of the room, her tractamorphic arms branching into five or six tentacles apiece, all of which were wound through an electronics cabinet.

Ione was quite proud she could recognize the Kiint immediately. **Good morning, Lieria, I thought you worked in the Physiology Division.**

The tentacle appendages uncoiled from the cabinet, flowing back into one solid pillar of flesh again. Lieria turned ponderously, careful not to knock into anything. **Welcome, Ione Saldana. I am here because Oski Katsura requested my input in this programme. I have been able to contribute to the analysis of data stored in the Laymil crystals; there is some crossover into my primary field of study.**

Excellent.

I note your cranial hair carries a residue of salt water; have you been swimming?

Yes, I gave Haile a scrub down. She's getting impatient to look around Tranquillity. You'll have to let me know when you think she's ready.

Your kindness is most welcome. We judge her mature enough to be allowed outside parental restriction providing she is accompanied. But do not permit her to impose upon your own time.

She's no bother.

One of Lieria's arms lengthened to pick up a slender white wafer ten centimetres square from the bench. The unit emitted a single whistle, then spoke. "Greetings, Director Parker Higgens."

He gave the xenoc a small bow.

Oski Katsura tapped the environment bubble with a fingernail. "We cleaned and tested all the components before we reassembled it," she told Ione. "That ice wasn't pure water, there were some peculiar hydrocarbons mixed in."

"Laymil faecal matter," Lieria said through the wafer.

"Quite. But the real challenge came from the data itself, it was like nothing we have found so far. It seemed almost totally randomized. At first we thought it might be some kind of artform, then we began to notice irregular trait repetition."

The same patterns repeated in different combinations, Tranquillity translated.

The science staff always go through this rigmarole, don't they? she asked, half amused.

It is their chance to demonstrate to you, their paymaster, the effort they put in. Don't disillusion them, it is impolite.

Ione kept her face neutral during the second-long exchange. "Which was enough to formulate a recognition program," she said smoothly.

"Quite," said Oski Katsura. "Ninety per cent of the data was garbage to us, but these patterns kept appearing."

- "Once we had enough of them clearly identified we held an interdisciplinary conference and asked for best guesses," Parker Higgens said. "Bit of a long shot, but it paid off handsomely. I'm pleased to say Lieria said they resembled Laymil optical impulses."

"Correct," Lieria said through the wafer. "Similarity approaching eighty-five per cent. The data packages represented colours to a Laymil eye."

"Once we'd established that, we ran a comparison on the rest of the data, trying to match it with other Laymil nerve impulses," Oski Katsura said. "Jackpot. Well, more or less. It took four months to write interpretation programs and build suitable interface units, but we got there in the end." A wave of her hand took in the benches and all their elaborate equipment. "We unravelled the first full sequence last night."

Dawning realization at what Oski Katsura was actually saying brought a sense of real excitement to Ione. Her eyes were drawn to the stack in its protective bubble. She touched the transparent surface reverently, it was warmer than the ambient temperature. "This is a recording of a Laymil sensorium?" she asked.

Parker Higgens and Oski Katsura grinned like ten-year-olds.

"Yes, ma'am," Parker Higgens said.

She turned to him sharply. "How much is there? How long does it go on for?"

Oski Katsura gave a modest shrug. "We don't quite understand the file sequences yet. The one which we have translated so far lasts a little over three minutes."

"How long?" Ione let a waspish note creep into her voice.

"If the bit rate holds constant for the other sequences . . . approximately eight thousand hours."

Did she say eight *thousand*?

Yes, said Tranquillity.

"Bloody hell!" An oafish smile appeared on Ione's face. "When you said translated, what did you mean?"

"The sequence has been adapted for human sensevise reception," Oski Katsura said.

"Have you reviewed it?"

"Yes. The quality is below normal commercial standards, but that ought to improve once we refine our programs and equipment."

"Can Tranquillity access your equipment through the communication net?" Ione asked urgently.

"It should be simple enough. One moment, I'll datavise the entry code," Oski Katsura said. "That's it."

Show me!

Senses which were fundamentally *wrong* engulfed her conscious thoughts, leaving her as a passive, faintly protesting, observer. The Laymil body was trisymmetric, standing one metre seventy-five high, possessing a tough, heavily crinkled slate-grey skin. There were three legs, with a double-jointed knee, and feet which ended in a hoof. Three arms with a bulbous shoulder which permitted a great deal of articulation, a single elbow, and hands with four triple-jointed fingers as thick as a human thumb and twice as long, bestowing considerable strength and dexterity. Most disturbing of all were the three sensor heads, emerging like truncated serpents between the shoulders. Each one had an eye at the front, with a triangular bat-ear above it, and a toothless breathing mouth below. All the mouths could vocalize, but one was larger and more sophisticated than the other two, which made up for their deficiency with a more acute sense of smell. The feeding mouth was on the top of the torso, in the cleft between the necks, a circular orifice equipped with sharp needle teeth.

The body Ione now wore constricted her own figure severely, pulping it below circular bands of muscle that flexed and twisted sinuously, squeezing protesting flesh and bone into a new shape, forcing her to conform to the resurgent identity suspended in the crystal matrix. She felt as though her limbs were being systematically twisted in every direction apart from the ones nature intended. But there was no pain inherent in the metamorphosis. Feverish thoughts, electrified by instinctive revulsion, began to calm. She started to look around, accepting the trinocular viewpoint input as best she could.

She was wearing clothes. The first surprise; born of prejudice, the foreign physique was *animal*, unhuman, no anthropomorphism could possibly exist here to build a bridge. But the trousers were easily recognizable, tubes of midnight-purple fabric, sleek as silk against the coarse skin. They came halfway down the lower leg, there was even a recognizable belt. The shirt was a stretchy cylinder of light green, with hoops that hung over the necks.

And she was walking, a three-legged walk that was so easy, so natural that she didn't even have to think how to move the limbs to avoid tripping. The sensor head with the speaking mouth was always at the front, swinging slowly from side to side. Her other two heads scanned the surrounding countryside.

Sights and sounds besieged her. There were few half-tones in her visual world, bright primary colours dominated; but the image was flecked with minute black fissures, like an AV projection running heavy interference; the myriad sounds sliced with half-second breaks of silence.

Ione glossed over the flaws. She was walking through a Laymil habitat. If Tranquillity was manicured perfection, this was manicured anarchy. The trees were at war, thrusting and clashing against each other. Nothing grew upright. It was like a jungle hit by a hurricane, but with the trunks packed so closely they couldn't fall, only topple onto their neighbours. She saw trees with their kinked trunks cupped together, trunks that spiralled round each other wrestling for height and light, young shoots piercing old flaking boles. Roots the size of a man's torso emerged from the trunks well above her head, stabbing down like fleshy beige fork prongs into the sandy soil, producing a buttress cone. The leaves were long ribbons, curled into spirals, a deep olive-green in colour. And down where she walked, where shadows and sunbeams alternated like incorporeal pillars, every nook and crevice was crammed with tiny cobalt-blue flowering mushrooms, their pilei fringed with vermilion stamens, swaying like sea anemones in a weak current.

Pleasure and peace soaked into her like sunlight through amber. The forest was in harmony, its life spirit resonating with the spaceholm mother essence, singing their madrigal in unison. She listened with her heart, thankful for the privilege of living.

Hoofs trod evenly along the meandering trail carrying her towards the fourth marriage community. Her husbands/mates awaited her, the eagerness inside her was woven into the forest song and rejoiced over by the mother essence.

She reached the borders of the jungle, saddened by the smaller trees, the end of song, jubilant that she had passed through cleanly, that she was worthy of a fourth reproduction cycle. The trees gave way to open land, a gentle valley swathed in high, lush grasses and speckled with vivid reds and yellows and blues of bell-shaped flowers. Spaceholm reared around her, a landscape of tangled greens, rampant vegetation choking the silver veins of streams and rivers, smeared with fragile tufts of cloud. Sunspires stabbed out along the axis from the centre of each endcap, thin sabres stretching for twenty kilometres, furiously radiant.

"Tree spirit song unity," she called with voice and mind. Her two clarion heads bugled gleefully. **"I await."**

"Richness reward embryo growth daughter," the spaceholm mother entity replied.

"Male selection?"

"Concord."

"Unison awaits."

"Life urge rapture."

She started to walk down the slope. Ahead of her on the floor of the valley was the fourth marriage community. Blue polyp cuboidal structures, rigidly symmetrical, arrayed in concentric rings. On the paths between the featureless walls she could see other Laymil moving about. All her heads craned forward.

The memory ended.

The lurch back into the conformity of the electronics lab was as abrupt as it was shocking. Ione put a hand on the bench to steady herself. Oski Katsura and Parker Higgens were giving her an anxious look, even Lieria's dark violet eyes were focused on her.

"That was . . . astonishing," she managed to say. The hot Laymil jungle lurked around the fringes of sight like a vengeful daydream. "Those trees, she seemed to think of them as alive."

"Yes," Parker Higgens said. "It was obviously some kind of mating selection test or ritual. We know Laymil females are capable of five reproductive cycles, it never occurred to anybody that they might be subject to artificial restraints. In fact I find it amazing that a culture so sophisticated should still indulge in what was almost a pagan rite."

"I'm not sure it was pagan," Oski Katsura said. "We have already identified a gene sequence similar to the Edenist affinity gene in the Laymil genome. However they are obviously far more Gaiaistic than Edenist humans; their habitat, the spaceholm, was virtually a part of the reproductive process. It certainly seemed to possess some kind of veto power."

"Like me and Tranquillity," Ione said under her breath.

Hardly.

Give us another five thousand years, and the birth of a new Lord of Ruin could easily become ritualized.

You are entirely correct, Ione Saldana, Lieria said. The Kiint continued speaking through her white wafer. "I note considerable evidence to indicate the Laymil mate-selection process is based on scientific eugenics rather than primitive spiritualism. Suitability is considerably more than possession of desirable physical characteristics, mental strength is obviously a prime requirement."

"Whatever, it opens up a fantastic window into their culture," Parker Higgens said. "We knew so little before this. To think that a mere three minutes could show us so much. The possibilities it reveals . . ." He looked at the electronics stack almost in worship.

"Will there be any problem in translating the rest of it?" Ione asked Oski Katsura.

"I don't see any. What you accessed was still pretty crude, the emotional analogues were only rough approximates. We'll tweak the program, of course, but I doubt we could have direct parallels with a race that alien."

Ione stared at the electronics stack. An oracle for a whole race. And possibly, just possibly, the secret was inside it: why they did it. The more she thought about it, the more puzzling it became. The Laymil were so vibrantly alive. What in God's name could ever make an entity like that commit suicide?

She shivered slightly, then turned to Parker Higgens. "Set up a priority budget for the Electronics Division," she said decisively. "I want all eight thousand hours translated as soon as possible. And the Cultural Analysis Division is going to have to be expanded considerably. We've concentrated far too much on the technological and physical side of the Laymil to date, that's going to have to change now."

Parker Higgens opened his mouth to protest.

"That wasn't a criticism, Parker," she said quickly. "The physical is all we've had to go on so far. But now we have these sensory and emotional memories we're entering a new phase. Extend invitations to whichever xenoc psychology experts you think will be of help, offer endowment sabbaticals from their current tenures. I'll add a personal message to the invitations if you think my name will carry any weight with them."

"Yes, ma'am." Parker Higgens appeared bemused by her speed.

"Lieria, I'd like you or one of your colleagues to assist with the cultural interpretation, I can see your viewpoints will be invaluable."

Lieria's arms rippled from root to tip (a Kiint laugh?). "It will be my pleasure to assist, Ione Saldana."

"One final thing. I want Tranquillity to be the first to review the memories as and when they are translated."

"Yes," Oski Katsura said uncertainly.

"Sorry," Ione said with an earnest smile. "But as Lord of Ruin I retain the right to embargo weapons technology. The cultural experts might argue over the finer nuances of what we see for months at a time, but a weapon is pretty easy to spot. I don't want any particularly unsavoury armaments released to the Confederation at large." And if it was an enemy's weapon that destroyed the Laymil habitats I want to know before I decide what to tell everybody.

15

Night had come to Durringham. It brought with it a thick grey mist which flowed down the slushy streets and over the mouldering roof slats, depositing an unctuous coating of droplets in its wake. The water filmed every exterior wall until the whole city was glistening darkly, droplets running together and dribbling off the eaves and overhangs. Doors and shutters were no protection, the mist penetrated buildings with ease, soaking into fabrics and condensing over furniture. It was worse than the rain.

The Governor's office was faring little better than the rest of the city. Colin Rexrew had turned up the conditioning until it made an aggravated rattling sound, but the atmosphere inside remained obstinately muggy. He was reviewing satellite images with Terrance Smith and Candace Elford, Lalonde's Chief Sheriff. The three big wall-screens opposite the curving window were displaying pictures of a riverside settlement village. They showed the usual collection of shambolic huts and small fields, large piles of felled trunks, and stumps which played host to ears of orange fungi. Chickens scratched around in the dirt between the huts, while dogs roamed free. The few people captured by the camera were dressed in dirty, ragged clothes. One child, about two years old, was completely naked.

"These are very poor images," Colin Rexrew complained. Most of the edges were blurred, even the colours appeared wan.

"Yes," Candace Elford agreed. "We ran a diagnostic check on the observation satellite, but there was no malfunction. The images from any other area it views are flawless. The satellite only has trouble when it's passing over the Quallheim."

"Oh, come on," Terrance Smith said. "You can't mean that the people in the Quallheim Counties can distort our observation, surely?"

Candace Elford considered her answer. She was fifty-seven, and Lalonde was her second appointment as chief sheriff. Both senior appointments had been won because of her thoroughness; she had worked her way up through various colony planet police services, and harboured a kind of bewildered contempt for colonists, who, she had discovered, were capable of damn near anything out in the frontier lands. "It's unlikely," she admitted. "The Confederation Navy ELINT satellites haven't detected any unusual emissions from Schuster County. It's probably a glitch, that satellite is fifteen years old, and it hasn't been serviced for the last eleven years."

"All right," Colin Rexrew said. "Point noted. We don't have the money for regular services, as you well know."

"When it breaks down, a replacement will cost the LDC a lot more than the expense of proper triennial maintenance," Candace Elford countered.

"Please! Can we stick with the topic in hand," Colin Rexrew said. He eyed the drinks cabinet longingly. It would have been nice to break open one of the chilled white wines and have a more relaxed session, but Candace Elford would have refused, which would make it awkward. She was such an uncompromising officer; one of his best though, someone the sheriffs respected and obeyed. He needed her, so he put up with her rigid adherence to protocol, counting his blessings.

"Very well," she said crisply. "As you can see, Aberdale has twelve burnt-out buildings. According to the sheriff in Schuster town, Matthew Skinner, there was some kind of Ivet disturbance four days ago, which is when the buildings were razed. The Ivets allegedly murdered a ten-year-old boy, and the villagers set about hunting them down. Supervisor Manani's communication block wasn't working, so an Aberdale villager visited Schuster the day after this murder, and Matthew Skinner reported it to my office. That was three days ago. He said he was riding to Aberdale to investigate; apparently most of the Ivets had been killed by that time. We heard nothing until this morning, when Matthew Skinner said the disturbance was over, and the Aberdale Ivets were all dead."

"I disapprove of vigilante action," Colin Rexrew said. "Officially, that is. But given the circumstances I can't say I blame the Aberdale villagers, those Ivets have always been a mixed blessing. Half of them should never be sent here, ten years' work-time isn't going to rehabilitate the real recidivists."

"Yes, sir," Candace Elford said. "But that's not the problem."

Colin Rexrew brushed back tufts of his thinning hair with clammy hands. "I didn't think it would be that simple. Go on."

She datavised an order into the office's computer. The screens started to display another village; it looked even more impecunious than Aberdale. "This is Schuster town itself," she said. "The image was recorded this morning. As you can see, there are three burnt-out buildings."

Colin Rexrew sat up a little straighter behind his desk. "They had Ivet trouble, too?"

"That is the curious thing," Candace Elford said. "Matthew Skinner never mentioned the fires, and he should have done, fires like that are dangerous in those kinds of communities. The last routine satellite images we have of Schuster are two weeks old, the buildings were intact then."

"It's pushing coincidence a long way," Colin Rexrew said, half to himself.

"That's what my office thought," Candace Elford said. "So we started checking a little closer. The Land Allocation Office divided the Quallheim territory up into three counties, Schuster, Medellin, and Rossan, which between them now have ten villages. We spotted burnt-out buildings in six of those villages: Aberdale, Schuster, Qayen, Pamiers, Kilkee, and Medellin." She datavised more instructions. The screens started to run through the images of the villages her office had recorded that morning.

"Oh, Jesus," Colin Rexrew muttered. Some of the blackened timbers were still smoking. "What's been happening up there?"

"First thing we asked. So we called up each of the village supervisors," Candace Elford said. "Qayen's didn't answer, the other three said everything was fine. So we called up the villages that didn't show any damage. Salkhad, Guer, and Suttal didn't answer; Rossan's supervisor said they were all OK, and nothing out of the ordinary was happening. They hadn't heard or seen anything from any of the other villages."

"What's your opinion?" Colin Rexrew asked.

The chief sheriff turned back to the screens. "One final piece of information. The satellite made seven passes over the Quallheim Counties today. Despite the shoddy images, at no time did we see anybody working in any of those fields; not in any of the ten villages."

Terrance Smith whistled as he sucked air through his teeth. "Not good. There's no way you'd keep a colonist from his field, not on a day with weather like it has been up there. They are utterly dependent on those crops. The supervisors make it quite plain from the start, once they're settled, they don't get any help from Durringham. They can't afford to leave the fields untended. Remember what happened in Arklow County?"

Colin Rexrew gave his aide an irritable look. "Don't remind me, I accessed the files when I arrived." He transferred his gaze to the screens, and the image of Qayen village. A black premonition was rising in his mind. "So what are you telling me, Candace?"

"I know what it looks like," she said. "I just can't believe it, that's all. An Ivet revolt which has successfully taken control of the Quallheim Counties, and in just four days, too."

"There are over six thousand colonists spread out in those counties," Terrance Smith said. "Most of them have weapons and aren't afraid to use them. Against that, there are a hundred and eighty-six Ivets, unarmed and unorganized, and without any form of reliable communication. They're Earth's junk, waster kids; if they could organize something like this they would never be here in the first place."

"I know," she said. "That's why I said I don't believe it. But what else could it be? Someone from outside? Who?"

Colin Rexrew frowned. "Schuster's been a problem before. What . . ." He trailed off, requesting a search through the files stored in his neural nanonics. "Ah, yes; the disappearing homestead families. Do you remember, Terrance, I sent a marshal up to investigate last year. Bloody great waste of money that was."

"It was a waste of money from our point of view because the marshal didn't find anything," Terrance Smith said. "That in itself was unusual. Those marshals are good. Which means either it was a genuine case of some animal carrying the families away, or some unknown group was responsible, and managed to cover their tracks to such an extent it fooled both the local supervisor and the marshal. If it was an organized raid, then the perpetrators were at least the equal of our marshal."

"So?" Colin Rexrew asked.

"So now we have another event, originating in the same county, that would be hard to explain away in terms of an Ivet revolt. Certainly the scale of the trouble argues against it being the Ivets by themselves. But an external group taking over the Quallheim Counties would fit the facts we have."

"We only have a secondhand report that it was Ivets anyway," Colin Rexrew said, pondering the unwelcome idea.

"It still doesn't make any sense," Candace Elford said. "I concede that the facts indicate the Ivets are getting help. But what external group? And why the Quallheim Counties, for God's sake? There's no wealth out there; the colonists are barely self-sufficient. There's no wealth anywhere on Lalonde, come to that."

"This isn't getting us anywhere," Colin Rexrew said. "Look, I've got three river-boats scheduled to leave in two days, they're taking six hundred fresh settlers up to Schuster County so they can start another village. You're my security adviser, Candace, are you telling me not to send them?"

"I think my advice would have to be, yes; certainly at this stage. It's not as if you're short of destinations. Sending unsuspecting raw colonists into the middle of a potential revolt wouldn't look good on any of our records. Is there a nearby alternative to Schuster where you can settle them?"

"Willow West County on the Frenshaw tributary," Terrance Smith suggested. "It's only a hundred kilometres north-west of Schuster; plenty of room for them there. It's on our current territory development list anyway."

"OK," Colin Rexrew said. "Get it organized with the Land Allocation Office. In the meantime, what do you intend to do about the Quallheim situation, Candace?"

"I want your permission to send a posse up there on the boats with the colonists. Once the colonists have been dropped off at Willow West, the boats can take them on to the Quallheim. As soon as I've got reliable people on the ground we can establish what's really going on and restore some order."

"How many do you want to send?"

"A hundred ought to be enough. Twenty full-time sheriffs, and the rest we can deputize. God knows, there's enough men in Durringham who'll jump at the chance of five weeks cruising the river on full pay. I'd like three marshals, as well, just to be on the safe side."

"Yes, all right," Colin Rexrew said. "But just remember it comes out of your budget."

"It'll be nearly three weeks before you can get your people up there," Terrance Smith said thoughtfully.

"So?" the chief sheriff asked. "I can't make the boats go any faster."

"No, but a lot can happen in that time. If we believe what we've seen so far, this revolt spread down the Quallheim in four days. Taking a worst case scenario, the revolt could carry on growing at the same rate, leaving your initial hundred-strong posse heavily outgunned. What I suggest is that we get the posse out there as fast as physically possible, and stop any further expansion before it gets totally out of hand. We have three VTOL aircraft at the spaceport, BK133s that our ecology research team use for survey missions. They're subsonic, and they only seat ten, but they could run a relay out to the mouth of the Quallheim. That way we'd have your posse there in two days."

Colin Rexrew let his head rest on the back of the chair, and ran a cost comparison through his neural nanonics. "Bloody expensive," he said. "And one of those VTOLs is out of service anyway after last year's cuts reduced the Aboriginal Fruit Classification budget. We'll compromise, as always. Candace sends her sheriffs and deputies up to the Quallheim on the river-boats, and her office here in town continues to monitor the situation with the observation satellite. If this revolt, or whatever it is, looks like it's spreading down out of the Quallheim Counties, we'll use the VTOLs to reinforce the posse before they get there."

The electrophorescent cells at the apex of Laton's singular study were darkened, eradicating external stimuli so he could focus himself on the inner self. Senses crept in on his glacial mind, impressions garnered via affinity from the servitor scouts spread throughout the jungle. The results displeased him enormously. In fact they were edging him towards worry. He hadn't felt like this since the Edenist Intelligence operatives had closed in, forcing him to flee his original habitat nearly seventy years previously. At that time he had felt fury, fear, and dismay the intensity of which he had never known as an Edenist; it had made him realize how worthless that culture truly was. His rejection had been total after that.

And now something was closing in on him again. Something he neither knew nor understood; something which acted like sequestration nanonics, usurping a human's original personality and replacing it with mechanoid warrior traits. He had watched the drastically modified behaviour of Quinn Dexter and the Ivets after the incident with the lightning in the jungle. They acted like fully trained mercenary troops, and others they came into contact with soon exhibited similar traits, though a minority of those usurped acted almost normally—most puzzling. Nor did they need weapons, they acquired an ability to throw sprays of photons like a holographic projector, light which could act like a thermal-induction field, but with tremendous power and reach. Yet there was no visible physical mechanism.

Laton had felt the first overspill of pain from Camilla

when the Ivets cremated her, mercifully shortened as she lost consciousness. He mourned his daughter as was proper, away in some subsidiary section of his mind, her absence from his life a sting of regret. But the important thing now was the threat he himself faced. In order to confront your enemy without fear, for fear is a bolt in the enemy's quiver, you must understand your enemy. And understanding was the one thing which had not come in four solid days of supreme cerebral effort.

Some of the glimpses he had snatched through the scouts defied physics. Either that or physics had advanced beyond all reasonable expectations during his exile. That was conceivable, he reasoned, weapons science was always kept very close to the government's chest, receiving the most funds and the least publicity.

Memory: of a man looking up at the sky and seeing the affinity bonded kestrel. The man laughed and raised his hand, snapping his fingers. Air around the kestrel solidified, entombing it in a matrix of frozen molecules, and sending it tumbling from the sky to dash its body against the rocks two hundred metres below. A snap of the fingers . . .

Memory: of a frantic terrified villager from Kilkee firing his laser hunting rifle at one of the usurped. The range had been fifteen metres, and the beam had no effect whatsoever. After the first few shots the rifle had died completely. Then the vennal Laton was using to scout with had curled up and sunk into some kind of coma.

The villages throughout the Quallheim Counties had been conquered with bewildering swiftness. That more than anything convinced Laton he was up against some kind of military force. There was a directing intelligence behind the usurped, expanding their numerical strength at an exponential rate. But what really baffled him was why. He had chosen Lalonde because it fitted his long-range goals; other than that it was a worthless planet. Why take control of people out here?

A test was the only explanation he could think of. Which begged the question what was it a preliminary to? The potential was awesome.

Laton? Waldsey's mental tone was fearful and uncertain, not like him at all.

Yes, Laton replied equitably. He could guess what was coming next. After sixty years he knew the way his colleagues' minds worked better than they did. He was only mildly surprised that it had taken them so long to confront him.

Do you know what it is yet?

No. I have been considering some kind of viral nanonic, but the number of demonstrated functions it possesses would be orders of magnitude above anything we even have theories for. And some of those functions are difficult to explain in terms of the physics we know and understand. In short, if you have a technology that powerful, why bother using it in this fashion? It is most puzzling.

Puzzling! Tao said angrily. **Father, it is bloody lethal, and it's right outside the tree. To hell with** *puzzling*, **we have to do something.**

Laton let the glimmer image of a smile penetrate their shared affinity. Only his children ever dared to contradict him, which pleased him after a fashion; obsequiousness was something he disapproved of almost as much as disloyalty. Which gave everybody a narrow, and perilous, balance to maintain. **No doubt you have an idea as to what we should do.**

Yeah. Load up the landcruisers, and head for the hills. Call it a strategic withdrawal, call it prudence, but just let's get *out* **of this tree. Now. While we still can. I don't mind admitting I'm frightened, if nobody else will.**

I would imagine that even this planet's chief sheriff will know that something odd is happening in Aberdale and the other Quallheim villages by now, Laton said. He sensed the others coming into the conversation, their minds carefully shielded from leaking too many emotions. **The LDC's surveillance satellite may be in a deplorable condition, but I assure you it would be quite capable of spotting the landcruisers. And it will be focused on the Quallheim Counties with considerable diligence.**

So? We just zap it. The old blackhawk masers you

brought down can reach it. It'll be weeks before the LDC replace it. By that time we'll be long gone. They'll see the track we made breaking through the jungle, but once we reach the savannah they'll lose us.

I would remind you just how close to success our immortality project is. Are you willing to sacrifice that?

Father, unless we get out of here, we aren't going to have a project left, or a life to immortalize. We can't defend ourselves against these usurped villagers. I've watched what happens when anyone shoots them. They don't even notice it! And even if somebody does manage to beat them, the Quallheim Counties are going to be searched a centimetre at a time afterwards. Either way, we can't stay here.

The lad's got a point there, Laton, Salkid said. We can't cling on here simply out of sentiment.

You always told me knowledge can't be destroyed, Tao said. We know how to splice a parallel-processing brain together. What we need is a secure location in which to do it. The tree certainly isn't it, not any more.

Well argued, Laton said. Except I'm not sure anywhere on Lalonde can be classed as safe any more. This technology is fearsome. He deliberately allowed his emotional shield to slip, and felt the shocked recoil of their thoughts that he who never demonstrated weakness was so deeply perturbed.

We can hardly walk into Durringham's spaceport and ask for a lift outsystem, Waldsey said.

The children can, Laton said. They have been born here, the intelligence agencies have no record of them. Once in orbit they can secure a starship for us.

Bloody hell, you mean it.

Indeed. It is the logical course. At the ultimate extreme, I am prepared to contact the intelligence agencies in Durringham and report the situation to them. They will take me seriously, and that way a warning will get out.

Is it that bad, Father? Salsett asked anxiously.

Laton projected a burst of reassuring warmth at the fifteen-year-old girl. **I don't think it will come to that, darling.**

Leaving the tree, she said wonderingly.

Yes, he said. **Tao, that was a good suggestion of yours; you and Salkid take a blackhawk maser out of storage, and be ready to eliminate that observation satellite. The rest of you have ten hours to pack. We start for Durringham tonight.**

He couldn't detect a single whiff of dissension. Minds retreated from the affinity contact.

In the hours which followed, the gigantea tree was subject to the kind of coordinated activity it hadn't seen since their arrival. Orders were flung frantically at the incorporated and the housechimps as the residents attempted to dismantle the work of thirty years in the short hours they had left. Heartbreaking decisions were made over what could go and what must stay, several couples arguing. The landcruisers had to be checked over and prepared after thirty years' unemployment. Laton's younger children scampered about getting in the way, nervous and elated at the prospect of leaving; the older members of the fellowship started thinking about the Confederation worlds again. Thermal charges were set throughout the rooms and corridors, ready to obliterate all trace of the gigantea's secrets.

The hectic activity registered as a background burble amid Laton's steely thoughts. Occasionally someone would intrude into his contemplation to ask for instructions.

After designating the few personal items he wanted to accompany them, he spent his time reviewing the memory of what happened in the clearing when Quinn Dexter killed Supervisor Manani. That strange lightning was the start of it. He ran and re-ran Camilla's memory images, which were stored in the tree's sub-sentient bitek processor array. The lightning seemed to be flat, almost compressed, some sections darker than others. As he ran the memory again the dark areas moved, sliding down the glaring streamers of rampaging electrons. The lightning bolts were acting as conduits to some kind of energy pattern, one which behaved outside the accepted norm.

A draught of air stroked his face. He opened his eyes to

darkness. The study was as it always had been. He switched his retinal implants to infrared. Jackson Gael and Ruth Hilton stood on the curving wood before him.

"Clever," Laton said. His contact with the processors faded away. Affinity was reduced to a whisper rattling round the closed confines of his skull. "It's energy, isn't it? A self-determining viral program that can store itself in a non-physical lattice."

Ruth bent down, and put her hand under his chin, tilting his face up so she could examine him. "Edenists. Always so rational."

"But where did it come from, I wonder?" Laton asked.

"What will it take to break his beliefs?" Jackson Gael asked.

"It's not of human origin," Laton said. "I'm sure of that; nor any of the xenoc races we know."

"We'll find out tonight," Ruth said. She let go of Laton's chin, and held out her hand. "Come along."

The morning after Governor Rexrew's briefing with Candace Elford, Ralph Hiltch was sitting behind his own desk in the Kulu Embassy dumper receiving a condensed version of events from Jenny Harris. One of the ESA assets she ran in the sheriff's office had asked for a meeting and told her about the trouble brewing in the Quallheim Counties.

All well and good, it was nice to see the Governor couldn't fart without the ESA knowing, but like Rexrew before him, Ralph was having a lot of trouble with the concept of an Ivet uprising.

"An open revolt?" he asked the lieutenant sceptically.

"It looks that way," she said apologetically. "Here, my contact gave me a flek of the surveillance satellite images." She loaded it into the processor block on Ralph's desk, and the screens on the wall began to show the Quallheim's motley collection of villages.

Ralph stood in front of them, hands on his hips as the semicircular clearings cut into solid jungle appeared. The treetops looked like green foam, broken by occasional glades, and virtually sealing over streams and the smaller rivers. "There's been a lot of fires," he agreed unhappily.

"And recently, too. Can't you manage a better resolution than this?"

"Apparently not, and that's the second cause for alarm. Something is affecting the satellite every time it passes over the Quallheim tributary. No other section of Amarisk is affected."

He gave her a long look.

"I know," she said. "It sounds ridiculous."

Ralph gave his neural nanonics a search request and returned his attention to the screens while it was running. "There's certainly been some kind of fight down there. And this isn't the first time Schuster County has come to our attention." The neural nanonics reported a blank; so he opened a channel to access his processor block's classified military systems file, extending the search.

"Captain Lambourne reported that nothing ever came out of the marshal's visit last year," Jenny Harris said. "We still don't know what happened to those homestead families."

Ralph's neural nanonics told him that the processor block file couldn't find a match for his request. "Interesting. According to our files, there is no known electronic warfare system which can distort a satellite image like this."

"How up to date are the files?"

"Last year's." He walked back to his seat. "But you're missing the point. Firstly it's a wholly ineffective system, all it does is fuzz the image slightly. Secondly, if you've gone to all the trouble to tamper with the satellite why not knock it out altogether? Given the age of Lalonde's satellite, everyone would assume it was a natural malfunction. This method actually draws attention to the Quallheim."

"Or draws attention away from somewhere else," she said.

"I'm paranoid, but am I paranoid enough?" he muttered. Outside the window the dark rooftops of Durringham were steaming softly in the bright morning sun. It was all so cheerfully primitive, the residents walking through the tacky streets, power bikes throwing up fans of mud, a teenage couple lost in each other, the tail end of a new colonist group making their way down to the transients' dormitories. Every morning for the last four years he'd seen variants on the same scene. Lalonde's inhabitants got on with their basic, modestly corrupt lives, and never bothered anyone. They couldn't, they didn't have the means. "The thing which disturbs me most is Rexrew's idea that it could be an external group attempting some kind of coup. I almost agree with him, it's certainly more logical than an Ivet revolt." He rapped his knuckles on the desktop, trying to think. "When is this posse of Candace Elford's setting off?"

"Tomorrow; she's going to start recruiting her deputies this morning. And incidentally, the *Swithland* is one of the boats that will be carrying them. Captain Lambourne can keep us updated if you allow her to use a communication block."

"OK, but I want at least five of our assets in that group of deputies, more if you can manage. We need to know what's going on up in the Quallheim Counties. Equip them with communication blocks as well, but make sure they understand they must only use them if the situation is urgent. I'll speak to Kelven Solanki about the issue, he's probably as keen as we are to know what's going on."

"I'll get onto it," she said. "One of the sheriffs Elford is sending belongs to me anyway, that'll make placing assets among the deputies a lot easier."

"Good, well done."

Jenny Harris saluted professionally, but before she got to the door she turned back and said, "I don't understand. Why would anyone want to stage a coup out in the middle of the hinterlands?"

"Someone with an eye to the future, maybe. If it is, our duty is very clear cut."

"Yes, sir; but if that is the case, they'd need help from out-system."

"True. Well, at least that's easy enough to watch for."

Ralph occupied himself with genuine embassy attaché work for the next two hours. Lalonde imported very little, but from the list of what it did require he tried to secure a reasonable portion for Kulu companies. He was trying to find a supplier for the high-temperature moulds a new glass-works factory wanted when his neural nanonics alerted him to an unscheduled starship that had just jumped into

Lalonde's designated emergence zone, fifty thousand kilometres above the planet's surface. The dumper's electronics
tapped the downlink from Lalonde's two civil spaceflight
monitor satellites, giving him access to the raw data. What
it didn't provide was system command authority, he was a
passive observer.

Lalonde's traffic control took a long time to respond to
the monitor satellite's discovery. There were three starships
in an equatorial parking orbit, two colonist transports from
Earth, and a freighter from New California, nothing else was
due for a week. The staff probably hadn't even been in the
control centre, he thought impatiently as he waited for them
to get off their arses and provide him with more information.

Starship visits outside the regular LDC contracted vessels, and the voidhawk supply run for Aethra, were rare
events, there were never more than five or six a year. That
this one should appear at this time was a coincidence he
couldn't put out of his mind.

The starship was already under power and heading for a
standard equatorial parking orbit when traffic control eventually triggered its transponder and established a communication channel. Data flooded into Ralph's mind, the standard
Confederation Astronautics Board registration and certification. It was an independent trader vessel called *Lady Macbeth*.

His suspicion deepened.

Rumour hit Durringham and spread with a speed that a news
company's distribution division would have envied. It
started when Candace Elford's staff went out for a drink
after a hard day assessing the scrambled information they
were getting from the Quallheim Counties. Durringham's
strong beer, sweet wines from nearby estates, and running
mild mood-stimulant programs through their neural nanonics liberated a quantity of almost accurate information about
exactly what had been going on all day in the chief sheriff's
office.

It took half of Lalonde's long night to filter out of the
pubs the sheriffs used and down into the more basic taverns
the agricultural workers, port labourers, and river crews

favoured. Distance, time, alcohol, and weak hallucinogens distorted and amplified the story in creative surges. The end results which were shouted and argued over loudly through the riverside drinking dens would have impressed any student of social dynamics. The following day, it proliferated through every workplace and home.

The main exchanges of conversations went thus.

The colonists in the Quallheim Counties had been ritually massacred by the Ivets, who had taken up Devil worship. A Satanic theocracy had been declared to the Governor and demanded recognition as an independent state, and all the Ivets were to be sent there.

An army of radical anarchistic Ivets was marching downriver, razing villages as they went, looting and raping. They were kamikazes, sworn to destroy Lalonde.

Kulu Royal Marines had landed upriver and established a beachhead for a full invasion force: all the locals who resisted had been executed. The Ivets had welcomed the marines, betraying colonists who resisted. Supplementary: Lalonde was going to be incorporated into the Kulu Kingdom by force. (Pure crap, people said, why would Alastair II want this God-awful shit-tip of a planet?)

The Tyrathca farmers had suffered a famine and they were eating humans, starting with Aberdale. (No, not possible. Weren't the Tyrathca herbivores?)

Waster kids from Earth had stolen a starship, and after zapping the sheriff's surveillance satellite they'd landed to help their old gang mates, the Ivets.

Blackhawks and mercenary starships had banded together; they were invading Lalonde, and they were planning on turning it into a rebel world which would be a base for raiding the Confederation. Colonists were being used for slave labour to build fortifications and secret landing sites out in the jungle. Ivets were captaining the work parties.

Two things remained reasonably constant amid all the wild theorizing. One: colonists had been killed by Ivets. Two: Ivets were heading/helping the revolt.

Durringham was a frontier town, the vast majority of its population scraping their living with long hours of hard labour. They were poor and proud, and the only group which stood between them and the bottom rung were those evil, workshy, criminal, daughter-raping Ivets; and by God that's where the Ivets were going to stay: underfoot.

When Candace Elford's sheriffs started to recruit deputies for the posse, tension and nervousness was already gripping the town. Seeing the posse actually assembling down at the port, confirming there really was something going on up-river, tipped unrest into physical aggression.

Darcy and Lori were lucky to miss the worst of the mayhem. On Lalonde they acted as the local representatives for Ward Molecular, a Kulu company that imported various solid-state units as well as a lot of the electron-matrix power cells which the capital's embryonic industries were incorporating into an increasing number of products. The Kulu connection was an ironic added touch to their cover; the deeply religious Kulu and the Edenists were not closely allied in the Confederation. Edenists were not permitted to germinate their habitats in any of the Kingdom's star systems, which made it unlikely that anyone would think of them as anything other than loyal subjects of King Alastair II.

They handled their business from a long wooden warehouse structure, a standard industrial building with an overhanging roof, and a floor which was supported on raised stone pillars a metre above the muddy gravel. Built entirely from mayope, it was strong enough to resist any casual break-in attempt by the capital's slowly increasing population of petty criminals. The single-storey cabin which they lived in sat in the middle of a half-acre plot of land at the back, which like most of Durringham's residents they used to grow vegetables and fruit bushes.

Warehouse and cabin were situated on the western edge of the port, five hundred metres from the water. The majority of nearby buildings were commercial premises—sawmills, lumber-yards, a few forges, and some relatively new cloth factories, their bleak ranks broken by streets of cabins to accommodate their workers. This end of town had stayed the same for years. It was the eastern end and long southern side which were expanding, and no one seemed keen to develop out towards the coastal swamps ten kilometres down the Juliffe. Nor were there any farms to the west; the raw jungle was less than two kilometres away.

But their proximity to the port did put them on the fringe of the trouble. They were in the office at the side of the warehouse when Stewart Danielsson, one of the three men who worked for them, came barging in.

"People outside," he said.

Lori and Darcy swapped a glance at the agitation in his tone, and went to see.

There was a loose progression of men from the nearby factories and mills heading towards the port. Darcy stood on the ramp outside the big open doorway at the front of the warehouse; there was a work area just inside, where they would pack orders and even perform repairs on Ward Molecular's simpler units. Cole Este and Gaven Hough, the company's other two employees, had both left their benches to join him.

"Where are they all going?" Lori asked. **And why do they look so angry?** she addressed Darcy on singular engagement.

"Going down to the port," Gaven Hough said.

"Why?"

He hunched his shoulders up, embarrassed. "Sort the Ivets out."

"Bloody right," Cole Este mumbled sullenly. "Wouldn't mind going on that posse myself. The sheriffs've been recruiting deputies all morning."

Damnation, trust this town to think with its arse, Darcy said. He and Lori had only been told about the Quallheim Counties revolt by one of their contacts in the Land Allocation Office the previous evening. **Those bloody sheriffs must have been shouting the news about Schuster.** "Gaven, Stewart, let's get these doors shut. We're closing for the day."

They started to slide the big doors shut, while Cole Este stood on the ramp, grinning and exchanging a few shouted comments with the odd person he knew. He was nineteen, the youngest of the three workers, and it was obvious he wanted to join the crowd.

Just look at the little idiot, Lori said.

Easy. We don't involve ourselves, nor criticize. Prime rule.

Tell me about it. They'll kill the Ivets down in the transients' dormitories. You know that, don't you?

Darcy slammed the bolt home on the door, and locked it with a padlock keyed to his finger pattern. **I know.**

"You want us to stay?" Stewart Danielsson asked dubiously.

"No, that's all right, Stewart, you three get off home. We'll take care of things here."

Darcy and Lori sat in the office with all but one of the windows shuttered on the inside. A partition with a line of tall glass panes in wooden frames looked out over the darkened warehouse. The furniture was basic, a couple of tables and five chairs Darcy had made himself. A conditioner whirred almost silently in one corner, keeping the atmosphere cool and dry. The office was one of the few rooms on the planet that was actually dusty.

Once is acceptable, Lori said. **Twice is not. Something strange is happening in Schuster County.**

Possibly. Darcy put his maser carbine on the table between them. The solitary shaft of sunlight shining through the window made the smooth grey composite casing glimmer softly. Protection, just in case the riot spread back through the town.

They could both hear the distant growl of the crowd down in the port; the newly arrived Ivets being hunted down and killed. Beaten into the mud with makeshift clubs, or gored by baying sayce to the sound of cheers. If they looked through the window at an angle they would be able to see boats of all sizes sailing hurriedly out of the circular polyp harbours for the safety of the water.

I hate Adamists, Lori said. **Only Adamists could do this to one another. They do it because they don't know one another. They don't love, they can only lust and fear.**

Darcy smiled, and reached out to touch her, because her mind was leaking a longing for the reassurance of physical contact. His hand never bridged the gap. An affinity voice with the power of a thunderstorm roared into their minds.

ATTENTION INTELLIGENCE OPERATIVES ON

LALONDE, I AM LATON. THERE IS A XENOC ENERGY VIRUS LOOSE IN THE QUALLHEIM COUNTIES. HOSTILE AND EXTREMELY DANGEROUS. LEAVE LALONDE IMMEDIATELY. THE CONFEDERATION NAVY MUST BE INFORMED. THIS IS YOUR ONLY PRIORITY NOW. I CANNOT LAST LONG.

Lori was whimpering, her hands clutching at her ears, mouth frozen open in a horrified wail. Darcy saw her dissolve under a discharge of chaotic mental images, each of them bright enough to dazzle.

Jungle. A village seen from the air. More jungle. A little boy hanging upside-down from a tree, his stomach sliced open. A bearded man hanging upside-down from a different tree, lightning flaring wildly.

Heat, excruciating heat.

Darcy grunted at the pain, he was on fire. Skin blackening, hair singeing, his throat shrivelling.

It stopped.

He was prone on the floor. Flames in the background. Always flames. A man and a woman were leaning over him, naked. Their skin was changing, darkening to green, becoming scaled. Eyes and mouth were scarlet red. The woman parted her lips and a serpent's forked tongue slipped out.

His children were crying all around.

Sorry, so sorry I failed you at the last.

Father shame: ignominy that extended down to a cellular level.

Leathery green hands began to run across his chest, a parody of sensuality. Where the fingers touched he could feel the ruptures begin deep below his skin.

NOW DO YOU BELIEVE?

And voices, audible above his agony. Coming from within, from a deeper part of his brain than affinity originated. Whisperers in chorus: "We can help, we can make it stop. Let us in, let us free you. Give yourself."

WARN THEM, CURSE YOU.

Then nothing.

Darcy found himself curled up on the mayope planks of

the office floor. He had bitten his lip; a trickle of blood wept down his chin.

He touched himself gingerly, fingers probing his ribs, terrified of what he would find. But there was no pain, no open wounds, no internal damage.

"It was him," Lori croaked. She was in her chair, head bowed, hugging her chest, hands clenched into tight fists. "Laton. He's here, he really is here."

Darcy managed to right himself into a kneeling position, it was enough for now, if he tried to stand he was sure he'd faint. "Those images . . ." Did you see them?

The reptile people? Yes. But the power in that affinity. It . . . it damn near overwhelmed me.

The Quallheim Counties, that's where he said it was. That's over a thousand kilometres away upriver. Human affinity can only reach a hundred at most.

He's had thirty years to perfect his diabolical genetic schemes. Her thoughts were contaminated with fright and revulsion.

"A xenoc energy virus," Darcy muttered, nonplussed. What did he mean? And he was being tortured, along with his children. Why? What is going on upriver?

I don't know. All I know is I wouldn't trust him, not ever. We saw images, fantasy figures. He's had thirty years to construct them, after all.

But they were so real. And why reveal himself? He knows we will eliminate him whatever the cost.

Yes, he knows we will come in force. But with that affinity power he could probably compel even a void-hawk. It would allow himself and his cronies to spread through the Confederation.

It was so real, Darcy repeated numbly. And now we know he is so powerful we can guard against him. It makes no sense, unless he really has run into something he can't handle. Something more powerful than he.

Lori gave him a sad, almost defeated look. We need to know, don't we?

Yes.

They let their thoughts flow and entwine like the bodies

of amorous lovers, reinforcing their strengths, eliminating weaknesses. Gathering courage.

Darcy used a chair as support, and pulled himself up. Every joint felt ponderously stiff. He sat heavily and dabbed at his bitten lip.

Lori smiled fondly, and handed him a handkerchief.

Duty first, he said. **We have to inform Jupiter that Laton is here. That takes precedence over everything. We're not due a voidhawk visit for another couple of months. I'll see Kelven Solanki and request he sends a message to Aethra and the support station out at Murora immediately, his office has the equipment to do that direct. The Confederation Navy would have to be told anyway, so it might as well be now. He can also include a report in the diplomatic flek on a colonist-carrier ship that's heading back to Earth. That ought to cover us.**

And after that we go upriver, Lori said.

Yes.

"Next!" the sheriff called.

Yuri Wilkin stepped up to the table, keeping the leash tight on his sayce, Randolf. Rain pattered on the empty warehouse's roof high above his head. Outside the open end, behind the sheriff, the yellow-brown polyp crater of harbour five was returning to a semblance of normality. Most of the boats had returned after their night on the river. A work crew from one of the shipyards were surveying the fire-ravaged hull that was bobbing low in the water. Some captain who hadn't been fast enough to cast off when the rioters came boiling along the polyp in search of Ivets.

The smell of burnt wood mingled with more exotic smells from the stored goods that had caught fire in several warehouses. The flames shooting out of the doomed buildings had been tremendous, even Lalonde's rain had taken hours to extinguish them.

Yuri had milled around watching along with the rest of the rioters last night, mesmerized with the destruction. The flames had lit something inside him, something that felt joyful at the sight of a young terrified Ivet reduced to a bloody chunk of unrecognizable meat beneath the crowd's clubs. He had yelled encouragement until his throat was hoarse.

"Age?" the sheriff asked.

"Twenty," Yuri lied. He was seventeen, but he already had a reasonable beard. He crossed his fingers, hoping it would be enough. There were over two hundred people waiting behind him, all wanting their chance now the sheriffs had started recruiting again.

The sheriff glanced up from his processor block. "Sure you are. You ever used a weapon, son?"

"I eat chikrows every week, shoot them myself. I know how to move around in the jungle OK. And I got Randolf, trained him all by myself, he's an ace baiter, knows how to fight, knows how to hunt. He'll be a big help upriver, you get two of us for the price of one."

The sheriff leant forwards slightly, peering over the edge of the table.

Randolf bared his stained fangs. "Killl Ivezss," the beast snarled.

"OK," the sheriff grunted. "You willing to take orders? We don't need people who aren't prepared to work in a team."

"Yes, sir."

"Reckon you might, at that. You got a change of clothes?"

Grinning, Yuri twisted round to show him the canvas duffle bag slung over his shoulder; his laser rifle was strapped to it.

The sheriff picked a vermilion-coloured deputy's badge from the pile beside his processor block. "There you go. Get yourself down to the *Swithland* and find a bunk. We'll swear you in officially once we're underway. And muzzle that bloody sayce, I don't want him chewing up colonists before we get there."

Yuri rubbed the black scales between Randolf's battered ears. "Don't you worry about old Randolf, he ain't going to hurt no one, not till I tell him to."

"Next!" the sheriff called.

Yuri Wilkin settled his hat firmly on his head, and headed for the sun-drenched harbour outside, a song in his heart and mayhem in mind.

*   *   *

"Gods, I've seen some rough planets in my time, Joshua," Ashly Hanson said. "But this one takes the biscuit. There isn't even anyone at the spaceport who wanted to buy copies of Jezzibella's MF album, let alone a black-market distribution net." He took a drink of juice from his long glass, it was a purplish liquid with plenty of ice bobbing around, some aboriginal fruit. The pilot never touched alcohol while the *Lady Macbeth* was docked to a station or in a parking orbit.

Joshua sipped his glass of bitter, which was warm and carried a punch almost as strong as some spirits he'd tasted. At least it had a decent head.

The pub they were drinking in was called the Crashed Dumper, a wooden barnlike structure at the end of the road that linked the spaceport with Durringham. Various time-expired spaceplane components were fastened up against the walls, the most prominent a compressor fan from one of the McBoeings that took up most of the end wall, with a couple of the fat blades buckled from a bird impact. The pub was used by spaceport staff along with the pilots and starship crews. It was, allegedly, one of the classier pubs in Durringham.

If this was refinement, Joshua didn't like to think what the rest of the city's hostelries must be like.

"I've been on worse," Warlow growled. The bass harmonics set up vibrations on the surface of the brightlime in his bulbous brandy glass.

"Where?" Ashly demanded.

Joshua ignored them. This was their second day in Durringham, and he was starting to worry. The day Ashly had flown them down there had been some sort of riot next to the river. Everything had shut down, shops, warehouses, government offices. Spaceport procedures had been minimal, but then he suspected they were always like that on Lalonde. Ashly was right, this was one massively primitive colony. Today had been little better; the Governor's industrial secretary had put him in touch with a Durringham timber merchant. The address turned out to be a small office down near the waterfront. Closed, naturally. Enquiries had eventually traced the owner, Mr Purcell, to a nearby pub. He assured

Joshua a thousand tonnes of mayope was no problem. "You can't give it away down here, we've got stocks backlogged halfway up the Juliffe." He quoted a price of thirty-five thousand fuseodollars inclusive, and promised deliveries could start to the spaceport tomorrow. The wood was a ridiculous price, but Joshua didn't argue. He even paid a two thousand fuseodollar deposit.

Joshua, Ashly, and Warlow had gone back to the spaceport on their hired power bikes (and the rental charge on those was bloody legalized robbery) to try to arrange for a McBoeing charter to ship the wood up to *Lady Mac*. That had taken the rest of the day, and another three thousand fuseodollars in bribe money.

It wasn't the money which bothered him particularly; even taking Lalonde's necessary lubrication into account the mayope was only a small percentage of the cost of a Norfolk flight. Joshua was used to datavised deals, and instant access to anybody he wanted via the local communication net. On Lalonde, where there was no net, and few people with neural nanonics, he was beginning to feel out of his depth.

When he had ridden back into town in the late afternoon to find Mr Purcell and confirm they had a McBoeing lined up, the timber merchant was nowhere to be found. Joshua retreated to the Crashed Dumper in a dark mood. He wasn't at all sure the mayope would even turn up tomorrow; and they had to leave in six days to stand any chance of securing a cargo of Norfolk Tears from a roseyard merchant. Six days, and he didn't have any alternative to mayope. It had seemed such a good idea.

He took another gulp of his bitter. The pub was filling up as the spaceport staff came off shift. Over in one corner an audio block was playing a ballad which some of the customers were singing along to. Large fans spun listlessly overhead, trying to circulate some of the humid air.

"Captain Calvert?"

Joshua looked up.

Marie Skibbow was dressed in a tight-fitting sleeveless green stretch blouse, and a short pleated black skirt. Her thick hair was neatly plaited. She was carrying a circular tray loaded with empty glasses.

"Now this is what I call improved service," Ashly said brightly.

"That's me," Joshua said. Jesus, but she had tremendous legs. Nice face too, ever so slightly wiser than her age.

"I understand you're looking for a cargo of mayope, is that right?" Marie asked.

"Does everybody in town know?" Joshua asked.

"Just about. A visit from an independent trader starship isn't exactly common around here. If we weren't having all this trouble with the Quallheim Counties and the anti-Ivet riots you'd be the most gossiped over item in Durringham."

"I see."

"Can I join you?"

"Sure." He pushed out one of the vacant chairs. People had tended to avoid their table, it was one of the reasons he'd brought Warlow down. Only someone who was stoned out of his brain would try and tangle with the amount of boosted muscle the old cosmonik packed into his giant frame.

Marie sat down and fixed Joshua with an uncompromising gaze. "Would you be interested in taking on an extra crew-member?"

"You?" Joshua asked.

"Yes."

"Do you have neural nanonics?"

"No."

"Then, I'm sorry, but the answer's no. I have a full complement anyway."

"How much do you charge for a trip?"

"Where to?"

"Wherever you're going next."

"If we can acquire a cargo of mayope, I'm going to Norfolk. I'd charge you thirty thousand fuseodollars for passage in zero-tau, more if you wanted a cabin. Starflight isn't cheap."

Marie's air of sophisticated confidence faltered slightly. "Yes, I know."

"You want to leave pretty badly?" Ashly asked sympathetically.

She dropped her gaze and nodded. "Wouldn't you? I lived

on Earth until last year. I hate it here, I'm not staying no matter what it costs. I want civilization."

"Earth," Ashly mused whimsically. "Lord, I haven't been there for a couple of centuries. Wouldn't call it particularly civilized even back then."

"He's a time hopper," Joshua explained as Marie gave the pilot a confused look. "And if you hate this place as much as you say, then Norfolk isn't where you want to go either. It's strictly a pastoral planet. They have a policy of minimal technological usage, and the government enforces it pretty rigorously from what I hear. Sorry."

She gave a small shrug. "I never thought it would be that easy."

"The idea of signing on with a ship is a good one," Ashly said. "But you really need neural nanonics before a captain will consider you."

"Yes, I know, I'm saving up for a set."

Joshua put on a neutral expression. "Good."

Marie actually laughed, he was being so careful not to hurt her feelings. "You think I waitress for a living? That I'm a dumb waster girl saving up tips and dreaming of better days?"

"Er . . . no."

"I waitress here in the evenings because it's the place the starship crews come. This way I get to hear of any openings before the rest of Durringham. And yes there are the tips, too, every little helps. But for real money I bought myself a secretarial job at the Kulu Embassy, in their Commercial Office."

"Bought a job?" Warlow rumbled. His sculpted dark-yellow face was incapable of expression, but the voice booming from his chest diaphragm carried a heavy query. People turned to look as he drowned out the ballad.

"Of course. You think they give away a gig like that? The embassy pays its staff in Kulu pounds." It was the second hardest currency in the Confederation after fuseodollars. "That's where I'm going to get the money to pay for my neural nanonics."

"Ah, now I see." Joshua raised his glass in salute. He admired the girl's toughness—almost as much as he admired her figure.

"That, or the deputy ambassador's son might get me off," Marie said quietly. "He's twenty-two, and he likes me a lot. If we married then obviously I'd go back to Kulu with him once his father's tour was over."

Ashly grinned and knocked back some of his fruit juice. A suspect grumble emerged from Warlow's chest.

Marie gave Joshua a questioning glance. "So. Do you still want your mayope, Captain?"

"You think you can get me some?"

"Like I said, I work in the Commercial Office. And I'm good at it, too," she said fiercely. "I know more about this town's economic structure than my boss. You're buying your cargo from Dodd Purcell, right?"

"Yes," Joshua said cautiously.

"Thought so; he's the nephew of the governor's industrial secretary. Dodd Purcell is a complete screwup, but he's a good partner for his uncle. All official tenders for timber go through the company he owns, except it's actually his uncle's, and all it consists of is an office down at the port. They don't actually own a yard, or even any timber. The LDC pays through the nose, but nobody queries it because no lower quotes ever make it past the industrial secretary's office. All that happens is Purcell contracts a real lumberyard to supply whatever project the LDC is paying for; they do all the work while he and uncle cream off thirty per cent. No effort, and all profit."

Warlow's chair creaked alarmed protests as his bulk shifted round. He tilted the brandy glass to his mouth aperture, the brightlime surged out, almost sucked down into his inlet nozzle. "Smart bastards."

"Jesus," Joshua said. "And I'll bet the price goes up tomorrow."

"I expect so," Marie said. "And then again the day after, then it will become a rush order to meet your deadline, so you'll have to pay a surcharge."

Joshua put his empty glass down on the stained table. "All right, you win. What's your counter-offer?"

"You are paying Purcell thirty-five thousand fuseodollars,

which is about thirty per cent over the odds. I'm offering to
put you in touch with a lumber-yard direct, they'll supply
the wood at the market rate, and you pay me five per cent of
the difference."

"Suppose we just go to a lumber-yard direct now you've
told us what's happening?" Ashly asked.

Marie smiled sweetly. "Which one? Are you going back
to the Governor's industrial secretary for a list? Once you've
picked one, do you know if it was burnt down in the riots?
Where is it, and how do you get to it? Parts of this town are
very unhealthy for visitors, especially after the riots. Does it
have that much mayope in stock or is the owner stringing
you along? What are you going to use to transport it out to
the spaceport? And how much time can you spend sorting
all that out? Even a relatively honest lumber-yard owner is
going to catch on that you've got a deadline once you start
fretting because you haven't got permits and procedures
smoothed out in advance. I mean, God, it took you almost a
day to hire a McBoeing. Bet you didn't buy energy for it either, they'll hit you for that tomorrow. And when they scent
blood it'll be Purcell all over again."

Joshua held up a warning hand to Ashly. Nobody at the
spaceport had mentioned energy for the McBoeing. Jesus!
On a normal planet it would be part of the charter; and of
course he couldn't use his neural nanonics to access the contract and run a legal program check because his copy of the
fucking thing was printed out on paper. *Paper*, for Christ's
sake. "I'll deal with you," he told Marie. "But I only pay on
delivery to orbit, and that includes your fee. So you're going
to have to clear all those obstacles you mentioned out of our
way, because I don't pay a single fuseodollar once those six
days are up."

She stuck out her hand, and after a moment's hesitation
Joshua shook.

"We're sleeping in my spaceplane, seeing as how it has
the only functional air-conditioner on the entire planet," he
told her. "I want you there at seven o'clock tomorrow morning ready to take us to this lumber-yard of yours."

"Aye, aye, Captain." She stood and picked up her tray.

Joshua pulled a wad of Lalonde francs from his jacket

pocket and peeled a few off. "We'll have the same again, and have a large one yourself. I think you've just earned it."

Marie plucked the notes from him and stuffed them in a side pocket on her skirt. She gave them all a ludicrously sassy twitch with her backside as she walked off to the bar.

Ashly watched her go with a lugubrious expression, then drained his juice in one gulp. "God help that ambassador's son."

Darcy and Lori spent the day after the riots preparing for their trip. There was Kelven Solanki to brief on the situation, and their eagles Abraham and Catlin to take out of zero-tau, equipment to make ready. Above all, they had to find transport. The harbour-master's office had been damaged in the riot, so there was no list available of the boats in dock. In the afternoon they sent the eagles skimming over the polyp rings searching for something they could use.

What do you think? Darcy asked. Abraham was turning lazy circles over harbour seven, his enhanced retinas providing an uncluttered image of the boats moored up against the quays.

Them? Lori exclaimed in dismay.

Have you found someone else?

No.

At least we know we can bully them with money.

The port still hadn't recovered from the riot when they made their way down to harbour seven first thing the next morning. Huge piles of ashes which used to be buildings were still radiating heat from their smouldering cores, giving off thin streamers of acrid smoke. Long runnels of mushed ashes meandered away from their bases, sluiced out by the rain; they had coagulated under the morning sunlight, looking like damp lava flows.

Gangs of workers were raking through the piles with long mayope poles, searching for anything salvageable. They passed one ruined transients' warehouse where a stack of cargo-pods had been pulled from the gutted remains, the warped composite resembling surrealistic sculptures. Darcy watched a forlorn family prise open a badly contorted marsupium shell with deep scorch marks on the oyster-coloured casing. The infant quadruped had been roasted in its chemical sleep, reduced to a shrivelled black mummy. Darcy couldn't even tell what species it was.

Lori had to turn away from the empty-faced colonists scrabbling at the pods' distorted lids, shiny new ship-suits smeared with dirt and sweat. They had come to Lalonde with such high hopes, and now they were faced with utter ruin before they'd even been given a chance at a life.

This is awful, she said.

This is dangerous, Darcy replied. **They are numbed and shocked now, but that will soon give way to anger. Without their farmsteading gear they can't be sent up-river, and Rexrew will be hard pushed to replace it.**

It wasn't all burnt, she said sorrowfully. The afternoon and evening of the riot there had been a steady stream of people walking past the Ward Molecular warehouse carrying pods and cartons of equipment they had looted.

They walked round harbour seven until they came to the quay where the *Coogan* was moored. The ageing tramp trader was in a dilapidated state, with holes in its cabin roof and a long gash in the wood up at the prow where it had struck some snag. Len Buchannan had only just managed to get out of the harbour ahead of the rioters, flinging planks from the cabin walls into the furnace hopper in his desperation.

Gail Buchannan was sitting in her usual place outside the galley doorway, coolie hat shading her sweating face, a kitchen knife almost engulfed by her huge hand. She was chopping some long vegetable root, slices falling into a pewter-coloured pan at her feet. Her eyes fastened shrewdly on Darcy and Lori as they stepped onto the decking. "You again. Len! Len, get yourself out here, we've got visitors. Now, Len!"

Darcy waited impassively. They had used the Buchannans as an information source in the past, occasionally asking them to pick up fleks from assets upriver. But they had proved so unreliable and cranky, Darcy hadn't bothered with them for the last twenty months.

Len Buchannan walked forward from the little engine-room, where he'd been patching the cabin walls. He was wearing jeans and his cap, a carpenter's suede utility belt hanging loosely round his skinny hips, with only a few tools in its hoops.

Darcy thought he looked hungover, which fitted the talk he'd heard around the port. The *Coogan* had hit hard times of late.

"Have you got a cargo to take upriver?" Darcy asked.

"No," Len said sullenly.

"It's been a difficult season for us," Gail said. "Things aren't like they used to be. Nobody shows any loyalty these days. Why, if it wasn't for us virtually giving our goods away half of the settlements upriver would have starved to death. But do they show any gratitude? Ha!"

"Is the *Coogan* fit to be taken out?" Darcy asked, cutting through the woman's screed. "Now? Today?"

Len pulled his cap off and scratched his head. "Suppose so. Engines are OK. I always service them regular."

"Of course it's in tiptop shape," Gail told him loudly. "There's nothing wrong with the *Coogan*'s hull. It's only because this drunken buffoon spends all his time pining away over that little bitch-brat that the cabin's in the state it is."

Len sighed irksomely, and leant against the galley doorframe. "Don't start," he said.

"I knew she was trouble," Gail said. "I told you not to let her on board. I warned you. And after all we did for her."

"Shut up!"

She glared at him and resumed slicing up the cream-white vegetable.

"What do you want the *Coogan* for?" Len asked.

"We have to get upriver, today," Darcy said. "There's no cargo, only us."

Len made a play of putting his cap back on. "There's trouble upriver."

"I know. That's where we want to go, the Quallheim Counties."

"No," Len Buchannan said. "Sorry, anywhere else in the tributary basin, but not there."

"That's where *she* came from," Gail hissed venomously. "That's what you're afraid of."

"There's a bloody war going on up there, woman. You saw the boats with the posse leaving."

"Ten thousand fuseodollars," Gail said. "And don't you two try haggling with me, that's the only offer you'll get, I'm starving myself as it is. I'll take you up on my own if Lennie's too frightened."

If that's starvation, I'd like to see gluttony, Darcy said.

"This is my boat," Len said. "Made with my own hands."

"Half yours," Gail shouted back, waving the knife at him. "Half! I have a say too, and I say *Coogan* is going back to the Quallheim. If you don't like it, go and cry in her skirts if she'll have you. Drunken old fool."

If this is the way they carry on, they'll kill each other before we get out of the harbour, Lori said. She watched Len staring at the burnt-out sections of the port, his brown weathered face lost with longing.

"All right," he said eventually. "I'll take you to the mouth of the Quallheim, or as near as we can get. But I'm not going anywhere near the trouble."

"Fair enough," Darcy said. "How long will it take us at full speed?"

"Going upriver?" Len closed his eyes, lips moving around figures. "Without stopping to trade, ten or twelve days. Mind, we'll have to moor in the evenings, and cut logs. You'll have to work your passage."

"Forget that," Darcy said. "I'll have some firewood delivered this afternoon, enough to get us there in one go; we can store it in the forward hold instead of a cargo. And I'll spell you at night, I don't need much sleep. How long travelling like that?"

"A week, maybe," Len Buchannan said. He didn't seem terribly happy with the idea.

"That's fine. We'll start this afternoon."

"We'll take half of the money now, as a deposit," Gail said. A Jovian Bank disk appeared from nowhere in her hand.

"You'll get a thousand now as a deposit, plus five hundred to buy enough food and water for three weeks," Lori said. "I'll pay another two thousand once we leave the harbour this afternoon, two more when we get to Schuster, and the sum when we get back here."

Gail Buchannan made a lot of indignant noise, but the sight of actual cash piling up in her disk silenced her.

"Make sure it's decent food," Lori told her. "Freeze dried, I'm sure you know where to get stocks of that from."

They left the Buchannans bickering and went on to a lumber-yard to arrange for the logs to be delivered. It took an hour longer than it should have done to get their order sorted out; the only reason they got it at all was because they were regular customers. The yard was frantically busy with an order for a thousand tonnes of mayope. The laughing foreman told them a lunatic starship captain was planning to carry it to another star.

They were going to make Joshua Calvert's deadline. Marie Skibbow couldn't keep the thought out of her mind. It was mid-afternoon, and she was sitting up at the bar in the nearly deserted Crashed Dumper having a celebratory drink. What she really felt like doing was singing and dancing, it was a wonderful experience. All the contacts she'd meticulously built up over the last few months had finally paid off. The deals she put together had clicked into place all the way down the line, smoothing the way for the wood to get from the lumber-yard into orbit with minimum fuss and maximum speed. In fact it had turned out they were being limited by how fast Ashly Hanson could load the foam-covered bundles into the *Lady Macbeth*'s cargo holds. The starship only carried one MSV, which imposed a two hundred and fifty tonne per day restriction. The pilot simply couldn't work any faster; and not even Marie could obtain a MSV from Kenyon, which was the only other place they were in use within the Lalonde star system. But even so, they should have the last bundle loaded tomorrow, a day before the deadline.

Her Jovian Bank disk was burning like a small thermal-induction field in her sawn-off jeans pocket. Joshua had paid her on the nose, every McBoeing flight that lifted off the spaceport's metal grid runway saw another batch of fuseodollars added to her account. And he'd given her a bonus for arranging the lorries. The drivers were taking colonists' farmsteading gear from the spaceport down to the harbour and returning half-empty; it didn't take much organization or money to fix it so they brought the mayope with them when they came back. That way Joshua saved money on an official contract with the haulage company that owned them.

Her first major-league deal. She sipped her iced brightlime, enjoying the bitter taste as it went down her throat. Was this how millionaires felt every day? The total satisfaction which came from tangible accomplishment. And all the famous merchant names in history must have started with a first deal like this, even Richard Saldana, who founded Kulu. Now there was a thought.

But there weren't many opportunities for deals this big on Lalonde. She simply had to leave, that goal had never changed. The money from the deal would be a hefty slice towards the eighteen thousand fuseodollars she needed for a basic set of neural nanonics. Joshua would probably pay her an overall bonus as well. He was honest enough.

Which brought her to the real question of the day: whether or not she was going to go to bed with him. He had certainly asked her often enough over the last four days. He was handsome, if a trifle gaunt, with a good-looking body; and he must be talented after all the girls he'd been with. An owner-captain under twenty-five years old, it would surely run into hundreds. Especially with that grin. He must practise it; so sexy. She rather liked the notion of what they'd be capable of doing to each other if they flung off every inhibition. There had been rumours back at the arcology about the prowess of people geneered for spaceflight, something to do with enhanced flexibility.

And if she did—which she probably would—he might just take her with him when he left. It really wasn't a possibility she could afford to ignore. After Norfolk he said he was planning on returning to Tranquillity. That habitat was premier real estate, superior even to Earth and Kulu. I've already whored my way down the river; whoring to Tranquillity would hardly be a hardship after that.

The Crashed Dumper's door creaked open. A young man

in a blue and red checked shirt and long khaki shorts walked in, and sat down at the other end of the bar. He never even glanced at Marie, which was odd. She was wearing her sawn-off jeans and a dark-orange singlet, long limbs on show. His face looked familiar, early twenties, ruggedly attractive with a neatly trimmed beard. His clothes were new, and clean, made locally. Was he one of Durringham's new generation of merchants? She'd met a lot of them since she got the job at the embassy, and they were always keen to talk while they waited for Ralph Hiltch, her boss.

She pouted slightly. There, if she had neural nanonics she'd have no trouble placing the name.

"Beer, please," he told the barkeeper.

The voice fixed him, it just took a moment for her incredulity to die down. No wonder she hadn't recognized him to start with. She went over to him.

"Quinn Dexter, what the bloody hell are you doing here?"

He turned slowly, blinking at her uncertainly in the pub's filtered light. She held back on a laugh, because it was obvious he didn't recognize her either.

His fingers clicked, and he smiled. "Marie Skibbow. Glad to see you made it to the big city. Everybody wondered if you would. They didn't stop talking about you for a month."

"Yeah, well . . ." She sat on the stool next to him as he paid for his beer from a thick wad of Lalonde francs. That wasn't right, Ivets didn't have hard cash. She waited until the barkeeper went away then dropped her voice. "Quinn, don't tell people who you are. They're killing Ivets in this town right now. It's pretty nasty."

"No problem. I'm not an Ivet any more. I bought myself out of my work time contract."

"Bought yourself out?" Marie had never known you could do that.

"Sure," he winked. "Everything on this planet is financially orientated."

"Ah, right. How did you buy it? Don't tell me dear old Aberdale started being successful."

"No, not a chance, it never changed. I found some gold in the river."

"Gold?"

"Yes, a nugget you wouldn't believe." He held up his hand, making a fist. "This big, Marie, and that's the honest truth. So I kept going back, there was nothing ever as big as that first one, but I built up quite a little hoard. They thought it must have washed down from the mountains on the other side of the savannah, remember them?"

"God, don't remind me. I don't want to remember anything about that village."

"Can't say I blame you. First thing I did was get out. Sailed straight down the Juliffe on a trader boat; took me a week and I got ripped off by the captain, but here I am. Arrived today."

"Yeah, I got ripped off too." Marie studied her glass of brightlime. "So what's happening upriver, Quinn? Have the Ivets really taken over the Quallheim Counties?"

"It was all news to me when we docked this morning. There was nothing like that in the offing when I left. Maybe they're fighting over the gold. Whoever owns the motherlode is going to be seriously rich."

"They've sent a load of sheriffs and deputies up there, armed to the teeth."

"Oh, dear. That doesn't sound good. Guess I'm lucky I got out when I did."

Marie realized how hot she had become in the last couple of minutes. When she glanced up she saw the fans had stopped spinning. Bloody typical, right when the sun was at its zenith. "Quinn? How are my family?"

"Well . . ." He pulled a sardonic face. "Your father's not changed much."

She lifted her glass level with her face. "Amen."

"Let's see; your mother's OK, your brother-in-law is OK. Oh yes, Paula's pregnant."

"Really? God, I'll be an aunt."

"Looks like it." He took a swig of his beer.

"So what are you going to do now?"

"Leave. Get on a starship and go, some planet where I can start over."

"There was that much gold?" she asked.

"Yeah, that much, and then some."

Marie thought fast, weighing up her options. "I can get

you off Lalonde by tomorrow afternoon, and not back to Earth either, this is a fresh planet the captain is heading for. Clean air, open spaces, and a rock-solid economy."

"Yeah?" Quinn brightened considerably. The overhead fans began to turn again.

"Yes. I have a contact in the ship, but I charge commission for introducing you."

"You really landed on your feet, didn't you?"

"I do OK."

"Marie, there weren't any girls on the boat down the river."

She wasn't sure how he had suddenly got so close. He was pressed up beside her, and his presence was sending fissures of doubt straight through her self-confidence. Something about Quinn was monstrously intimidating, verging on menacing. "I can help there, I think. I know a place, the girls are clean."

"I don't want a *place*, Marie. Dear God, seeing you sitting there triggered all those memories I thought I'd put behind me."

"Quinn," she said laconically.

"You think I can help it? You were every Ivet's wet dream back at Aberdale, we'd spend hours talking about you. There'd be fights over who got on the work detail to your homestead. I did, I got it every time, I made bloody sure I did."

"Quinn!"

"You were everything I could never have, Marie. Damn Christ, I worshipped you, you were perfection, everything that was right and good in the world."

"Don't, Quinn." Her head was spinning, making her dizzy. What he was saying was crazy, he'd never even noticed her when he walked in the Crashed Dumper. It was so hot, the sweat was running down her back. His arm went round her, making her look into fevered eyes.

"And now here you are again. My very own idol. Like God gave me a second chance. And I'm not giving up this chance, Marie. Whatever it takes, I want you. I want you, Marie." Then his lips were on hers.

She was shaking against him when he finished the kiss.

"Quinn no," she mumbled. He tightened his grip, squashing her against him. His chest felt as though it was carved from rock, every muscle a steel band. She couldn't understand why she wasn't pushing him away. But she wasn't, the thought was inconceivable.

"I'm going to make it so good you're never going to leave me," he said in a frantic whisper. "I'm going to make you see I'm the one for you, that there is no one else in the whole galaxy who can replace me. I'm going to take you from this atrocity of a planet when I go; and we're going to live somewhere sweet and beautiful, where there isn't any jungle, and people are happy. And I'm going to buy us a big house, and I'm going to make you pregnant, and our children are going to be so lovely it hurts to look at them. You'll see, Marie. You'll see what true love can bring when you give yourself up to me."

There were tears in her eyes at the terrible wonderful words. Words that spoke out every dream she owned. And how could he possibly know? Yet there was only desire and yearning in his face. So maybe—please God—just maybe it was true. Because nobody could be so cruel as to lie about such things.

They leant together as they stumbled out of the Crashed Dumper, the pair of them drunk with their own brand of desire.

The Confederation Navy office on Lalonde was a two-storey structure, an oblong box sixty-five metres broad, twenty deep. The outer walls were blue-silver mirrors, broken by a single black band halfway up, which ran round the entire circumference. The flat roof had seven satellite uplinks covered by geodesic weather casings that resembled particularly virile bright orange toadstools. Only five of them actually housed communication equipment, the other two covered maser cannon which provided a short-range defence capability. The building was situated in the eastern sector of Durringham, five hundred metres from the dumper which housed the Governor's office.

It was a class 050-6B office, suitable for phase one colonies and non-capital missions (tropical); a programmed silicon structure made by the Lunar SII. It had arrived on Lalonde in a cubic container five metres to a side. The Fleet marine engineers who activated it had to sink corner foundations fifteen metres deep into the loam in order to secure it against the wind. The silicon walls might have been as strong as mayope, but they were only as thick as paper; it was terribly vulnerable to even mild gusts. And given Lalonde's temperature there was some speculation that warm air accumulating inside might actually provide sufficient lift to get it airborne.

There were fifty Confederation Navy staff assigned to Lalonde: officers, NCOs, and ratings, who ate, worked, and slept inside. The most active department was the recruitment centre, where fifteen permanent staff dealt with youngsters who shared Marie Skibbow's opinion of their world, but lacked her individual resourcefulness. Enlistment offered a golden ticket offplanet, away from the rain, the heat, and the remorseless physical labour of the farms.

Every time Ralph Hiltch walked through the wide automated entrance doors and breathed in clean, dry, conditioned air he felt just that fraction closer to home. Back in a world of right angles, synthetic materials, uniforms, humming machinery, and government-issue furniture.

A pretty rating barely out of her teens was waiting to escort him from the entrance hall where all the farmboy and -girl hopefuls were queueing in their hand-stitched shirts and mud-stained denim trousers. He opened his lightweight cagoule and shook some of the rain from it as she escorted him up the stairs and into the security zone of the second floor.

Lieutenant-Commander Kelven Solanki was waiting for Ralph Hiltch in his large corner office. A career officer who had left his Polish-ethnic world of Mazowiecki twenty-nine years previously, he was forty-seven: a narrow-faced man with a lean build, several centimetres shorter than Ralph, with thick raven-black hair trimmed to a regular one centimetre. His dark-blue port uniform fitted well, although he'd left the jacket on the back of his desk chair.

Ralph was given a genuinely warm handshake when he

came in, and the rating was dismissed. She saluted smartly and closed the door.

Kelven Solanki's welcoming smile faded considerably as he gestured Ralph to the imitation-leather settee. "Who's going to start?"

He hung his cagoule on the edge of the settee and leaned back. "We're on your home territory, so I'll tell you what I know first."

"OK." Kelven sat on the chair opposite.

"First, Joshua Calvert and the *Lady Macbeth*; stunning though it appears, he is actually genuine as far as we can make out. I've got an inside track: my secretary, Marie, is running a deal for him, so she's keeping a strong tab on him for me. He's bought a thousand tonnes of mayope, got himself an export licence, and he's loading the stuff into his starship as fast as the McBoeing he hired can boost it into orbit. He's made no attempt to get in touch with any known fence, he didn't bring any cargo down in his own spaceplane, legal or illegal, and he'll be gone tomorrow."

Kelven found he was more interested in the independent trader captain than the situation really required. "He's genuinely transporting timber to another star?"

"Yes. To Norfolk, apparently. Which, given their import restrictions, isn't quite as insane as it sounds. They may just have a use for it with their pastoral tech. I haven't decided if he's an idiot or a genius. I'd love to know how he gets on."

"Me too. But he isn't quite the innocent you think he is. The *Lady Macbeth* has an antimatter drive unit. And my last general security file update from Avon carried a report that he was intercepted by a navy voidhawk a couple of months back; Fleet Intelligence was convinced he was trying to smuggle proscribed technology. They actually watched the units being loaded into his cargo bay. Yet when the voidhawk captain searched his ship—nothing. So it doesn't look like he's an idiot."

"Interesting. He's not due to leave until tomorrow, so he might still try something. I'll keep him under close observation. Will you?"

"I have been keeping a quiet eye on Captain Calvert since his arrival, and I'll continue to do so. Now, the Quallheim

Counties situation. I don't like it at all. We've been reviewing the images the chief sheriff's observation satellite has been downloading this morning, and the trouble is spreading into Willow West County. There are several burnt-out buildings in the villages, evidence of fighting, and the fields are being ignored."

"Hell, I didn't know that."

"Well, this time Candace Elford has managed to keep it quiet, at least for now. But the sheriffs and supervisors in the Quallheim Counties and Willow West still insist there's nothing wrong. Those that answer their communication blocks. I think that's the strangest aspect of this situation; I can't see the Ivets pointing a laser at their heads all day every day."

"I find it very hard to believe the Ivets could take over a whole county in the first place, let alone four. Rexrew might be right about an external group being behind it. Were these new Willow West images fuzzed like the last batch from the Quallheim?"

Kelven gave his counterpart a significant look. "Yes, unfortunately they were; and my technical officer can't work out how it was done. She's not the greatest electronic warfare expert in the navy, but she says there isn't even a theory which could account for it. I have to give serious consideration to the fact that Rexrew is right. And there's something else, too."

Ralph broke out of his reverie at the tone.

"I have been *authorized*"—he emphasized the word—"to tell you that Edenist Intelligence agents believe Laton is still alive, and may be on Lalonde, specifically in Schuster County. They say he contacted them to warn them of some kind of xenoc incursion. They left Durringham three days ago, heading upriver to investigate, but not before they made me contact Aethra to update it on the situation. And, Ralph, they looked worried."

"Edenist Intelligence is operative here?" Ralph asked. He'd never had the slightest hint.

"Yes."

"Laton, I think I know the name, some kind of Serpent insurrectionist; but he's not stored in my neural nanonics files.

Probably got him in my processor block back in the embassy."

"I'll save you the trouble. His file's in the computer. It's not nice reading, but be my guest."

Ralph datavised the request into the office computer, and sat in a disturbed silence as the information ran through his brain. His training had covered Edenist Serpents, but in a remote, academic fashion. He was used to dealing with mercenaries, blackhawks, smugglers, and devious politicians, not someone like this. The datavise seemed to be pumping cryogenic liquid down his spinal cord. "And the Edenists think he's on Lalonde?" he asked Kelven, aghast.

"That's right. They were never sure, but he showed an interest in the place decades ago, so they kept a watch. Now it's confirmed, he survived the navy assault and came here. According to the agents he called them because whatever is behind the Quallheim disturbances was breaking through his defences."

"Jesus wept!"

"There is a remote possibility that it was some kind of bluff to attract voidhawks here so he could take them over and get himself and his associates offplanet. But I have to say it's not likely. It looks like there really is some kind of external influence at work in the Quallheim Counties."

"The Edenists wanted me to know?"

"Yes. They thought it was important enough to override minor political constraints—their words. They want the First Admiral and your senior Saldanas warned as well as their Jupiter Consensus. Laton by himself would require a major military action, something which can defeat him would probably mean deployment at Fleet level."

Ralph stared at Kelven Solanki. The navy officer was badly frightened. "Have you told the Governor?"

"No. Rexrew has enough problems. There are over four thousand colonists in the transients' dormitories who have had their farmsteading gear either burnt or looted. He can't ship them upriver, and he hasn't got any replacement gear—nor is he going to get any in the near future. There are three colonist-carrier starships in orbit with their Ivets left in zero-tau; Rexrew can't bring them down because they'll be murdered as soon as they step out of the McBoeings. The starship captains aren't authorized to take them back to Earth. There are still sectors in the east of Durringham where full civil order hasn't been re-established. Frankly, given the state of the city, we're expecting widespread civil disobedience within three weeks, sooner if word about the Quallheim revolts spreading downriver reaches town. And with the way those idiot sheriffs leak confidential information, it will. We're looking at virtual anarchy breaking out. I don't consider the Governor as someone we can turn to with this information. He's between the classic rock and a hard place right now."

"You're right," Ralph agreed unhappily. God, why Lalonde? He'd hated the place when it was a seedy backward colony going nowhere. But right now a return to that state would have been a blessing. "I consider it my priority to inform Kulu what's happened, and what may happen with regards to Laton and these possible xenocs in the Quallheim Counties."

"Good. I have the legal authority to declare a system-wide emergency and commandeer any available starship. Hopefully it won't come to that, but I am sending one of my officers up to a colonist-carrier starship and diverting it to Avon. That's in hand now, the *Eurydice* finished unloading all its colonists yesterday, it only has about fifty Ivets left in zerotau. They'll be transferred over to the *Martijn*, where they can stay until Rexrew works out what he's going to do with them. Barring anything totally unforeseen, *Eurydice* should be leaving within another twelve hours. It'll carry my report to the First Admiral on a diplomatic flek, with another flek for the Edenist Ambassador on Avon. You can include a flek to Kulu's mission at the Confederation Assembly."

"Thank you. Although I haven't got a clue how to compile a report like that. They'll think we're crazy."

Kelven glanced out at the rain bouncing on the dark rooftops. The simplicity of the scene made the events in the distant Quallheim Counties seem surreal. "Maybe we are. But we have to do something."

"The first thing our respective bosses will do is send back for confirmation and more information."

"Yes, I thought about that. We must have that information ready for them."

"Somebody has to go to the Quallheim Counties."

"The Edenists are already on their way, but I'd like to send my own team. The marines are itching for the chance, of course. Do you have anyone capable of performing this kind of scout mission? I really think we need to pool resources."

"I agree with you on that. Hell, I even agree with the Edenists." And he had to smile cynically at that. "A joint venture would produce the best results. I have a couple of people trained to perform a covert penetration and scout mission. In fact, if you let me have access to the communication circuits on your ELINT satellites I can activate some assets I have upriver, see if they can fill us in on what's happening."

"I'll see you get that."

"OK, I'll send my Lieutenant Jenny Harris over to supervise the operation. How were you planning on getting the scout teams upriver?"

Kelven datavised an instruction to the office computer and a wall-mounted screen lit up, showing a map of the Juliffe basin tributary network. The Quallheim Counties showed as a red slash clinging to the southern side of the tributary; Willow West glowed a warning amber to the north-west. The next county along was outlined in black, the name Kristo blinking in white script. "A fast boat up to Kristo County, then horses into the trouble zone. If they left by tomorrow, they ought to arrive around only a day or so after the *Swithland* and its posse, perhaps even a little beforehand."

"Couldn't we airlift them in? I can obtain one of the BK133s, they could be there by tonight."

"And how would they get about? This is a scouting mission, remember. You can't take horses in a VTOL, and nothing else can get through that jungle."

Ralph scowled at the map on the screen. "Bugger, you're right. Hell, this planet is bloody pitiful."

"Convenient, though. One of the few places in the Confederation where a thousand kilometres makes a mockery of our usual transportation systems. We're so used to instantaneous response, it spoils us."

"Yes. Well, if any planet can bring us back to fundamentals, it's Lalonde."

The bundle of mayope trunks on the payload-handling truck had been assembled by the ground crew in one of the spaceport's hangars. A simple enough job, even for this planet's meagre cargo-preparation facilities; the trunks were almost perfectly cylindrical, a metre wide, cut to the same fifteen-metre length. Bright yellow straps held them together; ten load pins had been spaced correctly around the outside. Yet so far, two of the bundles had fallen apart when Ashly used the MSV's waldo arm to manoeuvre them from the spaceplane into the *Lady Macbeth*'s hold. The delay had cost them eight hours, and replacement wood had to be ordered and paid for.

Since then Warlow had inspected every bundle before it was loaded into the McBoeing. He'd sent three back to the hangar to be reassembled after he found loose straps, his enhanced audio senses picking up the ground crew's grumbles when they thought they were out of earshot.

But this bundle seemed satisfactory. The grapple socket plugged into his lower left arm closed around the last loading pin. He braced himself on the truck's base, and tried to shift the pin. The metal below his feet emitted a hesitant creak as his boosted muscles exerted their carefully measured force. The pin remained perfectly steady.

"OK, load it in," he told the waiting ground crew. His grapple socket disengaged, and he jumped down onto the rough tarmac.

The truck driver edged the vehicle back under the waiting McBoeing. Hydraulics began to slide the bundle into the lower fuselage cargo hold. Warlow stood beside the spaceplane's rear wheel bogies, in the shade. His body's thermal-distribution system had more than enough capacity to cope with Lalonde's blue-white sun, but he *felt* cooler here.

A power bike rounded the corner of the hangar and turned towards the spaceplane. Two people were riding on it, Marie Skibbow and a young man wearing a check shirt and khaki shorts. She drew to a halt in front of Warlow, giving the big cosmonik a breezy grin.

Cradles in the spaceplane's hold started to snap shut around the bundle's load pins. The truck's payload-handling mechanism slowly withdrew.

"How's it going?" Marie asked.

"One more flight after this, and we'll be finished," Warlow said. "Ten hours, maximum."

"Great." She swung her leg over the bike's saddle. The young man dismounted a moment later. "Warlow, this is Quinn Dexter."

Quinn smiled amicably. "Warlow, pleasure to meet you. Marie here tells me you're heading for Norfolk."

"That's right." Warlow watched the truck drive off back to the hangar; the bright orange vehicle looked strangely washed out. His neural nanonics reported a small data drop-out from his optical sensors, and he ordered a diagnostics program interrogation.

"This could be fortunate for both of us, then," Quinn Dexter said. "I'd like to buy passage on the *Lady Macbeth*, Marie said you're licensed for passengers."

"We are."

"OK, fine. So how much is a berth?"

"You want to go to Norfolk?" Warlow asked. His optical sensors had come back on line, the diagnostics had been unable to pinpoint the glitch.

"Sure." Quinn's happy smile broadened. "I'm a sales agent for Dobson Engineering. It's a Kulu company. We produce a range of basic farm implements—ploughshares, wheel bearings for carts, that kind of thing. Suitable for low-technology worlds."

"Well, you definitely came to the right place when you came to Lalonde," Warlow said, upping the diaphragm's bass level, his best approximation of irony.

"Yes. But I think I need to wait another fifty years before Lalonde even gets up to low technology. I haven't been able to break into the official monopoly, not even with the embassy's help, so it's time to move on."

"I see. One moment." Warlow used his neural nanonics

to open a channel to the spaceplane's flight computer, and requested a link to the *Lady Macbeth*.

"What is it?" Joshua datavised.

"A customer," Warlow told him.

"Give me a visual," he said when Warlow finished explaining.

Warlow focused his optical sensors on Quinn's face. The smile hadn't faded, if anything it had expanded.

"Must be pretty keen to leave if he's willing to buy passage on *Lady Mac* rather than wait for his berth on a company ship," Joshua said. "Tell him it's forty-five thousand fuseodollars for a zero-tau passage."

There were times when Warlow regretted losing the ability to give a really plaintive sigh. "He'll never pay that," he retorted. If Joshua didn't always try to extort clients they might win more business.

"So?" Joshua shot back. "We can haggle. Besides he might, and we need the money. The expenses I've shelled out on this bloody planet have just about emptied our petty cash account. We'll be breaking into our Norfolk fund if we're not careful."

"My captain is currently charging forty-five thousand fuseodollars for a zero-tau flight to Norfolk," Warlow said out loud.

"Zero-tau?" Quinn sounded puzzled.

"Yes."

He glanced at Marie, who remained impassive.

Warlow waited patiently while the spaceplane's cargo hold doors began to swing shut. His neural nanonics relayed the background chitter of the pilot running through the flight-prep sequence.

"I don't want to travel in zero-tau," Quinn said woodenly.

"Got him. Fifty-five thousand for a real-time cabin," Joshua datavised.

"Then I'm afraid cabin passage will cost you fifty-five thousand," Warlow recited laboriously. "Consumables, food, environmental equipment maintenance, it all adds up."

"Yes, so I see. Very well, fifty-five thousand it is then."
Quinn produced a Jovian Bank disk from his shorts pocket.

"Jesus," Joshua datavised. "This guy has an expense account a Saldana princeling would envy. Grab the money off him now, before he comes to his senses, then send him up on the McBoeing." The channel to *Lady Macbeth* closed.

Warlow took his own Jovian Bank credit disk from a small pouch in his utility belt, and proffered it to Quinn Dexter. "Welcome aboard," he boomed.

16

Oenone reduced and refocused its distortion field, allowing the wormhole terminus to close behind it. It looked round curiously with its many senses. Norfolk was a hundred and sixty thousand kilometres away; and the contrasting light from two different stars fell upon its hull. The upper hull was washed in a rosy glow from Duchess, the system's red-dwarf sun two hundred million kilometres away, darkening and highlighting the blue polyp's elaborate purple web pattern. Duke, the K2 primary, shone a strong yellowish light across the environmentally stabilized pods clasped in *Oenone*'s cargo bay from a hundred and seventy-three million kilometres in the opposite direction.

Norfolk was almost in direct conjunction between the binary pair. It was a planet that was forty per cent land, made up of large islands a hundred to a hundred and fifty thousand square kilometres each, and uncountable smaller archipelagos. *Oenone* hung over the only sliver of darkness which was left on the surface; for the approaching conjunction had banished night to a small crescent extending from pole to pole, measuring about a thousand kilometres wide at the equator, almost as if a slice had been taken out of the planet. Convoluted seas and winding straits sparkled blue and crimson in their respective hemispheres, and cloud swirls were divided into white and scarlet. Under Duke's glare the land was the usual blend of browns and greens, cool and welcoming, whereas the land illuminated by Duchess had turned a dark vermilion, creased with black folds, a harshly inhospitable domain in appearance.

Syrinx requested and received permission to enter a parking orbit from the civil spaceflight authority. *Oenone* swooped towards the planet in high spirits, chattering happily to the huge flock of voidhawks ahead of it. Three hundred and seventy-five kilometres above the equator a diamante ring was shimmering delicately against the interstellar blackness as twenty-five thousand starships reflected fragments of light from the twin suns off their mirror-bright thermal panels and communication dishes.

Norfolk's star system wasn't an obvious choice for a terracompatible world. When the Govcentral scoutship *Duke of Rutland* emerged into the system in 2207 a preliminary sensor sweep revealed six planets, all of them solid. Two of them were in orbit twenty-eight million kilometres above Duchess; Westmorland and Brenock, forming their own binary as they tumbled round each other at a distance of half a million kilometres. The other four—Derby, Lincoln, Norfolk, and Kent—orbited Duke. It was soon obvious that only Norfolk with its two moons, Argyll and Fife, could support life.

The already cluttered interplanetary space played host to a pair of major asteroid belts, and five minor belts, as well as innumerable rocks which traded stars as their gravity fields duelled for adherents. There was also a considerable quantity of comets and small pebble-sized debris loose in the system. The scoutship's cosmologist was heard to say that it was almost as though it hadn't quite finished condensing out of the whirling protostar disk.

One final point against colonization was the lack of a gas giant for the Edenists to mine for He3. Without a cheap local source of fuel for fusion, industry and spaceflight would be prohibitively expensive.

With this gloomy prognosis in mind, the *Duke of Rutland* went into orbit around Norfolk to conduct its obligatory resources and environment survey. It was bound to be an odd planet, with its seasons governed by conjunction between the Duke and Duchess rather than its sidereal period: midwinter, which came at a distance of a hundred and seventy-three million kilometres from the coolish primary, was Siberian, while midsummer, at equipoise between two stars, was a time when night vanished completely, bringing a Mediterranean balm. There was no distinction between the usual geographical tropical and temperate zones found on ordinary worlds (although there were small polar ice-caps); instead the seasons were experienced uniformly across the whole planet. Naturally, the aboriginal life followed this cycle, although there were no wild variants from standard evolutionary patterns. Norfolk turned out to have a lower than usual variety of mammals, marine species, and insects. Hibernation was common, in avian species it replaced migration, and they all bred to give birth in the spring. Nothing unusual there. But the plants would only flower and ripen when they were bathed in both yellow and pink light throughout the twenty-three hour, forty-three minute day. That wasn't a condition which could be duplicated easily anywhere, even on Edenist habitats. It made the plants unique. And uniqueness was always valuable.

The discovery was sufficient for Govcentral's English State to fund a follow-up ecological assessment mission. After three months classifying aboriginal plants for edibility and taste, midsummer came to Norfolk, and the team hit paydirt.

Oenone slipped into orbit three hundred and seventy-five kilometres above the eccentrically coloured planet, and contracted its distortion field until it was only generating a gravity field for the crew toroid and gathering in cosmic energy. The nearby starships were mostly Adamist cargo vessels, big spheres performing slow balletic thermal rolls; with their dump panels extended they looked bizarrely like cumbersome windmills. Directly ahead of *Oenone* was a large cargo clipper with the violet and green loops of the Vasilkovsky line prominent on its hull.

The voidhawk was still conversing eagerly with its fellows when Syrinx, Ruben, Oxley, and Tula took the ionfield flyer down to Kesteven, one of the larger islands seven hundred kilometres south of the equator. Its capital was Boston, a trade centre of some hundred and twenty thousand souls, nestling in the intersection of two gentle valleys. The area was heavily forested, and the inhabitants had only thinned the trees out to make room for their houses, almost camouflaging the city from the air. Syrinx could see some parks, and several grey church spires rising up above the trees. The city's aerodrome was a broad greensward set aside a mile and a half (Norfolk refused to use metric measurements) to the north of its winding leafy boulevards.

Oxley brought the craft in from the north-west, careful not to overfly the city itself. Aircraft were banned on Norfolk, except for a small ambulance and flying doctor service, and ninety per cent of its interstellar trade was conducted at midsummer, which was the only time the planet ever really saw spaceplanes. Consequently, Norfolk's population were a little sensitive to twenty-five-tonne objects shooting through the sky over their rooftops.

There were over three hundred spaceplanes and ion-field flyers already sitting on the grassy aerodrome when they arrived. Oxley settled three-quarters of a mile from the small cluster of buildings that housed the control tower and aerodrome administration.

The airlock stairs unfolded in front of Syrinx revealing the distant verdant wall of trees, and she saw someone pedalling a bicycle along the long rank of spaceplanes, with a dog running alongside. She breathed in, tasting dry, slightly dusty air with a distinct coppery tang of pollen.

The city's larger than I remember, Ruben said, with a mild sense of perplexity jumbled in with his thoughts.

What I saw looked very orderly, quaint almost. I love the way they've incorporated the forest rather than obliterated it.

He raised his eyebrows in dismay. **Quaint, she says. Well, don't tell the natives that.** He cleared his throat. "And don't use affinity too much while you're around them, they consider it very impolite."

Syrinx eyed the approaching cyclist. It was a boy no more than fourteen years old, with a satchel slung over his shoulder. **I'll remember.**

"They are fairly strict Christians, after all. And our facial expressions give us away."

"I suppose they do. Does the religious factor affect our chances of getting a cargo?"

"Definitely not, they're English-ethnic, far too polite to be prejudiced, at least in public." **And while we're on the subject,** he broadcast to his three shipmates, **no passes, please. They like to maintain the illusion they have high**

moral standards. Let them make the running, they invariably do.

"Who, me?" Syrinx asked in mock horror.

Andrew Unwin rode his bicycle up to the group of people standing beside the gleaming purple flyer and braked to a halt, rear wheel squeaking loudly. He had gingerish hair and a sunny face swamped by freckles. His shirt was simple white cotton, with buttons down the front and the arms rolled up to his elbows; his green shorts were held up by a thick black leather belt with an ornate brass buckle. There wasn't a modern fabric seal anywhere in sight. He glanced at Syrinx's smart blue ship-tunic with its single silver epaulette star, and stiffened slightly. "Captain, ma'am?"

"That's me." She smiled.

Andrew Unwin couldn't quite keep his formal attitude going, and the corners of his mouth twitched up towards a grin. "Aerodrome Manager's compliments, Captain, ma'am. He apologizes for not meeting you in person, but we're chocker busy right now."

"Yes, I can see that. It's very kind of him to send you."

"Oh, Dad didn't send me. I'm the Acting Passport Officer," he said proudly, and drew himself up. "Have you got yours, please? I've got my processor block." He dived into his satchel, which excited the dog, who started barking and jumping about. "Stop it, Mel!" he shouted.

Syrinx found she rather liked the idea of a boy helping out like this, walking up to utter strangers with curiosity and awe, obviously never thinking they might be dangerous. It spoke of an easy-going world which had few cares, and trust was prevalent. Perhaps the Adamists could get things right occasionally.

They handed their passport fleks over one at a time for Andrew to slot into his processor block. The unit looked terribly obsolete to Syrinx, fifty years out of date at least.

"Is Drayton's Import business in Penn Street still going strong?" Ruben asked Andrew Unwin, overdoing his wide I-want-to-be-friends smile.

Andrew gave him a blank stare, then his pixie face was alive with mirth. "Yes, it's still there. Why, have you been to Norfolk before?"

"Yes, it was a few years ago now, though," Ruben said.

"All right!" Andrew handed Syrinx her passport flek as his dog sniffed round her feet. "Thank you, Captain, ma'am. Welcome to Norfolk. I hope you find a cargo."

"That's very kind of you." Syrinx sent a silent affinity command to the dog to desist, only to feel foolish when it ignored her.

Andrew Unwin was looking up expectantly.

"For your trouble," Ruben murmured, and his hand passed over Andrew's.

"Thank you, sir!" There was a silver flash as he pocketed the coin.

"Where can we get a ride into town?" Ruben asked.

"Over by the tower, there's lots of taxi cabs. Don't take one that asks for more than five guineas. You can get your money changed in the Admin block after you get through Customs, as well." A small delta spaceplane flew low overhead, compressors whistling as the nozzles started to rotate to the vertical, already deploying its undercarriage. Andrew turned to watch it. "I think there's still some rooms at the Wheatsheaf if you're looking for lodgings." He hopped back on his bicycle and pedalled off towards the spaceplane that was landing, the dog chasing after him.

Syrinx watched him go in amusement. Passport control was obviously a serious business on Norfolk.

"But how do we get to the tower?" Tula asked querulously. Her hand was shielding her eyes from the Duke's golden radiance.

"One guess," Ruben said happily.

"We walk," Syrinx said.

"That's my girl."

Oxley went back into the spaceplane to collect the coolbox loaded with samples of food from Atlantis, and then rummaged through the lockers for their personal shoulderbags. He sent a coded order to the flyer's bitek processor as he came out, and the stairs folded away, the airlock closing silently. Tula picked up the coolbox, and they started off towards the white control tower that was wobbling in the heat shimmer.

"What did he mean about overpaying the taxis?" Syrinx asked Ruben. "Surely they have a standard tariff metre?"

Ruben started chuckling, He slipped Syrinx's arm through his. "When you say taxi, I suppose you mean one of those neat little cars Adamists always use on developed planets, with magnetic suspension, and maybe air-conditioning?"

Syrinx nearly said: "Well of course." But the gleam in his eyes cautioned her. "No . . . What do they use here?"

He just pulled her closer and laughed.

The bridge of heaven had returned to the skies. Louise Kavanagh wandered across Cricklade Manor's paddock with her sister Genevieve, the two of them craning their necks to look up at it. They had come out early every Duke-day morning for the past week to see how it had grown during Duchess-night.

The western horizon was suffused with a huge deep-red corona thrown out by the Duchess as she sank below the wolds, but in the northern quadrant orbiting starships sparkled and shone. Glint-specks of vivid ruby light that raced through the sky, strung together so tightly they formed a near-solid band, like a rainbow of red sequins. The western horizon, where the Duke was rising, had a similar arc, one of pure gold. Directly to the north, the band hung low over the rolling dales of Stoke County, lacking the brightness of the two horizon arcs where the reflection angle was most favourable, but still visible by Duke-day.

"I wish they'd stay for ever," Genevieve said forlornly. "Summer is a truly lovely time." She was twelve (Earth) years old, a tall, spindly girl with an oval face and inquisitive brown eyes; she had inherited her mother's dark hair, which hung halfway down her back in the appropriate style for a member of the land-owning class. Her dress was a pale blue with tiny white dots and a broad lacework collar, complemented with long white socks, and polished navy-blue leather sandals.

"Without winter, summer would never come," Louise said. "Everything would be the same all year round, and we'd have nothing to look forward to. There are lots of worlds like that out there." They looked up together at the ribbon of starships.

Louise was the elder of the two sisters, sixteen years old, the heir to the Cricklade estate which was their home, and an easy fifteen inches taller than Genevieve, with hair a shade lighter and long enough to reach her hips when it was unbound. They shared the same facial features, with small noses and narrow eyes, although Louise's cheeks were now more pronounced as her puppy fat burned away. Her skin boasted a clear complexion though to her dismay her cheeks remained obstinately rosy—just like a fieldworker.

This morning she was wearing a plain canary-yellow summer dress; and, wonder of all, this was the year Mother had *finally* allowed her to have a square-cut neck on some of her clothes, although her skirt hems had to remain well below her knees. The audacious necks allowed her to show how she was blossoming into womanhood. This summer there wasn't a young male in Stoke County who didn't look twice as she walked past.

But Louise was quite used to being the centre of attention. She had been since the day she was born. The Kavanaghs were Kesteven's premier family; one of the clanlike network of large rich land-owner families who when acting in concert exerted more influence than any of the regional island councils, simply because of their wealth. Louise and Genevieve were members of an army of relatives who ran Kesteven virtually as a private fiefdom. And the Kavanaghs also had strong blood ties with the royal Mountbattens, a family descended from the original British Windsor monarchy, whose prince undertook the role of planetary constitutional guardian. Norfolk might have been English-ethnic, but it owed its social structure to an idealized version of sixteenth-century Britain rather than the federal republic state of Govcentral which had founded the original colony four centuries ago.

Louise's uncle Roland, the senior of her grandfather's six children, owned nearly ten per cent of the island's arable land. Cricklade Manor's estate itself sprawled over a hundred and fifty thousand acres, incorporating forests and farmland and parkland, even whole villages, providing employment to thousands of labourers who toiled in its fields and woods and rosegroves, as well as tending to its herds and flocks. Another three hundred families farmed tithed crofts within its capacious boundaries. Craftsmen right across Stoke County were dependent on the industry it generated for their livelihood. And, of course, the estate owned a majority share in the county roseyard.

Louise was the most eligible heiress on Kesteven island. And she adored the position, people showed her nothing but respect, and willingly extended favours without expecting any return other than her patronage.

Cricklade Manor itself was a resplendent three-storey grey-stone building with a hundred-yard frontage. Its long stone-mullioned windows gazed out across a vast expanse of lawns and spinneys and walled orchards. An avenue of terrestrial cedars had been set out to mark out the perimeter of the grounds, geneered to endure Norfolk's long year and peculiar dual bombardment of photons. They had been planted three hundred years ago, and were now several hundred feet in height. Louise adored the stately ancient trees; their graceful layered boughs possessed a mystique which the smaller aboriginal pine-analogues could never hope to match. They were a part of her heritage that was for ever lost among the stars, alluding to a romantic past.

The paddock the sisters were walking through lay beyond the cedars on the western side of the manor, taking up most of a gentle slope that led down to a stream which fed the trout lake. Jumps for their horses were scattered around, unused for weeks in the excitement of the approaching rose crop. Midsummer was always a fraught time for Norfolk, and Cricklade seemed to be at the centre of a small cyclone of activity as the estate geared itself up for the roses when they ripened.

When they tired of the starships' grandeur, Louise and Genevieve carried on down to the water. Several horses with rust-red coats were wandering round the paddock, nuzzling amongst the tufty grass. Norfolk's grass-analogue was reasonably similar to Earth's, the blades were all tubular, and throughout the summer conjunction they produced minute white flowers at their tips. Starcrowns, Louise had called them when she was much younger.

"Father says he's thinking of inviting William Elphinstone to act as an assistant estate manager to Mr Butterworth," Genevieve said slyly as they approached the mouldering wooden bar fence at the foot of the paddock.

"That was clever of Father," Louise replied, straight faced.

"How so?"

"William will need to learn the practicalities of estate management if he is to take over Glassmoor Hall, and he could have nobody finer than Mr Butterworth to tutor him. That puts the Elphinstones under obligation to Father, and they have powerful connections among Kesteven's farm merchants."

"And William will be here for two midsummers, that's the usual period of tutelage."

"Indeed he will."

"And you'll be here as well."

"Genevieve Kavanagh, silence that evil tongue this instant."

Genevieve danced across the grass. "He's handsome, he's handsome!" she laughed. "I've seen the way he looks at you, especially in those dresses you wear for the dances." Her hands traced imaginary breasts over her chest.

Louise giggled. "Devil child, you have a faulty brain. I'm not interested in William."

"You're not?"

"No. Oh, I like him, and I hope we can be friends. But that's all. In any case, he's five years older than me."

"I think he's gorgeous."

"Then you can have him."

Genevieve's face fell. "I'll not be offered anyone so grand. You're the heiress, after all. Mother will make me marry some troll from a minor family, I'm sure of it."

"Mother won't *make* us marry anyone. Honest to goodness, Genny, she won't."

"Really truly?"

"Really truly," Louise said, even though she couldn't quite bring herself to believe it. Truth to be told, there weren't that many eligible suitors for her on Kesteven. Hers was an invidious position: a husband should hold equal status, but someone of equal wealth would have his own estate and she would be expected to live there. Yet Cricklade was her life, it was beautiful even in midwinter's long barren months when yards of snow covered the ground, the pine trees on the surrounding wolds were denuded, and the birds buried themselves below the frostline. She couldn't bear the thought of leaving it. So who could she marry? It was probably something her parents had discussed; her uncles and aunts too, most likely.

She didn't like to think about what the outcome would be. At the very least she hoped they would give her a list rather than an ultimatum.

One of the butterflies caught her eye, a geneered red admiral sunning itself on one of the grass blades. It was freer than she was, she realized miserably.

"Will you marry for love, then?" Genevieve asked, all dewy eyed.

"Yes, I'll marry for love."

"That's super. I wish I were as bold."

Louise put her hands on the top rail of the fence, looking across the gurgling stream. Forget-me-nots had run wild on the banks, their blue flowers attracting hordes of butterflies. Some time-distant master of Cricklade had released hundreds of species across the grounds. Every year they flourished, invading the orchards and gardens with their fluttering harlequin colours. "I'm not bold, I'm a dithery dreamer. Do you know what I dream?"

"No." Genevieve shook her head, her face rapt.

"I dream that Father lets me travel before I have to take on any of my family responsibilities."

"To Norwich?"

"No, not the capital, that's just like Boston only bigger, and I'll be going there anyway for finishing school. I want to travel to other worlds and see how their people live."

"Gosh! Travel on a starship, that's stupendously wonderful. Can I come too? Please!"

"If I go, then I suppose Father will have to let you go when you reach your age. Fair's fair."

"He'll never let me go. I'm not even allowed to go to the dances."

"But you sneak past Nanny and watch them anyway."

"Yes!"

"Well, then."

"He won't let me go."

Louise grinned down at her sister's petulant tone. "It is only a dream."

"You always make your dreams come real. You're so clever, Louise."

"I don't want to change this world with new ideas," she said, half to herself. "I just want to be allowed out, just once. Everything here is so duty-bound, so regimented. Some days I feel as though I've already lived my life."

"William could get you away from here. He could ask for a star voyage as a honeymoon; Father could never refuse that."

"Oh! You impudent baby ogress!" She aimed a lazy swipe at her sister's head, but Genevieve had already skipped out of range.

"Honeymoon, honeymoon," Genevieve chanted so loudly that even the nearby horses looked up. "Louise is going on honeymoon!" She picked up her skirts and ran, long slender legs flying over the flower-laden grass.

Louise gave chase, the two of them giggling and squealing in delight as they gallivanted about, scattering the butterflies before them.

Lady Macbeth emerged from her final jump insystem, and Joshua allowed himself a breath of silent relief that they were still intact. The trip from Lalonde had been an utter *bitch.*

For a start Joshua found he neither liked nor trusted Quinn Dexter. His intuition told him there was something desperately wrong about him. Wrong in a way he couldn't define, but Dexter seemed to drain life from a cabin when he entered. And his behaviour was weird, too; he had no instinct, no natural rhythm for events or conversation, as though he was working on a two-second time-delay to reality.

In fact, if Joshua had met him in the flesh back down on Lalonde's spaceport he probably wouldn't have accepted him as a passenger no matter how much money was stashed in his credit disk. Too late now. Although, thankfully, Dexter had spent most of his time alone in his cabin down in capsule C, venturing out only for meals and the bathroom.

That was one of his more rational quirks. After he'd come on board, he had given the compact bulkheads a quick suspicious look, and said: "I'd forgotten how much mechanization there is on a starship."

Forgotten? Joshua couldn't work that one out at all. How could you forget the way a starship looked?

Yet the oddest thing of all was how inept Dexter was at free-fall manoeuvring. Had he been asked, Joshua would have said that the man had never been in space before. Which was ridiculous, because he was a travelling sales manager. One who didn't have neural nanonics. And one who wore a frightened expression the whole time. There had even been occasions when Joshua had caught him flinching from some sudden metallic sound rattling out of the capsule systems, or the creak of the stress structure as they were under acceleration.

Of course, given *Lady Mac*'s performance during the voyage, that part of Dexter's behaviour was almost understandable. Joshua had experienced enough nasty moments on the flight himself. It seemed like there wasn't a system on board that hadn't suffered from some kind of glitch since they boosted out of Lalonde's orbit. What should have been a simple four-day trip had stretched out to nearly a week as the crew tackled power surges, data drop-outs, actuator failures, and dozens of smaller niggling malfunctions. Joshua hated to think what was going to happen when he handed over the maintenance log to the Confederation Astronautics Board's inspectors, they'd probably insist on a complete overhaul. At least the jump nodes had functioned, though he'd even begun to have his doubts about them.

He datavised the flight computer to unfold the thermo-dump panels and extend the sensor booms. Fault alerts jangled in his mind; one of the thermo-dump panels refused to open past halfway, and three booms were jammed in their recesses.

"Jesus!" he snarled.

There were mutters from the rest of the crew strapped into their bridge couches on either side of him.

"I thought you fixed that fucking panel," Joshua shouted at Warlow.

"I did!" the answer thumped back. "If you think you can do any better, put on a suit and get out there yourself."

Joshua ran a hand over his brow. "See what you can do," he said sullenly. Warlow grunted something unintelligible, and ordered the couch's straps to release him. He pushed himself towards the open hatchway. Ashly Hanson freed himself, too, and went after the cosmonik to help.

Sensor data was coming in from the booms which were functional. The flight computer started tracking nearby stars to produce an accurate astrogration fix. Norfolk with its divergent illumination looked unusually small for a terracompatible planet. Joshua didn't have time to puzzle that, the sensors reported laser radar pulses were bouncing off the hull, and a voidhawk distortion field had locked on.

"Jesus, now what?" Joshua asked even as the astrogration fix slipped into his mind. *Lady Mac* had translated two hundred and ninety thousand kilometres above Norfolk, way outside the planet's designated emergence zone. He groaned out loud and hurriedly datavised the communication dish to transmit their identification code. The Confederation Navy ships patrolling Norfolk would start using *Lady Mac* for target practice soon.

Norfolk was almost unique among the Confederation's terracompatible planets in that it didn't have a strategic-defence network. There was no high-technology industry, no asteroid settlements in orbit, and consequently there was nothing worth stealing. Protection from mercenaries and pirate ships wasn't needed; except for the two weeks every season when the starships came to collect their cargoes of Norfolk Tears.

As the planet moved towards midsummer a squadron from the Confederation Navy's 6th Fleet was assigned to protection duties, paid for by the planetary government. It was a popular duty with the crews; after the cargo starships departed they were allowed shore leave, where they were entertained in grand style, and all the crews were presented with a special half-sized bottle of Norfolk Tears by the grateful government.

The *Lady Macbeth*'s main communication dish servos spun round once, then packed up. Power-loss signals appeared across the schematic the flight computer was datavising into Joshua's brain. "I don't fucking believe it. Sarha, get that bastard dish sorted out!" Out of the corner of his eye he saw her activate the console by her couch. He routed the *Lady Mac*'s identification code through her omnidirectional antenna.

An inter-ship radio channel came alive, and the communication console routed the datavise into Joshua's neural nanonics. "Starship *Lady Macbeth*, this is Confederation Navy ship *Pestravka*. You have emerged outside this planet's designated starship emergence zones, are you in trouble?"

"Thank you, *Pestravka*," Joshua datavised in reply. "We've been having some system malfunctions, my apologies for causing any panic."

"What is the nature of your malfunction?"

"Sensor error."

"That's simple enough to sort out; you should know better than to jump insystem with inaccurate guidance information."

"Up yours," Melvin Ducharme grumbled from his couch.

"The error percentage has only just become apparent," Joshua said. "We're updating now."

"What's wrong with your main communications dish?"

"Overloaded servo, it's scheduled for replacement."

"Well, activate your back-up."

Sarha let out an indignant snort. "I'll point one of the masers at him if he likes. They'll receive that blast loud and bloody clear."

"Complying now, *Pestravka*." Joshua glared at Sarha.

He launched a quiet prayer as the ribbed silver pencil of the second dish slid out of *Lady Macbeth*'s dark silicon hull, and opened like a flower. It tracked round to point at the *Pestravka*.

"I'm datavising a copy of this incident to the Confederation Astronautics Board office on Norfolk," the *Pestravka*'s officer continued. "And I'll add a strong recommendation that they inspect your spaceworthiness certificate."

"Thank you so much, *Pestravka*. Are we now cleared to contact civil flight control for an approach vector? I'd hate to be shot at for not asking your permission first."

"Don't push your luck, Calvert. I can easily take a fortnight searching your cargo holds."

"Looks like your reputation's preceding you, Joshua," Dahybi Yadev said after the *Pestravka* cut the link.

"Let's hope it hasn't reached the planet's surface yet," Sarha said.

Joshua aligned the secondary dish on the civil flight control's communication satellite, and received permission to enter a parking orbit. *Lady Mac*'s three fusion tubes came alive, sending out long rivers of hazy plasma, and the starship accelerated in towards the gaudy planet at a tenth of a gee.

Chinks of light were glinting down into Quinn Dexter's vacant world, accompanied by faint scratchy sounds. It was like intermittent squalls of luminous rain falling through fissures from an external universe. Some beams of light flickered in the far distance, others splashed across him. When they did, he saw the images they carried.

A boat. One of the grotty traders on the Quallheim, little more than a bodged-together raft. Speeding downriver.

A town of wooden buildings. Durringham in the rain.

A girl.

He knew her. Marie Skibbow, naked, tied to a bed with rope.

His heartbeat thudded in the silence.

"Yes," said the voice he knew from before, from the clearing in the jungle, the voice which came out of Night. "I thought you'd like this."

Marie was tugging frantically at her bonds, her figure every bit as lush as his imagination had once conceived it.

"What would you do with her, Quinn?"

What would he do? What *couldn't* he do with such an ex-quisite body. How oh how she would suffer beneath him.

"You are bloody repugnant, Quinn. But so terribly use-ful."

Energy twisted eagerly inside his body, and a phantasm come forth to overlay reality. Quinn's interpretation of the physical form which God's Brother might assume should He ever choose to manifest Himself in the flesh. And what flesh. Capable of the most wondrous assaults, amplifying every degradation the sect had ever taught him.

The flux of sorcerous power reached a triumphal peak, opening a rift into the terrible empty beyond, and so another emerged to take possession as Marie pleaded and wept.

"Back you go, Quinn."

And the images shrank back to the dry wispy beams of flickering light. "You're not the Light Brother!" Quinn shouted into the nothingness. Fury at the acknowledgement of betrayal heightened his perception, the light became brighter, sound louder.

"Of course not, Quinn. I'm worse than that, worse than any mythical devil. All of us are."

Laughter echoed through the prison universe, tormenting him.

Time was so different in here . . .

A spaceplane.

A starship.

Uncertainty. Quinn felt it run through him like a hormonal surge. The electrical machinery upon which he was now de-pendent recoiled from his estranged body, which made his dependence still deeper as the delicate apparatuses broke down one by one. Uncertainty gave way to fear. His body trembled as it tried desperately to quieten the currents of ex-otic energy which infiltrated every cell.

It wasn't omnipotent, Quinn realized, this thing which controlled his body, it had limits. He let the dribs and drabs of light soak into what was left of his mind, concentrating on what he saw, the words he heard. Watching, waiting. Trying to understand.

* * *

Syrinx thought Boston was the most delightful city she had
seen in fourteen years of travelling about the Confederation, and that included the sheltered enclaves of houses in
the Saturn-orbiting habitats of her birth. Every house was
built from stone, with thick walls to keep the heat out during the long summer, then keep it in for the equally long
winter. Most of them were two storeys high, with some of
the larger ones having three; they had small railed gardens
at the front, and rows of stables along the back. Terrestrial
honeysuckle and ivy were popular creepers for covering the
stonework, while hanging baskets provided cheerful dabs of
colour to most porches. Roofs were always steep to withstand the heavy snow, and grey slate tiles alternated with jet-
black solar panels in pleasing geometric patterns. Wood was
burnt to provide warmth and sometimes for cooking, which
produced a forest of chimneys thrusting out of the gable
ends, topped by red clay pots with elaborate crowns. Every
building, be it private, civic, or commercial, was individual,
possessing the kind of character impossible on worlds where
mass-production facilities were commonplace. Wide streets
were all cobbled, with tall cast-iron street lights spaced
along them. It was only after a while she realized that as
there were no mechanoids or servitors each of the little granite cubes must have been laid by human hand—the time and
effort that must have entailed! There were trees lining each
pavement, mainly Norfolk's pine-analogues, with some geneered terrestrial evergreens for variety. Traffic was comprised entirely of bicycles, trike scooters (very few, and
mostly with adolescent riders), horses, and horse-drawn
cabs and carts. She had seen power vans, but only on the
roads around the outskirts, and those were farm vehicles.

After they had cleared Customs (altogether more rigorous
than Passport Control) they'd found the horse-drawn taxi
coaches waiting by the aerodrome's tower. Syrinx had
grinned, and Tula had let out an exasperated groan. But the
one they used was well sprung, proving a reasonably smooth
trip into town. Following Andrew Unwin's advice, they had
rented some rooms at the Wheatsheaf, a coaching house on
the side of one of the rivers which the town was built
around.

Once they had unpacked and eaten a light lunch in the courtyard, Syrinx and Ruben had taken another coach to Penn Street, the precious coolbox on the floor by their feet.

Ruben watched the traffic and pedestrians parading past with a contented feeling. Starship crews strolling about were easy to spot: their clothes of synthetic fabric were curiously bland in comparison to the locals' attire. Bostonians in summer favoured bright colours and raffish styles; this year multicoloured waistcoats were in vogue among the young men, while the girls wore crinkled cheesecloth skirts with bold circular patterns (hems always below their knees, he noted sadly). It was like stepping back into pre-spaceflight history, though he suspected no historical period on Earth was ever as clean as this.

"Penn Street, guv'nor," the driver cried as the horse turned into a road parallel to the River Gwash. It was the commercial sector of the city, with wharves lining the river, and a lengthy rank of prodigious warehouses standing behind them. Here for the first time they encountered powered lorries. A railway marshalling yard was visible at the other end of the dusty road.

Ruben looked down the long row of warehouses and busy yards and offices, only too well aware of Syrinx's gaze hot on his neck. Mordant thoughts started pressing against his mind. Drayton's Import wasn't *in* Penn Street, it was Penn Street. The name was on signs across every building.

"Where to now, guv'nor?" the driver asked.

"Head Office," Ruben replied. The last time he'd been here, Drayton's Import had consisted of a single office in a rented warehouse.

Head Office turned out to be a building in the middle of the street, on the waterfront side, sandwiched between two warehouses. Its arched windows were all iron rimmed, and a large, brightly polished brass plaque was set in the wall next to the double doors. The cab pulled to a halt in front of its curving stone stairs.

"Looks like old Dominic Kavanagh is doing all right for himself," Ruben said as they climbed out. He handed the driver a guinea, with a sixpenny piece for a tip.

Syrinx's stare could have cut diamond.

"Old Dominic, one of the best. Boy, did we have some times together, he knows every pub in town." Ruben wondered who his bravado was intended to reassure.

"Exactly how long ago was this?" Syrinx asked as they walked into reception.

"About fifteen or twenty years," Ruben offered. He was sure that was it, although he had a horrible feeling that Dominic had been the same age as himself. That's the trouble with crewing a voidhawk, he thought, every day the same, and all of them squashed together. How am I supposed to know the exact date?

The reception hall had a black and white marble floor, and a wide staircase leading up the rear wall. A young woman sat behind a desk ten yards inside the door, a uniformed concierge standing beside her.

"I'd like to see Dominic Kavanagh," Ruben told her blithely. "Just tell him Ruben's back in town."

"I'm sorry, sir," she said. "I don't think we have a Kavanagh of that name working here."

"But he owns Drayton's Import," Ruben said forlornly.

"Kenneth Kavanagh owns this establishment, sir."

"Oh."

"Can we see him?" Syrinx asked. "I have flown all the way from Earth."

The woman took in Syrinx's blue ship-tunic with its silver star. "Your business, Captain?"

"As everyone else, I'm looking for a cargo."

"I'll ask if Mr Kenneth is in." The woman picked up a pearl handset.

Eight minutes later they were being ushered into Kenneth Kavanagh's office on the top floor. Half of one wall was an arched window giving a view out over the river. Broad barges were gliding over the smooth black water, as sedate as swans.

Kenneth Kavanagh was in his late thirties, a broad-shouldered man wearing a neat charcoal-grey suit, white shirt, and a red silk tie. His raven-black hair was glossed straight back from his forehead.

Syrinx almost paid him no attention at all. There was another man in the room, in his mid-twenties, with a flat, square-jawed face, and a mop of pale copper hair combed into a rough parting. He had the kind of build Syrinx associated with sportsmen, or (more likely on this world) outdoor labourers. His suit was made from some shiny grey-green material. The jacket's left arm was flat, pinned neatly to his side. Syrinx had never seen anyone with a limb missing before.

You're staring, Ruben warned her as he shook hands with Kenneth Kavanagh.

Syrinx felt the blood warm her ears. **But what's wrong with him?**

Nothing. They don't allow clone vats on this planet.

That's absurd. It forces him to go through life crippled, I wouldn't wish that on anyone.

Medical technology is where the big arguments rage about what they should and shouldn't permit. And wholesale cloning is pretty advanced.

Syrinx recovered and extended her hand to Kenneth Kavanagh. He said hello, then introduced the other man as: "My cousin Gideon."

They shook hands, Syrinx trying to avoid eye contact. The young man had such a defeated air it threatened to drag her down into whatever private misery he was in.

"Gideon is my aide," Kenneth said. "He's learning the business from the bottom upwards."

"It seems the best thing," Gideon Kavanagh said in a quiet voice. "I can hardly manage the family estate now. That requires a great deal of physical involvement."

"What happened?" Ruben asked.

"I fell from my horse. Bad luck, really. Falling is part of horse riding. This time I landed awkwardly, took a fence railing through my shoulder."

Syrinx gave him an ineffectual grimace of sympathy, unsure what to say. *Oenone* was in her mind, its presence alone immensely supportive.

Kenneth Kavanagh indicated the chairs in front of his pale wooden desk. "It's certainly a pleasure to have you here, Captain."

"I think you've said that to a few captains this week," she told him wryly as she sat down.

"Yes, a few," Kenneth Kavanagh admitted. "But a first-time captain is always welcome here. Some of my fellow exporters take a blasé approach about our planet's product, and say there will always be a demand. I think a little warmth in the relationship never comes amiss, especially as it is just the one product upon which our entire economy is so dependent. I'd hate to see anyone discouraged from returning."

"Am I going to have cause to be discouraged?"

He spread his hands. "We can always find the odd case or two. What exactly is your starship's capacity?"

"*Oenone* can manage seven hundred tonnes."

"Then I'm afraid that a little bit of disappointment is going to be inevitable."

"Old Dominic always kept some cases back for a decent trade," Ruben said. "And we certainly have a trade in mind."

"You knew Dominic Kavanagh?" Kenneth asked with a note of interest.

"I certainly did. Your father?"

"My late grandfather."

Ruben's shoulders sank back into his seat. "Hoh, boy, he was such a lovely old rogue."

"Alas, his wisdom is sorely missed by all of us."

"Did he go from natural causes?"

"Yes. Twenty-five years ago."

"Twenty-five . . ." Ruben appeared to lose himself in reverie.

I'm sorry, Syrinx told him.

Twenty-five years. That means I must have been here at least thirty-five years ago, probably more. Bugger, but there's no fool like an old fool.

"You mentioned a trade," Kenneth said.

Syrinx patted the coolbox on the floor by her chair. "The best Atlantis has to offer."

"Ah, a wise choice. I can always sell Atlantean delicacies; my own family alone will eat half of them. Do you have an inventory?"

She handed over a sheaf of hard copy. There was no desktop processor block, she noticed, although there was a keyboard and a small holoscreen.

Kenneth read down the list, his eyebrows raised in appreciation. "Excellent, I see you have brought some orangesole, that's one of my personal favourites."

"You're in luck, there are five fillets in this coolbox. You can see if they're up to standard."

"I'm sure they are."

"None the less, I'd like you to accept the contents as my gift for your hospitality."

"That's really most kind, Syrinx." He started touch-typing on the keyboard, looking directly at the holoscreen. She was sure her fingers couldn't move at such a speed.

"Happily, my family has interests in several roseyards on Kesteven," Kenneth said. "As you know, we can't officially sell any Norfolk Tears until midsummer when the new crop is in; however, there is an informal allocation system operating amongst ourselves which I can make use of. And I see my cousin Abel has several cases unclaimed, he owns the Eaglethorpe estate in the south of Kesteven. They produce a very reasonable bouquet in that district. Regrettably, I can't offer you a full hold, but I think possibly we can provide you with six hundred cases of bottled Tears, which works out at just under two hundred tonnes."

"That sounds quite satisfactory," Syrinx said.

"Jolly good. So, that just leaves us with the nitty-gritty of working out a price."

Andrew Unwin loaded Quinn Dexter's passport flek into his processor block, and the unit immediately went dead. He rapped on it with his knuckles, but nothing happened. The three men from the spaceplane were watching him keenly. Andrew knew his cheeks would be bright scarlet. He didn't like to think what his father would say. Passport Officer was an important job.

"Thank you, sir." Andrew meekly handed the unread flek back to Quinn Dexter, who took it without comment. Mel was still barking, from a distance, hiding behind the front wheel of his bike. The dog hadn't stopped since the group trotted down the spaceplane's airlock stairs.

And the day had been going so well until the spaceplane from the *Lady Macbeth* landed.

"Is that it?" Joshua asked, his voice raised above the barking.

"Yes, thank you, Captain, sir. Welcome to Norfolk. I hope you find a cargo."

Joshua grinned, and beckoned him over. The two of them walked away from Quinn Dexter and Ashly Hanson who waited at the foot of the stairs, the dog scampering after them.

"Good of you to deal with us so promptly," Joshua said. "I can see the aerodrome's busy."

"It's my job, Captain, sir."

Joshua took a bundle of leftover Lalonde francs from his ship-suit pocket, and slipped three out. "I appreciate it." The plastic notes were pressed into the boy's hand. A smile returned to his face.

"Now tell me," Joshua said in a low tone. "Someone who can be trusted with passport duty must know what goes on around here, where the bodies are buried, am I right?"

Andrew Unwin nodded, too nervous to speak. What bodies?

"I hear there are some pretty important families on Norfolk, do you know which is the most influential here on Kesteven?"

"That would be the Kavanaghs, Captain, sir. There's dozens and dozens of them, real gentry; they own farms and houses and businesses all over the island."

"Do they have any roseyards?"

"Yes, there's several of their estates which bottle their own Tears."

"Great. Now, the big question: do you know who handles their offworld sales for them?"

"Yes, Captain, sir," he said proudly. That wad of crisp notes was still in the captain's hand, he did his best not to stare at it. "You want Kenneth Kavanagh for that. If anyone can find you a cargo, he can."

Ten notes were counted off. "Where can I find him?"

"Drayton's Import company, in Penn Street."

Joshua handed over the notes.

Andrew folded them with practised alacrity, and shoved them in his shorts pocket. After he'd ridden twenty yards from the spaceplane his processor block let out a quiet bleep. It was fully functional again. He gave it a bewildered look, then shrugged and rode off towards the spaceplane that was just landing.

Judging by the receptionist's initial attitude, Joshua guessed he wasn't the first starship captain to come knocking at Drayton's Import this week. But he managed to catch her eye as she held the pearl handset to her ear, and earned a demure smile.

"Mr Kavanagh will see you now, Captain Calvert," she said.

"That's very kind of you to press my case."

"Not at all."

"I wonder if you could recommend a decent restaurant for tonight. My associate and I haven't eaten for hours, we're looking forward to a meal. Somewhere you use, perhaps?"

She straightened her back self-consciously, and her voice slid up a social stratum. "I sometimes visit the Metropole," she said airily.

"Then I'm sure it must be delightful."

Ashly raised his eyes heavenwards in silent appeal.

It was another quarter of an hour before they were shown into Kenneth Kavanagh's office. Joshua didn't shirk from eye contact with Gideon when Kenneth introduced them. He got the distinct impression the amputee victim was suppressing extreme nervousness, his face was held too rigidly, as if he was afraid of showing emotions. Then he realized that Kenneth was watching his own reaction. Something about the situation wasn't quite right.

Kenneth offered them seats in front of the desk as Gideon explained how he'd lost his arm. The restriction on medical cloning was a stiff one, Joshua thought, although he could appreciate the reasoning. Once the line was drawn, Norfolk had to stick to it. They wanted a stable pastoral culture. If you opened the doors to one medical technology, where did you stop? He was glad he didn't have to decide.

"Is this your first visit to Norfolk, Captain?" Kenneth asked.

"Yes. I only started flying last year."

"Is that so? Well, I always like to welcome first-time captains. I believe it's important to build up personal contacts."

"That sounds like a good policy."

"Exporting Norfolk Tears is our lifeblood, alienating starship captains is not a wise option."

"I'm hoping I won't be alienated."

"And so do I. I try not to send anyone away empty handed, although you must understand there is a high level of demand, and I do have long-established customers to whom I owe a certain loyalty. And most of them have been here a week or more already. I have to say, you have left it somewhat late. What sort of cargo size were you thinking of?"

"*Lady Mac* can boost a thousand tonnes without too much trouble."

"Captain Calvert, there are some of my oldest customers who don't get that many cases."

"I have a trade proposition for you, a part exchange."

"Well, a trade is always helpful; although Norfolk's import laws are rather strict. I couldn't countenance breaking, or even bending them. I have the family reputation to consider."

"I understand perfectly," Joshua said.

"Jolly good. What is it you've brought?"

"Wood."

Kenneth Kavanagh gave him a stupefied stare, then burst out laughing. Even Gideon's sombre expression perked up.

"Wood? Are you serious?" Kenneth asked. "Your starship hold is full of wood?"

"A thousand tonnes." Joshua turned the seal of the shoulder-bag and pulled out the black wedge of mayope he'd brought. He had chosen it specially in the lumberyard back on Lalonde. It was a standard slice, twenty-five centimetres long, but the bark was still attached, and more importantly, there was a small twig with a few shrivelled leaves. He dropped it on the middle of the desk, making a solid thud.

Kenneth stopped laughing and leaned forward. "Good Lord." He tapped it with a fingernail, then gave it a harder knock with his knuckles

Without speaking, Joshua handed over a stainless steel chisel.

Kenneth applied the sharp blade to the wood. "I can't even scratch it."

"You normally need a fission blade to cut mayope. But it can be cut with the mechanical power saws you have on Norfolk," Joshua said. "Though it's a brute of a job. As you can imagine, once it's cut into shape it's incredibly hard wearing. I expect your artisans could come up with a few interesting applications if they put their minds to it."

Kenneth picked the wedge up in one hand to test the weight, pulling thoughtfully on his lower lip with the other. "Mayope, you call it?"

"That's right, it comes from a planet called Lalonde. Which is tropical; in other words it won't grow here on Norfolk. Not without extensive geneering, anyway." He looked at Gideon who was standing behind Kenneth's chair. The man showed a certain admiration for the wood, but he wasn't particularly involved, not like his senior cousin. Surely an aide should at least ask one question? But then he hadn't said a word since they had been introduced. Why was he present? Joshua instinctively knew the reason was important. If the Kavanaghs were as eminent as they appeared, even an injured one wouldn't be wasting time standing about in an office doing nothing.

He thought of Ione again. "Trust yourself when it comes to people," she'd said.

"Have you been to any other importer with this?" Kenneth asked cautiously.

"I only arrived today. Naturally, I came to a Kavanagh first."

"That's most courteous of you to honour my family in such a fashion, Captain. And I'd very much like to return the gesture. I'm sure we can come to some arrangement. As you know, roseyards aren't legally allowed to sell their produce before the new crop comes in, but fortunately my family does have an unofficial allocation system. Let me see what I can find for you." He put the mayope down and began typing.

Joshua met Gideon's gaze levelly. "Did you lead a very physically active life before your accident?"

"Yes, we of the gentry do tend to enjoy our sports. There is little to do in Kesteven during the winter months, so we have an extensive range of events to amuse us. My fall was a sorry blow."

"So office life doesn't really suit you?"

"It's the best occupation given my circumstances, I felt." Kenneth had stopped typing.

"You know, you wouldn't be nearly so restricted in free fall," Joshua said. "There are many people with medical problems who lead very full lives on starships and industrial stations."

"Is that so?" Gideon asked tonelessly.

"Yes. Perhaps you'd care to consider it? I have a vacancy on board *Lady Macbeth* at the moment. Nothing technical, but it's decent work. You could try it for a Norfolk year, see if it's more agreeable to you than office work. If not, I'll bring you back when I return for another cargo of Tears next summer. The pay is reasonable, and I provide insurance for all my crew." Joshua looked straight at Kenneth. "Which includes complete medical cover."

"That is extraordinarily generous of you, Captain," Gideon said. "I'd like to accept those terms. I'll try shipboard life for a year."

"Welcome aboard."

Kenneth resumed typing, then studied the holoscreen display. "You're in luck, Captain Calvert. I believe I can supply you with three thousand cases of Norfolk Tears, which comes to approximately one thousand tonnes. My cousin Grant Kavanagh has some extensive rosegroves in his Cricklade estate, and he hasn't yet placed all the cases. That district produces an absolutely first-rate bouquet."

"Wonderful," Joshua said.

"I'm sure cousin Grant will want to meet such an important client," Kenneth said. "On behalf of the family, I extend an invitation to you and Mr Hanson to stay at Cricklade for the midsummer harvest. You can see our famous Tears being collected."

*   *   *

The light from Duchess was just making its presence felt as Joshua and Ashly walked out of the Drayton's Import office. Norfolk's short period of darkness was giving way to the light of the red dwarf. Walls and cobbles were acquiring a pinkish shading.

"You did it!" Ashly whooped.

"Yeah, I did," Joshua said.

"A thousand tonnes, I've never heard of anyone getting that much before. You are the sneakiest, most underhand, deviously corrupt little bugger I have met in all my centuries." He flung an arm round Joshua's neck and dragged him towards the main street. "God damn, but we're going to be rich. Medical insurance, by God! Joshua you are beautiful!"

"We'll put Gideon in zero-tau till we reach Tranquillity. It shouldn't take a clinic more than eight months to clone a new arm for him. He can enjoy himself with Dominique's party set for the rest of the time after that. I'll have a word with her."

"How's he going to explain away a new arm when he gets back?"

"Jesus, I don't know. Magic clockwork, I expect. This world is backward enough to believe it."

Laughing, the two of them waved for a taxi coach.

When Duchess had risen well above the horizon, sending her bold scarlet rays to discolour the city, Joshua settled himself on a stool in the Wheatsheaf's wharfside bar and ordered a local brandy. The view outside the window was fascinating, casting everything in tones of red. Some colours were almost invisible. A regular train of barges sailed down the willow-lined river, helmsmen standing by the big tillers at the rear.

It was wonderful to watch, the whole city was a giant tourist fantasy pageant. But some of the inhabitants must lead incredibly dull lives, doing the same thing day after day.

"We worked out how you did it eventually," a female voice said in his ear.

Joshua turned, putting his eyes level with a delightful

swelling at the front of a blue satin ship-tunic. "Captain Syrinx, this is a pleasure. Can I get you a drink? This brandy is more than passable, I can recommend it, or perhaps you'd like a wine?"

"Doesn't it bother you?"

"No, I'll drink anything."

"I don't know how you can sleep at night. Antimatter kills people, you know. It's not a game, it's not funny."

"A beer, maybe?"

"Good day, Captain Calvert." Syrinx started to walk past.

Joshua caught her arm. "If you don't join me for a drink, how can you brag about working *it* out? And incidentally demonstrate how superior you Edenists all are to us poor mud-chewing primitives. Or maybe you don't want to hear my counter-argument. After all, you've convinced yourself I'm guilty of something. I don't even know what that is yet. Nobody ever had the decency to tell me what you thought I was carrying. Have Edenists left justice behind as well as the rest of our poor flawed Adamist customs?"

Syrinx's mouth dropped open. The man was intolerable! How did he twist phrases like that? It was almost as if she was in the wrong. "I never said you were a mud-chewing primitive," she hissed. "That's not what we think at all."

Joshua's eyes slid pointedly to one side. Syrinx realized everyone in the bar was staring at them.

Are you all right? *Oenone* asked anxiously, picking up on the flustered thoughts in her skull.

I'm fine. It's this bloody Calvert man again.

Oh, is Joshua there?

"Joshua?" She winced. She'd been so surprised at *Oenone*'s use of his first name it had slipped out.

"You remembered," Joshua said warmly.

"I . . ."

"Have a stool, what are you drinking?"

Furious and embarrassed, Syrinx sat on a barstool. At least it would stop everyone from looking. "I'll try a wine."

He signalled the barmaid for drinks. "You're not wearing your naval stripe."

"No. Our duty tour finished a few weeks back."

"So you're an honest trader now?"

"Yes."

"Have you got yourself a cargo?"

"Yes, thank you."

"Hey, that's great news, well done. These Norfolk merchants are tough buggers to crack. I got the *Lady Mac* stocked up, too." He collected the drinks, and touched his glass to hers. "Have dinner with me tonight, we can celebrate together."

"I don't think so."

"Do you have a previous engagement?"

"Well . . ." she couldn't bring herself to lie outright, that would make her no better than him. "I was just on my way to bed. It's been a long day with some tough negotiations. But thanks for the invitation. Another time."

"That's a real shame," he said. "Looks like you've condemned me to a terminally dull evening, then. There's only my pilot down here, and he's too old for my kind of fun-seeking. I'm waiting for him now. We seem to have lost our paying passenger. Not that I'm complaining, he wasn't the party type. Apparently there's a good restaurant in town called the Metropole, we were going to check it out. It's our one night in town, we've been invited to an estate for the midsummer itself. So, tough negotiations, eh? How many cases did you get?"

"You were a decoy," Syrinx said, jumping at the chance to get a word in.

"I'm sorry?"

"You were smuggling antimatter-confinement coils into the Puerto de Santa Maria system."

"Not me."

"We were trailing you all the way from Idria, we'd got you in our sensors every kilometre. That's what we couldn't understand. It was a direct flight. The confinement coils were on board when you left, and they were gone when you arrived. At the time we assumed you hadn't rendezvoused with anybody, because we never detected them. But then you didn't know we were there, did you?"

Joshua drank some of his brandy, his eyes never leaving her over the rim of the glass. "No, you were in full stealth mode, remember?"

"So was your friend."

"What friend?"

"You took a long time to manoeuvre into each jump co-ordinate. I've never seen anyone so clumsy before."

"Nobody's perfect."

"No, but nobody's that imperfect either." She took a sip of the wine. Oh, he was a canny one, this Joshua Calvert; she could see why she'd been fooled before. "What I think happened was this. You had your friend waiting a light-month outside the New California system, in full stealth mode, at a very precise coordinate. When you left Idria you jumped to within a few thousand kilometres of him. It would be difficult, but you could do that. With the nodes the *Lady Macbeth* is equipped with, and your own astrogration skill, that sort of accuracy is possible. And who would suspect? Nobody is that accurate jumping out of a system; it's when you come insystem you need precision to jump into the correct emergence zones."

"Go on, this is riveting stuff."

She took another sip. "Once you jumped outsystem, you shoved the illegal coils out of the cargo hold, and jumped away again. We couldn't detect that sort of dump of inert mass, not by using passive sensors at the distance we were operating from. Then as soon as *Oenone* and *Nephele* jumped in pursuit, your friend moved in and picked them up. So while you were taking an age to get to Puerto de Santa Maria, and keeping us occupied tracking you, he was racing on ahead. The coils were already there by the time we arrived."

"Brilliant." Joshua tossed down the last of his brandy and called the barmaid over. "That would work, wouldn't it?"

"It did work."

"No, not really. You see, your hypothesis is based on one assumption. Tragically false."

Syrinx picked up the second glass of wine. "What's that?"

"That I'm an ace astrogrator."

"I think you are."

"Right, so on a normal commercial run I would use this alleged skill of mine to shave hours off the journey time, wouldn't I?"

"Yes."

"So I would have used this skill to get here, to Norfolk, wouldn't I? I mean, I brought a cargo to trade, I'm not going to waste time, money, and fuel getting it here, now am I?"

"No."

"Right, so first of all ask the captain on the good ship *Pestravka* when and where I emerged in the Norfolk system. Then you can go and check my departure time from Lalonde, and work out how long it took me. Tell me after that if you think I'm a good astrogrator." He gave her an annoying toothsome smile.

Thanks to *Oenone*, she was instantly aware of Lalonde's spacial location; how long it ought to take an Adamist starship of *Lady Macbeth*'s class and performance to make the trip. "How long did it take you?" she asked in resignation.

"Six and a half days."

It shouldn't have taken them that long, *Oenone* said.

Syrinx said nothing. She simply couldn't bring herself to believe he was innocent. His whole attitude spelt complicity.

"Ah, here's Ashly now." Joshua stood and waved at the pilot. "And simply because you committed an extraordinarily rude *faux pas* don't think you have to pay for the drinks to make up for it. They're on me, I insist." He raised his glass. "Here's to mutual understanding and future friendship."

The *Coogan*'s battered prow was riding heavily over the
steep wavelets the Zamjan tributary sent rushing down its
length towards the Juliffe. Lori could feel the length of the
light trader boat exaggerating each pitch as they drove
against the current. After four and a half days nothing about
the *Coogan* bothered her any more; it creaked continually,
the engines produced a vibration felt throughout every timber, it was hot, dark, airless, and cramped. But enforced routine had made it all inconsequential. Besides, she spent a lot
of time lying inertly on her cot, reviewing the images the eagles Abraham and Catlin provided her.

Right now the birds were six kilometres ahead of *Coogan*,
gliding five hundred metres above the water, with just the
occasional indolent flick of a wing needed to maintain their
flight. The jungle on either side of the swollen river was
choked with mist from the rain that had just fallen, swan-
white wisps clinging to the glistening green trees like some
kind of animate creeper. There was no understanding the
jungle's immensity, Lori thought. The sights she saw
through the eagles brought home how little impression the
settlers had made on the Juliffe basin in twenty-five years.
The timorous villages huddled along the riverbanks were a
sorry example of the human condition. Microscopic para-
sites upon the jungle biota rather than bold challengers out
to subdue a world.

Abraham saw a ragged line of smoke staining the sky
ahead. A village cooking pit, judging by the shape and
colour: she'd certainly had enough practice over the last few
days to recognize one. She consulted her bitek processor
block, and the visualization of the Zamjan eclipsed the
image from the eagles. A vast four-hundred-kilometre river

in its own right, the broad tributary was the one which the Quallheim emptied into. Inertial guidance coordinates flicked round. The village was called Oconto, founded three years ago. They had an asset planted there, a man by the name of Quentin Montrose.

Lori, Darcy called, **I think there's another one, you'd better come and have a look.**

The visualization withdrew into the bitek processor. **I'm on my way.** She opened her eyes, and looked out through the nearest slit in the side of the rickety cabin wall. All she could see was the grizzled water being lashed by the squall. Warm droplets ran along the inside of the roof, defying gravity before they plopped down on the cots where she and Darcy had spread their sleeping-bags. There was more room now a third of the logs had been fed into the insatiable hopper, but she still had to squirm out through the Buchannans' cabin and the galley.

Gail was sitting at the table on one of the special stools that could take her weight. Packets of freeze-dried food were strewn across the greasy wood in front of her. "What would you like tonight?" she asked as Lori hurried past.

"Doesn't matter."

"That's typically thoughtless. How am I supposed to prepare an adequate meal for people who won't help? It would serve all of you right if I was to do nothing but boiled rice. Then you'd all moan and complain, I'd be given no peace at all."

Lori gave her a grimace-smile and ducked through the hatch out onto the deck. The fat woman disgusted her, not just her size, but her manner. Gail Buchannan surely represented the antithesis of Edenism, everything her culture strove to distance themselves from in human nature.

Rain was pelting down on the little wheel-house's solar-cell roof. Darcy and Len Buchannan were inside, hunched against the drops which came streaking in through the open sides. Lori dashed the four metres round to the door, drenching her loose grey jacket in the process.

"It'll be over in a minute," Darcy said. Up ahead, the end of the steel rainclouds was visible as a bright haze band surmounting the river and jungle.

"Where's the boat?" she asked, screwing her eyes against the stinging rain.

"There." Len raised a hand from the wheel and pointed ahead.

It was one of the big paddle-boats used to take colonists upriver, slicing imperiously through the water towards them. It didn't pitch about like the *Coogan*, its greater mass kept it level as the wavelets broke against its side and stern. Smoke streamed almost horizontally from its twin stacks.

"Dangerous fast, that is," Len said. "Specially for these waters. Plenty of foltwine about; catch a bundle of that in the paddle and she'll do her bearings a ton of damage. And we're heading into the snowlily season now as well, they're as bad as foltwine when they stick together."

Lori nodded briefly in understanding. Len had pointed out the thin grasslike leaves multiplying along the shallow waters near the shores, fist-sized pods just beginning to rise above the surface. Snowlilies bloomed twice every Lalonde year. They looked beautiful, but they caused havoc with the boats.

In fact Len Buchannan had opened up considerably once the trip started. He still didn't like the idea of Lori and Darcy steering his precious boat, but had grudgingly come to admit they could manage it almost as well as himself. He seemed to enjoy having someone to talk to other than his wife; he and Gail hadn't shared ten words since they cast off from Durringham. His conversation was mostly about river lore and the way Lalonde was developing, he had no interest in the Confederation. Some of the information was useful to her when she took the wheel. He seemed surprised by the way she remembered it all. The only time he'd gone sullen on her was when she told him her age, he thought it was some kind of poor-taste joke; she looked about half as old as he did.

The three of them watched the paddle-boat race past. Len turned the wheel a couple of points, giving it a wide passage. Darcy switched his retinal implants up to full resolution and studied the deck. There were about thirty-five people milling about on the foredeck; farmer-types, the men with thick beards, women with sun-ripened faces, all in clothes made from local cloth. They paid very little attention to the *Coogan*, apparently intent on the river ahead.

Len shook his head, a mystified expression in place. "That ain't right. The *Broadmoor* ought to be in a convoy, three or more. That's the way them paddlers always travel. Captain didn't call us on the radio neither." He tapped the short-range radio block beside the forward-sweep mass-detector. "Boats always talk out here, ain't so much traffic as you can ignore each other."

"And those weren't colonists on the deck," Darcy said.

The *Coogan* pitched up hard as the prow reached the first of the deep furrows of water which the wayward *Broadmoor* produced in its wake.

"Not going downriver, no," Len said.

"Refugees?" Lori suggested.

"Possibly," Darcy said. "But if the situation is that bad, why weren't there more of them?" He replayed the memory of the paddle-boat. It was the third they had encountered in twenty hours; the other two had steamed past in the dark. The attitude of the people on deck bothered him. They just stood there, not talking, not clustered together the way people usually did for companionship. They even seemed immune to the rain.

Are you thinking the same as me? Lori asked. She conjured up an image of the reptile people from Laton's call, and superimposed them on the deck of the Broadmoor—rain running off their green skin without wetting it.

Yes, he said. **It's possible. Probable, in fact. Some kind of sequestration is obviously involved. And those people on board weren't behaving normally.**

If boats are carrying the sequestrated downriver, it would mean that the posse on the *Swithland* have been circumvented.

I never expected them to be anything other than a token, and a rather pathetic one at that. If this is a xenoc invasion, then obviously they will want to subdue the entire planet. The Juliffe tributaries are the only feasible transport routes. Naturally they would use the riverboats.

I can't believe that anyone with the technology to

cross interstellar space would then be reduced to using wooden boats to get about on a planet.

Human settlers do. Darcy projected an ironic moue.

Yes, colonists who can't afford anything better, but a military conquest force?

Point taken. But there's an awful lot about this situation we don't understand. For a start, why invade Lalonde?

True. But to return to the immediate, if we've already penetrated the incursion front, do we need to go on?

I don't know. We need information.

We have an asset in the next village. I suggest we stop there and see what he knows.

Good idea. And Solanki will have to be informed about the aberrant river traffic.

Lori left Darcy to feed the furnace hopper and made her way back to the space in the cabin they shared. She pulled her backpack from under the cot and retrieved the palm-sized slate-grey communication block from among her clothes. It took a couple of seconds for the Confederation Navy's ELINT satellite to lock on to the scrambled channel. Kelven Solanki's tired-looking face appeared on the front of the slim rectangular unit.

"We may have a problem," she said.

"One more won't make any difference."

"This one might. We believe the presence Laton warned us of is spreading itself downriver on the boats. In other words, it can't be confined by the posse."

"Bloody hell. Candace Elford decided last night that Kristo County has also been taken over, that's halfway down the Zamjan from the mouth of the Quallheim. And after reviewing the satellite images, I have to concur. She's reinforcing the posse by BK133. They have a new landing point, Ozark, in Mayhew County, fifty kilometres short of Kristo. The BK133s are lifting in men and weapons right now. The *Swithland* should reach them early tomorrow, they can't be far ahead of you."

"We're approaching Oconto village right now."

"About thirty kilometres, then. What are you going to do?"

"We haven't decided yet. We'll need to go ashore whatever the outcome."

"Well, be careful, this is turning out to be even bigger than my worst-case scenarios."

"We don't intend to jeopardize ourselves."

"Good. Your message flek was dispatched to your embassy on Avon, along with mine to the First Admiral, and one from Ralph Hiltch to his embassy. Rexrew sent one to the LDC office as well."

"Thank you. Let's hope the Confederation Navy responds swiftly."

"Yes. I think you should know, Hiltch and I have dispatched a combined scout team upriver. If you want to wait in Oconto for them to arrive, you're more than welcome to join them. They're making good time, I estimate they should be with you in a couple of days at the most. And my marines are carrying a fair amount of fire-power."

"We'll retain it as an option. Though Darcy and I don't believe fire-power is going to be an overwhelming factor in this case. Judging by what we gleaned from Laton, and what we've observed on the paddle-boats, it appears wide-scale sequestration is playing a major part in the invasion."

"Dear Christ!"

She smiled at his expletive. Why did Adamists always appeal to their deities? It wasn't something she understood. If there was an omnipotent god, why did he make life so full of pain? "You might find a prudent course of action is to review river traffic out of the affected areas over the last ten days."

"Are you saying they've already reached Durringham?"

"It is more than likely, I'm afraid. We are almost at Kristo, and we're travelling against the current on a decidedly third-rate boat."

"I see what you mean, if they left Aberdale right at the start they could have been here a week ago."

"Theoretically, yes."

"All right, thanks for the warning. I'll pull some people in and start analysing the boats that have come down out of the Zamjan. Hell, this is just what the city needs on top of everything else."

"How are things in Durringham?"

"None too good, actually. Everyone's starting to hoard food, so prices are going through the roof. Candace Elford is deputizing young men left, right, and centre. There's a lot of unrest among the residents about what's happening up-river. She's afraid it's going to spiral out of control. Then on Wednesday the transient colonists decided to hold a peaceful rally outside the Governor's dumper demanding new gear to replace what was stolen, and extra land in compensation for the upset. I could see it from my window. Rexrew refused to talk to them. Too scared they'd lynch him, I should think. It was that sort of mood. Things got a bit rough, and they clashed with the sheriffs. Quite a lot of casualties on both sides. Some idiot let a sayce loose. The power cables from the dumper's fusion generator were torn down. So there was no electricity in the precinct for two days, and of course that includes the main hospital. Guess what happened to its back-up power supply."

"It failed?"

"Yeah. Someone had been flogging off the electron-matrix crystals to use in power bikes. There was only about twenty per cent capacity left."

"Sounds like there's not much to choose between your position and mine."

Kelven Solanki gave her a measured stare. "Oh, I think there is."

Oconto was a typical Lalonde village: a roughly square clearing shorn straight into the jungle, with the official Land Allocation Office marker as its pivot; cabins with trim vegetable gardens clustered at the nucleus, while broader fields made up the periphery. The normally black mayope planks of the buildings were turning a lighter grey from years of exposure to the sun and heat and rain, hardening and cracking, like driftwood on a tropical shore. Pigs squealed in their pens, while cows munched contentedly at their silage in circular stockades. A line of over thirty goats were tethered to stakes around the border of the jungle, chomping away at the creepers which edged in towards the fields.

The village had done well for itself during the three years

since its founding. The communal buildings like the hall and church were well maintained; the council had organized the construction of a low, earth-covered lodge to smoke fish in. Major paths were scattered with wood flakes to stem the mud. There was even a football pitch marked out. Three jetties stuck out of the gently sloped bank into the Zamjan's insipid water; two of them responsible for mooring the village's small number of fishing boats.

When the *Coogan* nosed up to the main central jetty Darcy and Lori were relieved to see a considerable number of people working the fields. Oconto hadn't succumbed yet. Several shouts went up as the trader boat was spotted. Men came running, all of them carrying guns.

It took a quarter of an hour to convince the nervous reception committee that they posed no threat, and for a few minutes at the start Darcy thought they were going to be shot out of hand. Len and Gail Buchannan were well known (though not terribly popular), which acted in their favour. The *Coogan* was travelling upriver, heading towards the rebel counties, not bringing people down from them. And finally, Lori and Darcy themselves, with their synthetic fabric clothes and expensive hardware units, were accepted as some kind of official team. With what mandate was never asked.

"You gotta understand, people round here are getting mighty trigger happy since last Tuesday," Geoffrey Tunnard said. He was Oconto's acting leader, a lean fifty-year-old with curly white hair, wearing much-patched colourless dungarees. Now he was satisfied the *Coogan* wasn't bringing revolution and destruction, and his laser rifle was slung over his beefy shoulder again, he was happy to talk.

"What happened last Tuesday?" Darcy asked.

"The Ivets." Geoffrey Tunnard spat over the side of the jetty. "We heard there'd been trouble up Willow West way, so we shoved ours in a pen. They've been good workers since we arrived. But there's no point in taking chances, right?"

"Right," Darcy agreed diplomatically.

"But on Monday we had some people visit, claimed they were from Waldersy village, up in Kristo County. They said the Ivets were all rebelling in the Quallheim Counties and Willow West, killing the men and raping the women. Said plenty of younger colonists had joined them, too. They was nothing but a vigilante group, you could see that, all hyped up they were, on a high. I reckoned they'd been smoking some canus; that'll send you tripping if you dry the leaves right. Trouble they were, just wanted to kill our Ivets. We wouldn't have it. A man can't kill another in cold blood, not just on someone else's say so. We sent them on downriver. Then blow me if they didn't creep back that night. And you know what?"

"They let the Ivets out," Lori said.

Geoffrey Tunnard gave her a respectful look. "That's right. Stole back in here right under our noses. Dogs never even noticed them. Slit old Jamie Austin's throat, him that was standing guard on the pen. Our supervisor Neil Barlow went right off after them that morning. Took a bunch of fifty men with him, armed men they were, too. And we haven't heard a damn thing since. That ain't like Neil, it's been six days. He should have sent word. Them men have families. We've got wives and kiddies left here that are worried sick." He glanced from Darcy to Lori. "Can you tell us anything?" His tone was laboured; Geoffrey Tunnard was a man under a great deal of strain.

"Sorry, I don't know anything," Darcy said. "Not yet. That's why we're here, to find out. But whatever you do, don't go after them. The larger your numbers, the safer you are."

Geoffrey Tunnard pursed his lips and looked away, eyes raking the jungle with bitter enmity. "Thought you'd say something like that. Course, there's those that have gone looking. Some of the women. We couldn't stop them."

Darcy put his hand on Geoffrey Tunnard's shoulder, gripping firmly. "If any more want to go, stop them. Have a log fall on their foot if that's what it takes, but you must stop them."

"I'll do my best." Geoffrey Tunnard dipped his head in defeat. "I'd leave if I could, take the family downriver on a boat. But I built this place with my own hands, and no damn Govcentral interference. It was a good life, it was. It can be again. Bloody Ivets never were any use for anything, waster kids in dungarees, that's all."

"We'll do what we can," Lori said.

"Sure you will. You're doing what you tell me not to: go out in the jungle. Just the two of you. That's madness."

Lori thought Geoffrey Tunnard had been about to say suicide. "Can you tell us where Quentin Montrose lives?" she asked.

Geoffrey Tunnard pointed out one of the cabins, no different to any of the others; solar panels on the roof, a sagging overhang above the verandah. "Won't do you no good, he was in Neil's group."

Lori stood at the side of the wheel-house as the *Coogan* cast off; Darcy was aft, heaving more of the interminable logs into the furnace hopper. Len Buchannan whistled tunelessly as he steered his boat into the middle of the river. Oconto gradually shrank away to stern until it was nothing but a deeper than usual gash in the emerald cliff. Smoke from the cooking fires drifted apathetically across the choppy water.

We could send one of the eagles looking for them, Lori suggested.

You don't really mean that.

No. I'm sorry, I was just trying to save my own conscience.

Fifty armed men, and no trace. I don't know about your conscience, but my courage has almost deserted me.

We could go back, or even wait for Solanki's marines.

Yes, we could.

You're right. We'll go on.

We should have told Geoffrey Tunnard to leave, Darcy said. **I should have told him; take his family and flee back to Durringham. At least it would have been honest. None of this false hope we left him with.**

That's all right, I think he already knows.

Karl Lambourne woke without knowing why. It wasn't noon yet, and he hadn't got to go back on watch until two o'clock. The blinds on his cabin's port were still shut, reducing the light inside to a mysterious and enticing dusk. Booted feet thudded along the deck outside the door. Conversation was a persistent background hum, children calling out in their whiny voices.

Everything normal. So why was he awake with a vague feeling of unease?

The colonist girl—what was her name?—stirred beside him. She was a few months younger than him, with dark hair teased into ringlets around a dainty face. Despite his initial dismay with the *Swithland* carrying all those extra sheriffs and deputies it was turning out to be a good trip. The girls appreciated the space and privacy his cabin gave them; the boat was very crowded, with sleeping-bags clogging every metre of deck space.

The girl's eyelids fluttered, then opened slowly. She— Anne, no Alison; that was it, Alison! remember that—grinned at him.

"Hi," she said.

He glanced along her body. The sheet was tangled up round her waist, affording him a splendid view of breasts, lean belly muscles, and sharply curving hips. "Hi yourself." He brushed some of the ringlets from her face.

Shouts and a barking laugh sounded from outside. Alison gave a timid giggle. "God, they're only a metre away."

"You should have thought of that before you made all that noise earlier."

Her tongue was caught between her teeth. "Didn't make any noise."

"Did."

"Didn't."

His arms circled her, and he pulled her closer. "You did, and I can prove it."

"Oh yeah?"

"Yeah." He kissed her softly, and she started to respond. His hand stole downwards, pushing the sheet off her legs.

Alison turned over when he told her to, shivering in anticipation as his arm slid under her waist, lifting her buttocks up. Her mouth parted in expectation.

"What the hell was that?"

"Karl?" She bent her head round to see him kneeling behind her, frowning up at the ceiling. "Karl!"

"Shush. Listen, can you hear it?"

She couldn't believe this was happening. People were still clumping up and down the deck outside. There wasn't any other sound! And she'd never ever been so turned on before. Right now she hated Karl with the same intensity she'd adored him a second before.

Karl twitched his head round, trying to catch the noise again. Except it wasn't so much a noise, more a vibration, a grumble. He knew every sound, every tremble the *Swithland* made, and that wasn't in its repertoire.

He heard it again, and identified it. A hull timber quaking somewhere aft. The creak of wood under pressure, almost as if they had touched a snag. But his mother would never steer anywhere near a snag, that was crazy.

Alison was looking up at him, all anger and hurt. The magic had gone. He felt his penis softening.

The noise came again. A grinding sound that lasted for about three seconds. It was muted by the bilges, but this time it was loud enough even for Alison to hear.

She blinked in confusion. "What . . . "

Karl jumped off the bed, snatching up his shorts. He jammed his legs into them, and was still struggling with the button when he yanked the door lock back and rushed out onto the deck.

Alison squealed behind him, trying to cover herself with her arms as vibrant midmorning sunlight flooded into the cabin. She grabbed the thin sheet to wrap herself in, and started hunting round for her clothes.

After the seductive shadows of his cabin the sunlight on deck sent glaring purple after-images chasing down Karl's optic nerves. Tear ducts released their stored liquid, which he had to wipe away annoyingly. A couple of colonists and three deputies, barely older than him, were staring at him. He leaned out over the rail and peered down at the river. There was some sediment carried by the water, and shimmering sunlight reflections skittering across the surface, but he could see a good three or four metres down. But there was nothing solid, no silt bank, no submerged tree trunk.

Up on the bridge Rosemary Lambourne hadn't been sure about the first scrape, but like her eldest son she was perfectly in tune with the *Swithland*. Something had left her with heightened senses, a suddenly hollow stomach. She automatically checked the forward-sweep mass-detector. This section of the Zamjan was twelve metres deep, giving her a good ten metres of clearance below the flat keel, even overloaded like this. There was nothing in front, nothing below, and nothing to the side.

Then it happened again. The aft hull struck something. Rosemary immediately reduced power to the paddles.

"Mother!"

She bent over the starboard side to see Karl looking up at her.

"What was that?"

He beat her to it by a fraction.

"I don't know," she shouted down. "The mass-detector shows clear. Can you see anything in the water?"

"No."

The river current was slowing the *Swithland* rapidly now the paddles were stilled. Without the steady thrash of the blades, the racket the colonists made seemed to have doubled.

It came again, a long rending sound of abused wood. There was a definite crunching at the end.

"That was aft," Rosemary yelled. "Get back there and see what happened. Report back." She pulled a handset from its slot below the communication console, and dropped it over the edge of the rail. Karl caught it with an easy snap of his wrist and raced off down the narrow decking, slipping through the knots of colonists with urgent fluid movements.

"*Swithland*, come in, please," the speaker on the communication console said. "Rosemary, can you hear me? This is Dale here. What's happening, why have you stopped?"

She picked up the microphone. "I'm here, Dale," she told the *Nassier*'s captain. When she glanced up she could see the *Nassier* half a kilometre upriver, pulling ahead; the *Hycel* was downriver on the starboard side, catching up fast. "It sounds like we struck something."

"How bad?"

"I don't know yet. I'll get back to you."

"Rosemary, this is Callan, I think it would be best if we didn't get separated. I'll heave to until you know if you need any assistance."

"Thanks, Callan." She leant out over the bridge rail and waved at the *Hycel*. A small figure on its bridge waved back.

A screech loud enough to silence all the colonists erupted from the *Swithland*'s hull. Rosemary felt the boat judder, its prow shifting a degree. It was like nothing she had ever experienced before. They were almost dead in the water, it couldn't possibly be a snag. It couldn't be!

Karl reached the afterdeck just as the *Swithland* juddered. He could feel the whole boat actually lift a couple of centimetres.

The afterdeck was packed full of colonists and posse members. Several groups of men were lying down, playing cards or eating. Kids charged about. Eight or nine people were fishing over the stern. Cases of farmsteading gear were piled against the superstructure and the taffrail. Dogs ran about underfoot; there were five horses tethered to the side rail, and two of them started pulling at their harnesses as the brassy scrunching noise broke across the boat. Everybody froze in expectation.

"Out of the way!" Karl shouted. "Out of the way." He started elbowing people aside. The noise was coming from the keel, just aft of the furnace room which was tacked on to the back of the superstructure. "Come on, move."

A sayce snarled at him. "Killl."

"Get that fucking thing out of my way!"

Yuri Wilken dragged Randolf aside.

The whole afterdeck complement was watching Karl. He reached the hatchway over the feed mechanism that shunted logs into the furnace. It was hidden beneath a clutter of composite pods. "Help me move these," he yelled.

Barry MacArple emerged from the furnace room, a brawny twenty-year-old, sweaty and sooty. He had kept indoors for most of this trip, and carefully avoided any member of the posse. None of the Lambourne family had mentioned that he was an Ivet.

The noise came to an abrupt halt. Karl was very aware of

the apprehensive faces focusing on him, the silent appeal for guidance. He held up his hands as Barry started to haul the pods off the hatchway. "OK, we're riding on some sort of rock. So I want all the kids to slowly make their way forwards. Slowly mind. Then the women. Not the men. You'll upset the balance with that much weight forward. And whoever those horses belong to, calm them down now."

Parents hustled their children towards the prow. A hushed murmur swept round the adults. Three men were helping Barry clear the hatchway. Karl lifted off a couple of the pods himself. Then he heard the noise again, but it was distant this time, not from the *Swithland*'s hull.

"What the hell—" He looked up to see the *Hycel* a hundred metres astern.

"Karl, what's happening?" Rosemary's voice demanded from the handset.

He raised the unit to his mouth. "It's the *Hycel*, Mum. They've hit it as well."

"Bloody hell. What about our hull?"

"Tell you in a minute."

The last of the pods were cleared away, revealing a two-metre-square hatch. Karl bent down to unclip the latches.

That was when the second sound rang out, a water-muffled THUNK of something heavy and immensely powerful slamming into the keel. *Swithland* gave a small jolt, riding up several centimetres. Some of the more loosely stacked cases and pods tumbled over. The colonists shouted in panic and dismay, and there was a general surge for the prow. One of the horses reared up, forelegs scraping the air.

Karl ripped the hatch open.

THUNK

Ripples rolled away from the *Swithland* as it wallowed about.

"Karl!" the handset squawked.

He looked down into the hull. The log-feed mechanism took up most of the space below the hatch, a primitive-looking clump of motors, pulley loops, and pistons. Two grab belts ran away to the port and starboard log holds. The black mayope planks of the hull itself were just visible. Water was welling out of cracks between them.

THUNK

Karl stared down in stupefaction as the planks bowed inward. That was mayope wood, nothing could dint mayope.

THUNK

Splinters appeared, long dagger fingers levering apart.

THUNK

Water poured in through the widening gaps. An area over a metre wide was being slowly hammered upwards.

THUNK

THUNK

Swithland was rocking up and down. Equipment and pods rolled about across the half-abandoned afterdeck. Men and women were clinging to the rail, others were spread-eagled on the decking, clawing for a handhold.

"It's trying to punch its way in!" Karl bellowed into the handset.

"What? What?" his mother shouted back.

"There's something below us, something alive. For Christ's sake, get us underway, get us to the shore. The shore, Mum. Go! Go!"

THUNK

The water was foaming up now, covering the hull planks completely. "Get this shut," Karl called. He was terribly afraid of what would come through once the hole was big enough. Together, he and Barry MacArple slammed the hatch back down, dogging the latches.

THUNK

Swithland's hull broke. Karl could hear a long dreadful tearing sound as the iron-hard wood was wrenched apart. Water seethed in, gurgling and slurping. It ripped the log feeder from its mountings, crashing it against the decking above. The hatch quaked violently.

A gloriously welcome whine from the paddle engines sounded. The familiar slow thrashing of the paddles started up. *Swithland* turned ponderously for the unbroken rampart of jungle eighty metres away.

Karl realized people were sobbing and shouting out. A lot of them must have made it forward, the boat was riding at a downward incline.

THUNK

This time it was the afterdeck planks. Karl, lying prone
next to the hatch, yelled in shock as his feet left the deck
from the impact. He twisted round immediately, rolling over
three times to get clear. Pods bounced and pirouetted chaot-
ically. The horses were going berserk. One of them broke its
harness, and plunged over the side. Another was kicking
wildly. A blood-soaked body lay beside it.

THUNK

The planks beside the hatch lifted in unison, snapping
back as if they were elastic. Water started to seep out.

Barry MacArple was scrambling on all fours along the
deck, his face engorged with desperation. Karl held out his
hand to the Ivet, willing him on.

THUNK

The planks directly below Barry were smashed asunder.
They ruptured upwards, jagged edges puncturing the Ivet's
belly and chest, then ripping his torso apart like a giant claw.
A metre-wide geyser of water slammed upwards out of the
gap, buffeting the corpse with it.

Karl turned to follow the water rising, fear stunned out of
him by the incredible, impossible sight. The geyser roared
ferociously, shaking Karl's bones and obliterating the im-
passioned shouts from the colonists. It rose a full thirty metres above the decking, its crown blossoming out like a
flower. Water, silt, and fragments of mayope plank splattered down.

Clinging for dear life to one of the cable drums as the
Swithland bucked about like a wounded brownspine, Karl
watched the geyser chewing away at the ragged sides of the
hole it had bored. It was creeping forward towards the superstructure. The bilges must be full already. Slowly and
surely more and more wood was eroded by the terrific force
of the water. In another minute it would reach the furnace
room. He thought of what would happen when the water
struck all fifteen tonnes of the searingly hot furnace, and
whimpered.

Rosemary Lambourne had a hard struggle to stay upright
as the *Swithland* tossed about. Only by clinging to the wheel
could she even stay on her feet. It was the sheer fright in
Karl's voice which had spurred her into action. He wasn't

afraid of anything on the river, he had been born on the *Swithland*.

That deadly battering noise was knocking into her heart as much as the hull. The strength behind anything that could thump the boat about like this was awesome.

How much of the *Swithland* is going to be left after this? God damn Colin Rexrew, his laxness and stupidity. The Ivets would never dare to revolt with a firm, competent governor in charge.

A roar like a continual explosion made her jump, almost sending her feet from under her. It was suddenly raining on the *Swithland* alone. The entire superstructure was trembling. What was happening back there?

She checked the little holoscreen which displayed the boat's engineering schematics. They were losing power rapidly from the furnace. Reserve electron-matrix crystals cut in, maintaining the full current to the engines.

"Rosemary," the radio called.

She couldn't spare the time to answer.

Swithland's prow was pointing directly at the bank sixty-five metres away, and they were picking up speed again. Pods and cases were scattered in the boat's wake, jouncing about in the water. She saw a couple of people splashing among them. More people went falling from the foredeck; it was as tightly packed as a rugby scrum down there. And there wasn't a thing she could do, except get them to the shore.

Off on the port side, *Nassier* was floundering about, paddles spinning intermittently. Rosemary saw a giant fountain of water smash through the middle of its superstructure, debris whirling away into the sky. What the fuck could do that? Some kind of water monster skulking around the riverbed? Even as the fantasy germinated in her mind she knew that wasn't the real answer. But she did know what the roaring noise behind her was now. The knowledge sucked at the last of her strength. If it hit the furnace . . .

Nassier's prow lifted into the air, shoving the afterdeck below the water. The superstructure crumpled up, large chunks being flung aside by the tremendous jet of water.

Dozens of people were swept into the river, arms and legs twirling frantically. In her mind she could hear the screams.

There were just too many people on board the paddle-boats. Rexrew had already increased the numbers of colonists they were made to carry, refusing to listen to the warning from the captains' delegation. Then he dumped this posse on them as well.

If I ever get back to Durringham, you're dead, Rexrew, she promised herself. You haven't just failed us, you've condemned us.

Then the *Nassier* began to capsize, rolling ever faster onto her starboard side. The jet of water died away as the keel flipped up. Rosemary saw a huge hole in the planks amidships as it reached the vertical. That was when the water must have rushed in on the furnace. A massive blast of white steam devoured the rear of the boat, rolling out across the surface of the river. Mercifully, it shielded the final act in the *Nassier*'s convulsive death.

Swithland's prow was fifteen metres from the trees and creepers which were strangling the bank. Rosemary could hear the sound of their own bedevilling geyser reducing. She fought the wheel to keep the boat lined up straight on the bank. The bottom was shelving up rapidly, the forward-sweep mass-detector emitting a frantic howl in warning. Five metres deep. Four. Three. They struck mud eight metres from the long flower-heavy vines trailing in the water. The big boat's awesome inertia propelled them along, slithering and sliding through the thick black alluvial muck. Bubbles of foul-smelling sulphurous gas churned around the sides of the hull. The geyser had died completely. There was a moment of pure dreamy silence before they hit the bank.

Rosemary saw a huge qualtook tree dead ahead; one of its thick boughs was the same height as the bridge. She ducked—

The impact threw Yuri Wilken back onto his belly just as he was starting to get up again. His nose slammed painfully against the deck. He tasted warm blood. The boat was making hideous crunching sounds as it ploughed into the frill of vegetation along the bank. Long vine strands lashed through the air with the brutality of bullwhips. He tried to bury himself into the hard decking as they slashed centimetres above his head. *Swithland*'s blunt prow rammed the low bank, jolting upwards to ride a good ten metres across the dark-red sandy earth. The paddle-boat finally came to a bruising halt with its forward deck badly mangled, and the qualtook tree embedded in the front of the superstructure.

Screams and wailing gave way to moans and shrill cries for help. Yuri risked glancing about, seeing the way in which the jungle had shrink-wrapped itself around the forward half of the boat. The superstructure looked dangerously unstable, it was leaning over sharply, with tonnes of vegetation pressing against the front and side.

His limbs were shaking uncontrollably. He wanted to be home in Durringham, taking Randolf for walks or playing football with his mates. He didn't belong here in the jungle.

"Are you all right, son?" Mansing asked.

Sheriff Mansing was the one who had signed him on for the expedition. He was a lot more approachable than some of the sheriffs, keeping a fatherly eye out for him.

"I think so." He dabbed at his nose experimentally, sniffing hard. There was blood on his hand.

"You'll live," Mansing said. "Where's Randolf?"

"I don't know." He climbed shakily to his feet. They were standing at the front corner of the superstructure. People were lying about all around, slowly picking themselves up, asking for help, wearing a numb, frightened expression. Two bodies had been trapped between the qualtook trunk and the superstructure; one was a small girl aged about eight. Yuri could only tell because she was wearing a dress. He turned away, gagging.

"Call for him," Mansing said. "We're going to need all the help we can get pretty soon."

"Sir?"

"You think this was an accident?"

Yuri hadn't thought it was anything. The notion sent a tremble down his spine. He put his lips together, and managed a feeble whistle.

"Twelve years I've been sailing up and down this river," Mansing said grimly. "I've never seen anything like that geyser before. What the hell can shoot water about like that? And there was more than one of them."

Randolf came lumbering up over the gunwale, his sleek black hide covered in smelly mud. The sayce had lost all of his usual aggressive arrogance, slinking straight over to Yuri and pressing against his master's legs. "Waaterrr baddd," he growled.

"He's not far wrong there," Mansing agreed cheerlessly.

It took quarter of an hour to establish any kind of order around the wrecked paddle-boat. The sheriffs organized parties to tend to the wounded and set up a makeshift camp. By general consensus they moved fifty metres inland, away from the river and whatever prowled below the water.

Several survivors from the *Nassier* managed to swim to the stern of the *Swithland* which was half submerged; the boat formed a useful bridge over the stinking quagmire which lined the bank. The *Hycel* had managed to reach the Zamjan's far bank; it had been spared the destructive geyser, but its hull had taken a dreadful pounding. Radio contact was established and both groups decided to stay where they were rather than attempt to cross the river and join forces.

Sheriff Mansing located an unbroken communication block amongst the remnants of the posse's gear, and patched a call through the LDC's single geostationary satellite to Candace Elford. The shocked chief sheriff agreed to divert the two BK133s to the *Swithland* and fly the seriously injured back to Durringham straight away. What she never mentioned was the possibility of reinforcing the forsaken boats. But Sheriff Mansing was above all a pragmatic man, he really hadn't expected any.

After making three trips to the camp, carrying pods of gear from the paddle-boat, Yuri was included into a small scout party of three sheriffs and nine deputies. He suspected they only included him because of Randolf. But that was OK, the other detail of deputies was now removing bodies from the *Swithland*. He preferred to take his chances with the jungle.

When Yuri and the scouts marched away, colonists with fission-blade saws were felling trees on one side of the camp's glade so the VTOL aircraft could land. A fire was burning in the centre.

It didn't take long for the groans of the casualties to fade away, blocked by the density of the foliage. Yuri couldn't get over how dark this jungle was, very little actual sunlight penetrated down to ground level. When he held his hand up the skin was tinted a deep green, the cinnamon-coloured jacket they had issued him with to protect him from thorns was jet black. The jungle around Durringham was nothing like this. It was tame, he realized, with its well-worn paths and tall trees spiralled with thin colourful vines. Here there were no paths, branches jutted out at all heights, and the vines were slung between boughs either at ankle height or level with his neck. A sticky kind of fungal mould slimed every leaf for three metres above the ground.

The scouts paired up, fanning out from the camp. The idea was to familiarize themselves with the immediate area out to five hundred metres, search for any more survivors from *Nassier*, and verify that no hostiles were near the camp.

"This is stupid," Mansing said after they had gone fifty metres. He was leading, chopping at the vines and small branches and bushes with a fission-blade machete. "I couldn't see you if you were three metres away."

"Perhaps it thins out up ahead," Yuri said.

Mansing slashed at another branch. "You're giving away your age again, son. Only the very young are that hopelessly optimistic."

They took turns to lead. Even with the fission blade hacking out every metre of path it was tiring work. Randolf loped along behind, occasionally butting against Yuri's calves.

According to Mansing's guidance block they had travelled about three hundred metres when the sayce stood still, head held up, sniffing the humid air. The species didn't have quite the sense of smell terrestrial canines possessed, but they were still excellent hunters in their own territory: the jungle.

"Peeeople," Randolf grunted.

"Which way?" Yuri asked.

"Here." The sayce pushed into the severed branches that

made up the walls of the path. He turned to look at them. "Here."

"Is this for real?" Mansing asked sceptically.

"Sure is," Yuri answered, stung by the doubt. "How far, boy?"

"Sooon."

"All right," Mansing said. He started to hack at the jungle where the sayce indicated.

It was another two minutes of sweaty labour before they heard the voices. They were high and light, female. One of them was singing.

Mansing was so intent on cutting the cloying vegetation away, swinging the heavy machete in endless rhythm, that he nearly fell head first into the stream when the creepers came to an abrupt end. Yuri grabbed his jacket collar to stop him slipping down the small grassy slope. Both of them stared ahead in astonishment.

Sunlight poured down through the overhead gap in the trees, hovering above the water like a thin golden mist. The stream widened out into a rock-lined pool fifteen metres across. Creepers with huge ruffed orange blooms hung like curtains from the trees on the far side. Tiny turquoise and yellow birds fluttered about through the air. It was a scene lifted from Greek mythology. Seven naked girls were bathing in the pool, ranging from about fifteen years up to twenty-five. All of them were slender and long limbed, sunlight glinting on their skin. White robes were strewn over the black rocks at the water's edge.

"Nooo," Randolf moaned. "Baddd."

"Bollocks," Yuri said.

The girls caught sight of them and shrieked with delight, smiling and waving.

Yuri shouldered his laser rifle, grinning deliriously at the seven pairs of wet breasts bouncing about.

"Bloody hell," Mansing muttered.

Yuri pushed past him, and scuttled down the slope into the stream. The girls cheered.

"Nooo."

"Yuri," Mansing gestured ineffectually.

He turned round, face illuminated with delight. "What?

We've got to find out where their village is, haven't we? That's our assignment, scout the terrain."

"Yes. I suppose so." He couldn't keep his eyes from the naiads sporting about.

Yuri was plunging on, legs sending up a wave of spray.

"Nooo," Randolf bayed urgently. "Baddd. Peeeople baddd."

Mansing watched the girls whooping encouragement to Yuri as the lad ploughed through the water towards them. "Oh, to hell with dignity," he said under his breath, and splashed down into the stream.

The first girl Yuri reached was about nineteen, with scarlet flowers tucked into her wet hair. She smiled radiantly up at him, hands holding his. "I'm Polly," she laughed.

"All right!" Yuri cried. The water only came halfway up her thighs; she really was completely naked. "I'm Yuri."

She kissed him, damp body pressing against his sleeveless shirt, leaving a dark imprint. When she broke off another girl slipped a garland of the orange vine flowers round his neck. "And I'm Samantha," she said.

"You gonna kiss me too?"

She twined her arms round his neck, tongue slipping hungrily into his mouth. Other girls were circling round, scooping up handfuls of spray and showering them. Yuri was in the midst of a warm silver rain with raw ecstasy pounding down his nerves. Here in the middle of nowhere, paradise had come to Lalonde. The droplets fell in slow motion, tinkling sweetly as they went. He felt hands slip the rifle strap from his shoulder, more hands pulled at his shirt buttons. His trousers were undone, and his penis stroked lovingly.

Samantha took a pace back looking at him in adoration. She cupped her breasts, lifting them up towards him. "Now, Yuri," she pleaded. "Take me now."

Yuri pulled her roughly against him, his soaking trousers tangling round his knees. He heard an alarmed shout that was cut off. Three of the girls had pushed Mansing under the water, his legs were thrashing above the surface. The girls were laughing hysterically, muscles straining with the effort of keeping him down.

"Hey—" Yuri said. He couldn't move because of his stupid trousers.

"Yuri," Samantha called.

He turned back to her. She was opening her mouth wider than he would have believed physically possible. Long bands of muscle writhed around her chin as if fat worms were tunnelling through her veins. Her cheeks started to split, beginning at the corners of her mouth and tearing back towards her ears. Blood leapt out of the wounds in regular beats, and she was still hinging her jaw apart.

Yuri stared for one petrified second then let loose a guttural roar of fright that reverberated round the impassive sentinel trees. His bladder gave out.

Samantha's grisly head darted forward, carmine teeth clamping solidly round his throat, her blood spraying against his skin.

"Randolf—" he yelled. Then her teeth tore into his throat, and his own blood burst out of his carotid artery to flood his gullet, quashing any further sounds.

Randolf howled in rage as his master fell into the water with Samantha riding him down. But one of the other girls looked straight at him and hissed in warning, flecks of saliva spitting out between her bared teeth. The sayce turned tail and sprinted back into the jungle.

"Power's going. Losing height. Losing height!" The BK133 pilot's frantic voice boomed out of the command centre's AV pillars.

Every sheriff in the room stared at the tactical communication station.

"We're going down!"

The carrier wave hissed for another couple of seconds, then fell silent. "God Almighty," Candace Elford whispered. She was sitting at her desk at the end of the rectangular room. Like most of the capital's civic buildings, the sheriff's headquarters was made of wood. It sat in its own square fortified enclosure a couple of hundred metres from the governor's dumper, a simplistic design that any pre-twentieth-century soldier would have felt at home in. The command centre itself formed one side of the parade ground, a long single-storey building with four grey composite spheres housing the satellite uplinks spaced along the apex of the roof. Inside, plain wooden benches ran around the walls, supporting an impressive array of modern desktop processor consoles operated by sheriffs seated in composite chairs. On the wall opposite Candace Elford's desk a big projection screen displayed a street map of Durringham (as far as it was possible to map that conglomeration of erratic alleyways and private passages). Conditioners hummed unobtrusively to keep the temperature down. The atmosphere of technological efficiency was spoilt slightly by the fans of yellow-grey fungus growing out of the skirting-board underneath the benches.

"Contact lost," Mitch Verkaik, the sheriff sitting at the tactical communication station reported, stone faced.

Candace turned to the small team she had assigned to monitor the posse's progress. "What about the sheriffs on the ground? Did they see it come down?"

Jan Routley was operating the satellite link to the *Swithland* survivors; she loaded an order into her console. "There is no response from any communicator on the *Swithland* or the *Hycel*. I can't even raise a transponder identity code."

Candace studied the situation display projected by her own console's AV pillar, more out of habit than anything else. She knew they were all waiting for her to rap out orders, smooth and confident, producing instant perfect solutions like an ambulatory computer. It wasn't going to happen. The last week had been a complete nightmare. They couldn't contact anyone in the Quallheim Counties or Willow West any more, and communications with villages along the Zamjan were patchy. The reinforcement flights to Ozark were a stopgap at best; privately she had intended that the fresh men and weapons would simply safeguard an evacuation of settlers down the river. She had long since abandoned the idea of restoring order to the Quallheim Counties, confinement was her best hope. Now it looked like Ozark was inside the affected zone. Seventy men and almost a quarter of her armoury.

"Call the second BK133 back to Durringham right away," she said shortly. "If the invaders can bring down one, they can bring down another." And at least ten sheriffs with their heavy-duty weapons would be saved. They might need them badly in the weeks to come. It was pretty obvious the invaders were intent on complete domination of the planet.

"Yes, ma'am." Mitch Verkaik turned back to his console.

"How long before the observation satellite makes a pass over the paddle-boats?" Candace asked.

"Fifteen minutes," Jan Routley answered.

"Program it for an infrared overscan fifty kilometres either side of its orbital track, see if it can locate the downed BK133. It shouldn't be too hard to spot." She rested her chin in her hands, staring blankly at her desktop processor. Protecting Durringham was her priority now, she decided. They must hold on to the city until the LDC sent a combat force capable of regaining the countryside. She was convinced they were faced with an invasion, the hour-long briefing she'd had with Kelven Solanki that morning had put paid to any final doubts. Kelven was badly worried, which wasn't like him at all.

Candace hadn't told her staff what Kelven had said to her, about the possible use of sequestration and river-boats that might have already brought a preliminary platoon of invaders to Durringham. It didn't bear thinking about. There were three chairs conspicuously empty in the command centre today; even the sheriffs were reverting to a self-protective mentality. She couldn't blame them; most had a family in the city, and none had signed on to fight a well-organized military force. But she'd agreed to cooperate with the Confederation Navy office in reviewing satellite image records of river traffic for the last fortnight.

"We're receiving the images now," Jan Routley called out.

Candace stirred herself, and walked over to the woman's position. Kilometre after kilometre of jungle streamed across the high-definition holoscreen; the green treetops were overlaid by transparent red shadows to indicate the temperature profile. The Zamjan leapt into view at the bottom of the screen, *Swithland*'s stern jutting out onto the water from under the bankside canopy of vegetation. Graphics flashed across the holoscreen, drawing orange circles around a glade close to the water.

"It's a fire," Jan Routley said. She datavised an order into the desktop processor to centre on the infrared source. The clearing expanded on the screen, showing a bonfire burning in its centre. There were blankets and the unmistakable white cargo-pods of homesteading gear littered about. Several trees had been felled on one side. "Where have all the people gone?" she asked in a small voice.

"I don't know," Candace said. "I really don't."

It was midafternoon, and the *Coogan* was twenty-five kilometres downriver from the abandoned paddle-boats when Len Buchannan and Darcy spotted the first pieces of flotsam bobbing about in the water. Crates of farmsteading gear, lengths of planking, fruit. Five minutes later they saw the first body: a woman in a one-piece ship-suit, face down, with arms and legs spread wide.

"We're turning back now," Len informed him.

"All the way to the mouth of the Quallheim," Darcy reminded him.

"Shove your money and your contract." He started turning the wheel. "You think I'm blind to what's going on? We're already in the rebel area. It's gonna take a miracle to get us downriver if we start now, never mind from another hundred and fifty kilometres further east."

"Wait," Darcy put his hand on the wheel. "How far to Ozark?"

Scowling, Len consulted an ancient guidance block sitting on a shelf in the wheel-house. "Thirty kilometres, maybe thirty-five."

"Put us ashore five kilometres short of the village."

"I dunno—"

"Look, the eagles can spot any boat coming down the river ten kilometres ahead of us. If one does come, then we turn round immediately and sail for Durringham. How does that sound?"

"Why didn't the eagles spot all this, then? Hardly something you could miss."

"They're out over the jungle. We'll call them back now.

Besides, it could be a genuine accident. There might be people hurt up ahead."

The lines around Len's mouth tightened, reflecting his indecision. No true captain would ignore another boat in distress. A broken chunk of yellow foam packaging scraped down the side of the *Coogan*. "All right," he said, clutching at the wheel. "But the first sign of trouble, and I'm off downriver. It's not the money. *Coogan*'s all I've got, I built her with my own hands. I ain't risking the old girl for you."

"I'm not asking you to. I'm just as anxious as you that nothing happens to the boat, or you. No matter what we find in the villages, we've still got to get back to Durringham. Lori and I are too old to walk."

Len grunted dismissively, but started feeding the wheel round again, lining the prow up on the eastern horizon.

The affinity call went out, and Abraham and Catlin curved through the clear air, racing for the river. From their vantage point seven kilometres ahead of the *Coogan* they could see tiny scraps of debris floating slowly in the current. They were also high enough for the water to be almost completely transparent. Lori could see large schools of brownspines and reddish eel-analogues swimming idly.

It wasn't until the sun was a red-gold ball touching the treetops ahead of the little trader boat that the eagles found the paddle-boats jammed into opposite banks. Lori and Darcy guided them in long spirals above the surrounding jungle, searching for the colonists and crew and posse. There was nobody on the boats, or in the camps that had been set up.

There's one, Lori said. She felt Darcy come into the link with Abraham, looking through the bird's enhanced eyes. Down below, a figure was slipping through the jungle. The tightly packed leaves made observation difficult, granting them only the most fleeting of glimpses. It was a man, a new colonist they judged, because he was wearing a shirt of synthetic fabric. He was walking unhurriedly westwards, parallel to the river about a kilometre inland.

Where does he think he's going? Darcy asked. **There isn't another village on this side for fifty kilometres.**

Do you want to send Abraham down below the tree level for a better look?

No. My guess is this man's been sequestrated. They all have.

There were nearly seven hundred people on those three boats.

Yes.

And there are close to twenty million people on Lalonde. How much would it cost to sequestrate them all?

A lot, if you used nanonics.

You don't think it is nanonics?

No; Laton said it was an energy virus. Whatever that is.

And you believe him?

I hate to say it, but I'm giving what he said a great deal of credence right now. There's certainly something at work here beyond our normal experience.

Do you want to capture this man? If he is a victim of the virus we should learn all we need to know from him.

I'd hate to try chasing anyone through this jungle, especially a lone man on foot who obviously has colleagues nearby.

We go on to Ozark, then?

Yes.

The *Coogan* advanced up the river at a much slower pace, waiting for the sun to set before passing the two paddleboats. For the first time since he arrived on the planet, Darcy actually found himself wishing it would rain. A nice thick squall would provide extra cover. As it was they had to settle for thin clouds gusting over Diranol, subduing its red lambency to a sourceless candle-glow which reduced ordinary visibility to a few hundred metres. Even so the trader's wheezing engines and clanking gearbox sounded appallingly loud on the night-time river where silence was sacrosanct.

Lori engaged her retinal implants as they crept thieflike between the two boats. Nothing moved, there were no lights. The two derelicts set up cold resonances in her heart she couldn't ignore. The ships brooded.

"There should be a small tributary around here," Darcy said an hour later. "You can moor the *Coogan* in it; that ought to make it invisible from anyone on the Zamjan."

"How long for?" Len asked.

"Until tomorrow night. That should give us plenty of time, Ozark is only another four kilometres east of here. If we're not back by 04:00 hours, then cast off and get home."

"Right you are. And I ain't spending a minute more, mind."

"Make sure you don't cook anything. The smell will give you away if there's any trained hunting beasts in the area."

The little tributary stream was only twice the width of the *Coogan*, with tall cherry oak trees growing on the boggy banks. Len Buchannan backed his boat down it, cursing every centimetre of the way. Once cables had secured it in the middle of the channel, Len, Lori, and Darcy worked for an hour cutting branches to camouflage the cabin.

Len's dark mood became apprehensive when Darcy and Lori were finally set to leave. Both of them had put on their chameleon suits; matt grey, tight fitting, with a ring of broad equipment pouches around the waist. He couldn't see an empty one.

"Look out for yourselves," he mumbled, embarrassed at what he was saying, as they walked down the plank to the jungle.

"Thank you, Len," Darcy said. "We will. Just make sure you're here when we get back." He pulled the hood over his head.

Len raised a hand. The air around the Edenists turned impenetrably black, flowing like oily smoke around their bodies. Then they were gone. He could hear their feet squelching softly in the mud, slowly fading into the distance. A sudden chill breeze seemed to rise out of the cloying jungle humidity, and he hastened back into the galley. Those chameleon suits were too much like magic.

Four kilometres through the jungle in the dead of night.

It wasn't too bad, their retinal implants had low-light and infrared capability. Their world was a two-tone of green and red, shot through with strange white sparkles, like interference on a badly tuned holoscreen. Depth perception was the trickiest, compressing trees and bushes into a flat mantle of landscape.

Twice they came across sayces on a nocturnal prowl. The animals' hot bodies shone like a dawn star amongst the lacklustre vegetation. Each time, Darcy killed them with a single shot from his maser carbine.

Lori's inertial guidance block navigated them towards the village, its bitek processor pumping their coordinates directly into her brain, giving her the mindless knowledge and accuracy of a migratory bird. All she had to watch out for was the lie of the land; even the most exhaustive satellite survey couldn't reveal the folds, rillets, and gullies that hid below the treetops.

Two hundred metres from the edge of Ozark's clearing, their green and red world began to grow lighter. Lori checked through Abraham high overhead, keeping the bird circling outside the clearing. There were a number of fires blazing in open pits outside the cabins.

Seems pretty normal, she told Darcy.

From here, yes. Let's see if we can get in closer and spot any of the sheriffs and their weapons.

OK. One minute, I'll bring Kelven in. We'll update him as we go. In case anything happens and we don't get back, that way they'll have some record—but she tried not to think that. She ordered her communication block to open a channel to the naval ELINT satellite. The unit had a bitek processor, so the conversation wouldn't be audible.

We're at Ozark village now, she told the navy commander.

Are you all right? Kelven Solanki asked.

Yes.

What's your situation?

Right now we're on our hands and knees about a hundred metres from the fields around the village. There are several fires burning in the village, and a lot of people moving round for this time of night. There must be three or four hundred of them outside, can't be many in the cabins. Apart from that it looks pretty ordinary. She wormed her way forward through the tangle of long grass and creepers, avoiding the bushes. Darcy was a metre to her left. It had been a long time since her last fieldcraft training session, she was moderately pleased by how little noise she was making.

Kelven, I want you to datavise a list of the sheriffs the BK133s landed at Ozark, Darcy said. **We'll see if we can identify any of them.**

Right away, here they come.

Lori pressed the twigs of a low-hanging branch to the ground, and slithered over them. There was the trunk of a large mayope four metres ahead, its roots sloping up out of the soil. Light from the fires fluoresced the bark to a lurid topaz.

The list of sheriffs streamed into her mind; facts, figures, and profiles, most importantly the holograms. Mirages of seventy men shimmered over the vapid low-light image of Ozark. Lori reached the mayope trunk and looked out over the lines of seedy cabins, trying to match the visual patterns in her mind with what she could see.

There's one, Darcy said. His mind indicated one of the men squatting in a circle of people around a fire. Some kind of animal carcass was roasting above the flames.

And another, Lori indicated.

They swiftly located a further twelve sheriffs at various fires.

None of them look particularly concerned that their communications with Candace Elford have been cut off, she said.

Have they been sequestrated? Kelven Solanki asked.

There's no way of knowing for sure, but my best guess is yes, Darcy said. **Given their current situation, their behaviour is abnormal. They should at least have posted a perimeter guard.**

The bitek processor in Lori's back-up communication block reported a power loss in the unit's electron-matrix crystal. She automatically ordered the reserve crystal to be brought on line, the thought was virtually subconscious.

I concur, Lori said. **I think our original primary goal of verifying Laton's presence is irrelevant in these circumstances.**

Seconded. We'll attempt to seize one of these people and bring them back to Durringham for examination. The mimetic governor circuitry on Darcy's chameleon suit indicated a databus glitch in his right leg; alternative channels were brought on line by the master processor.

Our best bet will be that cabin there, it's reasonably isolated, and I saw someone go in just now. Lori evinced a five-room building standing apart from the others. It was a hundred and twenty metres from the edge of the jungle, but the intervening ground was mostly allotments, providing as much cover as the trees. She took an image enhancer out of a pouch on her waist, and brought it up to her eyes. **Bloody thing's broken. Try yours, we need to know how many are inside.**

Darcy's chemical/biological agent detector shut down. **It hasn't broken,** he said in consternation. **We're in some kind of electronic warfare field!**

Damn it! Lori's back-up communicator and target-laser-acquisition warning sensors dropped out. **Kelven, did you hear that? They're using highly sophisticated electronic warfare systems.**

Your signal strength is fading, Kelven said.

Darcy felt his affinity link with his maser carbine's controlling processor vanish. When he looked at the gun its LCD display panel was dead. **Come on, move it! Back to the Coogan.**

Darcy!

He twisted round to see five people standing in a semicircle right-behind them. One woman, four men. All of them with strange placid smiles; dressed like settlers in denim trousers and cotton shirts, the men with thick beards. Even with shock paralysing his nerves he retained enough presence of mind to glance at his own arm. Infrared showed him a faint pink outline, but low-light simply revealed long blades of grass. The chameleon circuitry was still functional.

"Shit!" **Kelven, they can see chameleon suits. Warn your people. Kelven?** The hardware units he wore round his waist were all failing in rapid succession, affinity filling his mind with processor caution warnings. They started to wink out. There was no reply from Kelven Solanki.

"You must be the pair Laton called," one of the men said. He looked from Lori to Darcy. "You can get up now."

The power supply to Lori's chameleon suit ebbed to nothing, and the fabric reverted to its natural dull grey. She rolled to one side and stood in one smooth motion. Implant glands were feeding a gutsy brew of hormones into her blood supply, hyping her muscles. She dropped both her maser carbine and the image enhancer, freeing her hands. Five wouldn't be a problem. "Where do you come from?" she asked. "I'm talking to you that's in charge of them. Is your origin in your memory?"

"You're an atheist," the woman replied. "It would be kinder to spare you the answer."

Take them out, Darcy said.

Lori stepped forwards, turning, arms and legs moving fast. Left ankle swinging into the man's kneecap with her full bodyweight behind it—satisfying crackle of breaking bone; right hand chopping the woman's larynx, slamming her Adam's apple into her vertebrae. Darcy was wreaking similar mayhem on his targets. Lori spun round on one foot, left leg kicking out again, back arching supplely, and her boot's toecap caught a man just below and behind his ear, splitting his skull.

Hands gripped at her arms from behind. Lori yelped in shock. Nobody should be there. But reflexes took over, a fast back-kick which connected with a thigh, and she completed the turn with her arms locking into a defensive posture in time to see the woman staggering back. She blinked in incomprehension. The woman had blood pouring out of her mouth, her throat was severely disfigured from the first blow. As she watched, the skin inflated out, Adam's apple reappearing. The gush of blood stopped.

Sweet shit, what does it take to stop them?

The two men Darcy had knocked over were regaining their feet. One had a shattered shin bone, its jagged end protruding from the flesh just below his knee; he stood on it and walked forwards.

Electrodes, Darcy ordered. The first of the men was

reaching for him, the side of his face caved in where Darcy's boot had impacted, eyeball mashed in its socket, shedding tears of syrupy yellow fluid, but still smiling. He deliberately stepped inside the groping embrace, bringing his hands up, fingers wide, and clamping his palms on either side of the man's head. The long cords of eel-derived electroplaque cells buried in his forearms discharged through organic conductors that emerged from his fingertips in the form of tiny warts. The man's head was crowned with a blinding flare of purple-white static accompanied by a gunshot crack as the full two-thousand-volt charge slammed into his brain.

A vicious tingling erupted across Darcy's hands as some of the current leaked through the subcutaneous insulation. But the effect on the man was like nothing Darcy had ever seen before. The discharge should have felled him instantly, nothing living could withstand that much electricity. Instead he lurched backwards clutching at his mangled head, emitting a soprano keening. His skin began to glow, shining brighter and brighter. The shirt and jeans flamed briefly, falling away from the incandescent body as blackened petals. Darcy shielded his eyes with his hand. There was no heat, he realized, with a light so bright he ought to feel a scorch wave breaking across his chameleon suit. The man had become translucent now, so powerful was the surge of photons, revealing bones and veins and organs as deep scarlet and purple shadows. Their solidity dissolved, as if they were different coloured gases caught in a hurricane. He managed one last wretched wail as his body gave a massive epileptic spasm.

The light snuffed out, and the man fell flat on his face.

The other four assailants began to howl. Lori had heard a dog lamenting the death of its master once; their voices had that same bitter resentful grieving. She realized some of her hardware units were coming back on-line, the disruption effect was abating. Her chameleon suit circuitry sent psychedelic scarlet and green fireworks zipping over the fabric.

"Kelven!" she shouted desperately.

Alone in his darkened office a thousand kilometres away Kelven Solanki jerked to attention behind his desk as her static-jarred voice crashed into his neural nanonics.

"Kelven, he was right, Laton was right, there is some kind of energy field involved. It interfaces with matter somehow, controls it. You can beat it with electricity. Sometimes. Hell, she's getting up again."

Darcy's voice broke in. "Run! Now!"

"Don't let them gang up on you, Kelven. They're powerful when they group together. It's got to be xenocs."

"Shit, the whole village is swarming after us," Darcy called.

Static roared along the satellite link like a rogue binary blitzkrieg, making Kelven wince.

"Kelven, you must quarantine . . ." Lori never finished, her signal drowning below the deluge of rampaging whines and hisses. Then the racket ended.

TRANSPONDER SIGNAL DISCONTINUED, the computer printed neatly on Kelven's desk screen.

"I told you we shouldn't have come up here, didn't I?" Gail Buchannan said. "Plain as day, I said no, I said you can't trust Edenists. But you wouldn't listen. Oh no. They just waved their fancy credit disk in front of your eyes, and you rolled over like a wet puppy. It's worse than when she was on board."

Sitting on the other side of the galley's table, Len covered his eyes with his hands. The diatribes didn't bother him much now, he had learnt to filter them out years ago. Perhaps it was one of the reasons they had stayed together so long, not from attraction, simply because they ignored each other ninety per cent of the time. He had taken to thinking about such things recently, since Marie had left.

"Is there any coffee left?" he asked.

Gail never even glanced up from her knitting needles. "In the pot. You're as lazy as she was."

"Marie wasn't lazy." He got up and walked over to the electric hotplate where the coffee-pot was resting.

"Oh, it's *Marie* now, is it? I bet you can't name ten of the others we ferried downriver."

He poured half a mug of coffee and sat back down. "Neither can you."

She actually stopped knitting. "Lennie, for God's sake,

none of them had this effect on you. Look at what's happened to us, to the boat. What was so special about her? There must have been over a hundred brides in that bunk of yours down the years."

Len glanced up in surprise. With her bloated features rendering her face almost expressionless it was difficult to know what went on behind his wife's eyes, but he could tell how confused she was. He dropped his gaze to the steaming mug, and blew on it absently. "I don't know."

Gail grunted, and resumed her knitting.

"Why don't you go to bed?" he said. "It's late, and we ought to stay awake in shifts."

"If you hadn't been so eager to come here we wouldn't have to mess our routine up."

Arguing just wasn't worth the effort. "Well, we're here now. I'll keep watch until midmorning."

"Those damn Ivets. I hope Rexrew has every one of them shot."

The lighting panel screwed into the galley's ceiling began to dim. Len gave it a puzzled glance; all the boat's electrical systems ran off the big electron-matrix crystals in the engine-room, and they were always kept fully charged. If nothing else, he did keep the boat's machinery in good order. Point of honour, that was.

Someone stepped onto the *Coogan*'s deck between the wheel-house and the long cabin. It was only the slightest sound, but Len and Gail both looked up sharply, meeting each other's gaze.

A young-looking teenage lad walked into the galley. Len saw he was wearing a sheriff's beige-coloured jungle jacket, the name Yuri Wilken printed on the left breast. Darcy had told him about the invaders using sequestration techniques. At the time he'd listened cynically; now he was prepared to believe utterly. There was a vicious wound on the lad's throat, long scars of red tender skin all knotted up. A huge ribbon of dried blood ran down the front of his sleeveless shirt. He wore the kind of dazed expression belonging to the very drunk.

"Get off my boat," Len growled.

Yuri Wilken parted his mouth in a parody of a smile. Liq-

uid rasps emerged as he tried to speak. The lighting panel
was flashing on and off at high frequency.

Len stood up and calmly walked over to the long counter
fitted along the starboard wall.

"Sit," Yuri grated. His hand closed on Gail's shoulder.
There was a sizzling sound, and her dress strap ignited,
sending licks of yellow flame curling round his fingers. His
skin remained completely unblemished.

Gail let out an anguished groan at the pain, her mouth
yawning open. Wisps of blue smoke were rising from
below Yuri's hand as her skin was roasted. "Sit or she's
dead."

Len opened the top drawer next to the fridge, and pulled
out the 9mm, semi-automatic pistol he kept for emergen-
cies. He never had trusted lasers and magnetic rifles, not
exposed to the Juliffe's corrosive humidity. If anyone came
aboard looking for trouble after a deal went sour, or a village got worked up about prices, he wanted something that
would be guaranteed to work first time.

He flicked the safety catch off, and swung the heavy
blue-black gun around to point at Yuri.

"No," the lad's malaised voice croaked. He brought his
hands up in front of his face, cowering back.

Len fired. The first bullet caught Yuri on his shoulder,
spinning him round and pushing him into the wall. Yuri
snarled, furious eyes glaring at him. The second was aimed
at Yuri's heart. It hit his sternum and the planks behind him
were splashed with crimson as two of his ribs were blown
apart. He began to slide down the wall, breath hissing
through feral teeth. The lighting panel jumped up to its full
brightness.

Len watched with numb dismay as the shoulder wound
closed up. Yuri squirmed round, trying to regain his feet
with slow tenacity. He grinned evilly. The grip on the pistol
was growing alarmingly warm inside Len's hand.

"Kill him, Lennie!" Gail shouted. "Kill, kill!"

Feeling preternaturally calm, Len took aim at the lad's
head and squeezed the trigger. Once. Twice. The first
punched Yuri's nose into his skull, ripping through his
brain. He sucked air in, warbling frantically. Blood and

gore slurped out of the hole. The second shot caught the right side of his temple, driving splinters of bone into the wood behind like a flight of Stone Age darts. His feet began to drum on the deck.

Len was seeing it through a cold mist. The punished, mutilated body just refused to give up. He yelled a wordless curse, finger tugging back again and again.

The pistol was clicking uselessly, its magazine empty. He blinked, trying to pull the world back into focus. Yuri had finally fallen still, there was very little left of his head. Len turned aside, grasping the side of the basin for support as a flush of nausea travelled through him. Gail was whimpering softly, a hand stroking the terrible blisters and long blackened burn marks that mottled her shoulder.

He went over and cradled her head with a tenderness he hadn't shown in years.

"Get us out of here," she pleaded. "Please, Lennie."

"Darcy and Lori . . ."

"Us, Lennie. Get us out of here. You don't think they're going to live through tonight, do you?"

He licked his lips, making up his mind. "No." He brought her the first aid kit and applied a small anaesthetic patch to her shoulder. She let out a blissful little sigh as it discharged.

"You go start the engines," she said. "I'll see to this. I've never held you back yet." She started to rummage through the kit box, hunting for a medical nanonic package.

Len went out onto the deck and untied the silicon-fibre cables mooring the *Coogan*, slinging the ends over the side. They were expensive, and hard to come by, but it would take another quarter of an hour if he went stumbling round the banks coiling them all up properly.

The furnace was quite cool, but the electron-matrix crystals had enough power to take *Coogan* an easy seventy kilometres downstream before they were drained. He started the motors, shoving the trader boat out from under the lacework awning of cut branches veiling it from casual eyes. As if there were any of those left on the river, he mused.

Getting underway was a miraculous morale booster. Alone on the lively Zamjan amid the first tinges of dawn's

grey light he could almost believe they were trading again.
Simple times, watching the wheel-house's basic instrumentation, and enjoying the prospect of milking another batch
of dumb dreamers at the next village. He even managed to
keep his mind from the macabre corpse in the galley.

They had gone six kilometres almost due west, helped by
the broad river's swift current, when Len saw two dark
smudges on the water up ahead. *Swithland* and *Hycel* were
steaming towards him. A great cleft had been made in the
Swithland's prow, and the superstructure was leaning over
at a hellish angle; but neither seemed to be affecting her
speed.

The short-range radio block beside the forward-sweep
mass-detector let out a bleep, then the general contact band
came on. "Hoi there, Captain Buchannan, this is the *Hycel*.
Reduce speed and prepare to come alongside."

Len ignored it. He steered a couple of degrees to starboard. The two paddle-boats altered course to match.
Blocking him.

"Come on, Buchannan, what do you hope to gain? That
pitiful little boat can't out-race us. One way or the other,
you're coming on board. Now heave to."

Len thought of the burns the lad had inflicted with his
bare hand, the flickering lighting panel. It was all way beyond anything he could hope to understand or resolve.
There was no going back to life as it had been, not now.
And in the main it had been a good life.

He increased the power to the motors, and held the
course steady, aiming for the *Hycel*'s growing prow. With a
bit of luck Gail would never know.

He was still standing resolutely behind the *Coogan*'s
wheel when the two boats collided. The *Hycel* with its
greater bulk and stalwart hull rode the impact easily, smashing the flimsy *Coogan* apart like so much kindling, and
sucking the debris below its hull in a riot of bubbles.

Various chunks of wood and plastic bobbed about in the
paddle-boat's wake, spinning in the turbulent water. Thick
black oil patches welled up among them. The current
slowly pushed the scraps of wreckage downriver, dispers-

ing them over a wide area. Within quarter of an hour there was no evidence left to illustrate the trader boat's demise.

Swithland and *Hycel* continued on their way upriver without slowing.

18

Joshua Calvert was surprised to find himself enjoying the train journey. He had almost expected to see a nineteenth-century steam engine pumping out clouds of white smoke and clanking pistons spinning iron wheels. Reality was a sleek eight-wheel tractor unit with magnetic axle-motors powered from electron matrices, pulling six coaches.

The Kavanaghs had provided him with a first-class ticket, so he sat in a private compartment with his feet up on the opposite seat, watching the sprawling forests and picturesque hamlets go past. Dahybi Yadev sat next to him, eyelids blinking heavily as a mild stimulant program trickled through his neural nanonics. In the end they had decided that Ashly Hanson should remain behind to operate the *Lady Mac*'s MSV as the crew emptied the mayope from her cargo holds. Dahybi had volunteered to take his place quickly enough, and as the nodes had been glitch free on the trip to Norfolk, Joshua had agreed. The rest of the crew had been detailed to maintenance duty. Sarha had sulked at the prospect, she'd been looking forward to an extended leave exploring the gentle planet.

The train compartment's PA came on to announce they were pulling in to Colsterworth Station. Joshua stretched his limbs, and loaded a formal etiquette program into his neural nanonics. He had found it in *Lady Mac*'s memory cores; his father must have visited the planet at some time, though he had never mentioned it. The program might well turn out to be a saviour, country-dwelling Norfolk was supposed to be even more stuffy than swinging cosmopolitan Boston. Pursing his lips at the prospect, Joshua shook Dahybi Yadev's shoulder. "Come on, cancel the program. We've arrived."

Dahybi's face lost its narcotic expression, and he squinted out of the window. "This is it?"

"This is it."

"It looks like a field with a couple of houses in it."

"Don't yell that kind of comment about, for God's sake. Here." He datavised a copy of the etiquette program over. "Keep that in primary mode. We don't want to annoy our benefactor."

Dahybi ran through some of the social jurisprudence listed in the program. "Bloody hell, I think *Lady Mac* fell through a time warp to get here."

Joshua rang for the steward to carry their cases. The etiquette program said the man should be tipped five per cent of the ticket price, or a shilling, whichever was the larger sum.

Colsterworth Station consisted of two stone platforms, covered with broad wooden canopies supported by ornate wrought-iron pillars. The waiting-room and ticket office were built from red brick, and a row of metal brackets along the front wall were used to hold big hanging baskets full of bright flowering plants. Appearance was a priority to the stationmaster; the scarlet and cream paintwork was kept gleaming the whole year round, brasswork was polished, and his staff were always smartly turned out.

Such persistence had paid off handsomely today. He was standing next to the heir to Cricklade herself, Louise Kavanagh, who had remarked how nice it all looked.

The morning train from Boston pulled in slowly, and the stationmaster checked his watch. "Thirty seconds late."

Louise Kavanagh inclined her head graciously at the stout little man. On her other side William Elphinstone shuffled his feet impatiently. She silently prayed for him not to make a complete mess of things. He was so impetuous at times, and he looked totally out of place in his grey suit; field working clothes were much more apposite on him.

For herself, she'd carefully chosen a pale lavender dress with puff sleeves to wear. Nanny had helped to pleat her hair into an elaborate weave at the back of her head which ended in a long pony-tail. Hopefully the combination would give her a suitably dignified appearance.

The train halted, its first three coaches taking up the entire length of the platform. Doors banged open noisily, and passengers started to climb down. She straightened her back to get a better look at the people emerging from the first-class coach.

"There they are," William Elphinstone said.

Louise wasn't entirely sure what she'd been expecting, although she was pretty sure in her own mind that starship captains were wise, serious, and mature responsible men, perhaps a bit like her father (except without the temper). Who else would be entrusted with such a fearsome responsibility? What a captain did not look like, even in her most fantastical dreams, was a young man with strong regular features, six foot tall, wearing a smart, exotically stylish uniform that emphasized his powerful build. But there was the silver star on his shoulder, plain for all the world to see.

Louise swallowed hard, tried to remember the words she was supposed to say, and stepped forwards with a polite smile in place. "Captain Calvert, I'm Louise Kavanagh; my father apologizes for not being here to greet you in person, but the estate is very busy right now and requires his full attention. So I'd like to welcome you to Cricklade myself, and hope you enjoy your stay." Which was almost what she'd rehearsed, but there was something about enjoying his train journey which had been missed out. Oh, well . . .

Joshua took her hand in an emphatic grip. "That's very kind of you, Louise. And I must say I consider myself most fortunate that your father is so occupied, because there simply cannot be a nicer way of being welcomed to Cricklade than by a young lady as beautiful as yourself."

Louise knew her cheeks would be colouring, and wanted to turn and hide. What a juvenile reaction. He was only being polite. But so utterly charming. And he sounded sincere. Could he really think that about her? Her discipline had gone all to pieces. "Hello," she said to Dahybi Yadev. Which was so dreadfully gauche. Her blush deepened. She realized Joshua was still holding her hand.

"My starflight engineering officer," Joshua said, with a slight bow.

Louise recovered, and introduced William Elphinstone as

an estate manager, not mentioning he was only a trainee. Which he should have been grateful for, but she got the distinct impression he wasn't terribly impressed with the starship captain.

"We have a carriage laid on to take you to the manor," William said. He signalled to the driver to take Joshua's bags from the steward.

"That's really most thoughtful of you," Joshua told Louise.

Dimples appeared in her cheeks. "This way." She gestured to the platform exit.

Joshua thought the waiting carriage looked like an oversized pram fitted with modern lightweight wheels. But the two black horses moved it along at a fair clip, and the ride over the rutted track was comfortably smooth. There hadn't been much to Colsterworth, it was a rural market town with very few industries; the countryside economy revolved around the farms. Its houses were mostly built from locally quarried stone with a bluish tinge. Doors and windows were almost always arched.

When they rode down the busy High Street, pedestrians nudged one another and glanced over as the carriage went by. At first Joshua thought they were looking at him and Dahybi, but then he realized it was Louise who drew their attention.

Outside Colsterworth the rolling countryside was a patchwork of small fields separated by immaculately layered hedges. Streams wound down through the gentle valleys, while spinneys clung to the rounded heights and deeper folds. The wheat and barley had already been harvested, he saw. Plenty of haystacks were dotted about, steeply sloping tops netted against the expected winter winds. Tractors were ploughing the stubble back into the rich red soil before drilling the second crop. There would be just enough time for the stalks to ripen before the long autumn and winter seasons began.

"You don't have any proscription against power tractors, then?" Joshua asked.

"Certainly not," William Elphinstone replied. "We're a stable society, Captain, not a backward one. We use whatever is appropriate to maintain the status quo, and give people a decent standard of living at the same time. Using horses to plough every field would be pure drudgery. That's not what Norfolk is about. Our founders wanted pastoral life to be enjoyable for all." To Joshua's ears he sounded defensive, but then he had been on edge since they'd been introduced.

"Where does all the power come from?" Joshua asked.

"Solar cells are sufficient for domestic utilities, but ninety per cent of the electricity used for industry and agriculture is geothermal. We buy in thermal-potential fibres from the Confederation and drill them three or four miles down into the mantle. Most towns have five or six heat shafts; they're virtually maintenance free, and the fibres last for a couple of centuries. It's a much neater solution than building hydro dams everywhere and flooding valleys."

Interesting how he said Confederation, Joshua thought, almost as if Norfolk wasn't a part of it.

"All this must seem terribly cumbersome to you, I expect," Louise said.

"Not at all," Joshua answered. "What I've seen so far is admirable. You should visit some of the so-called advanced worlds I've been to. Technology comes with a very high price in terms of society, they have dreadful levels of crime and vice. Some urban areas have decayed into complete no-go zones."

"Three people were murdered on Kesteven last year," Louise said.

William Elphinstone frowned as if to object, but let it pass.

"I think your ancestors got your constitution about right," Joshua said.

"Hard on people who are sick," Dahybi Yadev observed.

"There aren't many illnesses," William Elphinstone said. "Our lifestyle means we're a very healthy people. And our hospitals can cope with most accidents."

"Including cousin Gideon," Louise said slyly.

Joshua pressed down on a smile as William Elphinstone gave her a curtly censorious look. The girl wasn't quite as meek as he'd first supposed. They were sitting opposite each other in the carriage, which gave him a good opportunity to study her. He had thought that she and William pain-in-the-arse Elphinstone were an item, but judging from the way she virtually ignored him it didn't seem too likely. William Elphinstone appeared none too happy with the cold-shoulder treatment, either.

"Actually, William isn't being entirely honest," she went on. "We don't catch diseases because most of our first-comer ancestors were recipients of geneering before they settled here. It stands to reason, on a planet which deliberately excludes the most advanced medical treatments it's wise to protect yourself in advance. So in that respect we don't quite match up to the simplistic pastoral ideal. You probably couldn't have built a society as successful as Norfolk before geneering; people would have insisted on continuing technical and medical research to better their lot."

William Elphinstone made a show of turning his head and staring out over the fields.

"Fascinating idea," Joshua said. "You can only have stability once you've passed a certain technological level, and flux is the natural order until that happens. Are you going to take politics at university?"

Her lips depressed fractionally. "I don't think I'll be going. Women don't, generally. And there aren't many universities anyway; there's no research to be done. Most of my family go to agricultural colleges, though."

"And will you be joining your relatives there?"

"Maybe. Father hasn't said. I'd like to. Cricklade is going to be mine one day, you see. I want to be more than just a figurehead."

"I'm sure you will be, Louise. I can't imagine you as just a figurehead for anything." He was surprised at how earnest his voice had become.

Louise cast her eyes down to see she was knotting her fingers in her lap in a most unladylike manner. Whatever was making her babble like this?

"Is this Cricklade now?" Joshua asked. The fields had given way to larger expanses of parkland between the small woods. Sheep and cattle were grazing placidly, along with

some xenoc bovine-analogue that looked similar to a very
hairy deer, with fat legs and hemispherical hoofs.

"We've been riding through the Cricklade estate since we
left town, actually," William Elphinstone said snidely.

Joshua gave Louise an encouraging smile. "As far as the
eye can see, is it?"

"Yes."

"Then I can see why you love it so much. If I ever settle
down, I'd want it to be in a land like this."

"Any chance we can see some roses?" Dahybi Yadev
asked loudly.

"Yes, of course," Louise said, suddenly brisk. "How
dreadfully remiss of me. Cousin Kenneth said this was your
first time here." She turned round and tapped the driver on
his shoulder. The two of them exchanged a few words.
"There's a grove beyond the forest up ahead," she said.
"We'll stop there."

The grove took up ten acres on a northern-facing slope.
To catch the suns, Louise explained. It was marked out by
a dry-stone wall that was host to long patches of moss-
analogue which sprouted miniature pink flowers. The flat
stones themselves were often crumbling from frost ero-
sion; little attempt had been made at repairs except in the
worst sections of subsidence. In one corner of the grove
there was a long barn with a thatched roof; moss had
clawed its way into the reeds, loosening the age-black-
ened bundles. New wooden pallets stacked with what
looked like thousands of conical white plant pots were just
visible through the barn's open doorway.

Still, dry air magnified the grove's placid composure,
adding to the impression of genteel decay. If it hadn't been
for the perfectly regimented rows of plants, Joshua would
have believed the grove had been neglected, simply treated
as a hobby by an indulgent landowner rather than the vital
industry it was.

Norfolk's weeping rose was unarguably the most famous
plant in the Confederation. In its natural state it was a thorn-
less rambling bush that favoured well-drained peaty soil.
But when cultivated and planted in groves it was trained up
wire trellises three metres high. The jade-green leaves were

palm sized, reminiscent of terrestrial maples with their deep serrations, their tips coloured a dull red.

But it was the flowers which drew Joshua's scrutiny; they were yellow-gold blooms, twenty-five centimetres in diameter with a thick ruff of crinkled petals hugging a central onion-shaped carpel pod. Each plant in the grove had produced thirty-five to forty flowers, standing proud on fleshy green stems as thick as a man's thumb. Under Duke's unremitting glare they had acquired a spectral lemon-yellow corona.

The four of them walked a little way down the mown grass between the rows. Careful pruning of the bushes had ensured that each flower was fully exposed to the sunlight, none of them overlapped.

Joshua pressed his toe into the wiry grass, feeling the solid earth. "It's very dry," he said. "Will there be enough water to fill them out?"

"It never rains at midsummer," Louise said. "Not on the inhabited islands, anyway. Convection takes all the clouds up to the poles; most of the ice-caps melt under the deluge, but the temperature is still only a couple of degrees above freezing. It's considered frightfully bad luck if it even drizzles here in the week before Midsummer's Day. The roses store up all the moisture they need for fruition in their roots during springtime."

He reached up and touched one of the big flowers, surprised by how stiff the stem was. "I had no idea they were so impressive."

"This is an old grove," she said. "The roses here are fifty years old, and they're good for another twenty. We replant several groves each year from the estate's nurseries."

"That sounds like quite an operation. I'd like to see it. Perhaps you could show me, you seem very knowledgeable about their cultivation."

Louise blushed again. "Yes, I do; I mean, I will," she stammered.

"Unless you have other duties, of course. I don't wish to impose." He smiled.

"You're not," she assured him quickly.

"Good."

She found herself smiling back at him for no particular reason at all.

Joshua and Dahybi had to wait until late afternoon before they were introduced to Grant Kavanagh and his wife, Marjorie. It was an opportunity for Joshua to be shown round the big manor house and its grounds, with Louise continuing her role of informative hostess. The manor was an impressive set-up; an unobtrusive army of servants was employed to keep the rooms in immaculate condition, and a lot of money had been spent making the decor as tasteful as possible. Naturally enough, the style was based prominently on the eighteenth-century school of design, history's miniature enclave.

Thankfully, William Elphinstone left them, claiming he had to work in the groves. They did, however, meet Genevieve Kavanagh as soon as their carriage drew up outside the entrance. Louise's young sister tagged along with them for the entire afternoon, giggling the whole time. Joshua wasn't used to children that age, in his opinion she was a spoilt brat who needed a damn good smack. If it wasn't for Louise he would have been mighty tempted to put her over his knee. Instead he suffered in silence, making the most of the way Louise's dress fabric shifted about as she moved. There was precious little else to absorb his attention. To the uninitiated eye the estate beyond the grounds was almost deserted.

Midsummer on Norfolk was a time when almost everybody living in the countryside helped out with the weeping rose crop. The travelling Romany caravans were in high demand, with estates and independent grove owners competing for their labour. Even school terms (Norfolk didn't use didactic laser imprints) were structured round the season, giving children time off to assist their parents, leaving winter as the principal time for studying. As the whole Tear crop was gathered in two days, preparation was an arduous and exacting business.

With over two hundred groves in his estate (not counting those in the crofts), Grant Kavanagh was the most industrious man in Stoke County during the days leading up to midsummer. He was fifty-six years old; modest geneering had produced a barrel-chested physique, five feet ten inches tall, with brown hair that was already greying around his mutton-chop sideboards. But a lifetime of physical activity and keeping a strict watch on what he ate meant he retained the vigour of a man in his twenties. He was able to chase up his flock of junior estate managers with unnerving doggedness. Which, as he knew from sore experience, was the only way of achieving anything in Stoke County. Not only did he have to supervise the teams which went round the groves setting up the collection cups, but he was also responsible for the county's bottling yard. Grant Kavanagh did not tolerate fools, slackers, and family sinecurists, which in his view described a good ninety-five per cent of Norfolk's population. Cricklade estate had run smoothly and profitably for the last two hundred and seventy years of its distinguished three-hundred-year existence, and by God that superb record wasn't going to end in his lifetime.

An afternoon spent in the saddle riding round some of the rosegroves closest to the manor, with the eternally enduring Mr Butterworth accompanying him, did not put him in the best frame of mind for trotting out glib niceties to dandies like visiting starship captains. He marched into the house slapping dust from his riding breeches and shouting for a drink, a bath, and a decent meal.

Having this red-faced martinet figure bearing down on him across the large airy entrance hall put Joshua in mind of a Tranquillity serjeant—only lacking the charm and good looks.

"Bit young to be skippering a starship, aren't you?" Grant Kavanagh said when Louise introduced them. "Surprised the banks gave you the loan to fly one."

"I inherited *Lady Mac*, and my crew made enough money in our first year of commercial flying to make the run to this planet. It's the first time we've been, and your family turned somersaults to give me three thousand cases of the best Tears on the island. What criteria would you judge my competence by?"

Louise closed her eyes and wished herself very, very small.

Grant Kavanagh stared at the utterly uncompromising expression of the young man who had answered him back in his own home, and burst out laughing. "By Christ, now that's the sort of attitude we could do with a hell of a lot more of around here. Well done, Joshua, I approve. Don't give ground, and bite back every time." He put a protective arm around both his daughters. "See that, you two rapscallions? That's what you've got to have to run commercial enterprises; starships or estates, it doesn't matter which. You just have to be the boss man each and every time you open your mouth." He kissed Louise on her forehead, and tickled a giggling Genevieve. "Glad to meet you, Joshua. Nice to see young Kenneth hasn't lost his touch when it comes to judging people."

"He puts together a tough deal," Joshua said, sounding unhappy.

"So it would seem. This mayope wood, is it as good as he says? I couldn't shut him up about it when he was on the phone."

"Yes, it's impressive. Like a tree that's grown out of steel. I brought some samples with me, of course, you can have a look for yourself."

"I'll take you up on that later." The manor's butler came into the hall carrying Grant's gin and tonic on a silver tray. He picked it up and took a sip. "I suppose this damned Lalonde planet will start charging a premium once they know how valuable it is to us?" he said in a disgruntled tone.

"That depends, sir."

"Oh?" Grant Kavanagh widened his eyes with interest at the humorously furtive tone. He let go of Genevieve, and patted her fondly. "Run along, poppet. It looks like Captain Calvert and I have something to discuss."

"Yes, Daddy." Genevieve capered past Joshua, giving him a sidelong glance, and breaking into giggles again.

Louise showed him a lopsided grin as she started to walk away. She had seen the other girls at school do that when they wanted to be coquettish with their boys. "You will be joining us for dinner, won't you, Captain Calvert?" she asked airily.

"I imagine so, yes."

"I'll tell cook to prepare some iced chiplemon. You'll like that; it's my favourite."

"Then I'm sure I'll like it too."

"And don't be late, Daddy."

"Am I ever?" Grant Kavanagh retorted, enchanted as ever by his little girl's playfulness.

She rewarded them both with a sunlight smile, then skipped off across the hall tiles after Genevieve.

An hour later Joshua was lying on his bed, fathoming the mysteries of the planet's communication system. His bedroom was in the west wing, a large room with *en suite* bathroom, its walls papered with a rich purple and gold pattern. The bed was a double, with a carved oak headboard and a horribly solid mattress. It required very little imagination on his part to picture Louise Kavanagh lying on it beside him.

There was a phone on the bedside table, but the impossibly antique gadget didn't have a standard processor; he couldn't use his neural nanonics to datavise the communication net control computer. It didn't even have an AV pillar, just a keyboard, a holoscreen, and a handset. He did think that Norfolk had written a wonderfully realistic Turing program into the exchange's processor array to deal patiently with requests, until he finally realized he was actually talking to a human operator. She patched him into the geostationary relay satellite circuit and opened a channel to *Lady Macbeth*. What the call must be costing Grant Kavanagh was an item he managed to put firmly at the back of his mind. Humans operating a basic computer management routine!

"We've unloaded a third of the mayope already," Sarha said; the link was audio only, no visual. "Your new merchant friend Kenneth Kavanagh has hired half a dozen spaceplanes from other starships to ferry it down to the surface. At this rate we'll be finished by tomorrow."

"Great news. I don't want to sound premature, but after this run is over it looks like we'll be coming back here to finalize that arrangement we were kicking around earlier."

"You're making progress, then?"

"Absolutely."

"What's Cricklade like?"

"Astonishing, it's enough to make a Tranquillity plutocrat jealous. You'd love it."

"Thanks, Joshua. That really makes me feel good."

He grinned and took another sip of the Norfolk Tears his thoughtful host had provided. "How are you and Warlow coping with the maintenance checks?"

"We've finished."

"What?" He sat up abruptly, nearly spilling some of the precious drink.

"We've finished. There isn't a system on board that isn't as smooth as a baby's bum."

"Jesus, you must have been working your arses off."

"It took us five hours, grand total. And most of that was spent waiting for the diagnostics programs to run. There's nothing wrong with *Lady Mac*, Joshua. Her performance rating is as good as the day the CAB awarded us our space-worthiness certificate."

"That's ridiculous. We were so glitch prone after Lalonde we were lucky to get here at all."

"You think I don't know how to load a diagnostics program?" she asked, her voice sounding very tetchy.

"Of course you know your job," he said in a conciliatory tone. "It just doesn't make a lot of sense, that's all."

"You want me to datavise the results down to you?"

"No. You can't, anyway; this planet's net couldn't handle anything like that. What does Warlow say, is *Lady Mac* up to a CAB inspection?"

"We'll pass with flying colours."

"OK, I'll leave it up to the pair of you what you do."

"We'll get the inspectors up here tomorrow morning. Norfolk's CAB office only runs stage D checks in any case. Our own diagnostics are stricter than that."

"Fine. I'll call tomorrow for an update."

"Sure. 'Bye, Joshua."

Tehama asteroid was one of the most financially and industrially successful independent industrial settlements in the New Californian star system. A stony iron rock twenty-eight kilometres long and eighteen wide, tracing an irregular fifty-day elliptical orbit within the trailing Trojan point of Yosemite, the system's largest gas giant, it had all the elements and minerals necessary to support life, barring hydrogen and nitrogen. But that deficiency was made good from a snowball-shaped carbonaceous chondritic asteroid, one kilometre wide, which had been nudged into a fifty-kilometre orbit around Tehama in 2283. Since then its shale had been mined and refined; hydrogen was combined with oxygen to produce water, plain and simple; nitrogen underwent more complex bonding procedures to form useable nitrates; hydrocarbons were an essential. They were all introduced to the caverns being bored out of Tehama's metallic ore, producing a habitable biosphere capable of supporting the increasing population.

By 2611 there were two major caverns inside Tehama; and its small companion had been reduced to a sable lump two hundred and fifty metres wide, with a silver-white refinery station, almost as large, clinging to it barnacle-fashion.

The *Villeneuve's Revenge* jumped into an emergence zone a hundred and twenty thousand kilometres away, and began its approach manoeuvres. After months tending the starship's ageing, failure-prone systems, Erick Thakrar was grateful for any shore time. Shipboard life was one long grind, he'd lost count of how many times he'd falsified the maintenance log so they could avoid CAB penalties and keep flying. There was no doubt about it, the *Villeneuve's Revenge* was operating dangerously close to the margin, both mechanically and financially. Genuine independence was proving an elusive goal; Captain Duchamp was in debt to the banks to the tune of a million and a half fuseodollars, and charters were hard to find.

Some small part of Erick felt sorry for the old boy. Commercial starflight was a viciously tough business, a tightly woven web of large cartels and monopolies that resented the very existence of independent traders. Starships like the *Villeneuve's Revenge* forced the major carrier fleets to keep their own prices down, reducing profits. They retaliated with semi-legal syndicates in an attempt to lock out small ships.

Duchamp was an excellent captain, but his business acumen was highly questionable. His crew was loyal, though, and Erick had heard enough stories of past missions to know they had few qualms about how they earned money. If he wanted to, he could have had them arrested within a week of coming on board—neural-nanonics recorded conversation was admissible evidence in court. But he was after bigger prizes than a worn-out ship with its loser crew. The *Villeneuve's Revenge* was his access code to whole strata of illegal operations. And it looked like Tehama was going to be the start of the game.

After docking at the asteroid's non-rotating axis spaceport, four crew members from the *Villeneuve's Revenge* descended on the Catalina bar in the Los Olivos cavern, the first to be dug, a cylindrical hollow nine kilometres long and five in diameter. The Catalina was one of the spaceport crew bars, with aluminium tables and a small stage for a band. At three in the afternoon, local time, it was almost dead.

The bar was a cave drilled into the cavern's vertical cliff-face endwall, one of thousands forming an interconnected cave city, producing a band of glass windows and foliage-wrapped balconies that encircled the base of the endwall. Like an Edenist habitat, nobody lived on the cavern floor itself, it was a communal park and arable farm. But there the resemblance stopped.

Erick Thakrar sat at an alcove table near the balcony window with two of his shipmates, Bev Lennon and Desmond Lafoe, and their captain, André Duchamp. The Catalina was near the top of the city levels, giving it a seventy-five per cent gravity field, and a good view out into the cavern. Erick wasn't impressed by what he could see. The axis was taken up by a hundred-metre diameter gantry, most of which was filled by the thick black pipes of the irrigation-sprinkler nozzles. It was ringed at two hundred and fifty metre intervals by doughnut-shaped solartubes that shone with a painful blue-white intensity. They lacked the warm incandescence of an Edenist habitat's axis light-tube, which was dramatically illustrated by the plants far below. The cavern floor's grass shaded towards the yellow, while trees and shrubs were spindly, missing their full complement of leaves. Even the fields of crops were hungry looking (one reason why imported delicacies were so popular and profitable in all asteroid settlements). It was as though an unexpected autumn had visited the tropical climate.

The whole cavern was cramped and clumsy, a poor copy of a bitek habitat's excellence. Erick found himself thinking back to Tranquillity with nostalgia.

"Here he comes," André Duchamp muttered. "Be nice to the *Anglo*, remember we need him." The captain came from Carcassonne, a die-hard French nationalist, who blamed the ethnic English in the Confederation for everything from failed optical fibres in the starship's flight computer to his current overdraft. At sixty-five years old his geneered DNA maintained his physique in the lean mould which was the staple criterion of the space adapted, as well as providing him with a face that was rounded all over. When André Duchamp laughed, everyone in the room found themselves smiling along, so powerful was the appeal; he had the same emotional conviction as a painted clown.

Right now he put on his most welcoming smile for the man sidling anxiously up to the table.

Lance Coulson was a senior flight controller in Tehama's Civil Astronautics Bureau; in his late fifties, he lacked the political contacts necessary to gain senior management ranking. It meant he was stuck in inter-system tracking and communications until retirement now; that made him resentful, and agreeable to supplying people like André Duchamp with information—for the right price.

He sat at the table and gave Erick Thakrar a long look. "I haven't seen you before."

Erick started recording his implant-enhanced sensorium directly into a neural nanonics memory cell, and ordered a file search. Image: of an overweight man, facial skin a red tinge of brown from exposure to the cavern solartubes; grey suit with high circular collar, pinching the neck flesh; light brown hair, colour-embellished by follicle biochemical treatments. Sound: of slightly wheezy breathing, heartbeat rate above average. Smell: sour human sweat, beads standing out on a high forehead and the back of chubby hands.

Lance Coulson was nerving himself up. A weakling ruffled by the company he kept.

"Because I haven't been here before," Erick replied, unyielding. His CNIS file reported a blank, Lance Coulson wasn't a known criminal. Probably too petty, he thought.

"Erick Thakrar, my systems generalist," André Duchamp said. "Erick is an excellent engineer. Surely you don't question my judgement when it comes to my own crew?" There was just enough hint of anger to make Lance Coulson shift round in his seat.

"No, of course not."

"Excellent!" André Duchamp was all smiles again; he clapped Lance Coulson on the back, winning a sickly smile, and pushed a glass of Montbard brandy over the scratched aluminium slab to him. "So what have you got for me?"

"A cargo of micro-fusion generators," he said softly.

"So? Tell me more."

The civil servant rolled the stem of his glass between his thumb and finger, not looking at the captain. "A hundred thousand." He slid his Francisco Finance credit disk across the table.

"You jest!" André Duchamp said. There was a dangerous glint to his eyes.

"There were . . . questions last time. I'm not doing this again."

"You're not doing it this time at that price. If I had that kind of money do you think I would be here crawling to a tax-money leech like you?"

Bev Lennon put a restraining hand on Duchamp's shoulder. "Easy," he said smoothly. "Look, we're all here because money is tight, right? We can certainly pay you a quarter of that figure in advance."

Lance Coulson picked up his credit disk and stood up. "I see I have been wasting my time."

"Thank you for the information," Erick said in a loud voice.

Lance Coulson gave him a frightened look. "What?"

"That's going to be enormously useful to us. How would you like to be paid? Cash or commodities?"

"Shut up."

"Sit down, and stop fucking about."

He sat, checking the rest of the tables with twitchy glances.

"We want to buy, you want to sell," Erick said. "So let's stop the drama queen tactics, assume you've shown us what a tough negotiator you are, and we're all shitting bricks. Now what's your price? And be realistic. There are other flight controllers."

He overcame his agitation for just long enough to shoot Erick a look of one hundred per cent hatred. "Thirty thousand."

"Agreed," André Duchamp said immediately. He held out his Jovian Bank disk.

Lance Coulson gave a last furtive glance round before shoving his own disk in André's direction.

"*Merci*, Lance." André's grin was scathing as he received the datavised flight vector.

The four crewmen watched the civil servant retreating, and laughed. Erick was congratulated for calling the other man's bluff, Bev Lennon fetching him half a litre of of imported Lübeck beer.

"You had me panicking!" the wiry fusion specialist protested as he dropped the tankards down on their table.

Erick took a sip of the icy beer. "I had me panicking."

It was going well, they accepted him, reservations (and he knew some still had them) were fading, breaking down. He was becoming one of the lads.

Along with Bev Lennon and Desmond Lafoe, the ship's node specialist, a brawny two-metre-tall bear of a man, Erick spent the next ten minutes talking trivia while André Duchamp sat back with a blank expression reviewing the vector he had just bought.

"I don't see any problem," the captain announced eventually. "If we use a Sacramento orbit to jump from we can rendezvous any time in the next six days. Fifty-five hours from now would be the ideal . . ." His voice trailed off.

Erick turned to follow his gaze. Five men wearing copper-coloured one-piece ship-suits walked into the Catalina bar.

Hasan Rawand caught sight of André Duchamp as he was about to sit at the bar. He tapped Shane Brandes, the

Dechal's fusion engineer, on the side of his arm and flicked a finger in the direction of the master of *Villeneuve's Revenge*. His other three crew-members, Ian O'Flaherty, Harry Levine, and Stafford Charlton, caught the gesture and turned to look.

The two crews regarded each other with mutual hostility and antagonism.

Hasan Rawand walked over to the window booth table, his crew right behind him. "André," he said with mock civility. "So nice to see you. I trust you have brought my money. Eight hundred thousand, wasn't it? And that's before interest. It has been seventeen months after all."

André Duchamp gazed straight ahead, his hands cupping his beer tankard. "I owe you no money," he said darkly.

"I think you do. Cast your mind back; you were carrying plutonium initiators from Sab Biyar to the Isolo system. *Dechal* waited in Sab Biyar's Oort cloud for thirty-two hours for you, André. Thirty-two hours in stealth mode, with freezing air and iced food, pissing into tubes that leaked, not even allowed a personal MF player in case the navy ships picked up its electronic emission. That's not nice, André; it's about as close as you can get to a Confederation penal colony without being shot down to the surface in a drop capsule. We waited for *thirty-two hours* in the stinking dark for you to show so we could take the initiators in, doing your dirty work for you and carrying all the risk. And when we got back to Sab Biyar what did I find?"

André Duchamp grinned round at his own crew, trying to brazen it out. "I'm sure you'll tell me, *Anglo*."

"You went to Nuristan and sold the initiators to one of their naval contractors, you Gallic *shithead*! I was left trying to explain to the Isolo Independence Front where their nukes had gone, and why their poxy rebellion was going to fail because they hadn't got the fire-power to back up their demands."

"You can show me the contract?" André Duchamp asked mockingly.

Hasan Rawand glared down at him, lips compressed in rage. "Just hand over the money. A million will see you clear."

"To hell with you, *Anglo* filth. I, André Duchamp, owe nobody money." He stood up and tried to barge past the *Dechal*'s captain.

It was the move Erick Thakrar was waiting for and dreading. Sure enough, Hasan Rawand shoved André Duchamp back in the booth. The back of the older captain's knee struck a seat which almost tipped him off balance. He recovered and launched himself at Hasan Rawand, fists flying.

Desmond Lafoe rose to his feet drawing a frantic gasp from Ian O'Flaherty when his size, weight, and strength became apparent. Huge hands reached forward, and Ian O'Flaherty was jerked off his feet. He kicked out wildly, toecap striking Desmond Lafoe's shin. The giant merely grunted, and then threw his victim across the room. He landed awkwardly on one of the aluminium tables, his shoulder taking the brunt of his momentum before he crashed down backwards onto a pair of chairs.

Erick felt a hand close around the neck fabric of his shipsuit. It was Shane Brandes who was hauling him out of the booth; a forty-year-old with a bald head and small gold earrings, smiling with ugly anticipation. The unarmed combat file in Erick's neural nanonics went into primary mode. His instinctive thought routines were superseded by logic-based patterns, calculating inertia and intent with an ease surpassing any kung fu master. Nanonic supplement boosted muscles powered up.

Shane Brandes was surprised how easy it was to pull his opponent out of the booth. Gratification became alarm when he kept on coming. Shane had to backstep to keep balance, his own neural nanonics assuming command of his mass positioning. He cocked a fist back to smash into Erick's face, only to have a nanonic warning blare in his mind as Erick's forearm swung up with incredible speed. His punch was blocked, arm chopped painfully to one side. A furious kick to Erick's groin—his knee nearly fractured from the impact of the counter-kick. He reeled to one side, banging into Harry Levine and Bev Lennon, who were locked together.

Erick slammed an elbow into Shane's ribs, hearing bone break. He let out an agonized grunt.

The unarmed combat file said that speed was essential,

take out your opponent as soon as possible. His neural nanonics analysed Shane's movements, the half twist as he clutched at his ribs, bending over. The motion was projected two seconds into the future. Interception points were computed. A list materialized in his consciousness, and he selected a blow that would cause temporary incapacitation. His right leg shot out, booted foot aiming for a patch of empty air. Shane's head fell into it.

A threat assessment sub-routine shifted his peripheral senses into priority focus. André Duchamp and Hasan Rawand were still battering away at each other on the side of the booth's table. Neither was inflicting much damage in the confined space.

Harry Levine had got Bev Lennon into a head lock. The two of them were on the floor, squirming round like theatrical wrestlers, sending chairs spinning. Bev Lennon sent a flurry of elbow jabs into Harry Levine's stomach, attempting to knock his navel into his spine.

Stafford Charlton obviously had a boosted musculature. He was standing in front of Desmond Lafoe, landing blow after blow on the big man, arms moving with programmed efficiency. He had almost doubled up from the pain, his right arm hung limply, the shoulder broken. Blood ran out of his flattened nose.

Ian O'Flaherty rose behind Desmond Lafoe, berserk loathing contorting his face, a pocket fission blade in his right hand. With his enhanced retinas on full amplification, the yellow haze emitted by the activated blade dazzled Erick for an instant. The threat assessment sub-routine activated the defensive nanonic implant in his left hand. A targeting grid of fine blue lines flipped up across his vision. A rectangular section flashed red, and wrapped itself around Ian O'Flaherty, adapting to his movements like elastic thread.

"Don't!" Erick Thakrar shouted.

Ian O'Flaherty had already raised the blade high above his head when the shout came. In his wired state he probably wouldn't have obeyed even if he heard. Erick saw the muscles in his lower arm begin to contract, the knife quivered as it started on its downward slash.

The neural nanonics program reported that even with

boosted muscles Erick couldn't reach Ian O'Flaherty in time. He made his decision. A small patch of skin above the second knuckle of his left hand dilated, and the implant spat out a dart of nanonic circuitry, barely as large as a wasp stinger. It struck the bare skin of Ian O'Flaherty's neck, penetrating to a depth of six millimetres. The fission blade had already descended twenty centimetres towards Desmond Lafoe's broad back. As soon as it sensed it was buried inside the flesh, and its momentum was spent, the dart sprouted a fur of microscopic filaments. They quested round on a pre-programmed search pattern for nerve strands, tips wriggling between the close-packed honeycomb of cells. Ganglions were located, and the sharp filament tips forced their way through gossamer membranes sheathing the individual nerves. At this time the knife had descended twenty-four centimetres. Ian O'Flaherty's right eyelid gave an involuntary twitch at the small sting from the dart's entry. The dart's internal processor analysed the chemical and electrical reactions flashing along the nerves; it began to broadcast its own signal into the brain. His neural nanonics detected the signal at once, but the circuitry was powerless to help, it could only override natural impulses originating from within the brain.

Ian O'Flaherty had brought the blade thirty-eight centimetres down towards Desmond Lafoe when he felt a million lacework rivulets of fire igniting inside his body. The blade fell another four centimetres before his muscles were convulsed by the besieging deluge of impulses. His nerves were burning out, overloaded by the nanonic dart's diabolical signal, ordering the massive uncontrolled release of energy along each strand, a simultaneous chemical detonation inside every neuron cell.

Breath rasped out of his wide mouth, aghast eyes looking round the room in a final plea for life. His skin turned red, as if afflicted by instant sunburn. His muscles lost all strength, and he toppled limply onto the floor. The fission blade skittered about, shaving flakes of rock from the floor whenever it touched.

No one else was fighting any more.

Desmond Lafoe gave Erick a puzzled, pain-filled glance. "What . . ."

"He would have killed you," Erick said in a quiet voice; he lowered his left arm. Everyone in the bar seemed to be staring at the offending limb.

"What did you do to him?" a horrified Harry Levine asked.

Erick shrugged.

"Screw that," André Duchamp rasped. There was blood running out of his left nostril, and his eye was swelling rapidly. "Come on."

"You can't just go!" Hasan Rawand shouted. "You killed him."

André Duchamp tugged Bev Lennon to his feet. "It was self-defence. That *Anglo* bastard tried to kill one of my crew."

"That's right," Desmond Lafoe rumbled. "It was attempted murder." He waved Erick on towards the door.

"I'll call the cops," Hasan Rawand said.

"Yes, you would, wouldn't you?" André Duchamp sneered. "That's your level, *Anglo*. Lose and weep, run to the law." He fixed the shock-frozen barkeeper with a warning stare, then jerked his head for his crew to go through the door. "Why were we fighting, Hasan? Ask yourself that. The *gendarmes* certainly will."

Erick stepped out into the rock tunnel which connected the Catalina with the rest of the vertical city's corridors and lifts and lobbies, helping a white-faced Desmond Lafoe to limp along.

"Run and hide then, Duchamp," Hasan Rawand's voice echoed after them. "And you, murderer. But this universe isn't so large. Remember that."

True night, with its darkness and lordly twinkling stars, had come and gone above Cricklade. It lasted less than eight minutes before the red blaze of Duchess-night began, and even those scant minutes hadn't been particularly dim. The ring of orbiting starships had looked spectacular, dominating the cloudless northern sky with their cold sparkle. Joshua had gone out onto the manor's balcony with the Kavanagh family to see the bridge of heaven after they'd finished their five-course dinner. Louise had worn a cream dress with a tight bodice; it had come alive with a pale blue fire under the cometary light showering down. The amount of attention she had shown him during the meal verged on the embarrassing, it was almost as bad as the hostility he got from William Elphinstone. He was rather looking forward to being shown round the estate by her tomorrow. Grant Kavanagh had been enthusiastic about the idea once it was announced. Without consulting his neural nanonics he couldn't be quite sure who had brought the subject up at the dinner table.

There was a light knock on his bedroom door, and it opened before he could say anything. Hadn't he turned the key?

He rolled over on the bed where he'd been lying watching the holoscreen with its inordinately bland drama programmes. Everything was set on Norfolk, where nobody swore and nobody screwed and nobody scrapped; even the one news programme he'd caught earlier was drearily parochial, with only a couple of references to the visiting starships and nothing at all about Confederation politics.

Marjorie Kavanagh slipped into the room. She smiled and held up a duplicate key. "Scared of things that go bump in the night, Joshua?"

He grunted in dismay, and flopped back down on the bed.

They had met for the first time just before dinner, a formal drinks session in the drawing-room. If the line hadn't been so antique and passé he would have said: "Louise didn't tell me she had an elder sister." Marjorie Kavanagh was a lot younger than her husband, with thick raven hair and a figure which showed that even Louise had still got quite a way to go yet. Thinking about it logically, he should have realized that someone as rich and aristocratic as Grant Kavanagh would have a beautiful young wife, especially on a planet where status ruled. But Marjorie was also a flirt, which her husband seemed to find highly amusing, especially as she delivered her teasing innuendos while clinging to his side. Joshua didn't laugh; unlike Grant he knew she was serious.

Marjorie came over to stand by the side of the bed, looking down at him. She was wearing a long blue silk robe, loosely tied around her waist. The heavy curtains were drawn against the red gleam of Duchess-night, but he could see enough of her cleavage to know she wasn't wearing anything underneath.

"Er . . ." he began.

"Not sleeping? Something on your mind, or southwards of there?" Marjorie asked archly; she looked pointedly at his groin.

"I have a lot of geneering in my heritage. I don't need much sleep."

"Oh, goodie. Lucky me."

"Mrs Kavanagh—"

"Knock it off, Joshua. Playing the innocent doesn't suit you." She sat on the edge of the bed.

He raised himself up on his elbows. "In that case, what about Grant?"

A long-fingered hand ran back through her hair, producing a dark cascade over her shoulders. "What about him? Grant is what you might call a man's man. He excels in the more basic male pursuits of hunting, drinking, filthy jokes, gambling, and women. If you haven't yet noticed, Norfolk isn't exactly a model of social enlightenment and female emancipation. Which gives him full licence to indulge himself while I sit at home playing the good wifey. So while he's off rogering a pair of teenage Romany girls he spotted helping out in the groves this afternoon, I thought: Fuck it, I'm going to have some fun myself for once."

"Do I get a say?"

"No, you're too perfect for me. Big, strong, young, handsome, and gone in a week. How could I possibly let that opportunity go by? Besides, I'm fiercely protective when it comes to my daughters, a proper hax bitch."

"Er . . ."

"Ah ha!" Marjorie grinned. "You're blushing, Joshua." Her hand found the hem of his shirt, and slid across his abdomen. "Grant can be so very idiotic when it comes to the girls. He had quite a chortle at the way Louise took to you at dinner. He doesn't think, that's his problem. You see, here on Norfolk they are in no danger at all from the local boys, they don't need chaperones for dances nor guardian aunts when they stay with friends. Their name protects them. But you're not a local boy, and I saw exactly what was going on inside that testosterone-fuelled mind of yours. No wonder you and Grant get on so well together, I can barely tell you apart."

Joshua squirmed from her hand as she stroked the sensitive skin at the side of his ribs. "I think Louise is very sweet. That's all."

"Sweet." Marjorie smiled softly. "I was just eighteen when I had her. And I'll thank you not to work out how old that makes me! So you see I know exactly what she's thinking right now. Captain Romance from beyond the sky. Norfolk girls of my class are virgins in more ways than one. I'm not about to let some over-sexed stranger ruin her future, she has a slim enough chance of a happy one as it is, what with arranged marriages and minimal education, which is the lot of females on this planet, even for our class. And I'm doing you a favour into the bargain."

"Me?"

"You. Grant would kill you if you ever laid a finger on her. And, Joshua, I don't mean metaphorically."

"Er . . ." He couldn't believe that; not even in this society.

"So I'm going to sacrifice my virtue to save both of you." She undid the belt, and slipped the robe from her shoulders. Sultry red light gleamed on her body, embellishing the erotic allure. "Isn't that just so *terribly* noble of me?"

The emergent snowlily plants were starting to be a problem around the village jetties along the length of the Juliffe and its multitudinous tributaries. The tightly clumped red-brown fronds occupied the shallows, the banks, and the mud-banks. None of which affected the *Isakore* as it sailed its unerringly straight course along the Zamjan towards the Quallheim Counties, carrying its boisterous passenger complement of four Confederation Navy Marines, and three Kulu ESA tactical operation agents. *Isakore* hadn't put ashore once since it left Durringham. It was an eighteen-metre-long fishing boat, with a carvel hull of mayope, sturdy enough for its original owners to take it down to the mouth of the Juliffe and catch sea fish in their nets. Ralph Hiltch had ordered its

thermal-conversion furnace to be taken out, and got the
boatyard to install the micro-fusion generator which the
Kulu Embassy used as its power reserve. With one high-
pressure gas canister of He3 and deuterium for fuel, *Isakore*
now had enough power to circumnavigate the globe twice
over.

Jenny Harris was lying on her sleeping-bag under the
plastic awning they had rigged up over the prow, out of the
light drizzle sweeping the river. The sheeting didn't make
much difference, and her shorts and white T-shirt were soaking. Four days of sailing without a break from the humidity
left her vainly trying to remember whether she had ever
been dry.

A couple of the marines were on their sleeping-bags beside her, Louis Beith and Niels Regehr, barely out of their
teens. They were both 'vising their personal MF players,
eyes closed, fingers tapping out chaotic rhythms on the
deck. She envied their optimism and confidence. They
treated the scouting mission with an almost schoolboyish
enthusiasm; although she admitted they were well trained
and physically impressive with their boosted muscles. A
tribute to their lieutenant, Murphy Hewlett, who had kept
his small squad's morale high even on a dead-end posting
like Lalonde. Niels Regehr had confided they all thought the
mission upriver was a reward not a punishment.

Her communication block datavised that Ralph Hiltch
was calling. She got to her feet and walked out from under
the awning, giving the young marines some privacy. The
dampness in the air wasn't noticeably increased. Dean
Folan, her deputy, waved from the wheel-house amidships.
Jenny acknowledged him, then leant on the gunwale and accepted the channel from the communication block.

"I'm updating you on the Edenist agents," Ralph
datavised.

"You've found them?" she queried. It had been twenty
hours since they had gone off air.

"Chance would be a fine thing. No, and the observation
satellite images show that Ozark village is being abandoned.
People are just drifting away—walking into the jungle, as
far as we can tell. We must assume they have been either se-

questrated or eliminated. There is no trace of the boat they were using, the *Coogan*, the satellite can't see it anywhere on the river."

"I see."

"Unfortunately, the Edenists knew you were coming up-river behind them."

"Hellfire!"

"Exactly, so if they have been sequestrated the invaders will be watching out for you."

Jenny ran a hand over her head. Her ginger hair had been shaved down to a half-centimetre stubble, the same as everyone else on board. It was standard procedure for jungle missions, and her combat shell-helmet would make better contact. But it did mean anyone who saw them would immediately know what they were. "We weren't exactly inconspicuous anyway," she datavised.

"No, I suppose not."

"Does this change our mission profile?"

"Not the directive, no. Kelven Solanki and I still want one of these sequestrated colonists brought back to Durringham. But the timing has certainly altered. Where are you now?"

She datavised the question into her inertial guidance block. "Twenty-five kilometres west of Oconto village."

"Fine, put ashore at the nearest point you can. We're a little worried about the boats coming out of the Quallheim and Zamjan tributaries. When we reviewed the satellite images we found about twenty that have set off downriver in the last week, everything from paddle-steamers to fishing ketches. As far as we can make out they're heading for Durringham, they certainly aren't stopping."

"You mean they're behind us as well?" Jenny asked in dismay.

"It looks that way. But, Jenny, I don't leave my people behind. You know that. I'm working on a method of retrieving you that doesn't include the river. But only ask if you really need it. There are only a limited number of seats," he added significantly.

She stared across the grey water at the unbroken jungle, and muttered a silent curse. She liked the marines, a lot of trust had been built up between the two groups in the last four days; there were times when the ESA seemed too duplicitous and underhand even for an Intelligence agency. "Yes, boss, I understand."

"Good. Now, remember; when you put ashore, assume everyone is hostile, and avoid all groups of locals. Solanki is convinced it was sheer numbers which overwhelmed the Edenists. And, Jenny, don't let prejudice inflate your ego, the Edenist operatives are good."

"Yes, sir." She signed off and picked her way past the wheel-house to the little cabin which backed onto it. A big grey-green tarpaulin had been rigged over the rear of the boat to screen the horses. She could hear them snorting softly. They were agitated and jumpy after so long cooped up in their tiny enclosure. Murphy Hewlett had kept them reasonably comfortable, but she'd be glad when they could let them loose on land again. So would the team which had to shovel their crap overboard.

Murphy Hewlett was sheltering in the lee of the tarpaulin, his black fatigue jacket open to the waist, showing a dark green shortsleeved shirt. She started to explain the change in schedule.

"They want us to go ashore right now?" he asked. He was forty-two years old, and a veteran of several combat campaigns both in space and on planets.

"That's right. Apparently people are deserting the villages in droves. Picking one of them up shouldn't be too big a problem."

"Yeah, you're right about that." He shook his head. "I don't like this idea that we're already behind enemy lines."

"I didn't ask my boss what the situation was like in Durringham right now, but to my mind this whole planet is behind the lines."

Murphy Hewlett nodded glumly. "There's real trouble brewing here. You get to recognize the feeling after a while, you know? Combat sharpens you, I can tell when things ain't right. And they're not."

Jenny wondered guiltily if he could guess the essence of what Ralph Hiltch had said to her. "I'll tell Dean to look out for a likely landing spot."

She hadn't even reached the wheel-house before Dean Folan was shouting urgently. "Boat coming!"

They went to the gunwale and peered ahead through the thin grey gauze of drizzle. The shape slowly resolved, and both of them watched it sail past with shocked astonishment.

It was a paddle-steamer which seemed to have ridden straight out of the nineteenth-century Mississippi River. Craft just like it were the inspiration behind Lalonde's current fleet of paddle-boats. But while the *Swithland* and her ilk were bland distaff inheritors utilizing technology instead of engineering craftsmanship, this *grande dame* could have been a true original. Her paintwork was white and glossy, black iron stacks belched out a thick, oily smoke, pistons hissed and clanked as they turned the heavy paddles. Happy people stood on the decks, the handsome men in suits with long grey jackets, white shirts, and slender lace ties, their elegant women in long frilly dresses, casually twirling parasols on their shoulders. Children ran about, sporting gaily; the boys were in sailor suits, and the girls had ribbons in their flowing hair.

"It's a dream," Jenny whispered to herself. "I'm living a dream."

The stately passengers were waving invitingly. Sounds of laughter and merrymaking rang clearly across the water. Earth's mythical golden age had come back to nourish them with its supreme promise of unspoilt lands and uncomplicated times. The paddle-steamer was taking all folk of good will back to where today's cares would cease to exist.

The sight was tugging at the hearts of all on board the *Isakore*. There wasn't one of them who didn't feel the urge to jump into the river and swim across the gulf. The gulf: between them and bliss, an eternal joy of song and wine which waited beyond the cruel divide which was their own world.

"Don't," Murphy Hewlett said.

Jenny's euphoria shattered like crystal as the discordant voice struck her ears. Murphy Hewlett's hand was on hers, pressing down painfully. She found her arms were rigid, tensed, ready to propel her over the side of the fishing boat.

"What is that?" she asked. At some deep level she was bemoaning the loss, being excluded from the journey into a different future; now she would never know if the promise was true . . .

"Don't you see?" he said. "It's them, whatever they are. They're growing. They don't care about us seeing them unmasked any more, they don't fear us."

The colourful solid mirage sailed on regally down the river, its wake of joyous invocation tarrying above the brown water like a dawn mist. Jenny Harris stayed at the gunwale for a long time, staring into the west.

The grove was a site of intense activity. Over two hundred people were working their way along the rows, positioning the collection cups around the weeping roses. It was early Duke-day; Duchess had just set, leaving a slight pink fringe splashing the western horizon. Between them, the two suns had banished all trace of moisture from the torrid air. Most of the men and women tending the big weeping roses wore light clothes. The younger children ran errands, bringing new stacks of collection cups to the teams, or supplying iced fruit juice from large jugs.

Joshua was feeling the heat despite being dressed in a burgundy sleeveless T-shirt and black jeans. He sat on the back of his horse watching the cupping teams at work. The cups that were being hung so carefully were white cardboard cones, with a waxed shiny inner surface, thirty centimetres wide at the open end, tapering down to a sealed point. Stiff hoops pasted onto the side were used to wire them onto the trellis below the weeping rose flowers. Everyone he could see carried a thick bundle of wires tucked into their belt. It didn't take more than thirty seconds for them to fix each cup.

"Is there one collection cup for every single flower?" he asked.

Louise was sitting on her horse next to him, dressed in jodhpurs and a plain white blouse, hair held by a single band at the back. She had been surprised when he accepted her invitation to take the horses rather than use a carriage to get about the estate. Where would a starship captain learn how to ride? But ride he could. Not as well as her, which gave her a little thrill, that she should be better than a man at anything.

Especially Joshua. "Yes," she said. "How else could you do it?"

He gave the stacks of collection cups piled up at the end of each row a puzzled frown. "I don't know. Jesus, there must be millions of them."

Louise had grown accustomed to his casual swearing now. It had shocked her a little at first, but people from the stars were bound to have slightly different customs. Coming from him it didn't seem profane, just exotic. Perhaps the most surprising thing was the way he could suddenly switch from being himself to using the most formal mannerisms.

"Cricklade alone has two hundred groves," she said. "That's why there are so many cuppers. It has to be done entirely in the week before midsummer when the roses are in bloom. Even with every able-bodied person in the county drafted in there's only just enough to get it finished in time. A team like this takes nearly a day to complete a grove."

Joshua leant forwards in the saddle, studying the people labouring away. It all seemed so menial, yet every one of them looked intent, devoted almost. Grant Kavanagh had said that a lot of them worked through half of Duchess-night, they would never have got the work finished otherwise. "I'm beginning to see why a bottle of Norfolk Tears costs so much. It's not just the rarity value, is it?"

"No." She flicked the reins, and guided the horse along the end of the rows, heading for the gate in the wall. The foreman touched his wide-brimmed hat as she passed. Louise gave a reflex smile.

He rode beside her after they left the grove. Cricklade Manor's protective ring of cedars was just visible a couple of miles away across the wolds. "Where now?" It was parkland all around, sheep clustering together under the lonely trees for shade. The grass was furry with white flowers. Everywhere he looked there seemed to be blooms of some kind—trees, bushes, ground plants.

"I thought Wardley Wood would be nice, you can see what wild Norfolk looks like." Louise pointed at a long stretch of dark-green trees a mile away, following the bottom of a small valley. "Genevieve and I often walk there. It's lovely." She dropped her head. As if he would be interested in the glades with their multicoloured flowers and sweet scents.

"That sounds good. I'd like to get out of this sunlight. I don't know how you can stand it."

"I don't notice it, really."

He spurred his horse on, breaking into a canter. Louise rode past him easily, moving effortlessly with her horse's rhythm. They galloped across the wolds, scattering the somnolent sheep, Louise's laughter trilling through the heavy air. She beat him easily to the edge of the wood, and sat there smiling as he rode up to her, panting heavily.

"That was quite good," she said. "You could be a decent rider if you had a bit of practice." She swung her leg over the saddle and dropped down.

"There are some stables on Tranquillity," he said, dismounting. "That's where I learnt, but I'm not there very often."

A big mithorn tree stood just outside the main body of the wood, its coin-sized dark red flowers sprinkling the end of every twig. Louise wrapped the reins round one of its lower branches, and started off into the wood along one of the little animal tracks she knew. "I've heard of Tranquillity. That's where the Lord of Ruin lives, Ione Saldana. She was on the news last year; she's so beautiful. I wanted to cut my hair short like hers, but Mother said no. Do you know her?"

"Now that's the trouble when you really do know someone famous; no one ever believes you when you say yes."

She turned round, eyes wide with delight. "You do know her!"

"Yes. I knew her before she inherited the title, we grew up together."

"What's she like? Tell me."

An image of a naked sweaty moaning Ione bent over a table while he was screwing her appeared in his mind. "Fun," he said.

The glade she led him to was on the floor of the valley; a stream ran through it, spilling down a series of five big rock-pools. Knee-high flower stems with tubular yellow and lavender blooms clotted the ground, giving off a scent similar to orange blossom. Water-monarch trees lined the stream below the pools, fifty yards tall, their long, slender branches swaying in the slight breeze, fernlike leaf fronds drooping. Birds flittered about in the upper boughs, uninspiring dun-coloured bat-analogues with long, powerful forelimbs for tunnelling into the ground. Wild weeping roses boiled over the stones along the side of two of the pools; years of dead petrified branches overlaid by a fresh growth of new living shoots to produce hemispherical bushes. Their flowers were crushed together, disfigured as they vied for light.

"You were right," Joshua told her. "It is lovely."

"Thank you. Genevieve and I often bathe here in the summer."

He perked up. "Really?"

"It's a little place of the world that's all our own. Even the hax don't come here."

"What's a hax? I heard someone mention the name."

"Father calls them wolf-analogues. They're big and vicious, and they'll even attack humans. The farmers hunt them in the winter, it's good sport. But we've just about cleared them out of Cricklade now."

"Do the hunters all get dressed up in red jackets and charge around on horses with packs of hounds?"

"Yes. How did you know?"

"Lucky guess."

"I suppose you've seen real monsters on your travels. I've seen pictures of the Tyrathca on the holoscreen. They're horrible. I couldn't sleep for a week afterwards."

"Yes, the Tyrathca look pretty ferocious. But I've met some breeder pairs; they don't think of themselves like that. To them we're the cruel alien ones. It's a question of perspective."

Louise blushed and ducked her head, turning away from him. "I'm sorry. You must think me a frightful bigot."

"No. You're just not used to xenocs, that's all." He stood right behind her and put his hands on her shoulders. "But I would like to take you away from here some time and show you the rest of the Confederation. Some of it is quite spectacular. And I'd love to take you to Tranquillity." He looked round the glade, thoughtful. "It's a bit like this, only much much bigger. I think you'd like it a lot."

Louise wanted to squirm away from his grip, men simply shouldn't act in such a familiar fashion. But his customs were surely different, and he was massaging her shoulder muscles gently. It felt nice. "I always wanted to fly on a starship."

"You will, one day. When Cricklade is yours you can do anything you want." Joshua was enjoying the touch of her. Naïvety, a voluptuous body, and the knowledge that he should never, ever be even thinking about screwing her were combining to form a potent aphrodisiac.

"I never thought of that," she said brightly. "Can I charter the *Lady Macbeth*? Oh, but it will be simply ages yet. I don't want Father to die, that would be an absolutely awful thing to think. Will you still be coming to Norfolk in fifty years' time?"

"Of course I will. I have two things tying me here now. Business, and you."

"Me?" It came out as a frightened squeak.

He turned her round to face him, and kissed her.

"Joshua!"

He put two fingers over her lips. "Shush. No words, only us. Always us."

Louise stood rigidly still as he unbuttoned her blouse, all kinds of strange emotions battling in her head. I ought to run. I ought to stop him.

Sunlight fell onto her bare shoulders and back. It was a peculiar sensation, a tingling warmth. And the expression on his face as he gazed at her was scary, he looked so hungry, but anxious at the same time.

"Joshua," she murmured, half nervous, half amused. Her shoulders had hunched up of their own accord.

He pulled his T-shirt off over his head. They kissed again, his arms going around her. He seemed very strong. His skin pressing against her had started a trembling in her stomach that nothing was able to stop. Then she realized her jodhpurs were being peeled down.

"Oh God."

His finger lifted her chin up. "It's all right. I'll show you how." And his smile was at least as warm as the sun.

She took her black leather riding boots off herself, then helped him with the jodhpurs. Her brassiere and knickers were plain white cotton. Joshua removed them slowly, savouring the drawn-out exposure.

He spread their clothes out and laid her down. She was terribly tense to start with, her lower lip clamped between her teeth, narrow eyes peeking down fearfully at the length of her body. It took a long, pleasant time of soft caresses, kisses, stealthy whispers, and tickles before she began to respond. He coaxed a giggle from her, then another, then it was a squeal, a groan. She touched his body, curious and suddenly bold, a hand sliding down his belly to cup his balls. He shuddered and repaid her by massaging her thighs. There was another long interval while their hands and mouths explored each other. Then he slid above her, looking down at dishevelled hair, drowsy eyes, dark nipples standing proud, legs parted. He moved into her carefully, the damp warmth enveloping and squeezing his cock an erotic splendour. Louise writhed tempestuously below him, and he began a slow, provocative stroke. He used neural nanonic overrides to restrain his own body's responses, sustaining his erection as long as he wanted it, determined that she should reach a climax, that it should be as perfect for her as he could possibly make it.

After an age he was rewarded by her complete loss of control. Louise threw away every last inhibition as her orgasm built, shouting at the top of her voice, her body arching desperately below him, lifting his knees from the ground. Only then did he allow himself any release, joining her in absolute bliss.

Post-coital languor was a sweet time, one of tiny kisses, stroking individual strands of sticky hair from her face, single compassionate words. And he had been quite right all along, forbidden fruit tasted the best.

"I love you, Joshua," she whispered into his ear.

"And I love you."

"Don't leave."

"That's unfair. You know I'm coming back."

"I'm sorry." She tightened her grip around him.

He moved his hand up to her left breast and squeezed, hearing a soft hiss of indrawn breath. "Are you sore?"

"A bit. Not much."

"I'm glad."

"Me too."

"Do you want to have that swim now? Water can be a lot of fun."

She grinned cautiously. "Again?"

"If you want."

"I do."

Marjorie Kavanagh came to his bedroom again that Duchess-night. The prospect of Louise sneaking through the red-shaded manor to be with him and discovering him with her mother added a spice to his lovemaking that left her exhausted and delighted.

The next day Louise, eyes possessively agleam, announced at breakfast that she would show Joshua round the county roseyard, so he could see the casks being prepared for the new Tears. Grant declared this a stupendous idea, chuckling to himself that his little cherub was having her first schoolgirl crush.

Joshua smiled neutrally, and thanked her for being so considerate. There were another three days to go until midsummer.

At Cricklade, and all across Norfolk, they marked the onset of Midsummer's Day with a simple ceremony. The Kavanaghs, Colsterworth's vicar, Cricklade Manor's staff, the senior estate workers, and representatives from each of the cupper teams gathered at the nearest grove to the manor towards the end of Duke-day. Joshua and Dahybi were invited, and stood at the front of the group that assembled just inside the shabby stone wall.

The rows of weeping roses stretched out ahead of them; blooms and cups alike upturned to a fading azure sky, perfectly still in the breathless evening air. Time seemed to be suspended.

Duke was falling below the western horizon, a sliver of pyrexic tangerine, pulling the world's illumination down with it. The vicar, wearing a simple cassock, held his arms up for silence. He turned to face the east. On cue, a watery pink light expanded across the horizon.

A sigh went up from the group.

Even Joshua was impressed. There had been about two minutes of darkness the previous evening. Now there would be no night for a sidereal day, Duchess-night flowing seamlessly into Duke-day. It wouldn't be until the end of the following Duchess-night that the stars would come out again for a brief minute. After that it would be the evenings when the two suns overlapped, and the morning darkness would grow longer and longer, extending back into Duchess-night until Norfolk reached inferior conjunction and only Duke was visible: midwinter.

The vicar led his flock in a brief Harvest Thanksgiving service. Everybody knew the words to the prayers and psalms, and quiet, murmuring voices banded together to be heard right across the grove. Joshua felt quite left out. They finished by singing "All Creatures Great and Small". At least his neural nanonics had that in a memory file; he joined in heartily, surprised by just how good he felt.

After the service, Grant Kavanagh led his family and friends on a rambling walk along the aisles between the rows. He touched various roses, feeling their weight, rubbing petals between his thumb and forefinger, testing the texture.

"Smell that," he told Joshua as he handed over a petal he had just picked. "It's going to be a good crop. Not as good as five seasons ago. But well above average."

Joshua sniffed. The scent was very weak, but recognizable, similar to the smell which clung to a cork after a bottle of Tears had been opened. "You can tell from this?" he asked.

Grant put his arm around Louise as they sauntered along the aisle. "I can. Mr Butterworth can. Half of the estate workers can. It just takes experience. You need to be here for a lot of summers." He grinned broadly. "Perhaps you will be, Joshua. I'm sure Louise will ask you back if no one else does."

Genevieve shrieked with laughter.

Louise blushed furiously. "Daddy!" She slapped his arm.

Joshua raised a weak smile and turned to examine one of the rose plants. He found himself facing Marjorie Kavanagh. She gave him a languid wink. His neural nanonics sent out a volley of overrides to try and stop the rush of blood to his own cheeks.

After the inspection walk the manor staff served up an outdoor buffet. Grant Kavanagh stood behind one of the trestle tables, carving from a huge joint of rare beef, playing the part of jovial host, with a word and a laugh for all his people.

As Duchess-night progressed the rose flowers began to droop. It happened so slowly that the eye could detect no motion, but hour by hour the thick stems lost their stiffness, and the weight of the large petals and their central carpel pod made gravity's triumph inevitable.

By Duke-morning most of the flowers had reached the horizontal. The petals were drying out and shrivelling.

Joshua and Louise rode out to one of the groves close to Wardley Wood, and wandered along the sagging plants. There were only a few cuppers left tending the long rows, straightening the occasional collection cup. They nodded nervously to Louise and scurried on about their business.

"Most people have gone home to sleep," Louise said. "The real work will begin again tomorrow."

They stood aside as a man pulled a wooden trolley past them. A big glass ewer, webbed with rope, was resting on it. Joshua watched as he stopped the trolley at the end of a row and lifted the ewer off. About a third of the rows had a similar ewer waiting at the end.

"What's that for?" he asked.

"They empty the collection cups into those," Louise said. "Then the ewers are taken to the county roseyard where the Tears are casked."

"And they stay in the cask for a year."

"That's right."

"Why?"

"So that they spend a winter on Norfolk. They're not proper Tears until they've felt our frost. It sharpens the taste, so they say."

And adds to the cost, he thought.

The flowers were wilting rapidly now, the stems curving down into a U-shape. Their sunlight-fired coronal cloak had faded away as the petals darkened, and with it had gone a lot of the mystique. They were just ordinary dying flowers now.

"How do the cuppers know where to wire the cups?" he asked. "Look at them. Every flower is bending over above a cup." He glanced up and down the aisle. "Every one of them."

Louise gave him a superior smile. "If you are born on Norfolk, you know how to place a cup."

It wasn't just the weeping roses which were reaching fruition. As they trotted the horses over to Wardley Wood Joshua saw flowers on the trees and bushes closing up, some varieties leaning over in the same fashion as the roses.

In their peaceful glade the wild rose bushes along the rock pools seemed flaccid, as if their shape was deflating. Flowers lolled against each other, petals agglutinating into a quilt of pulp.

Louise let Joshua undress her as he always did. Then they spread a blanket down on the rocks below the weeping roses and embraced. Joshua had got to the point where Louise was shuddering in delighted anticipation as his hands roved across her lower belly and down the inside of her thighs when he felt a splash on his back. He ignored the first one and kissed Louise's navel. Another splash broke his concentration. It couldn't be raining, there wasn't a cloud in the barren blue sky. He twisted over. "What—?"

Norfolk's roses had begun to weep. Out of the centre of the carpel pod a clear fluid was exuded in a steady monotonous drip. It was destined to last for ten to fifteen hours, well into the next Duchess-night. Only when the pod was drained would it split open and release the seeds it contained. Nature had intended the fluid to soften the soil made arid by weeks without rain, allowing the seeds to fall into mud so they would have a greater chance of germination. But then in 2209 a woman called Carys Thomas, who was a junior botanist in the ecological assessment mission, acting against all regulations (and common sense), put her finger under a weeping pod, then touched the single pearl of glistening fluid to her tongue. Norfolk's natural order came to an immediate end.

Joshua wiped up the dewy bead from his skin and licked his finger. It tasted coarser than the Norfolk Tears he'd so relished back in Tranquillity, but the ancestry was beyond doubt. A roguish light filled his eyes. "Hey, not bad."

A snickering Louise was moved round until she was directly underneath the lax hanging flowers. They made love under a shower of sparkling droplets prized higher than a king's ransom.

The cuppers returned to the groves as the next Duchess-night ended. They cut away the collection cups, now heavy with Tears, and poured their precious contents into the ewers. It was a task that would take another five days of intensive round-the-clock labour to complete.

Grant Kavanagh himself drove Joshua and Dahybi down to the county roseyard in a four-wheel-drive farm ranger, a powerful boxy vehicle with tyres deep enough to plough through a shallow marsh. The yard was on the outskirts of Colsterworth, a large collection of ivy-clad stone buildings with few windows. Beneath the ground was an extensive warren of brick-lined cellars where the casks were stored throughout their year of maturation.

When he drove through the wide entrance gates the yard workers were already rolling out the casks of last year's Tears.

"A year to the day," he said proudly as the heavy iron-bound oak cylinders rattled and skipped over the cobbles. "This is your cargo, young Joshua. We'll have it ready for you in two days." He braked the farm ranger to a halt outside the bottling plant where the casks were being rolled inside. The plant supervisor rushed out to meet them, sweating. "Don't you worry about us," Grant told him blithely. "I'm just showing our major customer around. We won't get in the way." And with that he marched imperiously through the broad doorway.

The bottling plant was the most sophisticated mechanical set-up Joshua had seen on the planet, even though it lacked any real cybernetic systems (the conveyor belts actually used rubber pulleys!). It was a long hall with a single-span roof, full of gleaming belts, pipes, and vats. Thousands of the ubiquitous pear-shaped bottles trundled along the narrow belts, looping overhead, winding round filling nozzles, the racket of their combined clinking making conversation difficult.

Grant walked them along the hall. The casks were all blended together in big stainless-steel vats, he explained. Stoke County's bouquet was a homogenized product. No groves had individual labels, not even his.

Joshua watched the bottles filling up below the big vats, then moving on to be corked and labelled. Each stage added to the cost. And the weight of the glass bottles reduced the amount of actual Tears each starship could carry.

Jesus, what a sweet operation. I couldn't do it better myself. And the beauty of it is we're the ones most eager to cooperate, to inflate the cost.

At the end of the line, the yard manager was waiting with the first bottle to come off the conveyor. He looked expectantly at Grant, who told him to proceed. The bottle was uncorked, and its contents poured into four cut-crystal glasses.

Grant sniffed, then took a small sip. He cocked his head to one side and looked thoughtful. "Yes," he said. "This will do. Stoke can put its name to this."

Joshua tried his own glass. It chilled every nerve in his throat, and burst into flames in his stomach.

"Good enough for you, Joshua?" Grant clapped him on the back.

Dahybi was holding his glass up to the light, staring at it with greedy enchantment.

"Yes," Joshua declared staunchly. "Good enough."

Joshua and Dahybi took it in turns to oversee the cases the roseyard put together for them. For space travel the bottles were hermetically sealed in composite cube containers one metre square, with a thick lining of nultherm foam to protect them (more weight); the roseyard had its own loading and sealing machinery (more cost). There was a railway line leading directly from the yard to the town's station, which meant they were able to dispatch several batches to Boston every day.

All this activity severely reduced the amount of time Joshua spent at Cricklade Manor, much to Louise's chagrin.

Nor was there any believable reason why she should take him riding over the estate again.

He arranged the shifts with Dahybi so that he worked most of Duchess-night at the roseyard, which meant his tussles with Marjorie were curtailed.

The morning of the day he was leaving, however, Louise did manage to trap him in the stables. So he had to spend two hours in a dark, dusty hay loft satisfying an increasingly bold and adventurous teenager who seemed to have developed a bottomless reserve of physical stamina. She clung to him for a long time after her third climax, while he whispered assurances of how quickly he would come back.

"Just for business with Daddy?" she asked, almost as an accusation.

"No. For you. Business is an excuse, it would be difficult otherwise on this planet. Everything's so bloody formal here."

"I don't care any more. I don't care who knows."

He shifted round, brushing straw from his ribs. "Well, I *do* care; because I don't want you to be treated like a pariah. So show a little discretion, Louise."

She ran her fingertips over his cheeks, marvelling. "You really care about me, don't you?"

"Of course I do."

"Daddy likes you," she said uncertainly. Now probably wasn't the best time to press him on their future after he returned. He must have a lot on his mind with the awesome responsibility of the starflight ahead of him. But it did seem as though her father's plaudit was like an omen. So few people ever met with Daddy's approval. And Joshua had said how much he adored Stoke County. The kind of land I'd like to settle in: his exact words.

"I'm rather fond of the old boy myself. But God he's got a temper."

Louise giggled in the dark. Down below the horses were shuffling about. She straddled his abdomen, her mane of hair falling around the two of them. His hands found her breasts, fingers tightening until she moaned with desire. In a low, throaty voice he told her what he wanted her to do. She strained her body to accommodate him, trembling at her own daring. He was solid against her, wonderfully *there*, encouraging and praising.

"Tell me again," she murmured. "Please, Joshua."

"I love you," he said, breath teasingly hot on her neck. Even his neural nanonics couldn't banish the dawning guilt he felt at the words. Have I really been reduced to lying to trusting, hopelessly unsophisticated teenagers? Perhaps it's because she is so magnificent, what we all want girls to be like even though we know it's wrong. I can't help myself. "I love you, and I'm coming back for you."

She groaned in delirium as he entered her. Ecstasy brought its own special light, banishing the darkness of the loft.

Joshua only just managed to reach the manor's hall in time to kiss or shake hands with members of the large group of staff and family (William Elphinstone was absent) who had come to wish him and Dahybi farewell. The horse-drawn carriage carried the two of them back to Colsterworth Station, where they boarded the train back to Boston along with the last batch of their cargo.

Melvyn Ducharme met them when they arrived back in the capital, and told them that over half of the cases were already up in the *Lady Macbeth*. Kenneth Kavanagh had used his influence with captains whose spaceplanes were being under-used for their own smaller cargos. It hadn't generated much goodwill, but the loading was well ahead of schedule. Using *Lady Mac*'s small spaceplane alone would have meant taking eleven days to boost all the cases into orbit.

They returned up to the starship straight away. When Joshua floated into his cabin, Sarha was waiting with the free-fall sex cage expanded, and a hungry smile in place. "No bloody chance," he told her, and curled up into a ball to sleep for a solid ten hours.

Even if he had been awake he had no reason to focus the *Lady Macbeth*'s sensors on departing starships. So he would never have seen that out of the twenty-seven thousand eight hundred and forty-six starships which had come to Norfolk, twenty-two of them experienced an alarming variety of severe mechanical and electrical malfunctions as they departed for their home planets.

TIMELINE

2020 . . . Cavius base established. Mining of Lunar sub-crustal resources starts.

2037 . . . Beginning of large-scale geneering on humans; improvement to immunology system, eradication of appendix, organ efficiency increased.

2041 . . . First deuterium-fuelled fusion stations built; inefficient and expensive.

2044 . . . Christian reunification.

2047 . . . First asteroid capture mission. Beginning of Earth's O'Neill Halo.

2049 . . . Quasi-sentient bitek animals employed as servitors.

2055 . . . Jupiter mission.

2055 . . . Lunar cities granted independence from founding companies.

2057 . . . Ceres asteroid settlement founded.

2058 . . . Affinity symbiont neurons developed by Wing-Tsit Chong, providing control over animals and bitek constructs.

2064 . . . Multinational industrial consortium (Jovian Sky Power Corporation) begins mining Jupiter's atmosphere for He_3 using aerostat factories.

2064 . . . Islamic secular unification.

2067 . . . Fusion stations begin to use He_3 as fuel.

2069 . . . Affinity bond gene spliced into human DNA.

2075 . . . JSKP germinates Eden, a bitek habitat in orbit around Jupiter, with UN Protectorate status.

2077 . . . New Kong asteroid begins FTL stardrive research project.

2085 . . . Eden opened for habitation.

2086 . . . Habitat Pallas germinated in Jupiter orbit.

2090 . . . Wing-Tsit Chong dies, and transfers memories to Eden's neural strata. Start of Edenist culture. Eden and Pallas declare independence from UN. Launch buyout of JSKP shares. Pope Eleanor excommunicates all Christians with affinity gene. Exodus of affinity capable humans to Eden. Effective end of bitek industry on Earth.

2091 . . . Lunar referendum to terraform Mars.

2094 . . . Edenists begin exowomb breeding programme coupled with extensive geneering improvement to embryos, tripling their population over a decade.

2103 . . . Earth's national governments consolidate into Govcentral.

2103 . . . Thoth base established on Mars.

2107 . . . Govcentral jurisdiction extended to cover O'Neill Halo.

2115 . . . First instantaneous translation by New Kong spaceship, Earth to Mars.

2118 . . . Mission to Proxima Centauri.

2123 . . . Terracompatible plant found at Ross 154.

2125 . . . Ross 154 planet named Felicity, first multiethnic colonists arrive.

2125–2130 . . . Four new terracompatible planets discovered. Multiethnic colonies founded.

2131 . . . Edenists germinate Perseus in orbit around Ross 154 gas giant, begin He_3 mining.

2131–2205 . . . One hundred and thirty terracompatible planets discovered. Massive starship building programme initiated in O'Neill Halo. Govcentral begins large-scale enforced outshipment of surplus population, rising to $2 million a week in 2160: Great Dispersal. Civil conflict on some early multiethnic colonies. Individual Govcentral states sponsor ethnic-streaming colonies. Edenists expand their He_3 mining enterprise to every inhabited star system with a gas giant.

2139 . . . Asteroid Braun impacts on Mars.

2180 . . . First orbital tower built on Earth.

2205 . . . Antimatter production station built in orbit around sun by Govcentral in an attempt to break the Edenist energy monopoly.

2208 . . . First antimatter-drive starships operational.

2210 . . . Richard Saldana transports all of New Kong's industrial facilities from the O'Neill Halo to an asteroid orbiting Kulu. He claims independence for the Kulu star system, founds Christian-only colony, and begins to mine He_3 from the system's gas giant.

2218 . . . First voidhawk gestated, a bitek starship designed by Edenists.

2225 . . . Establishment of a hundred voidhawk families. Habitats Romulus and Remus germinated in Saturn orbit to serve as voidhawk bases.

2232 . . . Conflict at Jupiter's trailing Trojan asteroid cluster between belt alliance ships and an O'Neill Halo company hydrocarbon refinery. Antimatter used as a weapon; twenty-seven thousand people killed.

2238 . . . Treaty of Deimos; outlaws production and use of antimatter in the Sol system; signed by Govcentral, Lunar nation, asteroid alliance, and Edenists. Antimatter stations abandoned and dismantled.

2240 . . . Coronation of Gerrald Saldana as King of Kulu. Foundation of Saldana dynasty.

2267–2270 . . . Eight separate skirmishes involving use of antimatter among colony worlds. Thirteen million killed.

2271 . . . Avon summit between all planetary leaders. Treaty of Avon, banning the manufacture and use of antimatter throughout inhabited space. Formation of Human Confederation to police agreement. Construction of Confederation Navy begins.

2300 . . . Confederation expanded to include Edenists.

2301 . . . First Contact. Jiciro race discovered, a pre-technology civilization. System quarantined by Confederation to avoid cultural contamination.

2310 . . . First ice asteroid impact on Mars.

2330 . . . First blackhawks gestated at Valisk, independent habitat.

2350 . . . War between Novska and Hilversum. Novska bombed with antimatter. Confederation Navy prevents retaliatory strike against Hilversum.

2356 . . . Kiint homeworld discovered.

2357 . . . Kiint join Confederation as "observers".

2360 . . . A voidhawk scout discovers Atlantis.

2371 . . . Edenists colonize Atlantis.

2395 . . . Tyrathca colony world discovered.

2402 . . . Tyrathca join Confederation.

2420 . . . Kulu scoutship discovers Ruin Ring.

2428 . . . Bitek habitat Tranquillity germinated by Crown Prince Michael Saldana, orbiting above Ruin Ring.

2432 . . . Prince Michael's son, Maurice, geneered with affinity. Kulu abdication crisis. Coronation of Lukas Saldana. Prince Michael exiled.

2550 . . . Mars declared habitable by Terraforming office.

2580 . . . Dorado asteroids discovered around Tunja, claimed by both Garissa and Omuta.

2581 . . . Omuta mercenary fleet drops twelve antimatter planet-busters on Garissa, planet rendered uninhabitable. Confederation imposes thirty-year sanction against Omuta, prohibiting any interstellar trade or transport. Blockade enforced by Confederation Navy.

2582 . . . Colony established on Lalonde.